The **POPULAR MECHANICS**

ILLUSTRATED **HOME HANDYMAN**

ENCYCLOPEDIA & GUIDE

EDITED BY THE STAFF OF POPULAR MECHANICS

J. J. Little & Ives Co., Inc., New York — 1961

A LIGHTWEIGHT GARAGE DOOR

ARE YOU PLANNING to replace the heavy, hinged frame doors on your garage? Then why not build a lightweight overhead door using corrugated-aluminum sheets for facing? Square and plumb the opening before starting the installation of the door. Referring to the detail below, assemble the door to fit your particular garage. Taper the diagonal braces from full width at the center to the width of the side members at the ends. For ease in handling, the aluminum should not be applied until after the hardware and lifting mechanism have been installed and the door hung in place. The cheapest and simplest lifting mechanism can be fabricated with counterweights attached to the door with chains or ropes, concealing the weights between the studs on one wall of the garage. However, spring balance or power-driven mechanisms can be purchased complete with mounting instructions. The thickness of the wood stock used in the door may have to be increased to accommodate certain mechanisms. As a last step, install weather stripping on the bottom edge of the door and then apply the corrugated sheets, using aluminum nails or screws and overlapping the edges.

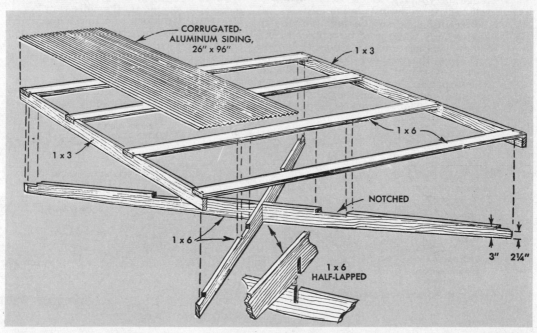

CORRUGATED-ALUMINUM SIDING, 26" x 96"

1 x 3

1 x 3

1 x 6

NOTCHED

1 x 6

3"   2¼"

1 x 6 HALF-LAPPED

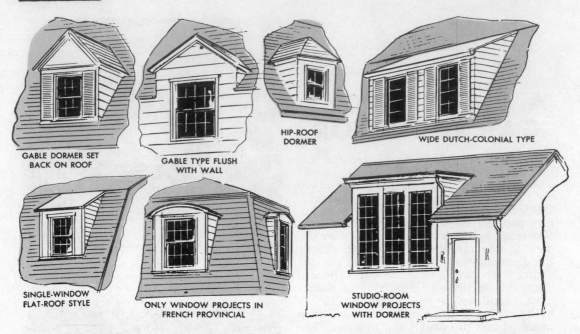

GABLE DORMER SET BACK ON ROOF

GABLE TYPE FLUSH WITH WALL

HIP-ROOF DORMER

WIDE DUTCH-COLONIAL TYPE

SINGLE-WINDOW FLAT-ROOF STYLE

ONLY WINDOW PROJECTS IN FRENCH PROVINCIAL

STUDIO-ROOM WINDOW PROJECTS WITH DORMER

How to Install DORMERS

IN ADDITION to the obvious advantages of increasing usable floor space and providing adequate ventilation for upstairs rooms, dormers also improve the appearance of a house when properly designed and installed. However, location or styling of the dormers can detract from the lines of the house and, therefore, should be given careful consideration. One effective way to plan your dormers is to sketch various types and sizes of dormers on tracing paper taped over a photograph of the house. Then judge for yourself which dormer lends itself best to your installation.

Precautions when starting: It's wise to have a large waterproof tarpaulin on hand before starting to install a dormer, so you can cover the roof opening or unfinished dormer overnight or when rain is probable. The tarpaulin should extend over shingles on either side of the opening and over the roof ridge. The opening is bridged with boards and the tarpaulin held down by sandbags and narrow boards, as in Fig. 1.

Remove shingles first: After measuring the location of the dormer from the roof edges, remove the shingles where the opening is to be made. You can start loosening shingles from a ladder set against the eave, a ladder hooked over the ridge, Fig. 2, or from an improvised roof scaffold, as in Fig. 3. When using a ladder set against the eave, provide footrests by nailing 2 x 4 cleats to the roof as the shingles are removed.

Strips of asphalt shingle are easy to remove after prying up the nails as in Fig. 4. Use a wooden block as a fulcrum to avoid damaging the shingles. Nails in wooden shingles are cut with a flat tool having a sharp V-notch at one end. It is pushed up under shingles and struck with a hammer to sever the nails. Remove shingles a foot or so beyond the limits of the opening to be made and cut the roofing paper a few

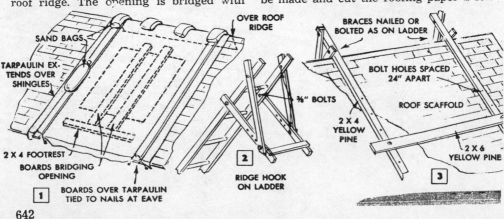

OVER ROOF RIDGE

SAND BAGS

TARPAULIN EX- TENDS OVER SHINGLES

2 X 4 FOOTREST

BOARDS BRIDGING OPENING

BOARDS OVER TARPAULIN TIED TO NAILS AT EAVE

1

RIDGE HOOK ON LADDER

2

⅜" BOLTS

2 X 4 YELLOW PINE

BRACES NAILED OR BOLTED AS ON LADDER

BOLT HOLES SPACED 24" APART

ROOF SCAFFOLD

2 X 6 YELLOW PINE

3

For house expansion and for appearance, dormers are important. Here is the step-by-step procedure for opening the roof, framing, sheathing, roofing and finishing

An example of what dormers can do for the appearance of a home having a large, unbroken expanse of roof. They also give light and air to attic rooms

Below, when opening up roof, shingles can be saved for use on dormer roof. Nails are lifted from roof without damaging shingles by using block as fulcrum

inches from the edges of the shingles, Fig. 5.

Cutting the opening: Start cutting the roof boards with a keyhole saw after boring holes to start. As soon as the kerf is long enough, use a crosscut saw. Cut closely along the rafters at each side of the opening, sawing on the side toward the opening, and remove the cut boards with a pry bar. The opening should extend the width of a roof board past the point where double headers are to be located top and bottom.

Next, cut the rafters that bridge the opening, as indicated by the dotted lines in Fig. 5. The lower edge of the upper double header should come at ceiling height as in Fig. 6. It's best to install headers on edge, marking the rafters with the aid of a level. Cut the header piece from the same size stock as rafters. Nail the rafters at the sides of the opening to one header first, then nail the header to the cutoff ends of the rafters. Install the second header piece the same

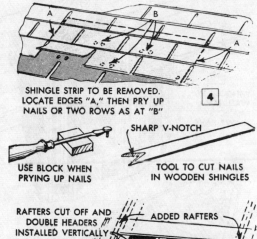

SHINGLE STRIP TO BE REMOVED. LOCATE EDGES "A," THEN PRY UP NAILS OR TWO ROWS AS AT "B" **4**

USE BLOCK WHEN PRYING UP NAILS

SHARP V-NOTCH

TOOL TO CUT NAILS IN WOODEN SHINGLES

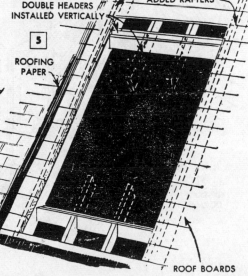

RAFTERS CUT OFF AND DOUBLE HEADERS INSTALLED VERTICALLY

ADDED RAFTERS

5

ROOFING PAPER

ROOF BOARDS

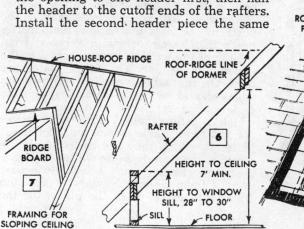

HOUSE-ROOF RIDGE

ROOF-RIDGE LINE OF DORMER

RAFTER

6

HEIGHT TO CEILING 7' MIN.

HEIGHT TO WINDOW SILL, 28" TO 30"

SILL

FLOOR

RIDGE BOARD

7

FRAMING FOR SLOPING CEILING

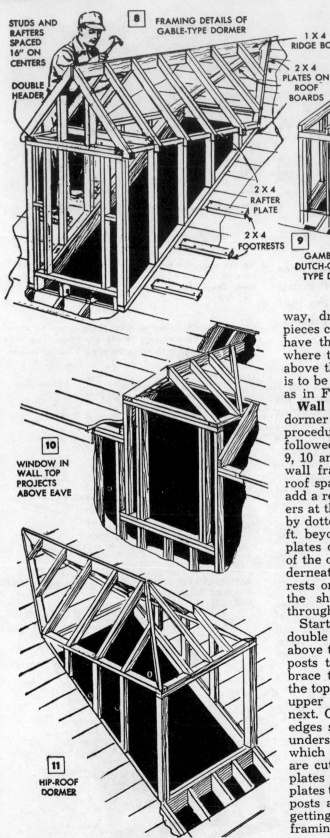

STUDS AND RAFTERS SPACED 16" ON CENTERS

DOUBLE HEADER

8 FRAMING DETAILS OF GABLE-TYPE DORMER

1 X 4 RIDGE BOARD

2 X 4 PLATES ON ROOF BOARDS

2 X 4 RAFTER PLATE

2 X 4 FOOTRESTS

9 GAMBREL OR DUTCH-COLONIAL TYPE DORMER

10 WINDOW IN WALL. TOP PROJECTS ABOVE EAVE

11 HIP-ROOF DORMER

way, dropping it as necessary. The two pieces comprising the lower header should have their top edges flush, at a location where the window will come about 30 in. above the floor. If the ceiling of a dormer is to be sloping, the top header is arranged as in Fig. 7.

Wall framing: Framing of a gable-type dormer is shown in Fig. 8, and the same procedure, with only slight differences, is followed on other types shown as in Figs. 9, 10 and 11. Use 2 x 4 stock for both the wall framing and rafters, although large roof spans may require 2 x 6 rafters. First add a reinforcing rafter to each of the rafters at the sides of the opening as indicated by dotted lines, Fig. 5. These project 3 or 4 ft. beyond the double headers. Next, nail plates on the roof boards along the sides of the opening, nailing into the rafters underneath, Fig. 8. Also nail temporary footrests on the roof, which can extend over the shingles but should not be nailed through them.

Start the wall framing by installing the double corner posts with a double header above them. Toenail the lower ends of the posts to the roof plates and temporarily brace this framework with a board from the top of the window header across to the upper roof header. The rafter plates are next. On the gable-type dormer their top edges should be at the same level as the underside of the upper header in the roof, which is ceiling height. The rafter plates are cut at an angle at one end to fit·roof plates to which they are nailed. Nail the plates to the front framing while the corner posts are checked with a level to assure getting them plumb. Now, with skeleton framing in place, mark the plates for the

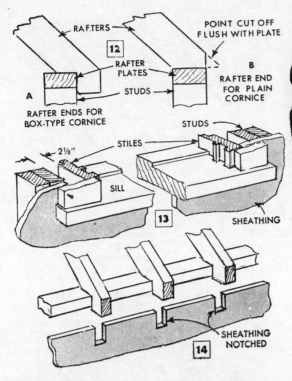

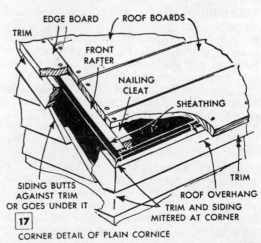

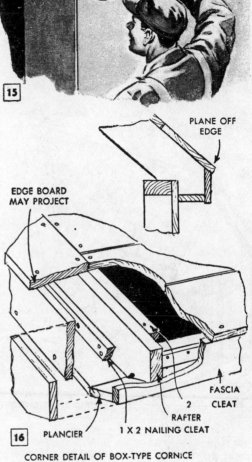

CORNER DETAIL OF BOX-TYPE CORNICE

CORNER DETAIL OF PLAIN CORNICE

studs which are spaced 16 in. on centers. Drive nails through the top plate into the studs and toenail the studs to the roof plate.

Roof framing: Next proceed with the roof framing, starting with the 1 x 6 ridge board nailed between the roof plates at the point where they meet, in line with the center of the dormer. Support the front of the ridge board temporarily so it is level and above the exact center of the dormer. Then take careful measurements of the rafters so they can all be precut. Nail them in place after marking the ridge board and the rafter plates to locate them 16 in. on centers. If you are making a box-type cornice, the rafters are notched and extended beyond the walls, Fig. 12-A, but for plain cornices the rafters are cut off flush with the plate as in detail B. Framing the gambrel-dormer roof as in Fig. 9 is the simplest and most rigid type of construction, but requires the installation of a false ceiling. To save this extra work, the center rafters may be butted against the header and the outer rafters mounted flush with the lower edge of the header.

Window framing: After the sides and roof are framed, nail the ceiling joists, spacing them 16 in. on centers, and install the window framing. The window opening is centered and should be 4¼ in. wider than the window frame at the stiles, thus providing a 2⅛-in. space from each stile to the frame as in Fig. 13. Usually the rough framing consists of double studs at the sides and a double header at the top. In Fig. 8 only

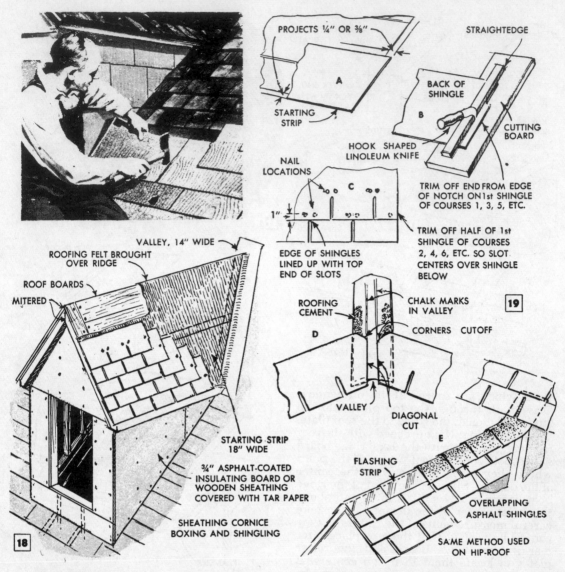

PROJECTS ¼" OR ⅜"

STRAIGHTEDGE

STARTING STRIP

A

BACK OF SHINGLE

B

CUTTING BOARD

HOOK SHAPED LINOLEUM KNIFE

TRIM OFF END FROM EDGE OF NOTCH ON 1st SHINGLE OF COURSES 1, 3, 5, ETC.

NAIL LOCATIONS

C

1"

EDGE OF SHINGLES LINED UP WITH TOP END OF SLOTS

TRIM OFF HALF OF 1st SHINGLE OF COURSES 2, 4, 6, ETC. SO SLOT CENTERS OVER SHINGLE BELOW

ROOFING CEMENT

CHALK MARKS IN VALLEY

CORNERS CUTOFF

19

D

VALLEY

DIAGONAL CUT

E

FLASHING STRIP

OVERLAPPING ASPHALT SHINGLES

SAME METHOD USED ON HIP-ROOF

VALLEY, 14" WIDE

ROOFING FELT BROUGHT OVER RIDGE

ROOF BOARDS MITERED

STARTING STRIP 18" WIDE

¾" ASPHALT-COATED INSULATING BOARD OR WOODEN SHEATHING COVERED WITH TAR PAPER

SHEATHING CORNICE BOXING AND SHINGLING

18

single studs are shown because of their proximity to the corner posts to which they are nailed with short blocks at the center.

Sheathing: The roof is sheathed and shingled before sheathing the walls, the roof boards projecting over the edges of the siding and trim. On roofs with box cornices, apply the wall sheathing first, then add the cornice and lastly the roof. You can use wooden sheathing or composition sheathing board for the walls. The top edge of side-wall sheathing is notched, Fig. 14, to fit over the rafters, or the rafter notches may extend ¾ in. over the plate so that the sheathing can be inserted.

Cornice construction: Rafter ends for box-type cornices must be identical. Mark the rafters along their top edges using a straightedge. Mark for vertical cuts by using a level or miter gauge, and for the bottom horizontal cuts by using a square. The

bottom board, or plancier, of the side cornice, Figs. 15 and 16, should extend at the front a distance equal to the width of the board. The side of the cornice (fascia) has its top edge beveled at an angle to fit snugly under the roof sheathing, which may project beyond it an inch or so. The side and front cornices are joined, as in Fig. 16. The edge board—also called drip edge—is nailed to the end rafter while the other roof boards butting against it are nailed to a 2 x 2 cleat nailed along the inside edge of the rafter. Dormer roof boards will fit snugly against the house roof boards if sawed at the correct angle and bevel. Construction of a plain cornice is shown in Fig. 17.

Shingling: First lay a 14-in. sheet-metal valley where dormer and house roof meet, Fig. 18, bending it with a straightedge so it lies flat on both roofs. Lay roofing felt on the roof in overlapping strips, the higher one covering 4 or 5 in. of the lower one. Then space a "starting" strip along the roof, as in Fig. 19-A, letting it project ¼ or ⅜ in. Sometimes regular strip shingles are used instead of a starter strip, the shingles being placed upside down so that the slots are on top. The first shingle of the bottom course and other alternate courses is trimmed, detail B, to eliminate the half slot, or notch, at the end. Cut shingles from the back side with a linoleum knife or heavy pocketknife. Cutting is easier, especially on hot days, if you keep the knife blade moistened with kerosene. You can use the edge of a shingling hatchet or a pair of tin snips instead of a knife. Use a straightedge and cut the shingles on a board to prevent damaging them. The first shingle of the second and alternate courses is trimmed so the slot comes halfway over the shingle below, detail C. Two nails are driven about an inch above and on either side of each slot. Mark the valley by snapping a chalk line to indicate where the shingles must be cut diagonally, detail D. This detail also shows how the top corners of shingles at the valley are cut at an angle to shed water. Nails should not be driven through the sheet metal, the ends of the shingles being cemented to the valley. Shingle courses are continued to the ridge, the nails of the last course being covered with the capping, which consists of a flashing strip and individual shingles overlapped, as in detail E. The last capping shingle is brought upward and under a shingle course of the house roof. When wooden shingles are used, courses overlap to expose about 5 in. to the weather. The shingles are spaced ¼ to ⅜ in. apart. Keep the side edges of the shingles at least 1¼ in. from the edges of shingles in the course below. Drive the shingle nails

21 WEDGE-SHAPED BLOCKS FOR SUPPORT AND LEVELING

TAR PAPER

THIS FLASHING UNDER SIDING AND TRIM BUT OVER SHINGLES

UNDER SHINGLES

22 FLASHING AT JOINTS OF DORMER AND HOUSE ROOF

A

B — TRIM OVER SIDING

C — SIDING BUTTS AGAINST TRIM

CORNERS MITERED FOR TIGHT FIT. NAILS COUNTERSUNK AND PUTTIED

24

SILL

CORNER TRIM

¾" SHEATHING

SIDING OR OTHER WALL COVERING

E

PLASTER OR OTHER WALL COVERING

2 X 2 STRIPS FOR NAILING

TRIM

WINDOW SILL

PLASTER GROUND

MINERAL WOOL

STOOL

WOODEN BLOCK

HEADER

D

PAPER FOLDED IN GROOVE

SHEATHING

APRON

PLASTER GROUND

PLASTER

SIDING

SHEET-METAL FLASHING

EDGE DOUBLED

DRIP CAP

23

MOLDING

WINDOW

25

26

NAILS TO USE

20d COMMON NAILS: Rafters to double headers and vice versa; roof plates to rafters underneath

16d COMMON NAILS: Rafter plates to ends of studs

10d COMMON NAILS: Reinforcing rafters or any double studs fastened together; toenailing studs, rafters, joists, etc.

8d COMMON NAILS: Wooden wall and roof sheathing, outside trim (countersunk and puttied)

8d ALUMINUM NAILS: Siding and exterior trim

8d FINISHING NAILS: For interior trim

1¾" LARGE, FLAT-HEAD, GALV. NAILS: For insulation-type sheathing

⅞" or 1" WIDE, FLAT-HEAD, GALV. NAILS: Asphalt shingles on roofing boards

3d GALV. SHINGLE NAILS: For wood shingles

about 6 in. above butt ends of the shingles and not closer than ¾ in. from the edges.

Installing window frames: Set the window frame in the opening so that the stiles are 2⅛ in. from studs, Fig. 13. Drive wooden wedges between the sill and the header as shown in Figs. 21 and 24-D to get the frame plumb and hold it securely in position while nailing the outer trim. Before nailing, check the window frame with a level, as in Fig. 20.

Flashing to prevent leaks: After reshingling the house roof to the front of the dormer, add a sheet-metal flashing strip along the dormer. The strip should be at least 8 in. wide and bent centrally to come over the shingle nails, as in Fig. 22. Fasten the upper edge to wooden sheathing or to studs under insulating-type sheathing. Also apply a flashing strip over the drip cap at the top of the window, as in Fig. 23. Use "metal shingles" where the dormer sides join the house roof, Fig. 22, starting at the front corners. Note that flashing piece No. 1 is applied before the front flashing strip and

is bent around the corner. Bring the roof shingling over flashing piece No. 1, which should lie flat on the roof about 4 in. beyond the dormer. Flashing piece No. 2 overlaps No. 1 and is similarly covered with the next shingle course. The same procedure is followed for pieces 3 and 4.

Application of siding: Outside wall covering should match that of the house or harmonize with its styling. If wooden sheathing is used, it is covered with tar paper before applying siding, clapboard or shingles. Siding at outside corners can be neatly mitered, Fig. 24-A, with the joining edges embedded in calking compound. Siding may be covered with trim, detail B, and spaces between the siding and trim tamped with mineral wool and calked. Another method is to butt the siding against the trim, detail C, the lower edge of the siding being kept about ½ in. above the roof to prevent absorption of water. It's best to use aluminum nails as they need not be countersunk and puttied to prevent rust spots. Siding under a window fits into the groove on the underside of the sill, detail D, and is pushed up tightly against a folded edge of the sheathing paper.

Finishing the inside: It's advisable to insulate walls and ceiling of a dormer, using a vapor-barrier insulation. Fig. 25 shows batt-type insulation being installed. When insulating, stuff mineral wool between the window sill and the header, Fig. 24-D. The inside wall may be finished with wallboard or plasterboard. If the wall is to be plastered, apply plaster grounds along all edges of the window, details D and E of Fig. 24, and along the floor edge of walls. These grounds come flush with the plaster. Apply perforated-metal corner beads at outside corners before plastering, and strips of metal lath along inside corners.

After plastering, install trim around the windows. A plywood subfloor is installed, over which any type of finish floor may be laid. Baseboards are applied after laying the finish floor. Fig. 26 shows an inside view of the finished dormer. ★ ★ ★

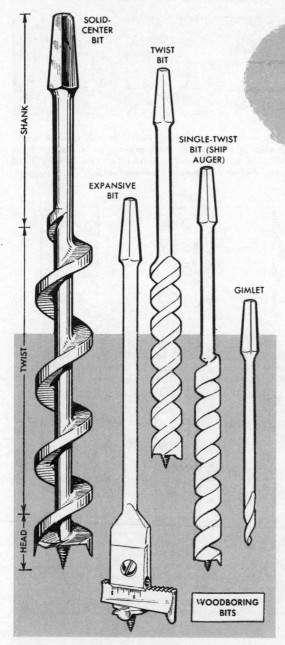

True Holes With Woodboring Bits

By C. W. Woodson

AS IT CUTS its way into wood, a wood-boring, or auger, bit performs several operations simultaneously. The screw point draws the bit into the wood at a uniform rate, the spurs make a circular cut of a given diameter, the cutters lift the waste and the twist, or auger, carries the chips upward. Common woodboring bits of several types are detailed at the left. These are made with squared and tapered shanks for use in a hand brace. Solid-center and twist bits for use in a brace are regularly supplied in sets from ¼ to 1 in., rising by 16ths. The expansive bit is designed to bore shallow holes of varying diameters as at A, B and C in the lower left-hand detail. It comes in several sizes. The single-twist bit, also referred to as a single-spiral bit and ship auger, is designed for boring deep holes. A machine bit similar to the brace type pictured also is available. Gimlet bits come in sizes by 32nds, from ¹⁄₃₂ in. up.

Power bits for use in drill presses and portable electric drills are designed for high speeds. Three common types are shown on the next page, but there are many variations designed for special purposes. The wing-type, or spade-type, bits usually are supplied in sets, the door-lock bit is generally purchased individually. The term "door lock" more often refers to this type of bit made with a squared shank for use in a brace. When made with straight or shouldered shank it is supplied in single and multiple-spur types. The Forstner bit is made with straight shank and also with squared shank. It has a continuous lip which guides the bit and severs the wood fibers ahead of the single cutter.

Above, common types of woodboring bits for use in a brace. Below, cutter of expansive bit is adjustable. Right-hand detail shows parts of standard auger bit

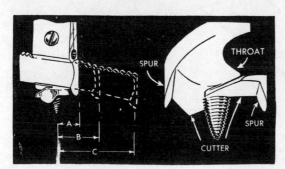

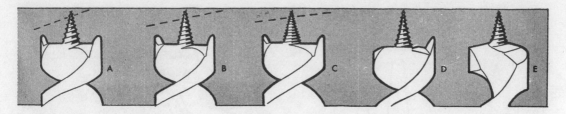

Screw point of auger bit is supplied in various pitches so that feed can be varied to suit type of work. Sharp pitch, detail A, feeds bit rapidly, makes heavy chip in soft wood. Medium-pitch screw, detail B, is used on general-purpose bits. Slow-pitch screw, detail C, feeds bit slowly, is best for use in very hard woods. Detail D shows fast-cutting bit with one spur. Detail E shows a fast-cutting bit without spurs

Below, typical of high-speed bits for use in drill presses and portable electric drills are the three types detailed. Forstner bit comes with ½-in. shank, others with ¼-in. shanks for use in portable drills

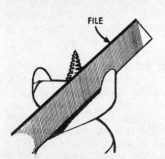

FORSTNER

WING TYPE

DOOR LOCK

POWER BITS

Details A, B and C above show how auger bit works. In detail A, screw pulls bit into wood. Detail B, spurs score wood to hole diameter. Detail C, lips cut and lift chips into the throat

To avoid splintering stock when bit comes through, stop boring when screw projects slightly as at left, above. Withdraw bit, invert stock and bore out waste as in center detail. In counterboring, bore small hole through. Select short length of dowel to fit small hole and turn onto lead screw to center counterbore

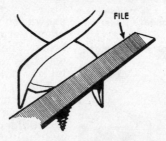

FILE

FILE

OILSTONE

Use a small single-cut file to sharpen spurs and lips of an auger bit or, better still, use an auger-bit file or a Swiss pattern file with a safe edge. Wing-type power bits can be sharpened with a small abrasive stick, or oilstone, as in right-hand detail. Auger bits in larger sizes also can be sharpened with abrasive stick

Photos Courtesy General Electric Co.

After electrical heating cables are positioned, the paving material—asphalt here—is poured over them

Electrically Heated Driveways

NOTING THE INCREASING acceptance of laborsaving devices as part of the cost of a home, a paving contractor in Bridgeport, Conn., now offers electrically heated snow-melting sidewalks and driveways as a "package." Heated paving is not, of course, a new idea. But having one contractor provide both paving and wiring is fairly unique, and the idea quite likely will spread to other areas where snow removal is a problem. Either concrete or asphalt can be heated, as the electric cables simply are embedded in the paving material by pouring it over them. No thermostats are required—it is the amount of snow that determines when the cables are to be energized, not the temperature—which keeps the wiring simple. An off-on switch in the house is the only control required. If you are considering having a sidewalk or driveway installed, consider installing these cables.

Workman uses marked plank to space loops of cable properly so maximum heating efficiency is assured

Individual lengths of cable are spliced together in junction boxes that are buried in the paving

5 TOY

SYNCHRONOUS MOTOR
(1)
TWO PIECES OF STEEL CLOCK SPRING
MAGNETS A & B FROM BUZZER CONNECTED IN SERIES
¾" MACH. SCREW
BRASS OR ALUMINUM
8"
3¾"
2¾"

(2) TIN-AND-NAIL MOTOR

(3) SYNCHRONOUS MOTOR

(4) INDUCTION MOTOR

(5) SERIES MOTOR

(6) TIN-AND-NAIL MOTOR
CONNECT WIRES A AND B TO DRY CELLS OR TRANSFORMER
CENTER-PUNCH MARK FOR BEARING
HEAVY TIN YOKE SUPPORTS ROTOR
COILS WOUND ON 2-IN. NAILS TO TWICE DIAMETER OF HEAD
BARE COPPER-WIRE BRUSH
ROTOR
¼ TWIST

TIN-AND-NAIL MOTOR: One of the simplest forms of an electric motor where small electromagnets cause a tin rotor to spin, is shown in Figs. 2 and 6. This motor runs on a couple of dry cells or will operate on 6 volts a.c. provided by a transformer. The rotor acts like a tiny switch as it wipes against a brush lightly, turning on current momentarily just before its arms pass over the electromagnets. This current impulse, which occurs at each half rotation, is just enough to keep the rotor going. The rotor is cut from tin to the cross shape shown and the side arms are twisted at right angles. The electromagnets or field coils are wound in series on two nails, both windings being in the same direction. The nails are 2 in. apart. One end of the wire is scraped bare and twisted to form a tight coil which serves as a binding post, it being tacked down to

MOTORS *convey basic ideas*

These simple electric motors, which run on low-voltage a.c. or d.c. as specified, are constructed from nails, wire and scraps of iron and tin. All of them have been built and made to operate; one provides ample power to drive small toys

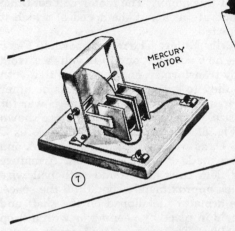

MERCURY MOTOR

①

the baseboard at point A, Fig. 6. At this point connections to a transformer or battery are made. The other end of the wire is tacked to the yoke that supports the upper end of the rotor. A length of bare copper wire is used as a brush, rubbing lightly against the edges of the rotor about ½ in. above the base. It is formed to a coil to provide flexibility. The other end of the brush wire is bared and formed into a binding-post coil at point B to which the other side of the transformer or battery is connected. Center-punch marks are made in the yoke and in a small tin base plate, halfway between the two nails. Then the rotor is set in place so that the arms are about ⅛ in. above the tops of the nails. The brush is adjusted so that it touches the edges of the rotor and also releases before the arms pass over the nail heads. After connecting the motor to the current supply, give the rotor a start by turning it and the motor should run.

Synchronous Motor: A synchronous motor is one that operates at a constant speed, which is equal to or a submultiple of the frequency of the alternating current supplied to it. A simple synchronous motor

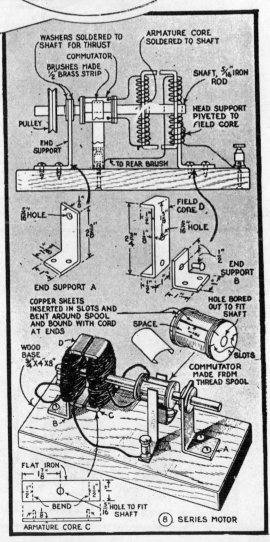

WASHERS SOLDERED TO SHAFT FOR THRUST

ARMATURE CORE SOLDERED TO SHAFT

COMMUTATOR

BRUSHES MADE ½ BRASS STRIP

SHAFT, 5/16" IRON ROD

HEAD SUPPORT PIVETED TO FIELD CORE

PULLEY

END SUPPORT

TO REAR BRUSH

5/16" HOLE

FIELD CORE D

5/16" HOLE

END SUPPORT A

END SUPPORT B

HOLE BORED OUT TO FIT SHAFT

COPPER SHEETS INSERTED IN SLOTS AND BENT AROUND SPOOL AND BOUND WITH CORD AT ENDS

SPACE

SLOTS

WOOD BASE ¾"X4"X8"

COMMUTATOR MADE FROM THREAD SPOOL

FLAT IRON

BEND

HOLE TO FIT SHAFT

ARMATURE CORE C

⑧ SERIES MOTOR

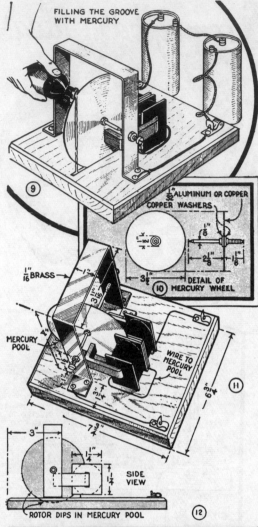

FILLING THE GROOVE WITH MERCURY

(9)

ALUMINUM OR COPPER
COPPER WASHERS

$\frac{1}{16}$"BRASS

$3\frac{1}{4}$"

DETAIL OF
(10) MERCURY WHEEL

MERCURY POOL

WIRE TO MERCURY POOL

(11)

$6\frac{3}{4}$"

$7\frac{3}{4}$"

3"

SIDE VIEW

ROTOR DIPS IN MERCURY POOL

(12)

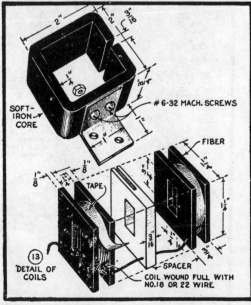

2"

SOFT-IRON CORE

6-32 MACH. SCREWS

FIBER

TAPE

SPACER

COIL WOUND FULL WITH NO.18 OR 22 WIRE

(13)

DETAIL OF COILS

operating on low-voltage a.c. from a bell transformer is shown in Figs. 1 and 3. The field coils A and B are two magnets from a buzzer or doorbell placed so that the windings run in the same direction. These are connected in series. The rotor consists of two pieces of steel clock spring and the shaft is a No. 6-32 machine screw filed to a point at each end. Two nuts hold the springs to the shaft as shown. The shaft is pivoted between center-punched marks in the base plate and the supporting arm. There is no electrical connection to the rotor of this motor. The motor will continue to operate at about the speed at which it is started.

Series Motor: The motor shown in Fig. 5 runs on 6 volts d.c. or 8 to 12 volts a.c. from a toy transformer, and it can be fitted with a pulley to operate small models or other devices, delivering considerable power for its size. Details of construction are shown in Fig. 8. The armature and field cores C and D, as well as the end supports A and B, are made of $\frac{1}{8}$-in. strap iron. Armature and field coils are wound with bell wire which approximately should fill the space. The armature is slipped on the shaft and is held in place by peening or with a drop of solder. The commutator is made from a thread spool and two strips of copper. Slots are sawed in opposite sides of the spool, the edges of the copper strips are inserted into the slots, and the strips are bent around the spools. There should be about $\frac{1}{4}$ to $\frac{3}{8}$-in. clearance between the two copper segments. The edges of the commutator should be wrapped securely with strong cord. The leads from the armature coil are soldered to the two copper segments of the commutator, and the armature is put in place. Two washers are soldered to the shaft on either side of the end support to limit end play. The brushes are made of spring brass, $\frac{1}{2}$ in. wide. It may be necessary to give the motor a start by hand. If it does not run as first assembled, turn the commutator on the shaft to a position which will cause the motor to take hold.

Mercury-Pool Motor: The mercury-pool motor shown in Figs. 7 and 9 is a type used in d.c. watt-hour meters and other meters. It operates on two or three dry cells connected in series. It will not operate on a.c. Details of construction are shown in Figs. 9 to 13 inclusive. The rotor is a disk of $\frac{1}{32}$-in. aluminum or copper mounted on a small shaft which is placed between two machine screws which are center-punched at one end to serve as bearings and are locked to the frame with nuts. The mercury pool is cut in the wooden base, directly under the rotor. Next, an electromagnet is made. The core is ¼-in. flat iron bent as shown in Fig. 13 and the two coils are wound full of No. 18 or No. 22 magnet wire, a spacer being placed between them. Both coils must be wound in the same direction. The electromagnet is mounted so that the rotor revolves freely between the coils, and the poles of the magnet are directly below the shaft of the rotor. Electrical connections are shown in Fig. 11. One terminal is connected to the coil, and the other side of the coil is connected to a wire dipping into the mercury pool. The rotor also dips into the pool. The second terminal is connected to the frame of the motor.

Induction Motor: Operated on low-voltage a.c. from a toy transformer, the disk-type induction motor shown in Fig. 4 exemplifies a principle used in meters of various types. It will not operate on d.c. Details of parts are given in Figs. 14 to 17 inclusive. The laminations used are approximately of the dimensions shown in Fig. 17 and can be obtained from an old audio transformer used in radio. Two stacks of laminations, each ⁹⁄₁₆ in. thick, are required for the lower and upper coil. The upper coil is wound with No. 28 d.c.c. wire, enough wire being wound on the coil to fill the winding space on the core. The lower coil is wound with No. 18 wire. The leads from each coil are brought out to a pair of binding posts on opposite sides of the motor. The core of the upper coil is drilled directly below the coil and a single turn of No. 8 bare copper wire is inserted as shown in Fig. 15. The ends of this wire should be lapped carefully and soldered together. The frame is made of No. 16-ga. sheet brass. The rotor is a disk of sheet copper or aluminum. It is moved up or down on the shaft until it is in the proper position between the two cores. The upper coil terminals are connected to a radio rheostat and the lower coil is connected to the transformer supplying 6 volts. It will be necessary to shift the upper coil slightly to one side or the other in order to get the motor to operate properly. Once the proper position has been found, the speed can be controlled by adjusting the rheostat.

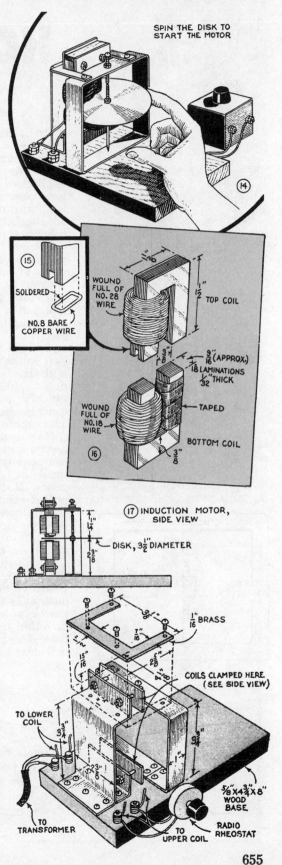

SPIN THE DISK TO START THE MOTOR

(14)

(15) SOLDERED — NO.8 BARE COPPER WIRE

WOUND FULL OF NO.28 WIRE — TOP COIL

⁹⁄₁₆ (APPROX.) — 18 LAMINATIONS ¹⁄₃₂" THICK — TAPED

WOUND FULL OF NO.18 WIRE — BOTTOM COIL

(16)

(17) INDUCTION MOTOR, SIDE VIEW

DISK, 3½" DIAMETER

¹⁄₁₆" BRASS

COILS CLAMPED HERE (SEE SIDE VIEW)

TO LOWER COIL

TO TRANSFORMER

TO UPPER COIL

RADIO RHEOSTAT

⁵⁄₈" X 4¾" X 8" WOOD BASE

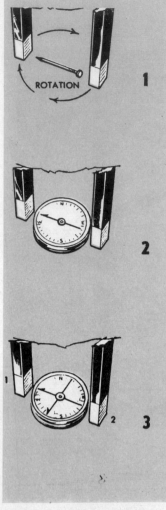

1

2

3

CURRENT

CONDENSER

A

C

POWER
SUPPLY

B

4

HOME REPAIR

By H. D. Eckerson

FAILURE of a home appliance motor can upset the daily schedule of any modern household. Everything must be put aside until the motor is fixed and running again. Electric motors powering home appliances and shop tools are extremely durable and long-lasting units, and under normal conditions they keep running for many years without attention. But occasionally they fail due to worn parts, hardened lubricant or some other abnormality that may have developed unobserved. It's then that you can save yourself money and time by knowing how the various types of motors work and how to make simple motor repairs.

Action, or power, of an electric motor results from interaction of the magnetic field of a stationary winding, usually called the stator, and a rotating member generally referred to as the rotor. Note the nail between the poles of the horseshoe magnet in Fig. 1. If you rotate the magnet very slowly the nail will turn with it, following the magnetic field rather jerkily due to inertia. If rotation of the magnet is started quickly the nail will not follow, as it cannot respond quickly enough to stay within the field of the magnet. This "motor" is not self starting.

Now note Fig. 2 and think first of the compass needle and then the body of the compass as being the components of the rotor. When the magnet is rotated, fast or slow, the needle will follow quite precisely. But think of the body of the compass being pulled around with the needle, making a slower start and following at its own pace. Several conclusions can now be drawn: The magnetic field still must rotate and, although the rotor is self starting it will not turn as fast as the magnet. It will lag, or "slip," a little.

Finally, think of the compass as having two needles fixed at right angles so they will rotate as one, Fig. 3. It will be noted that the needles start to turn when the magnet is placed in position. When the leading needle passes pole No. 1 it will be pulled in the opposite direction from the second needle which is approaching pole No. 1. The result will be a kind of pulsating movement. But suppose that polarity of the first

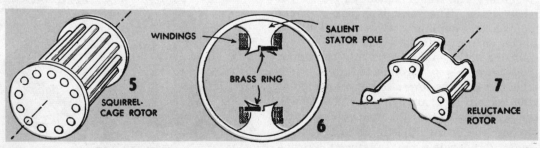

WINDINGS

SALIENT
STATOR POLE

BRASS RING

5

SQUIRREL-
CAGE ROTOR

6

7

RELUCTANCE
ROTOR

# of ELECTRIC MOTORS

needle is reversed the instant it passes pole No. 1. It then will continue to rotate toward pole No. 2. This action will set up a continuous rotation of the fixed needles and you have in effect, a d.c. motor, still assuming, of course, that the body of the compass is being pulled along with the needles and is rotating about a center. From this action it can be concluded that the stator field need not rotate, that the fields must switch, or reverse, polarity each time they pass a stator pole and, finally, that this type of motor also is self starting.

Fig. 4 shows how the stator fields of an induction motor are connected. Windings A and B are main field windings and the auxiliary winding C is connected into the circuit through a condenser. Operating on a.c. the condenser in effect keeps current in the auxiliary winding out of step with that in the main windings with the result that the stator field is oriented in the direction

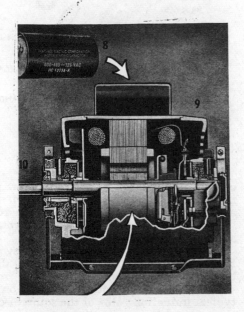

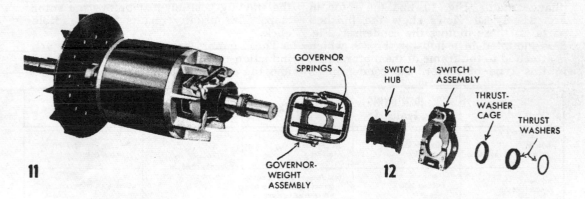

11

GOVERNOR SPRINGS

SWITCH HUB

SWITCH ASSEMBLY

THRUST-WASHER CAGE

THRUST WASHERS

GOVERNOR-WEIGHT ASSEMBLY

12

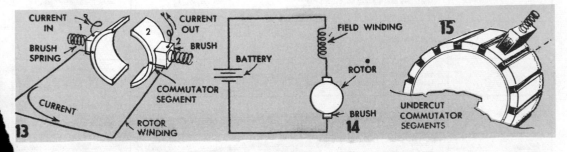

13

CURRENT IN

BRUSH SPRING

CURRENT OUT

BRUSH

CURRENT

COMMUTATOR SEGMENT

ROTOR WINDING

BATTERY

FIELD WINDING

ROTOR

BRUSH

14

15

UNDERCUT COMMUTATOR SEGMENTS

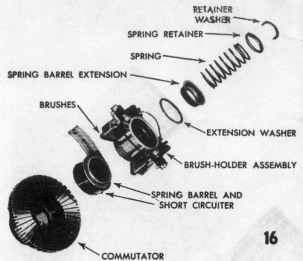

RETAINER WASHER
SPRING RETAINER
SPRING
SPRING BARREL EXTENSION
BRUSHES
EXTENSION WASHER
BRUSH-HOLDER ASSEMBLY
SPRING BARREL AND SHORT CIRCUITER
COMMUTATOR

16

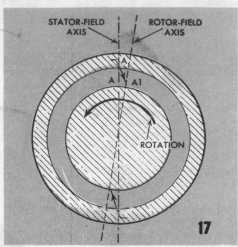

STATOR-FIELD AXIS
ROTOR-FIELD AXIS
ROTATION

17

of the arrow, Fig. 4, at one instant and in the direction of the secondary winding at a different instant. In effect, the rotor "follows" a magnetic field which rotates around the air gap.

The rotor's magnetic field, not shown in Fig. 4, is set up by induced currents, there being no connection between the main windings and the rotor. Fig. 5 shows a typical induction rotor of the squirrel-cage type, found in nearly all appliance motors of fractional hp. In this connection, refer also to the cutaway view of a typical appliance motor, Fig. 10, and the rotor in Fig. 11. These views show the finished parts. In these motors the condenser, Fig. 8, is mounted in a housing, Fig. 9, which is attached to the frame of the motor. Also, in this type of motor, the condenser is

used only for starting and is then automatically switched out of the circuit by the centrifugal switching device. This switch is shown in a pulled-apart view in Fig. 12 and assembled in Figs. 10 and 11.

After the rotor attains full speed and the condenser has been switched out of the circuit (this occurs when the rotor attains about half its normal speed) the rotor continues to spin by what might be termed straight induction. When the motor switch is turned off, the governor, Fig. 12, returns the centrifugal switch assembly to the starting position just before the rotor stops. This usually results in an audible click.

These motors are of the capacitor-start, induction-run type (see the table below) and the condenser and centrifugal switch

TYPE	IDENTIFYING FEATURES	CHARACTERISTICS	APPLICATIONS	REPAIR
Induction (capacitance & "split phase")	None of the features used below	Fair all-around operating qualities	Common household uses: fans, vac. cleaners, pumps	Check condenser and all terminals for good contact
Induction capacitance-start	Centrifugal switch	Good starting torque & good running qualities (especially if combined with permanent capacitor)		Check switch, change condenser
Induction shaded-pole	Salient-stator poles with brass ring	Low torque, low efficiency	Very small fans, etc.	If cleaning & checking contacts doesn't help, you're stuck for a rewinding job at the repair shop
Reluctance	Salient-rotor poles	Synchronous, large for HP rating	Very rare	Check condenser & switch
Hysteresis	Usually a smooth rotor Identified best by application	Low torque, synchronous speed quiet	Clocks, phonographs	Cleanliness essential & also check condenser. Try setting motor on its side for several hours
Universal	Brushes "AC or DC" on nameplate	Small, light wt., high speed	High-speed applications, hand tools, etc.	Check brushes & spring tension. Clean commutator segments & governor contacts
Repulsion-induction	Brushes, Brush-lifting device, Shorting ring	Good starting torque, but large & expensive for its horsepower rating	Only older motors are likely to be this type	Check brushes, commutators, springs, shorting clamp, brush-lifting device

are the parts most likely to fail. A burned-out condenser is easily replaced and careful use of a solvent generally restores the switch to efficient operation.

Variations of the induction motor include those with two condensers, one for starting and one for continuous running. These are sometimes called capacitor-start, capacitor-run motors, and are not commonly used to power home appliances. Other types have a brass ring around one half of each pole, Fig. 6, to change the magnetic properties of the halves and simulate the effect of an auxiliary winding. This motor is limited in application because of a very low starting torque.

Recall that in Fig. 3 it was noted that a change in polarity can cause the needles to rotate continuously in one direction and that the magnetic field does not rotate. Basically, this is the principle on which the universal, or d.c.-a.c., motor operates. The device for changing current direction in these motors is the brush and commutator, Figs. 13, 14 and 15. The rotor of such a motor consists of a group of current-carrying coils. Fig. 13 shows an elementary rotor winding, the latter terminating on the brass (or copper) segments which are called commutators. Current is fed through the brushes to the commutator segments and around the coil, thus setting up a rotor field. When the rotor turns, commutator segment No. 1 will eventually contact brush No. 2 and commutator No. 2 will contact brush No. 1 and thus the direction of the current around the coil will be reversed. Fig. 14 shows a series connection of such a motor with a battery as the power source. If the battery is replaced by an a.c. power source, the stator magnetic field will reverse its polarity periodically with the alternating current, but because of the series connection the rotor field will change its direction in step with the stator and the rotor will continue to turn.

This is the universal motor you find in nearly all portable power tools and about the only servicing it requires is a periodic cleaning to remove thrown lubricant and dust, and replacement of worn brushes.

In the repulsion-start, induction-run motor (see table on the opposite page) a centrifugal switch short circuits the commutator and in some motors lifts the brushes after the rotor has attained about half its normal speed. Fig. 16 is a pulled-apart view of the short-circuiting, brush-lifting mechanism showing the various parts. Other motors sometimes used on light equipment and in special applications are the "reluctance" motor, Fig. 7, and the "hysteresis" motor, Fig. 17, the latter used in clocks and phonographs. ★ ★ ★

THAT THIRD WIRE

By Ralph Treves

IN NEW HOMES wired with electrical systems of the continuous-ground type, which requires that appliances be equipped with three-prong plugs, the shock hazard is reduced to the minimum. On the other hand, in older homes having two-wire electrical systems there is always the possibility that defects in appliances and portable power tools due to wear, deterioration of insulation or other causes, can create a serious, if not dangerous, shock hazard. Any hazard that may exist due to these causes is increased in the presence of dampness, as in a basement where humidity is high during summer months.

Older appliances such as wringer-type washers and any motor-driven tools having two-wire power cords, A in Figs. 1 and 2, can be grounded with a third wire, B in Figs. 1 and 2. One end of the third wire, or ground wire, should be attached to bared metal on the appliance or tool as in the inset detail, Fig. 1. The other end should be attached to a water pipe with a suitable ground clamp as in Fig. 5. In this procedure it should be understood that you are not necessarily guarding against a defect in manufacture, but against the outside chance that an electrical defect may exist in the tool or appliance due to hard usage, undue wear or other causes of which you may not be aware.

Some tools and appliances made in later years come with a three-wire power cord having a two-prong plug and a pigtail (green ground wire) leading out from the

BRASS
SCREW

GROUND
WIRE

side of the plug, Fig. 4. Often this is fitted
with a special screw which replaces the
screw holding the cover plate of the receptacle. This is an effective ground on systems
installed in BX, rigid conduit or thin-wall
conduit. Late-model equipment comes with
a three-wire power cord, a three-prong
plug and an auxiliary plug, or jack, having
a two-prong end and a pigtail for attaching the ground to the receptacle as in Fig.
3. Be sure the screw is tight.

When a portable electric drill, saw or
other power tool must be operated at a distance from an outlet which is beyond the
reach of the regular power cord, an extension must be used. When the tool is
equipped with a three-wire cord, always
use a three-wire extension having plugs
as in Fig. 6. Use of such an extension will
assure that the tool is properly grounded
to insure working safety. ★★★

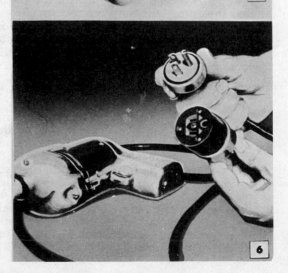

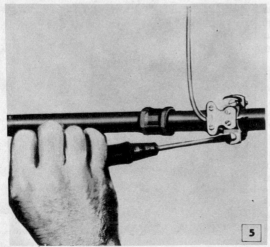

IS YOUR Wiring Adequate?

By J. B. Mullen

INCREASING USE OF home electrical appliances and also the higher current requirements of newer-type individual appliances make the wiring of many older homes inadequate to handle the load safely. Compare, as an example, the 300 to 500-watt rating of earlier electric irons with a modern iron which requires up to 1000 watts. The same increase in current requirements is true of certain other appliances. Also, the regular electric service of 20 or more years ago was planned before such electrically operated units as clothes driers, water heaters, home-shop power tools, kitchen ranges and air conditioners became standard household equipment.

Wires carrying current throughout the house have a certain resistance to the flow of current. This is greater for the smaller sizes of wire and less for the larger sizes. Table I, also Fig. 2. Thus when planning an all-new service, or additions to an older service, the wire size becomes important. Voltage drop on inadequate supply lines not only reduces the actual voltage available at the appliance, it also sets a definite limit to the amount of current that can be carried safely by a wire of a given size.

Table I gives safe capacities for the common sizes of house wiring, also the voltage

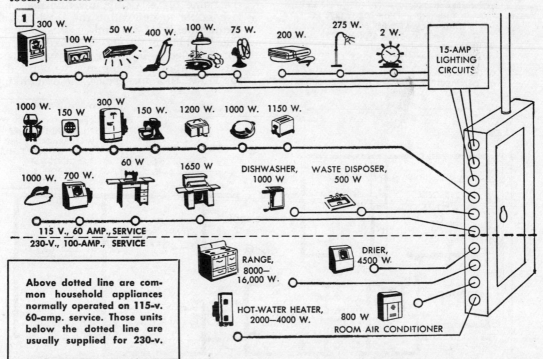

300 W. 100 W. 50 W. 400 W. 100 W. 75 W. 200 W. 275 W. 2 W.

15-AMP LIGHTING CIRCUITS

1000 W. 150 W. 300 W 150 W. 1200 W. 1000 W. 1150 W.

1000 W. 700 W. 60 W 1650 W DISHWASHER, 1000 W WASTE DISPOSER, 500 W

115 V., 60 AMP., SERVICE
230-V., 100-AMP., SERVICE

RANGE, 8000—16,000 W. DRIER, 4500 W.

HOT-WATER HEATER, 2000—4000 W. 800 W ROOM AIR CONDITIONER

Above dotted line are common household appliances normally operated on 115-v. 60-amp. service. Those units below the dotted line are usually supplied for 230-v.

TABLE I RESISTANCE, CURRENT LIMITS AND LINE LOSS FOR VARIOUS SIZES OF WIRE				
WIRE SIZE (No.)	RESISTANCE (ohms per 1000 ft.)	MAXIMUM AMPS (indoors)	VOLTAGE DROP PER 50' OF CIRCUIT AT MAX. AMPS.	POWER LOSS PER 50' OF CIRCUIT AT MAX. AMPS.
14	2.621	15	3.9	59
12	1.650	20	3.3	61
10	1.036	30	3.1	93
8	0.6574	40	2.6	105
6	0.4105	55	2.3	124
4	0.2588	70	1.81	127
3	0.2054	80	1.64	131
2	0.1618	95	1.53	138
1	0.1290	110	1.42	156
0	0.1019	125	1.27	159

TABLE II DEMAND LOAD AND WIRE SIZE FOR RANGES			
RATING OF RANGE	WATT-DEMAND LOAD	CURRENT DEMAND (at 230 v.)	WIRE SIZE OF RANGE FEEDERS (No.)
Up to 12 KW	8,000 w.	34.8 amp.	8
12-13 KW	8,400 w	36.6 amp.	8
13-14 KW	8,800 w.	38.2 amp.	8
14-15 KW	9,200 w.	40.0 amp.	8
15-16 KW	9,600 w.	41.7 amp.	6
16-17 KW	10,000 w.	43.5 amp.	6
17-18 KW	10,400 w.	45.2 amp.	6
18-19 KW	10,800 w	47.0 amp.	6
19-20 KW	11,200 w.	48.7 amp.	6
20-21 KW	11,600 w.	50.4 amp.	6

2

MINIMUM NUMBER OF GENERAL-PURPOSE CIRCUITS
1. FLOOR AREA = (24 x 10) + (28 x 15) + (27.5 x 23)
    = 240 + 420 + 632 = 1292 SQ. FT.
2. WATTS LOAD = 3 WATTS PER SQ. FT.
    = 3 × 1292 = 3900 WATTS
3. (A) USING 15-AMP. CIRCUITS (No. 14 WIRE)
 No. OF CIRCUITS = $\frac{3900}{1725}$ = 2.3, OR 3 CIRCUITS
 (B) USING 20-AMP. CIRCUITS (No. 12 WIRE)
 No. OF CIRCUITS = $\frac{3900}{2300}$ = 1.7, OR 2 CIRCUITS

drop at these currents per 50 ft. of circuit. Voltage drop should not exceed 2 percent on branch lines with lights or 5 percent under any conditions. A drop in voltage greater than these percentages is not only power wasted, it can become a hazard. Electric power is measured in watts and many appliances have the rated wattage and voltage stamped on the name plate. From this it is possible to calculate current requirements (amps.) simply by dividing the watts by the voltage. On fractional-hp. motors in such sizes as are used on household appliances, the amperage usually is stamped on the name plate. Using this information it is possible to determine the total current requirements of a number of appliances. Fig. 1, which is purely representative and not intended to be in any way typical, pictures the appliances commonly operated on the 115-v., 60-amp. service, the branch lines

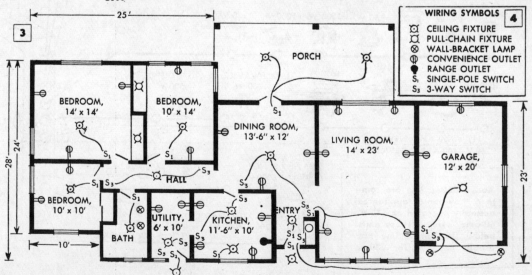

3

WIRING SYMBOLS **4**
- ☒ CEILING FIXTURE
- ☒ PULL-CHAIN FIXTURE
- ⊗ WALL-BRACKET LAMP
- ⦶ CONVENIENCE OUTLET
- ● RANGE OUTLET
- S₁ SINGLE-POLE SWITCH
- S₃ 3-WAY SWITCH

PORCH

BEDROOM, 14' x 14'

BEDROOM, 10' x 14'

DINING ROOM, 13'-6" x 12'

LIVING ROOM, 14' x 23'

GARAGE, 12' x 20'

BEDROOM, 10' x 10'

HALL

UTILITY, 6' x 10'

KITCHEN, 11'-6" x 10'

ENTRY

BATH

25'

28'

24'

23'

10'

TABLE III
CURRENT-CARRYING CAPACITY OF FLEXIBLE CORDS AND FIXTURE WIRE

WIRE SIZE	OHMS PER 1000 FT	ALLOWABLE CURRENT, FLEX CORD	VOLTAGE DROP PER 50-FT. LENGTH OF CORD (a)	MAXIMUM-USE FACTOR (AMPS x LENGTH) (c)	ALLOWABLE CURRENT, FIXTURE WIRE (b)
18	6.636	7 amp.	4.6	430	5 amp
16	4.174	10 amp	4.2	680	7 amp
14	2.621	15 amp.	3.9	1100	––
12	1.650	20 amp	3.3	1740	––

(a) At maximum allowable current
(b) As used to connect individual light fixtures to circuit
(c) For 5% voltage drop

being fused to 15 amps. Such units as the electric range, clothes drier, water heater and certain types of air conditioners require a 230-v., 100-amp. service.

The amount of current available at each outlet depends on the wire size of the supply lines, the number of branch lines carrying current to outlets throughout the house and also on the number of taps into current flowing to each branch line. With an inadequate service, overloading of one branch in effect robs others of current and may cause a voltage drop below the nominal limits throughout the system. Wattage used up in line loss heats the wires. The resistance of the overloaded wires increases as they warm up. Thus if overloading goes beyond safe limits for an appreciable length of time the wires may heat to the point of igniting the insulation. Over a long period of time there is equal hazard in the cumulative effect of a continuing overloaded condition, which is certain to cause a breakdown of the insulation.

When planning an adequate service for an older home, decide on the number of additional outlets, lights and switches. Then you can plan the special-purpose circuits and other wiring which are to be added. Figs. 3 and 4 suggest a procedure in planning. Minimum standards call for one outlet for each 20 ft. of wall, but usually it is better to reduce this to one outlet for each 12 ft. of wall, or simply plan enough outlets so that no point on a usable wall is more than 6 ft. from an outlet, and in the kitchen about 4 ft.

In older homes most of the branch circuits are general-purpose circuits supplying both lights and outlets for appliances.

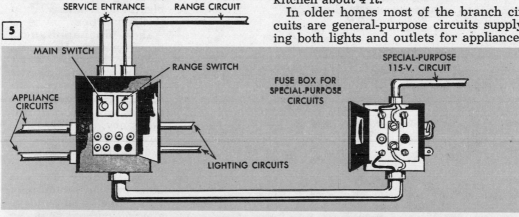

5

SERVICE ENTRANCE — RANGE CIRCUIT
MAIN SWITCH
RANGE SWITCH
APPLIANCE CIRCUITS
FUSE BOX FOR SPECIAL-PURPOSE CIRCUITS
SPECIAL-PURPOSE 115-V. CIRCUIT
LIGHTING CIRCUITS

TABLE IV
WHEN TO USE INDIVIDUAL BRANCH CIRCUITS

	CLASS OF EQUIPMENT	EXAMPLES
NECESSARY	Equipment over 16 amp.	Range, clothes drier
CONVENIENT	Equipment vital to home operation	Water pump, furnace
DESIRABLE	Motors, and appliances with large motors	Workshop, home freezer

663

TABLE V
BRANCH-CIRCUIT SPECIFICATIONS

Type of Circuit	General-Purpose Branch Circuit		Appliance Circuit	Individual-Appliance Circuit		
Max. rating	15 amp.	20 amp.	20 amp.	15 amp.	20 amp.	30 amp.
Wire size (minimum)	14	12	12	14	12	10
Size of fuse (maximum)	15 amp.	20 amp.	20 amp.	15 amp.	20 amp.	30 amp. not over 150% of appliance rating
Required rating of outlet receptacles	15 amp.	15 / 20	15 / 20	15 amp.	20 amp.	30 amp
Max. rating of appliance connected to a receptacle	12 amp. 1380 w	12 / 16 1380/1840	12 / 16 1380/1840	12 amp. 1380 w	16 amp. 1840 w	24 amp 2760 w
Max. rating of permanently connected appliances	7.5 amp.	10 amp	10 amp.	15 amp.	20 amp.	30 amp.
Lamps permitted on circuit?	Yes	Yes	No	No	No	No

TABLE VI
CHECK LIST OF ACTUAL LOAD
ON GENERAL-PURPOSE AND APPLIANCE CIRCUITS

Room	No. of Outlets	Fixtures and Appliances	Watts	Amperes	
				Gen. Purpose Circuits (a)	Appliance Circuits (b)
Living room	7	Table lamps (6)	1020	8.9	
		Radio	75	.7	
		TV	300	2.6	
Entry hall	1	Ceiling light	100	9	
Hall closet	1	Ceiling light	60	5	
Kitchen	7	Ceiling lights (2)	150	1.3	
		Toaster—1000 w.			
		French fryer—1050 w	1050		9.1
		Waffle iron—600 w.			
		Mixer	120		1.1
		Iron	1000		8.7
		Refrigerator	300		7.0
		Ventilator	150		1.2
		Coffee maker	525		4.6
Dining room	4	Ceiling light	150	1.3	
Hall	1	Ceiling light	100	9	
Attic	1	Ceiling light	60	.5	
Bedroom No. 1	4	Ceiling light	120	1 1	
		Radio	60	.5	
		Table lamp	100	.9	
Closet	1	Ceiling light	60	.5	
Bedroom No. 2	4	Ceiling light	120	1 1	
		Table lamps	120	1 1	
Closet	1	Ceiling light	60	.5	
Bathroom	3	Ceiling lights (2)	180	1.6	
		Portable heater	600	5.2	
Basement	3	Lights (7)	630	5.5	
		Freezer	350		4.8
Laundry	2	Washing machine	700		7.0
		Ironer	1500		13.0
Porch, outside	1	Lights (3)	220	1.9	
TOTAL				37.5	56.5

Total current: 94.0 amp.
Equivalent watts: 94 x 115 = 10,800 watts

Usually these will have a capacity of 15 amps., depending on the wire size. This means that the maximum power that can be taken from them is about 1725 watts, less if the wire size is smaller than No. 14. Modern homes will require at least one appliance circuit for outlets in the kitchen, dining room, breakfast room and laundry to handle heavy-current appliances. These outlets usually are wired with No. 12 wire and fused for 20 amps. The appliance circuit should carry all outlets in these rooms (except clock outlets), but no outlets in any other rooms and no light fixtures. Note Tables IV and V, the latter summarizing specifications for branch circuits.

A check list of the actual load on general-purpose and appliance circuits, of which Table VI is a sample, is helpful in planning wiring layout and calculating the total amperage. Note also Tables IV, VII and VIII in this connection.

Individual appliances drawing over 16 amps., such as a range, water heater and the electric drier, require special circuits, Fig. 5. Independent circuits, although not necessary, are desirable for large motors, or groups of motors, such as power tools in the home shop. Independent circuits prevent dimming of lights due to the heavy starting current required by the larger motors. When making up the check list of outlets, lighting fixtures and the wattage of lamps and appliances, include all those appliances you may add in the future. Where two appliances are of a type never used simultaneously, list only the one with the highest wattage. Convert watts to amps. by dividing the total by the line voltage and you have the current requirement. Since the load connected to any branch must not exceed its capacity—better slightly under full capacity—you can easily determine the number of branch circuits required to carry the estimated load. This method is reasonably accurate when estimating wiring requirements for both old and new homes, but before actual work is carried out you must make sure that the procedures are in accordance with local and national electrical codes.

When you plan to increase the demand on an existing installation the wire size, service capacity and the type of service, whether 2 or 3-wire, are important considerations. Appliance circuits on No. 12 wire are now required in most localities. Circuits on which lights are used cannot be fused for more than 20 amps. See Table V. Special-purpose circuits, Fig. 5, for larger appliances should use the size of wire required by their current demand. The total current requirement generally is used in determining the size of service-entrance conductors and the amp. rating of the service-entrance switch and the fuses required. The current demand of a range is determined separately from Table III and added to the other requirements. In figuring a new service entrance, either for new construction or for an existing installation, it's best to anticipate possible future demand and go beyond that required at present, both in wire size and type of service.

At present electricity is supplied to homes either by 2-wire 110, 115 or 120-v. systems or by 3-wire 110/220, 115/230 or 120/240-v. systems, 115/230-v. being perhaps the most common of the 3-wire services. The 2 and 3-wire systems are diagrammed in Figs. 6 and 7. The 3-wire system provides both voltages and should be installed wherever possible as it offers several advantages. Because the 3-wire system doubles the voltage, smaller wires can be used from entrance to main switch. Smaller fuses are required. As an example, a 13,000-watt service would require 120-amp. fuses and main switch and No. 0 wire size on a 2-wire, 115-v. system. The same

CHECK LIST – TABLE VII
EQUIPMENT ON INDIVIDUAL CIRCUITS

Equipment	Rating	Amperes 115 Volts	Amperes 230 Volts	Watts Demand on Branch Circuit
Clothes drier	4500 w		19.5	4500
Workshop				
Saw	3/4 hp., 10.2 amp.			
Jointer	1/3 hp., 6.0 amp.	16.2		1860
Drill press	1/4 hp., 4.6 amp.			
Water pump	1 hp.		5.3	1220
Furnace	1/6 hp.	2.9		
	1/4 hp.	4.8		
		7.7		885
Total of equipment on individual circuits (except range)				8465
Range	10.6 KW			8000*

* Range demand figured separately, as shown in Table II.

(Watts demand on all other branch circuits equal to appliance rating.)

TABLE VIII
GENERAL-PURPOSE CIRCUITS

(A) Using 15-amp (No 14 wire) circuits:

$$\text{No of circuits} = \frac{AMPS.}{10}$$

$$= \frac{37.5}{10} = 3.75 \text{ or } 4 \text{ circuits}$$

(B) Using 20-amp (No 12 wire) circuits:

$$\text{No of circuits} = \frac{AMPS.}{15}$$

$$= \frac{37.5}{15} = 2.5 \text{ or } 3 \text{ circuits}$$

APPLIANCE CIRCUITS

(20-amp., No 12 wire, circuits)

$$\text{No. of circuits} = \frac{AMPS}{15}$$

$$= \frac{56.5}{15} = 3 8 \text{ or } 4 \text{ circuits}$$

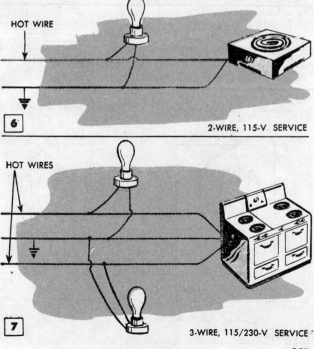

HOT WIRE

6   2-WIRE, 115-V. SERVICE

HOT WIRES

7   3-WIRE, 115/230-V SERVICE

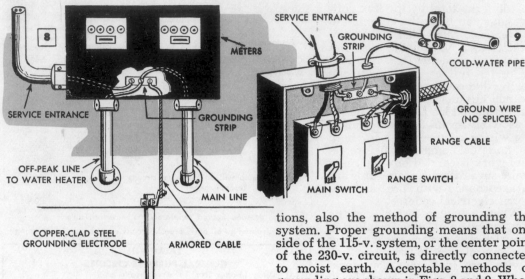

8 METERS

SERVICE ENTRANCE

GROUNDING STRIP

OFF-PEAK LINE TO WATER HEATER

MAIN LINE

COPPER-CLAD STEEL GROUNDING ELECTRODE

ARMORED CABLE

SERVICE ENTRANCE

GROUNDING STRIP

COLD-WATER PIPE

9

GROUND WIRE (NO SPLICES)

RANGE CABLE

MAIN SWITCH

RANGE SWITCH

service would require only 60-amp. fuses and No. 4 wire on a 3-wire 115-230-v. system. Appliances which take a heavier current, also larger shop motors, usually are designed for 230-v. current. Motors of ½ hp. and larger generally are arranged for operation on either 115 or 230-v. current. On the higher voltage the units require less current and can be operated with smaller sizes of wire.

Grounding is simple and 230 v. can be obtained even though the potential at no point exceeds 115 v. above ground. The 3-wire system also provides a better-balanced load condition. Most power suppliers require a 3-wire installation when new wiring is added to existing systems.

Existing installations, especially those in older homes, should be carefully checked over before planning new additions to the service. Condition of the existing wiring and the wire size are important considera-

tions, also the method of grounding the system. Proper grounding means that one side of the 115-v. system, or the center point of the 230-v. circuit, is directly connected to moist earth. Acceptable methods of grounding are shown in Figs. 8 and 9. When special-purpose circuits are added to an existing system, wiring through the special-purpose fuse boxes must be properly carried out. Fig. 10 shows acceptable methods.

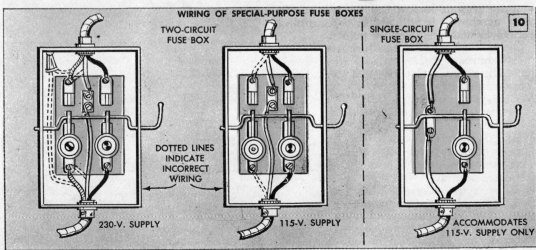

WIRING OF SPECIAL-PURPOSE FUSE BOXES

TWO-CIRCUIT FUSE BOX

SINGLE-CIRCUIT FUSE BOX

10

DOTTED LINES INDICATE INCORRECT WIRING

230-V. SUPPLY

115-V. SUPPLY

ACCOMMODATES 115-V. SUPPLY ONLY

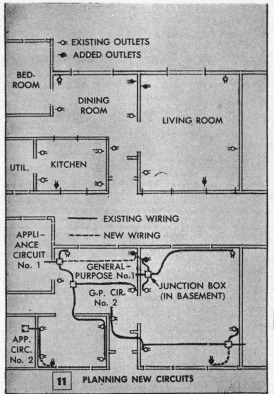

EXISTING OUTLETS
ADDED OUTLETS

BED-ROOM

DINING ROOM

LIVING ROOM

UTIL. KITCHEN

—— EXISTING WIRING
---- NEW WIRING

APPLIANCE CIRCUIT No. 1

GENERAL PURPOSE No. 1

G.P. CIR. No. 2

JUNCTION BOX (IN BASEMENT)

APP. CIRC. No. 2

11 PLANNING NEW CIRCUITS

MANY OLDER HOMES have 110 or 115-v. electrical service and the current that can be safely drawn from such existing systems is usually no more than adequate to handle the normal number of lighting fixtures and appliances which have been common for a number of years, and which are designed for comparatively low current requirements. Usually such systems were installed with the minimum number of circuits and convenience outlets and fall far short of present-day needs.

When newer appliances of heavy current requirements are to be added to the household equipment, it is important to plan adequate main and branch electrical service. Usually it is recommended that 3-wire service be installed from the power source to the service panel, making 115-230-v. current available at the main entrance switch. From this point on, the answer to the question of whether to rewire the house completely or to install new branch circuits is dependent on several factors and can be determined only by a complete survey of the existing installation. Inspection of existing wiring should include examination of wire splices and insulation in all junction boxes. Switches that fail to act

positively on make and break should be replaced, as defective switches may heat to the danger point if left on over long periods of time. Note also the length, location and number of extension cords that are normally used with the existing wiring, keeping in mind that all ordinary extension cords are No. 18 wire and will handle only limited current. Examine the system carefully to determine whether or not it is properly grounded. In some early installations the neutral, or grounded, wire was fused. This should never be done, as a blown fuse on the grounded, or neutral, wire removes the protection of grounding beyond that point.

A survey of the existing wiring conducted in the manner described (see also pages 661-666) will indicate wiring defects, show where new outlets are needed (also how many) and whether it is practical to regroup outlets into new circuits. Where additional outlets are necessary to bring the installation up-to-date, it will help to begin by making a simple floor plan, Fig. 11, indicating by symbols the existing outlets and those to be added.

Fig. 20, detail A, the upper plan, shows the wiring of four general-purpose circuits in a home. Circuits No. 3 and 4 are adequate, but circuits No. 1 and 2 are found to be overloaded. Because of this it is decided to take parts of these two circuits

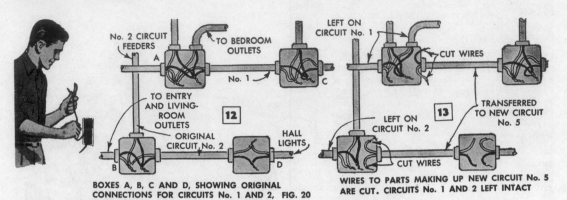

No. 2 CIRCUIT FEEDERS

TO BEDROOM OUTLETS

A

No. 1

C

TO ENTRY AND LIVING-ROOM OUTLETS

ORIGINAL CIRCUIT No. 2

B

HALL LIGHTS

D

LEFT ON CIRCUIT No. 1

CUT WIRES

LEFT ON CIRCUIT No. 2

TRANSFERRED TO NEW CIRCUIT No. 5

CUT WIRES

12

13

BOXES A, B, C AND D, SHOWING ORIGINAL CONNECTIONS FOR CIRCUITS No. 1 AND 2, FIG. 20

WIRES TO PARTS MAKING UP NEW CIRCUIT No. 5 ARE CUT. CIRCUITS No. 1 AND 2 LEFT INTACT

POINTS TO CONSIDER
WHEN PLANNING LOCATIONS OF OUTLETS, LIGHTS AND SWITCHES

FOR	CONVENIENCE OUTLETS	SPECIAL OUTLETS for	PERMANENT LIGHTING	SWITCHES
Living Room Recreation Room General Living Areas	Placed so that no point along floor line of usable wall space is more than 6 ft. from an outlet	FM radio Television Room air conditioner	From ceiling, wall, cove or valance lights Switched convenience outlets may be substituted in living rooms	On latch side of each frequently used doorway

Rooms with entrances more than 10 feet apart should have multiple control switches |
Dining Areas	Near hostess' chair. Placed so that no point along floor line of usable wall space is more than 6 ft. from an outlet. One above counter or table space when next to wall		Ceiling light over table	
Bedrooms	Place outlets on each side and within 6 ft. of each bed location. Apply Living Room rule to remaining space	Room air conditioner	From ceiling, wall, cove or valance lights	
Kitchen	For each 4 ft. of work counter For refrigerator For planning desk At table space	Electric range Dishwasher-disposer Home freezer Clock Ventilating fan	Provide general light and light over sink Others over work counters as needed	
Laundry	For hot-plate, etc.	Automatic washer Electric drier Iron or ironer Ventilating fan	At washing area At ironing area	
Bathrooms	Adjacent to mirror	Built-in heater Ventilating fan	Light both sides of face at mirror One in enclosed shower compartment	
Hallways	For each 15 ft. of hallway		One at least; two in long halls	
Entrances	Near front entrance (weatherproof)		At front entrance At trades entrance	Inside front entrance Inside trades entrance
Stairways			Light at head and foot	Switches at head and foot for each light
Closets			For each closet	
Porches, Terraces, Patios	For each 15 ft. of usable outside wall (weatherproof)		For each 150 sq. ft. of porch	Inside door to porch
Utility Room or Basement	One at workbench One near furnace	Fuel-fired heating equipment Electric water heater	For each enclosed space At workbench Near furnace At foot of basement stairs	At head of stairs or at entrance
Attic	One for general use	Summer cooling fan	One for each separate space	At bottom of stairs
Garage or Carport	One for general use	Food freezer Workbench Door opener	Interior light Exterior light if detached garage	At door Multiple switches at garage and house

NOTE: The requirements given here for number and placement of outlets, lights and switches are the bare minimum requirements. For additional suggestions and more details, ask your electric power supplier or an experienced electrical contractor about the accepted Standards of Wiring Adequacy, approved by the National Adequate Wiring Bureau.

Table courtesy National Adequate Wiring Bureau

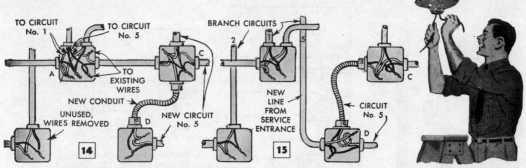

14 WIRES FISHED THROUGH EXISTING CONDUIT FEED NEW BRANCH. CABLE CONNECTS TO PART OF OLD CIRCUIT No. 2

15 ALTERNATE METHOD: CONDUIT FROM MAIN FUSE CENTER FEEDS NEW CIRCUIT. UNUSED CONDUIT, WIRES, PULLED OUT

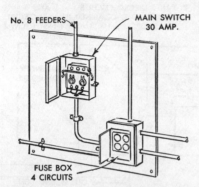

16 SERVICE, MAIN SWITCH AND BRANCH CIRCUITS INADEQUATE

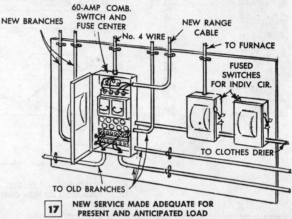

17 NEW SERVICE MADE ADEQUATE FOR PRESENT AND ANTICIPATED LOAD

and make a new circuit, No. 5, in the lower plan. Figs. 12 to 15 inclusive show how this can be done. Boxes A and B, Fig. 12, are opened and the wires to the parts of the old circuits beyond these points are cut. In some cases, additional wires can be fished through the same conduits from the service entrance to feed the new circuit, Fig. 14. In this instance, new wires from the fuse box are brought through junction box A to junction box C. The separated part of the old circuit No. 2 is connected to the new circuit by means of a new length of conduit running from box D to box C. An alternate method is to run a new conduit from the fuse box to box D and then to box C, Fig. 15. All conduits and cables not used should be removed, as they can no longer serve any practical purpose in the installation.

The plan for added circuits and new outlets may require that changes be made at the "service entrance," the term quite generally applied to the main service panel on which are mounted the main switch and fuse cabinet for the branch circuits. The units shown in Fig. 16 are more or less typical of the service entrance in older installations. Changes can be quite simple or more involved, depending on what extent it is necessary to enlarge the system. Variations, according to the requirements, are

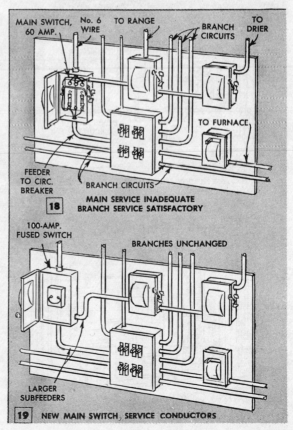

18 MAIN SERVICE INADEQUATE BRANCH SERVICE SATISFACTORY

19 NEW MAIN SWITCH, SERVICE CONDUCTORS

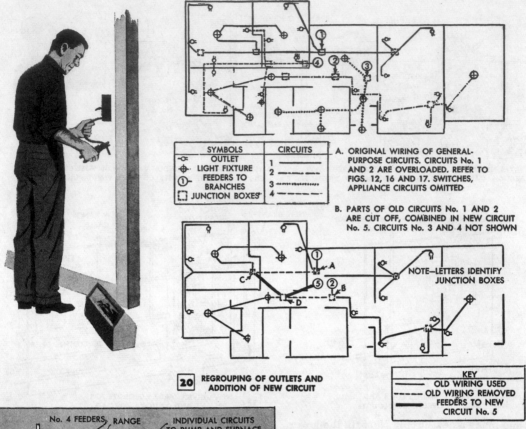

SYMBOLS		CIRCUITS	
⊸	OUTLET	1	
⊕	LIGHT FIXTURE	2	
①	FEEDERS TO BRANCHES	3	
⬚	JUNCTION BOXES	4	

A. ORIGINAL WIRING OF GENERAL-PURPOSE CIRCUITS. CIRCUITS No. 1 AND 2 ARE OVERLOADED. REFER TO FIGS. 12, 16 AND 17. SWITCHES, APPLIANCE CIRCUITS OMITTED

B. PARTS OF OLD CIRCUITS No. 1 AND 2 ARE CUT OFF, COMBINED IN NEW CIRCUIT No. 5. CIRCUITS No. 3 AND 4 NOT SHOWN

NOTE—LETTERS IDENTIFY JUNCTION BOXES

20 REGROUPING OF OUTLETS AND ADDITION OF NEW CIRCUIT

KEY	
	OLD WIRING USED
	OLD WIRING REMOVED
	FEEDERS TO NEW CIRCUIT No. 5

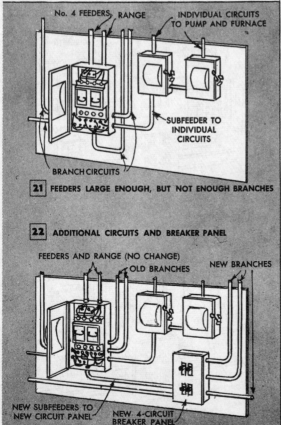

21 FEEDERS LARGE ENOUGH, BUT NOT ENOUGH BRANCHES

No. 4 FEEDERS — RANGE — INDIVIDUAL CIRCUITS TO PUMP AND FURNACE — SUBFEEDER TO INDIVIDUAL CIRCUITS — BRANCH CIRCUITS

22 ADDITIONAL CIRCUITS AND BREAKER PANEL

FEEDERS AND RANGE (NO CHANGE) — OLD BRANCHES — NEW BRANCHES — NEW SUBFEEDERS TO NEW CIRCUIT PANEL — NEW 4-CIRCUIT BREAKER PANEL

shown in Figs. 17, 18, 19, 21 and 22. Usually the installation in Fig. 17 is considered adequate for a 60-amp. service with fused switches on the individual circuits and main feeders of No. 4 wire. In making any change it's usually best to begin with a combination unit. This consists of a main switch and fuses and branch circuit fuses or circuit breakers, all enclosed in a single cabinet, or box, as such a unit is commonly called.

In planning additions to an existing installation always consider the necessary "balance" of the main service and branch service. Fig. 18 is an example. Fig. 19 shows the installation of a new main switch and service conductors, No. 2 feeders and larger subfeeders being installed to provide adequate main and branch service. Fig. 21 shows a panel with adequate main service but not enough branches to take care of requirements. Fig. 22 shows how a breaker panel and additional circuits are added to provide for present and possible future needs.

It should be understood, of course, that the methods detailed are purely representative and are not intended to in any way supplant the recommendations of your electrician or any electrical code. ★ ★ ★

HOME REWIRING

CURRENT CAPACITIES OF WIRES

Size		Size	
14—15 amperes		4—70 amperes	
12—20	"	3—80	"
10—30	"	2—95	"
8—40	"	1—110	"
6—55	"		

These are Code capacities. The sizes mentioned throughout this article are one size larger to compensate for voltage drop. For feeders use one size larger than table

Older homes usually are not wired to make full use of all electrical conveniences now available or being developed. In many houses, the wiring is not of approved sizes to carry modern appliance loads; there are too few switches for control of the lights and an insufficient number of convenience outlets.

Rewiring a home to take care of present and possible future requirements is quite simple to do. While most localities have no regulations prohibiting a homeowner from doing his own wiring, it generally is required that the completed job be inspected by a competent electrician for compliance with both the national and local electrical codes. Therefore, before going ahead with a wiring job, the homeowner should study all the local ordinances and codes and should be familiar with the requirements of the national electrical code.

A rewiring job requires careful planning, so the first thing to do is make rough pencil sketches of the present wiring. Make a separate diagram for each floor of the house. If there is a garage or other building wired for electricity, include this on the ground-floor sketch.

On each sketch, simply mark the approximate location of each lighting fixture, wall switch, convenience outlet, etc. Next, make pencil notes of the various conveniences and appliances desired. Among those that may be needed are fluorescent lighting, combination receptacles for radio power, aerial and ground, and switches that permit lights to be turned on and off from any entrance to a room or from the top or bottom of a stairway.

Other modern conveniences include door switches in all clothes closets, which turn on the lights when the doors are opened, and outlets that provide plug-in receptacles easily reached from any part of the room. Locate separate outlets for the kitchen clock, mantel clock, electric

A rough pencil sketch should be made of wiring of each floor in house before rewiring job is undertaken.

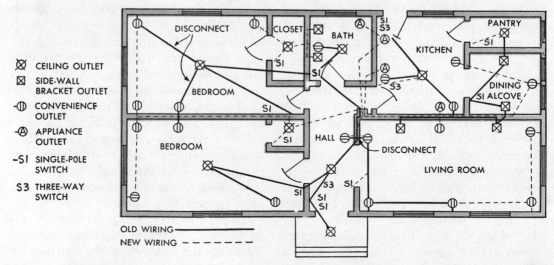

⊗ CEILING OUTLET

⊠ SIDE-WALL BRACKET OUTLET

-⊕ CONVENIENCE OUTLET

-Ⓐ APPLIANCE OUTLET

-SI SINGLE-POLE SWITCH

S3 THREE-WAY SWITCH

OLD WIRING ————
NEW WIRING - - - - -

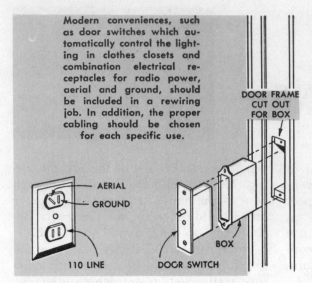

Modern conveniences, such as door switches which automatically control the lighting in clothes closets and combination electrical receptacles for radio power, aerial and ground, should be included in a rewiring job. In addition, the proper cabling should be chosen for each specific use.

DOOR FRAME CUT OUT FOR BOX

AERIAL
GROUND
110 LINE
BOX
DOOR SWITCH

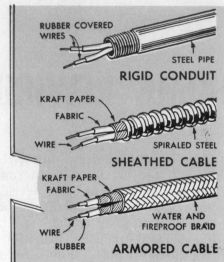

RUBBER COVERED WIRES
STEEL PIPE
RIGID CONDUIT

KRAFT PAPER
FABRIC
WIRE
SPIRALED STEEL
SHEATHED CABLE

KRAFT PAPER
FABRIC
WIRE
RUBBER
WATER AND FIREPROOF BRAID
ARMORED CABLE

iron, washing machine, dishwasher, garbage-disposal unit and a ventilating fan. Any other special lighting problems should be considered and provided for in the rough plan.

If wires are not large enough to handle maximum current requirements, lights and appliances will not deliver their rated output. The national code recommends No. 12 wire as the smallest size to be used on branch circuits.

In addition, the code specifies that wiring capacity be sufficient to provide at least 2 watts of lighting for every square foot of floor area in the house—excluding unfinished areas such as the basement and attic, unless these require special lighting.

In addition to lighting requirements, capacity for 1500 watts of appliance load must be provided on circuits separate from the lighting and convenience-receptacle circuits. Appliance circuits usually are provided for the kitchen, dining room, utility room and laundry, or whichever of these are on the floor plan. If a total of more than six receptacles is required in these locations, two or more circuits are provided.

When planning appliance circuits, remember that other heavy-load appliances such as a home freezer, clothes drier and perhaps a room-type air conditioner may be added in the future. If these extra units are being considered, plan one or

more extra circuits or provide sufficient capacity in the branch control center and feeders to take care of the requirements.

In deciding on the location of convenience outlets and circuits, the following suggestions may be helpful as they follow approved procedure:

Place a receptacle in each usable wall space 3 ft. or more in width. Have a receptacle located within 6 ft. (at the floor line) of any location in any usable wall space. Provide receptacles on enclosed porches. All outdoor receptacles must be of the weatherproof type. Receptacles for television sets should be located so that the set can be placed where light from windows will not strike the screen directly. Place at least one receptacle at each work space in the kitchen, workshop, garage and utility room. Locate separate receptacles for fixed appliances such as the garbage eliminator, dishwasher, ventilating fan and bathroom heater. Workshop motors should be on the shop-lighting circuit so that machines which happen to be in operation will stop if the lights go out.

The next planning step is to sketch in the new wiring system with a colored pencil on the wiring diagram. Make use, if possible, of all existing outlets to eliminate unnecessary work.

Then, opposite each permanently connected lamp mark the wattage required. Total up the wattage of the lighting fix-

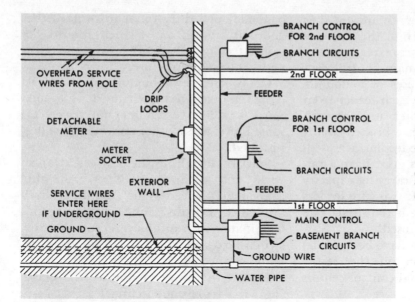

OVERHEAD SERVICE WIRES FROM POLE

DRIP LOOPS

DETACHABLE METER

METER SOCKET

EXTERIOR WALL

SERVICE WIRES ENTER HERE IF UNDERGROUND

GROUND

BRANCH CONTROL FOR 2nd FLOOR

BRANCH CIRCUITS

2nd FLOOR

FEEDER

BRANCH CONTROL FOR 1st FLOOR

BRANCH CIRCUITS

FEEDER

1st FLOOR

MAIN CONTROL

BASEMENT BRANCH CIRCUITS

GROUND WIRE

WATER PIPE

The best method of controlling electricity is to provide a branch control center for each floor in the house. These centers can be fed from a main control center located where the service feeders from the power lines enter the house.

tures. As 1725 watts are allowed on each circuit, divide the total wattage by 1725 to find the number of circuits required.

In wiring lights on two or more circuits, it is best, where possible, to arrange them so that all lights on each floor are not on one circuit. Otherwise, the blowing of a fuse will cause all the lights on that floor to go out. To figure the number of receptacle circuits required (other than the special ones feeding kitchen, laundry, etc.) allow one circuit for each six or seven receptacles. It is best to provide a branch control center for each floor in the house. These branch control centers are fed from a main control center located near the point where the service feeder enters the house.

When the number of lighting and convenience-receptacle circuits have been calculated for each floor, mark this information on the sketch.

Branch circuits should be of No. 12 wire, each circuit being rated at 15 amp. The rated amperage of all the circuits in a branch control center added together will give the total amperage required for that control center. This will apply where two-wire feeders are used between the branch control centers and the main control center. However, three-wire service lately has come into common use in new installations. With three-wire feeders, the amperage will be halved.

The correct size of wire required for each branch feeder can be determined easily from the table on the "Current Capacities of Wires."

The feeder circuits remaining to be calculated are the individual branch circuits which feed directly to heavy-load appliances such as a water heater or range. If the power company does not require a separate meter on the water-heater circuit, both the heater and the range may be connected to the same branch circuit.

To calculate the size of the feeders required, simply divide the wattage of each appliance by the voltage. This will give the amperage required. For example, a water heater consuming 3000 watts at 230 volts will require 13 amp. (3000 divided by 230). Use No. 10 wire for this load.

The range load is calculated in the same manner. While ranges usually operate on both 115 and 230 volts, depending upon how many burners are in use at a time, only the 230 voltage is used to calculate the amperage. For a range rated at 7000 watts, the load would be 30.4 amp. Use a three-wire feeder of No. 16 wire.

Branch control centers may be arranged in three ways. They may consist of only 15-amp. circuits for lamps and convenience receptacles. Secondly, they may contain one or more 15-amp. circuits and one or more 20-amp. appliance circuits. Or, they may contain only 20-

amp. circuits. A fuse or circuit breaker protects each circuit, but the fuse or breaker must be of no greater capacity than the circuit. The main control center will contain two fuses or a double-pole circuit breaker for each feeder from the branch control center and for each feeder from the appliance branch-circuit feeder where three-wire feeders are used.

The overload devices must have a rating no higher than the carrying capacity of the wires they feed. If two-wire feeders are used, only one fuse is required. The grounded wire is not fused.

After the calculations have been made, mark this information on the rough sketch of the circuits and control centers of the new system.

The installation of new conduit runs is not difficult. Some local codes permit only thin-wall conduit to be used in certain locations. Check before making the installation. In all conduit work, whether using rigid or flexible metal conduit, the structure of the house determines to some extent the procedure to be followed.

Usually, there is a way to feed flexible conduit either through or around ordinary obstructions, but sometimes it will be found impossible to run conduit to certain locations. Such outlets may have to be relocated or surface conduit, called metal molding, may have to be used. A suitable box should be installed in the basement or utility room to contain the doorbell transformer, which should be connected to a branch lighting circuit and protected with fuses.

Of course, rewiring an old house is more involved than wiring a new one. Service will have to be maintained to some lights while other circuits are being installed.

Start by installing the service-entrance wires and equipment. Next, run the branch-circuit feeders and the individual appliance circuits. The latter should terminate in suitable receptacles or switch boxes to which the appliances are to be connected.

Follow this by removing all the existing wires from one circuit at a time and installing new, larger-capacity wires. Where armored cable, nonmetallic cable or knob-and-tube wiring is to be replaced, remove all the old wiring. Next, fish in the new armored cable or flexible metal conduit and attach to the boxes. Larger-capacity armored cable may be installed, or three-wire armored cable substituted and the outlets divided evenly between the two circuits.

If rigid conduit is merely to be rewired, pull out the old wires and replace them with larger-capacity wiring of the new S.N. type having a smaller diameter. This can only be used for rewiring of existing conduits or metal molding. Either the

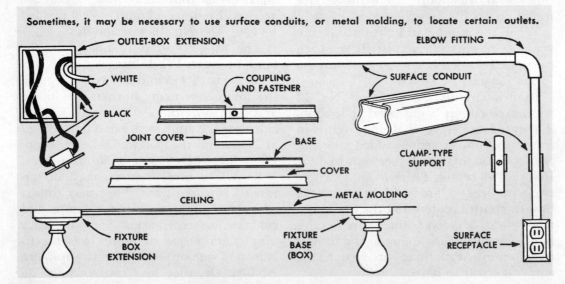

Sometimes, it may be necessary to use surface conduits, or metal molding, to locate certain outlets.

OUTLET-BOX EXTENSION
ELBOW FITTING
WHITE
COUPLING AND FASTENER
SURFACE CONDUIT
BLACK
JOINT COVER
BASE
CLAMP-TYPE SUPPORT
COVER
CEILING
METAL MOLDING
FIXTURE BOX EXTENSION
FIXTURE BASE (BOX)
SURFACE RECEPTACLE

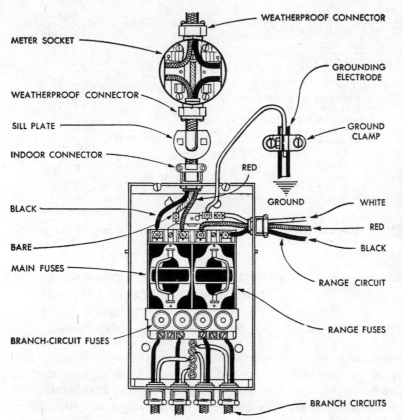

WEATHERPROOF CONNECTOR

METER SOCKET

GROUNDING ELECTRODE

WEATHERPROOF CONNECTOR

GROUND CLAMP

SILL PLATE

INDOOR CONNECTOR

RED

GROUND

WHITE

RED

BLACK

BLACK

BARE

MAIN FUSES

RANGE CIRCUIT

RANGE FUSES

BRANCH-CIRCUIT FUSES

BRANCH CIRCUITS

Service-entrance wire and equipment should be installed first in order to maintain the lighting when rewiring an old house. Therefore, the installation of this type of service switch, which is ideal for a house utility room where all the rooms are on one floor, is one of the primary jobs to be undertaken.

same number of wires of larger capacity can be used, or the circuits can be split into two parts and two circuits installed, using three or four wires of the same capacity.

Where three-wire branch circuits are used, they must be considered as two separate circuits. Each ungrounded wire is protected at the branch control center by a single-pole breaker or by a fuse.

As each circuit is completed and the connections made, it is tested and connected temporarily to the old distribution fuses. In splicing wires in outlet boxes, solder the joints and cover with

rubber tape and friction tape, or use approved solderless connectors.

When all the new circuits are finished they may be disconnected from the old fuses and connected to the new branch control centers, or main control center, as the case may be. The feeders are then connected and the branch control centers are mounted in their proper location. Then the feeders are connected to the main control center, but all circuit breakers are left in open-circuit position until the feeders and circuits have been tested.

To feed individual branch circuits,

Using a doorbell, two dry cell batteries and test prods, you can test various circuits.

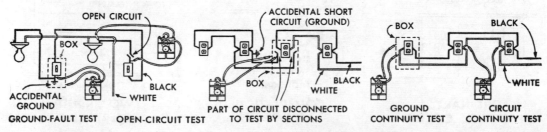

OPEN CIRCUIT

BOX

ACCIDENTAL SHORT CIRCUIT (GROUND)

BOX

BLACK

BOX

BLACK

WHITE

BLACK WHITE

WHITE

ACCIDENTAL GROUND

GROUND-FAULT TEST

OPEN-CIRCUIT TEST

PART OF CIRCUIT DISCONNECTED TO TEST BY SECTIONS

GROUND CONTINUITY TEST

CIRCUIT CONTINUITY TEST

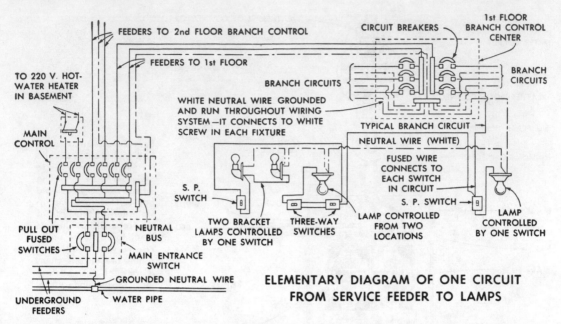

FEEDERS TO 2nd FLOOR BRANCH CONTROL

CIRCUIT BREAKERS

1st FLOOR BRANCH CONTROL CENTER

FEEDERS TO 1st FLOOR

TO 220 V. HOT-WATER HEATER IN BASEMENT

BRANCH CIRCUITS

BRANCH CIRCUITS

WHITE NEUTRAL WIRE GROUNDED AND RUN THROUGHOUT WIRING SYSTEM—IT CONNECTS TO WHITE SCREW IN EACH FIXTURE

TYPICAL BRANCH CIRCUIT

NEUTRAL WIRE (WHITE)

MAIN CONTROL

FUSED WIRE CONNECTS TO EACH SWITCH IN CIRCUIT

S. P. SWITCH

S. P. SWITCH

LAMP CONTROLLED BY ONE SWITCH

TWO BRACKET LAMPS CONTROLLED BY ONE SWITCH

THREE-WAY SWITCHES

LAMP CONTROLLED FROM TWO LOCATIONS

PULL OUT FUSED SWITCHES

NEUTRAL BUS

MAIN ENTRANCE SWITCH

GROUNDED NEUTRAL WIRE

UNDERGROUND FEEDERS

WATER PIPE

ELEMENTARY DIAGRAM OF ONE CIRCUIT FROM SERVICE FEEDER TO LAMPS

This is a wiring plan showing how various devices and fixtures are connected to circuits.

appliance circuits, feeders and service feeders, a simple test set uses a doorbell, two dry cells and test prods.

If a ground shows up, check all boxes through which the circuit feeds for the cause of the trouble. It may be caused by the end of a bare wire touching some metal part of an outlet box, or the insulation may have been cut on a wire where it enters a box. If the defective circuit can be tested in sections, this may save considerable time in locating the trouble.

The same general procedure is followed in searching for an open circuit, except that in the case of an open circuit a defective splice or broken wire usually is the cause of the fault. If all circuits test free of grounds and show complete circuit continuity, then test for ground continuity at each outlet.

These three types of receptacle units can be installed to improve the electrical system of the house.

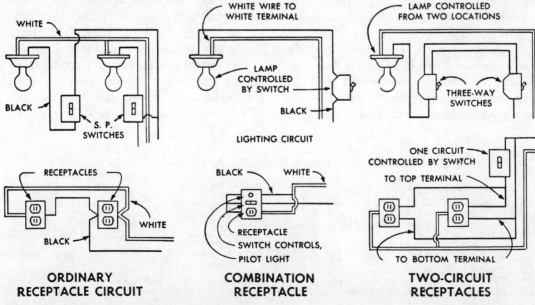

WHITE

BLACK

S. P. SWITCHES

RECEPTACLES

BLACK

WHITE

ORDINARY RECEPTACLE CIRCUIT

WHITE WIRE TO WHITE TERMINAL

LAMP CONTROLLED BY SWITCH

BLACK

LIGHTING CIRCUIT

BLACK

WHITE

RECEPTACLE SWITCH CONTROLS, PILOT LIGHT

COMBINATION RECEPTACLE

LAMP CONTROLLED FROM TWO LOCATIONS

THREE-WAY SWITCHES

ONE CIRCUIT CONTROLLED BY SWITCH

TO TOP TERMINAL

TO BOTTOM TERMINAL

TWO-CIRCUIT RECEPTACLES

MULTISTATION LIGHT CONTROL

By H. Alan Schwan

COMMONLY CALLED 3-way switches, single-pole, double-throw (s.p.d.t.) switches often are used at the upper and lower ends of a stairway leading to a second floor or to a basement, to permit turning a light on and off from two different locations. The method of wiring such switches is shown in the upper detail below. Should it be necessary or desirable to control a light, motor or appliance from three or more locations, two 3-way switches can be used, plus one or more 4-way switches — used as double-pole, double-throw switches (d.p.d.t.) in this wiring hookup—wired between them as indicated in the lower detail. Where small electrical loads are involved, such as lamps of 500 watts or less, or motors of ¼ hp. or less, heavy-duty, radio-type 4-way toggle switches can be used. The example shown in the illustration at the top of the page—controlling an outdoor light from three locations—could utilize this type of switch. Where electrical loads are heavier, regular house-type 3-way switches can be coupled together to provide a 4-way switch. The switch toggles are drilled and a small machine bolt and nut are used to lock the toggles together. The switches then are wired as shown in the lower right-hand detail. Wires C and D run to one of the 3-way switches, while wires E and F go either to another 4-way switch, or to a 3-way switch, as shown in the wiring diagram in the "typical section." These switches can, of course, be located wherever necessary. Three 4-way switches in the diagram shown produce a total of five locations. More or fewer switches may be used.

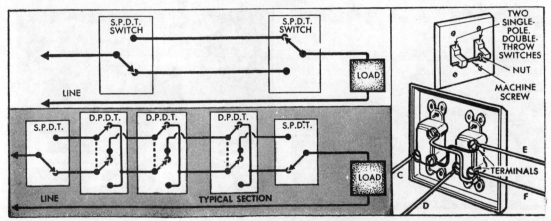

EXTENSION

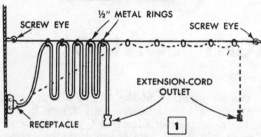

A ROUND YOUR HOME and workshop, the extension cords are as useful and valuable as any of the tools you own. Because so much depends on them, they deserve the same care as do your tools. Furthermore, if neglected, the extension cords can be numbered among the most dangerous items in the shop.

Extension wires trailing over the floor have caused more accidents than can be counted. The detail in Fig. 1 shows one good method of avoiding such a condition. The extension cord is strung through metal rings on a wire runner overhead. With this device, the cord can be pulled safely across the shop and yet be out of the way at all times.

Your extension cords should be checked occasionally for bad connections and broken wires. One way to do this is to turn on the radio at a spot between stations. Then, with the extension cord carrying current, roll it between your hands, and push and pull the cord at the points where it joins the plug and socket as well as at any suspected trouble spot. If the radio sputters during the test, the spot being checked needs repair. A typical source of trouble is indicated at A in Fig. 2, where the unsoldered strands of wire have frayed

SCREW EYE ½" METAL RINGS **SCREW EYE**

EXTENSION-CORD OUTLET

RECEPTACLE

1

Above, the extension cord is wired or taped to metal rings about 3 ft. apart when extended. This method keeps cord out of the way no matter where it is used

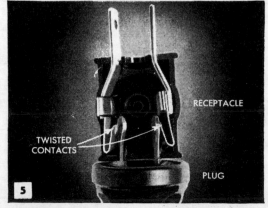

UNDERWRITERS' KNOT

B

A

2

LOOP

A

B

TAPE

3

RECEPTACLE

TWISTED CONTACTS

PLUG

5

CORDS

By Ed Packer

so the connection is poor. The proper condition of the wire is shown at B, where the strands of wire have been soldered before being wrapped around the terminal screw. Note the underwriter's knot in the same figure. When installing plugs, use such a knot inside of the plug to keep the wires from being pulled loose.

A neglected break in the insulation can cause a serious shock or a short circuit, and should be repaired immediately. A cord used in the shop is not easy to keep taped because of oil and grease, so the repair shown in Fig. 3 is useful. The broken area is taped, and the tape is held in place by a cord wrapping. A loop of cord is laid lengthwise on the wire and then the loop wrapped with cord. The end of the wrapping is brought through the loop at A. Then a pull on B, will tuck the end at A securely under the wrapping.

There are several ways of improving an extension cord's contact in the outlet. As in Fig. 4, the prongs can be notched with side cutters, which roughens the surface. Another method, Fig. 5, is to twist the prongs slightly, since bent contacts will wedge more tightly into the receptacle. The contact surfaces of a receptacle should be kept clean for best results. Fig. 6 shows how to clean them by sanding the inner surfaces with sandpaper rolled over a large nail.

Finally, for convenient storage and handling, every extension cord should have a winding reel. Figs. 7 to 9 show two such reels that are made easily from hardboard. The dimensions of the sides of the smaller one are 3½ x 5 in., and the large one is 6 x 12 in. The small reel accommodates 20 ft. of light cord, and has a night light which tells when power is coming through the line. The capacity of the large reel is 50 ft. of heavy cord, and it is made doubly handy by the receptacles mounted on it. ★ ★ ★

Reels are assembled from hardboard sides using copper tubing as spacer sleeves. 3-way outlet on small reel takes night light which acts as "on" indicator

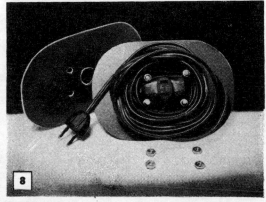

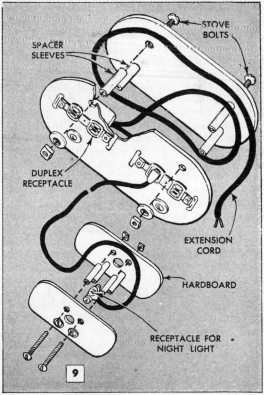

SPACER SLEEVES

STOVE BOLTS

DUPLEX RECEPTACLE

EXTENSION CORD

HARDBOARD

RECEPTACLE FOR NIGHT LIGHT

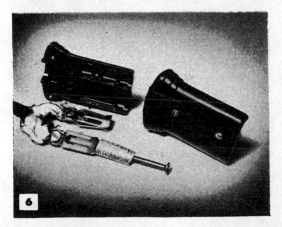

Portable Tester Uses AC or DC

By Frank Fritz

LIGHT AND COMPACT, this tester can be a real aid to the homeowner who does his own electrical-repair work and to anyone who utilizes electricity or electronics in a hobby. Photographers, especially, will find the tester useful for checking extension cords, flash guns and even flash bulbs. Testing unit can be operated with 110-volt house current, or by its own self-contained dry-cell power. This latter feature makes it possible to use the unit on equipment in the field, where other sources of electricity might not be available. Because of the circuitry, either the house current or dry-cell power can be used to test flash bulbs without firing them, and both circuits can be used on other devices that are powered by higher voltages.

As indicated in the wiring diagram, a recessed male plug is located in the 110-volt circuit of the tester. This permits the female end of an extension cord to be used to supply current. From this plug the current flows in series and parallel through a neon lamp and three resistors that reduce the voltage, so that when exposed test prods are used, upper left-hand photo on this page, touching the prods with bare hands does not present a hazard. However, even moderate voltages present a potential danger, so treat the tester with respect. When it is not being used, disconnect the 110-volt supply to eliminate the chance of anyone touching bare contacts. Prongs inserted in either of the flush-mounted receptacles for testing flash bulbs and house lamps consist of a paper clasp and one prong taken from a light plug. The latter also is available as a replacement prong for some types of plugs and can be purchased in hardware stores. The head of the paper clasp contacts the center of a lamp base, the prong touches the side. If a flash-bulb filament is good, the meter will register or the neon lamp will glow, depending on which circuit is used.

In the dry-cell circuit of the tester, a meter or miniature socket that will accept a No. 40 miniature lamp is used. The meter in the original tester was salvaged from an old radio. If you have such a meter, test it in the following manner: Plug into the socket of the circuit a test cord fitted with prods. Touch the prods together and the meter needle should swing across the dial. Next, touch the prods to the tip and side of the base of an ordinary lamp bulb. The needle should move about halfway across the dial. Finally, touch the prods to a photoflash bulb, holding the bulb in a gloved

hand in case it fires. If the bulb does fire, discard the meter, as it does not contain enough resistance. The miniature bulb will work as well, but the meter does not project from the tester as will the bulb.

The tester is housed in a metal box of standard 2 x 4 x 4-in. size, available from radio-supply houses. The dry cell, a penlight size used for power units utilizing transistors, also is obtainable at this source, as are the dry-cell holder, the recessed male plug, the two receptacles and the lamp sockets. Various types of test leads and prods can be made up to suit a particular use. For example, test leads with alligator clips would be handy when checking the continuity in the circuits of an electric motor. Or one lead could have a clip that could be snapped on a convenient ground, while the other lead could be a prod that is moved quickly from one spot to another to check for short circuits or to check continuity of a circuit that is supposed to be grounded. ★ ★ ★

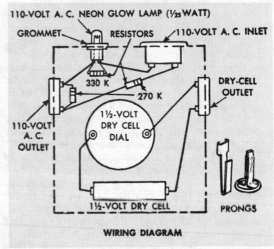

WIRING DIAGRAM

110-VOLT A. C. NEON GLOW LAMP (1/25 WATT)

GROMMET — RESISTORS — 110-VOLT A. C. INLET

330 K

270 K

110-VOLT A. C. OUTLET

1½-VOLT DRY CELL DIAL

DRY-CELL OUTLET

PRONGS

1½-VOLT DRY CELL

How to Calculate Home Power Costs

By J. B. Mullen

WHEN YOU PLAN to add new home electrical appliances or replace old equipment with more efficient units, it's interesting and often profitable to calculate accurately the total power requirements and, from this figure, average up the costs. In many instances the added wattage will entitle you to a lower rate classification, thus reducing rather than increasing costs.

A simple alignment chart you can make yourself will give the answer accurately without any involved computation. For purposes of illustration, suppose that your present rate is 5 cents per kilowatt hour for the first 100 kilowatt hours and 3 cents for over 100 kilowatt hours (k.w.h.). Then you would normally use the 3-cent rate in estimating the operating cost of additional appliances. On the other hand, if you are estimating the cost of operating present equipment or replacements, it usually is better to determine an average rate. This can be obtained by dividing the total bill by the total number of kilowatt hours used. In some cases the total may place you in an even lower rating. However, it should be understood that rates vary. Those given are only representative.

The table below lists average wattage requirements for common electrical appliances. Name plates on appliances usually give the electrical characteristics, model numbers and types in a manner similar to that shown. A typical example of how computations are made quickly by means of **the alignment chart is shown by dotted** lines on the opposite page. First determine the wattage requirements and the operating time. Connect these two values on the chart by means of a straightedge, noting that a 3000-watt unit operated 20 hours consumes 60 k.w.h. of electricity. Note that the second position of the straightedge gives an operating cost of $1.50 at a 2½-cent-per-kilowatt-hour rate. Again the values given are only representative, but they do show the very low cost of operating modern home appliances. A more graphic illustration is shown at the top of the opposite page. The appliances pictured can be operated for the time given on approximately 5 cents' worth of electricity at 2 cents per kilowatt hour. ★ ★ ★

POWER REQUIRED BY TYPICAL APPLIANCES

Appliance	Watts
Range	8,000 - 15,000
Clothes drier	4,400 - 4,800
Automatic washer	600 - 900
Ironer	1,200 - 1,600
Iron	900 - 1,200
Broiler or deep frier	600 - 1,800
Refrigerator	350 - 700
Freezer	350 - 1,000
Radiant heater	600 - 1,500
Toaster	900 - 1,200

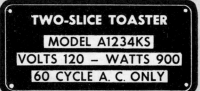

TWO-SLICE TOASTER
MODEL A1234KS
VOLTS 120 – WATTS 900
60 CYCLE A. C. ONLY

FIND WATTS ON NAME PLATE

UTILITY FREEZER
VOLTS 120 – AMPS. 5.8
50-60 CYCLE A. C.
MODEL L50   TYPE DM

IF WATTS ARE NOT SHOWN USE THE FORMULA WATTS = VOLTS X AMPS.

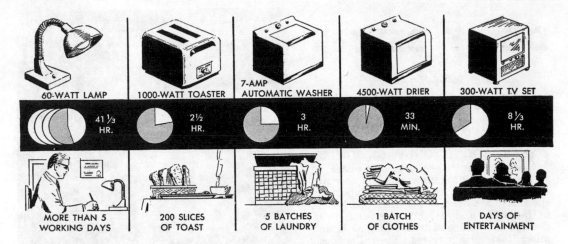

60-WATT LAMP	1000-WATT TOASTER	7-AMP AUTOMATIC WASHER	4500-WATT DRIER	300-WATT T.V SET
41⅓ HR.	2½ HR.	3 HR.	33 MIN.	8⅓ HR.
MORE THAN 5 WORKING DAYS	200 SLICES OF TOAST	5 BATCHES OF LAUNDRY	1 BATCH OF CLOTHES	DAYS OF ENTERTAINMENT

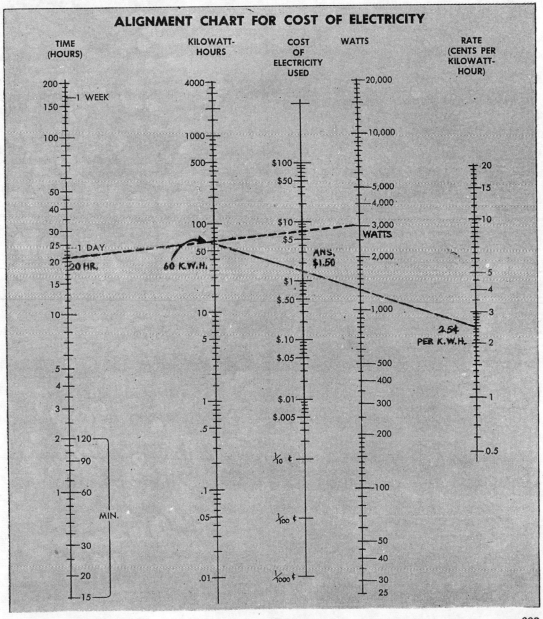

ALIGNMENT CHART FOR COST OF ELECTRICITY

DO IT BETTER
with a
STAPLER

ONCE FOUND ONLY ON DESKS, where they were used for fastening sheets of paper together, staplers now are available in a variety of shapes, types and sizes that are used in the home workshop, in factories and in the construction industry, to replace hammer and nails and other fastening devices. Even the desk stapler has become a multipurpose tool, no longer restricted to fastening just paper. The heads of most desk staplers can be pivoted back, or removed completely from the anvil, permitting the stapler to be used as a tacker. Attaching cloth or light sheet plastic to card tables is an example of one job that these staplers do quickly and neatly, Fig. 7. The young lady could do a better job on the table if she had a gun-type stapler, such as the one in Fig. 3. This inexpensive stapler drives fairly heavy ¼ or ⁵⁄₁₆-in. staples and will do many jobs around the average home and workshop, including most of those shown in Fig. 5. In this, as in all gun-type staplers, the staple driver is powered by a spring which is tightened to maximum pressure, then suddenly released by the single action of squeezing the trigger arm toward the base. Concentrating the total force of the spring on the narrow

Johns-Manville

1. Quick fastening of ceiling tile through blind flanges is just one job for which a staple gun is ideal

2. Right, top stapler is gun, center is hammer stapler, bottom is mallet-drive stapler. 3. Below is inexpensive, smaller-size staple gun having many uses around a home; it should be in every home workshop

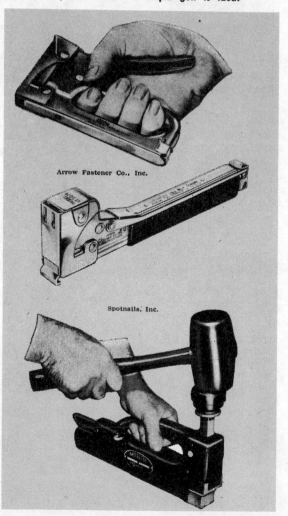

Arrow Fastener Co., Inc.

Spotnails, Inc.

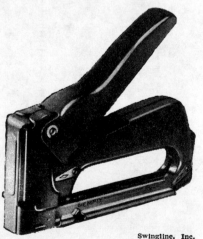

Swingline, Inc.

4. Attaching new screening to frames, whether it be metal or plastic, is a quick job with sure-holding staples. Screen trim also can be stapled in place

area of the head of a staple causes it to be driven with tremendous force.

When a job is beyond the capacity of the small gun-type stapler, a larger gun must be used. An example of this is shown in Fig. 1, where the flanges of the ceiling tiles are ¼ in. thick. The staples of the smaller gun would not penetrate deeply enough into the wood, after passing through the flanges, to provide adequate holding power. Larger guns use staples of lengths from $\frac{7}{16}$ to $\frac{5}{8}$ in. Heavier drive springs also are used in the larger guns. Compound leverage is used in the triggering mechanism, reducing the work effort required to operate the guns. These larger guns are more expensive and the staples used also cost more than those for smaller guns, but there are obvious advantages to the larger guns. Not only can they do the heavy jobs, but the lighter ones as well. Attaching screening, Fig. 4, upholstering, Fig. 8, and putting up insulation, Fig. 9, can be done with either the large or small guns.

Most staplers can use more than one size of staple. Thus, if one size does not drive flush in a fairly dense substance, a staple with shorter legs should be used to assure firm seating of the staples against the material being stapled. Deep penetration of staples is due to their strength and sharp points. Staples for work heavier than fastening paper usually are made of high-carbon-steel wire for maximum resistance to bending. Plain chisel points, Fig. 6, detail A, drive straight with the least tendency to spread. Divergent chisel points, detail B, have inclined straight edges in opposite directions that cause the staple to spread while cutting through the stock. Divergent points, detail C, also spread the legs, while convergent points, detail D, tend to bring the legs together for anchorage in the material.

Staples are made in a variety of shapes to suit special purposes. The heads may be square, round or oval. Thickness of the wire varies with staple size. In view of these variations, staples of a size other than those specifically made for a machine should not be used. Other staples will not fit or will jam in the plunger passage.

Staples are available plain, without any coating, or they may be rosin-coated or etched to provide greater holding power. Corrosion-resistant staples are galvanized or copper-clad. Stainless-steel staples also

5. Shown are a few of the many jobs that staplers can do. If you are a home handyman, a gardener or a housewife, staplers can do a job better for you

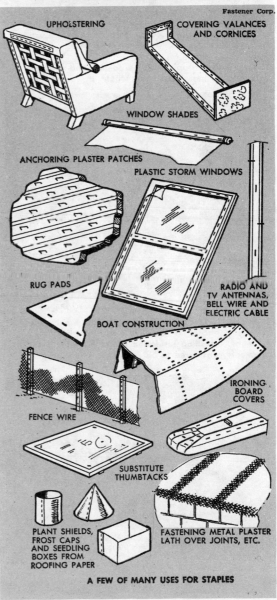

UPHOLSTERING

COVERING VALANCES AND CORNICES

WINDOW SHADES

ANCHORING PLASTER PATCHES

PLASTIC STORM WINDOWS

RUG PADS

RADIO AND TV ANTENNAS, BELL WIRE AND ELECTRIC CABLE

BOAT CONSTRUCTION

IRONING BOARD COVERS

FENCE WIRE

SUBSTITUTE THUMBTACKS

PLANT SHIELDS, FROST CAPS AND SEEDLING BOXES FROM ROOFING PAPER

FASTENING METAL PLASTER LATH OVER JOINTS, ETC.

A FEW OF MANY USES FOR STAPLES

Bostitch

7. Above, desk stapler can be opened and used as light-duty tacker. Small gun would do better job

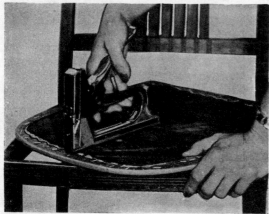

Heller Roberts Mfg. Corp.

8. Above reupholstering chair seats with either cloth or sheet plastic is another easy stapling job.
9. Below, installing insulation is job probably most commonly considered to be done best with a stapler

Bostitch

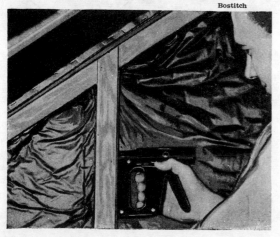

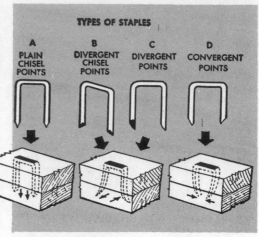

TYPES OF STAPLES

A
PLAIN
CHISEL
POINTS

B
DIVERGENT
CHISEL
POINTS

C
DIVERGENT
POINTS

D
CONVERGENT
POINTS

6. Various types of points are used on staples to provide holding power compatible with job requirements. Average gun staples have plain chisel points

are available for some types of guns.

As with most tools, a stapler must be used properly for best results, and with care to avoid mishaps. Keep your fingers clear of the channel through which the staples are driven. In use, hold a gun stapler flat and firmly against the work so the gun will not jump, which prevents it from delivering full power. As an aid in obtaining complete penetration, especially with the smaller guns, press the thumb of the hand not holding the gun on the head, to prevent the gun from jumping.

Larger staple guns often accommodate staples of several lengths. In some guns the depth of penetration can be controlled by an adjustment so that the material being fastened, such as electrical cable, copper or aluminum tubing, will not be damaged. Guns that are especially made for such purposes have lips that fit the work.

Big brother to the staple gun is the hammer stapler, center photo Fig. 2. This tool is swung like a hammer, and drives a staple with each blow. Some of the heavy-gauge staples used are ¾ in. long. Staplers of this type are useful for tacking down carpet pads, shingles, metal plaster lath, roofing paper and similar materials. Another type stapler is the mallet-drive stapler, lower photo Fig. 2. Some of these staplers are built to drive 16-ga. staples as much as 1½ in. long, for fastening stock ¾ in. thick. Fastening ¾-in. plywood would be one job for which they are suited.

Not shown are pneumatic staplers, which can drive staples 2 in. long. They are used in assembly and construction in the building industry, as well as in factories. Even sheet metal is fastened with staplers.

But for the homeowner, staplers provide a quick, sure method of attachment, with no skill required, as in nailing. No chance either of making hammer marks where not wanted on a finished surface, with a stapler. ★ ★ ★

A — INSERT IN HOLE

B — TIGHTEN FULLY

C — REMOVE BOLT

USE THE RIGHT HANGER

WHEN YOU PLAN to hang a picture, cabinet, shelf or other fixture on the wall it's important to use the right hanger for the job. The weight to be supported, the size and shape of the object and the type of wall construction must be considered when selecting the hanger. As an example, framed pictures and small mirrors weighing up to 15 lb. can be safely hung on conventional plastered walls with the right-size hanger of the type shown in Fig. 2. But such a hanger, or hook, designed for framed pictures, won't do for a cabinet or chest like that pictured in Fig. 1. You'll need a fastener with a sectional sleeve which expands into a series of radial locking lugs when the screw or bolt is tightened, Fig. 1, A, B and C. Such hangers come in three sizes and lengths for light, medium and heavy loads. Similar hanging problems are solved by use of the hanger shown in Fig. 3, detail C. Typical applications on plastered and hollow-tile walls are shown in details A and B. Such hangers, or toggle bolts as they are sometimes called, often are recommended for light and medium loads on plasterboard (dry-wall) walls.

Anchor plates, or "nails," that are fastened to masonry walls with a special adhesive often are used for attaching furring strips in preparation for installing solid-wood paneling. The individual fastener consists of a nail press-fitted in a perforated sheet-metal plate to which the adhesive is applied, Fig. 6. The plate is then pressed against the wall with the nail projecting outward. Ordinarily the plates are

Designed for plastered walls, this hanger, or hook, will hold pictures or mirrors weighing up to 15 lb.

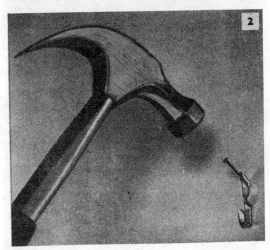

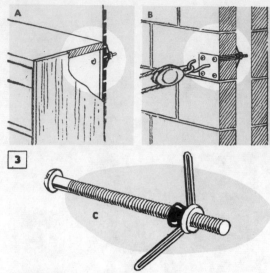

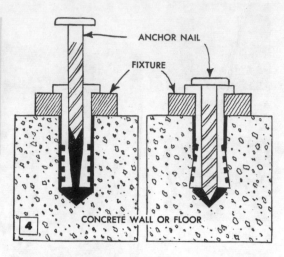

Above, fastener is similar to that pictured in Fig. 1. Suitable for light to medium loads. Below, special fastener is attached to wall with adhesive

spaced horizontally about 12 to 18 in. apart. When the adhesive is thoroughly dry the wooden strips are positioned and forced down over the nail points with light blows of a hammer. Then the nail points are clinched as in the right-hand detail, Fig. 6. This method of attaching furring strips to masonry walls is somewhat faster than the usual procedure.

Figs. 4, 7 and 8 show several newer fasteners of the expanding-sleeve type designed for installation in masonry walls and floors. The type shown in Fig. 4 employs a drive nail, similar in appearance to a masonry nail, which is driven into the anchor to expand the lower end of the sleeve as detailed. The type shown in Fig. 8 is quite similar except that a headless pin serves as an expander when driven in flush. Either type makes a neat installation of motor, bench or machine pedestal on floors, also holds fairly heavy loads on

A heavy-duty fastener of the expanding type is designed for heavy loads on masonry walls and floors

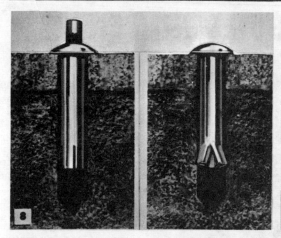

walls. The heavy-duty fastener shown in Fig. 7 is designed for heavy loads. It consists of two parts, a tapered sleeve and tapped expander into which a machine bolt is turned when making the installation. The fastener is installed with a special setting tool as in the left-hand view, Fig. 7. To install, it is necessary to drill a hole in the masonry with a carbide drill as in Fig. 9.

Small framed pictures and individual plate racks can be attached to the walls with the gummed-tape hanger shown in Fig. 10. These hangers are safe for very light loads. Also, for very light loads a prepared cement-asbestos compound pressed into a hole drilled in plastered walls makes a good anchor for a screw, Fig. 11. Another anchor, especially designed for light loads on hollow-tile, glass-block and marble walls, is shown in Fig. 12. It requires only a shallow hole. When the screw is tightened the rubber sleeve expands. ★ ★ ★

Cement-asbestos compound forced into hole provides secure anchor for wood screw which serves as hanger

Holes for expanding-type fasteners are drilled in masonry with a hand (star) drill or carbide drill

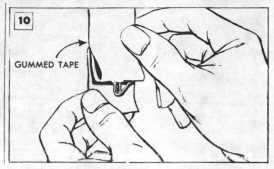

GUMMED TAPE

Below, this fastener is installed in a very shallow hole. Suitable for hollow-tile, glass-block, marble walls

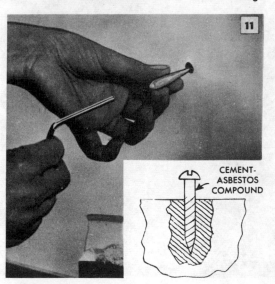

CEMENT-ASBESTOS COMPOUND

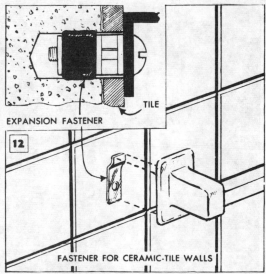

EXPANSION FASTENER

TILE

FASTENER FOR CERAMIC-TILE WALLS

SELECTING AND BUILDING FENCES

Above, this "rail" fence is made of square stock with hewn or adzed edges. Below, a low X-brace design frames a small cottage effectively

A FENCE does for the house what a frame does for a picture. It bounds the area, and just as a frame may add to or detract from a picture, so may the fence do much to improve or impair the appearance of a house. The style chosen should blend with the general architecture. To use extreme examples, a Georgian house would not look well with a split rail fence, nor would a log cabin appear natural surrounded by a brick wall. However, many of the styles shown here will blend with most types of architecture.

When building a fence, the posts should be spaced an even number of feet apart; 6, 8 or 10 feet, for example. The reason for this is that the 2 by 4-in. lumber that forms the top and bottom rails of most fences comes sawed in such lengths, or multiples of these dimensions, and can be cut without waste.

But if the design is best with the posts spaced an odd number of feet, as shown in the details of Fig. 7, a 7-ft. length can be cut from a 14-ft. piece and a 9-ft. span cut from 10-ft. stock without much waste due to the lap past the posts. Figs. 1, 2 and 3 show wide variations in the design of fencing which has been adapted to the setting. In Figs. 1 and 2 notice how the fence has been especially designed and located to complement structural details of the house in both cases. In Fig. 3 the heavy, massive architecture of the wall-and-fence combination borders a large landscaped area most effectively. In Fig. 4 the simple lines of the board fence unobtrusively supplement a landscape largely natural in its arrangement and add a foreground detail that is pleasing to the eye at any season. Moreover, the fence serves the additional dual purpose of defining the boundaries of the property and providing a backdrop detail for the low, flowering shrubs bordering the grassed area in the near foreground.

Fig. 5 shows how another fencing problem has been worked out with the architecture of the house and the boundaries of the property in mind. To break up the geometric pattern formed by the vertical and horizontal lines of both the picket

fence and the house, tops of the pickets have been cut and fitted on a radius and the regular curve thus formed is further accentuated by nailing a thin wood strip over the curved ends. The gate in this particular fence is so constructed that it forms part of the major curve, as you can see from the photo and the detail in Fig. 7. Thus the long sweep of the curved strip has the effect of lengthening the spans between the posts and makes the area enclosed appear larger and more spacious. Such a design is especially effective where the fence must be near the house, as on a small lot.

Other examples of the application of complementing designs are those shown in Figs. 6 and 8, both of these following to a certain degree the lines of the building. Both houses are of the rambling "ranch-

Long horizontal spans are broken up by adding the vertical lines of two uprights which are equally spaced between the main supporting posts

spaced, provide an arbor for intertwining shrubbery and the long spans obviously are calculated to complement the low roof lines of the house. Two other designs, not pictured but detailed in Fig. 9, not only are of wide utilitarian application but are particularly effective when judiciously arranged with frame homes of the colonial or Cape Cod styling located on medium to large landscaped grounds.

Notice that the fence detailed in the lower view, Fig. 9, features a wide board in the center between top and bottom boards of approximately half the width of the center member. The design detailed in the top view, Fig. 9, is of the popular X-brace style with a bottom board below the lower horizontal stretcher. This particular styling also is effective as a background for low, dense shrubbery due to the angular lines of the X-brace design, which give an open-panel effect.

house" styling and in each case the character and nature of the property made it necessary or desirable to locate the fence near the building. In the first design, Fig. 6, note that the long horizontal spans are broken by the addition of two uprights equally spaced between the posts and that the gate is clearly defined by an inverted "V" formed by slanting uprights framed into the panel of the gate. There being no shrubbery nearby, the fence was stained with creosote to a weathered brown color which gives pleasing contrasts.

In Fig. 8 the fence is more nearly a part of the architectural plan, inasmuch as it serves only as a partial enclosure. The horizontal boards, of equal widths equally

In building fences of the types pictured and detailed the selection of suitable materials and fastenings is quite important. Posts should be of enduring woods such as red cedar or oak, and the boards, pickets and rails may be of cedar, white pine or cypress. Either rough-sawed or surfaced

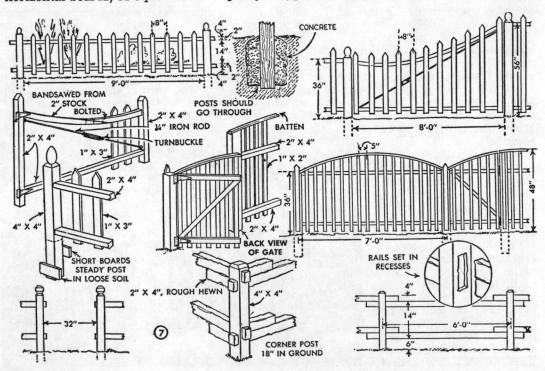

BANDSAWED FROM 2" STOCK BOLTED

2" X 4"

1" X 3"

2" X 4"

4" X 4"   1" X 3"

SHORT BOARDS STEADY POST IN LOOSE SOIL

32"

POSTS SHOULD GO THROUGH

¼" IRON ROD

TURNBUCKLE

2" X 4"

CONCRETE

8"   4"
2"
14"
2"   4"

BATTEN

2" X 4"

1" X 2"

2" X 4"

BACK VIEW OF GATE

2" X 4", ROUGH HEWN

4" X 4"

CORNER POST 18" IN GROUND

9'-0"

48"

36"

56"

8'-0"

5"

36"   48"

7'-0"

RAILS SET IN RECESSES

4"
14"
6'-0"
6"

boards can be used, although those of the former grade are much more difficult to paint. In setting posts permanently first creosote the lower ends up to the ground line and then set in concrete, making sure that the lower ends project as shown in the upper center detail of Fig. 7. Fasteners, such as nails, screws, bolts, hinges and hooks, used in assembling any of the fences shown should be zinc-coated or otherwise made rust-resistant. In any case, always use coated nails as they not only resist rust for long periods but hold much better in soft woods. Unless colors are demanded by some special outdoor decorative scheme, fences are commonly painted white, using an outside lead-and-oil paint, or are stained with creosote which also acts as a preserva-

tive. The fence will be much more enduring if you take the time to apply paint to the surfaces of all joining parts. If you assemble the fence first and then paint it you leave a portion of the surfaces unprotected. Moisture works into the joints and is absorbed through the uncoated wood. This causes swelling, loosening of the nails and eventual checking and decay. The best way is to prime the wood and then apply one finish coat before assembly, but if you're in a hurry apply the priming coat to the joining surfaces as you assemble the parts. It's advisable to do this when finishing with either lead-and-oil paint or creosote. The primer should be thoroughly dry before applying a second coat, otherwise peeling is likely to result.

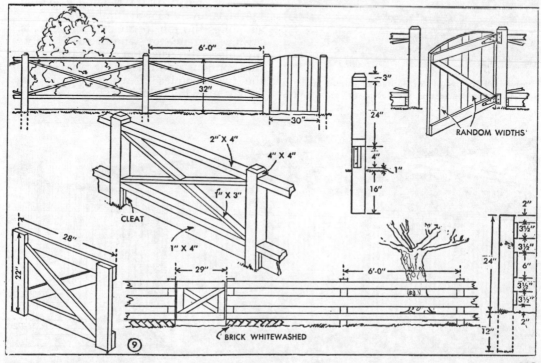

FENCES AND WINDBREAKS

Painted checkerboard style, this eye-stopper fence consists of aluminum panels applied to opposite sides

Attractive masonry wall combines regular 4-in. concrete building blocks with ornamental criss-cross ones
Courtesy National Concrete Masonry Association

Lightweight inserts of corrugated aluminum make a modern patio enclosure that requires no painting

Privacy is the best reason for having a fence around your patio. Screened from direct view of neighbors or passersby, you will feel less like a fish in a bowl and free to relax in solid comfort. In addition, a fence will serve as a windbreak and add a decorative touch as well. If you are handy with hammer and saw or a trowel, there are any number of attractive and simple fences you can build, a few of which are shown on these two pages. Stock fencing is available by the running foot at lumberyards, which simplifies the job to the setting of posts.

Since a fence or windbreak is only as durable as its posts, you should pick a wood that contains natural preservatives against the two enemies of wood—termites and fungus growths, which produce rot and de-

California Redwood Association photo

Louver pattern has redwood boards set at angle to control strong cross winds, assures complete privacy

Blocking adds decorative touch to plain fence. Posts are 4 x 4s, blocking between 1 x 4s is 2 x 4s

cay when the wood is in direct and prolonged contact with the ground. Redwood and cedar have these natural preservatives. Where other woods are used they first should be treated with an artificial chemical preservative of the paint-over type. A popular and fairly simple fence to build is a woven one. Here, the horizontal rows of boards are laced in and out through the posts, starting at the bottom and alternating the weave so that succeeding rows of boards fall on opposite sides of the posts.

Another simple fence to build is one where the rows of boards are nailed to opposite sides of the posts, the first row to one side, the second row to the opposite side and so on up to the top. The boards may be spaced an inch or so apart to make the fence partially open or kept tight by keeping the edges of the opposite rows even. Both of these fences are "good" both sides as compared to a picket fence, for example, where the posts are completely exposed on one side. Standard 1 x 6 and 1 x 8 boards need only be cut to length in building either of these fences.

Cleats, front and back, hold inserts of Diamond-Rib aluminum in square openings of fence framing. Posts are 4 x 4s, rails are 2 x 4s. Vertical corrugations of inserts, plus ribbed texture, add eye appeal
Kaiser Aluminum and Chemical Corp. photo

695

FENCE IT RIGHT

By William B. Eagan

ONE OF THE LEAST EXPENSIVE ways of keeping stray animals off your property and insuring that toddlers will not "escape" to the street is to enclose your land with a woven-wire fence. Of the many materials available, chain-link type fencing will do the job the best and last the longest.

Before buying material for your fence, make an accurate layout of the area to be enclosed, as shown in Fig. 6. Be sure to include all gates and locate them exactly as they are to be placed in the completed fence. If changes are made after ordering the material, some of it is likely to be wasted. Make certain that the desired location of the fence lines fall inside your property lines.

The first step of the layout procedure is to locate the terminal posts, which consist of end, corner and gate posts. Drive offset stakes and stretch lines between them as in Figs. 3 and 6. Next measure the overall distances between terminal-post locations and divide these distances into equal

spaces of less than 10 ft. as shown in the sample layout, Fig. 6. Then drive marking stakes exactly where each post is to be placed. The distances indicated by A-B and C-D, are controlled by the gate sizes used. Be sure the gateposts are set accurately for the actual opening. This is the distance measured from the inside face to the inside face of the posts on each side of a gate. All posts should be set approximately 2 in. inside your property line to be sure the fittings do not overhang the neighbors' property. To locate the fence positions, simply stretch lines on the exact boundary of the property lines and then set the posts 2 in. inside of them.

Heights for residential fences vary from 3½ to 4 ft.—the width of the fabric (woven-wire fencing). The fabric usually is finished with one edge knuckled, Fig. 5, and the other edge barbed, Fig. 8. The latter edge should be placed at the bottom of the fence. The standard gauge for such fence heights is No. 9 wire. For terminal posts, use 2-in. galvanized steel pipe, 1¼-in. for line posts

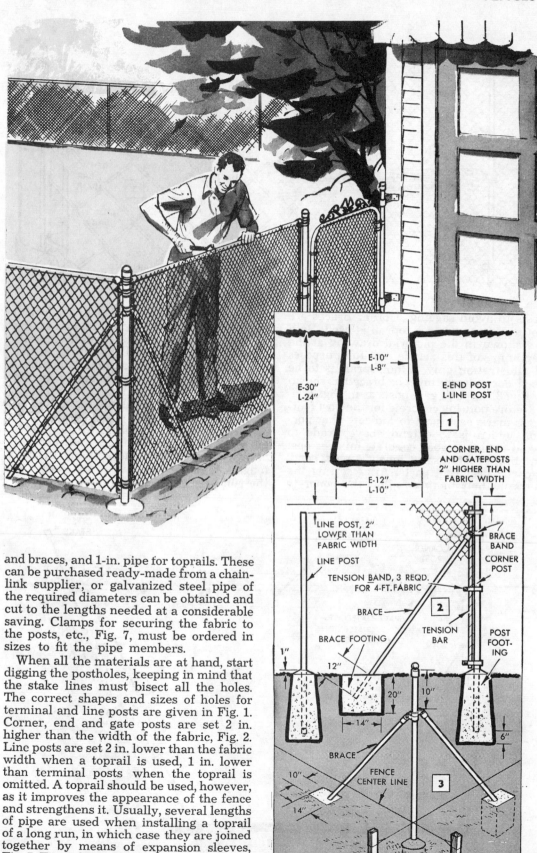

and braces, and 1-in. pipe for toprails. These can be purchased ready-made from a chain-link supplier, or galvanized steel pipe of the required diameters can be obtained and cut to the lengths needed at a considerable saving. Clamps for securing the fabric to the posts, etc., Fig. 7, must be ordered in sizes to fit the pipe members.

When all the materials are at hand, start digging the postholes, keeping in mind that the stake lines must bisect all the holes. The correct shapes and sizes of holes for terminal and line posts are given in Fig. 1. Corner, end and gate posts are set 2 in. higher than the width of the fabric, Fig. 2. Line posts are set 2 in. lower than the fabric width when a toprail is used, 1 in. lower than terminal posts when the toprail is omitted. A toprail should be used, however, as it improves the appearance of the fence and strengthens it. Usually, several lengths of pipe are used when installing a toprail of a long run, in which case they are joined together by means of expansion sleeves, Fig. 7. Try to have these joints occur at line

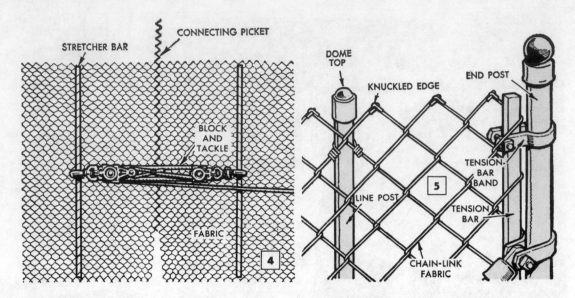

posts to avoid sagging. Corner braces are not necessary when a toprail is used. Both are shown in the pictorial drawing at the beginning of this article, but for purposes of illustration only. If no toprail is to be used, corner posts must be braced as shown in Fig. 3, end and gate posts as in Fig. 2.

Before pouring concrete for the post footings, mark each post to indicate that portion which is to extend above grade to avoid errors. A good concrete mix for post and brace footings is: Cement, 1 part; sand, 2 parts; gravel, 4 parts. After setting the posts in their footings, allow the concrete

to cure from 2 days to a week. Then pour the footings to take the braces, and after a similar waiting period, install toprails, most of the fittings and the fabric, in that order. All post footings should include a 1-in. crown above grade as shown in Fig. 2, to permit water to drain away from them.

There are two methods of attaching chain-link fabric to the posts. One involves securing a length of fabric to the post at each end of a run (distance between any two terminal posts) and splicing the two lengths together at or near the center of the run as shown in the pictorial illustra-

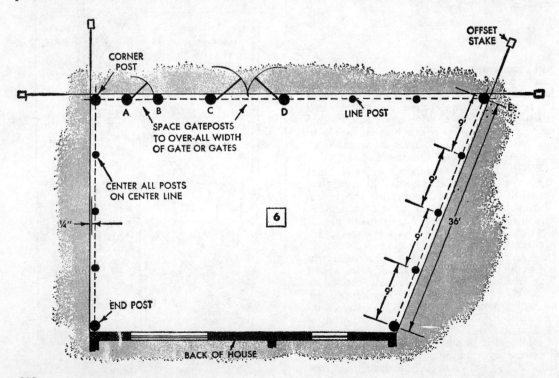

tion and in Fig. 4. To make such a splice, "cut" the overlapping lengths of fabric at the point selected for the joint by untwisting a wire spiral from each length. Then pull the fabric ends together and unite them by weaving one of the wire spirals into the mesh as in Fig. 4. The second method involves attaching the fabric to a terminal post at the beginning of a run and securing a block-and tackle to the terminal post at the other end so that the fabric can be pulled tight. Proper tension is with the fabric pulled just tight enough to take up the slack. A wire spiral is then untwisted from the fabric at the point it is to take the tension bar, Fig. 5, and used for connecting it to the post.

The first method of attaching the fabric to the posts usually is used for runs of 50 ft. and longer, when it is difficult to stretch the fabric properly. The second method is easiest and should be used on all runs of less than 50 ft. Both methods require the same fittings—a tension bar and three bands at each end of a run. The bands should be spaced as shown in Fig. 8. The fabric is fastened to the toprail and line posts with short lengths of wire as detailed in Fig. 8. Each run of fence fabric is applied in the same manner, regardless of length of run.

To complete the fence, hinges and latches are attached to the gateposts and the gates are hung in place. When doing this, place the top hinge in an upside-down position, fastening it to the gatepost while engaged in the gate fitting, This prevents the gate from being lifted off the hinges. Double-gate installations require a concrete pad in which a pipe nipple is submerged flush with the top to take the latching device, Fig. 9. Be sure all hinge bolts are tightened securely so that the gates do not sag. ★ ★ ★

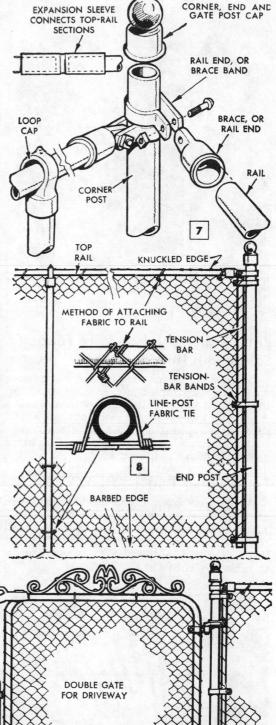

EXPANSION SLEEVE CONNECTS TOP-RAIL SECTIONS

CORNER, END AND GATE POST CAP

RAIL END, OR BRACE BAND

LOOP CAP

BRACE, OR RAIL END

RAIL

CORNER POST

7

TOP RAIL

KNUCKLED EDGE

METHOD OF ATTACHING FABRIC TO RAIL

TENSION BAR

TENSION-BAR BANDS

LINE-POST FABRIC TIE

8

END POST

BARBED EDGE

9

PIPE NIPPLE IN CONCRETE

DOUBLE GATE FOR DRIVEWAY

Paint Roller Used on Wire Fence Saves Both Time and Labor

Using a roller makes painting a woven-wire fence a simple task, as compared to the tedious job of painting it with a brush. Also, there is no mess, as compared with spray-gun application. Special roller covers with long-nap fibers are available, although a regular cover can be used.

Fan-Shaped Panel "Trims" Fence

. Assembled from the same size pickets that are used in the fence, this fan-shaped panel is fitted at right angles to the end of the fence to eliminate a "chopped-off" look. The lower ends of the pickets were tapered to make a tight fit at the fan base.

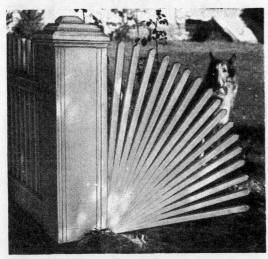

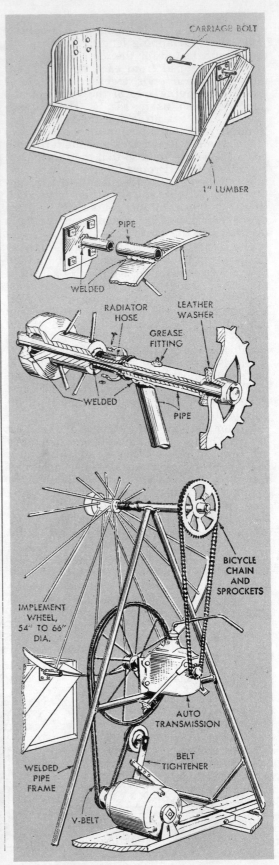

By J. V. Corder

Back-Yard Ferris Wheel Has Three Speeds

DRIVEN through an auto transmission by a ¾-hp. electric motor, this Ferris wheel may be operated at three different speeds by merely shifting the transmission. The frame consists of two A-frames of 2-in. pipe welded together, the two units being tied together at the lower ends by short lengths of pipe welded in place. The upper end of each A-frame terminates in a short horizontal pipe, which serves as a bearing for the wheel axle. Note in the lower center detail how a leather washer and a piece of radiator hose serve as grease retainers.

Seats swing between two large implement wheels, such as cultivator or hayrake wheels, which are welded to the axle. The seats are pivoted as shown in the upper detail on the facing page, and fitted with safety chains. Lower detail shows the drive mechanism. Sprockets and chain used on implements may be substituted for those of a bicycle if desired. Large belt wheel is about 30 in. in diameter. Note belt tension is provided by idler pulley. ★ ★ ★

BUILD YOUR HOME AROUND A
FIREPLACE

By Tom Riley

FEW HOMEOWNERS actually build their own fireplaces, which is a job for the experienced mason. But knowing how one should be built and what types are popular will be helpful when you decide to have a fireplace.

When planning to build or remodel it is important to choose a fireplace that will create the atmosphere you desire. A few years ago there was little choice. The fireplaces in all the homes along your block generally were quite similar, differing perhaps in their brick or tile facing and bookcase or shelf treatment at each side. Today you have a wonderful variety of types and designs from which to choose and can have a fireplace

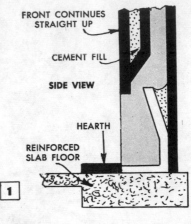

FRONT CONTINUES STRAIGHT UP

CEMENT FILL

SIDE VIEW

HEARTH

REINFORCED SLAB FLOOR

1

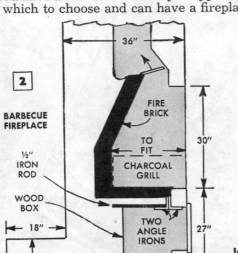

2

BARBECUE FIREPLACE

36"

FIRE BRICK

TO FIT

CHARCOAL GRILL

30"

½" IRON ROD

WOOD BOX

18"

TWO ANGLE IRONS

27"

12"

Island-wall fireplace of used brick divides living and dining rooms. Dining-room side of fireplace has charcoal grill and wood box

Excellent blend of modern and traditional. Raised hearth is most popular feature of today's fireplaces

Above, copper hood replaces considerable brickwork in this corner-type fireplace. Below, this fireplace is part of a curved living-room wall of Arizona fieldstone. Shelf-type hearth is black marble

that definitely belongs in a particular room of your home.

Most fireplaces built today, whether of brick, block or stone, use a conventional, time-tested firebox. Thus, manufactured dampers can be utilized, the firebrick lining is simple to install and there is a smoke shelf above (to baffle chimney downdrafts). This standardization of the firebox design has very little to do with the fireplace's exterior, which can vary in a hundred ways. In general, the traditional finish was intended to hide the masonry behind wood or plaster walls, leaving only a little masonry exposed around the edge of the fireplace and perhaps up to a mantel. The trend today is to expose as much of the brickwork as possible—the masonry is attractive so why not show it? And so, instead of slanting the brickwork back to slim it down to the size of the chimney, the brickwork of the front and sides of the fireplace now often continues straight up to the ceiling, or on up through the roof to have a generous-sized chimney on the exterior. Thus, some large spaces will appear between the brick of the upper fireplace shell and the chimney proper, which seems confusing when you look at a half-completed job. The spaces are often used for extra flues for the furnace or they may be filled with rubble and cement. If not exposed through the roof, these spaces often are simply left open in the attic.

Exposing all the masonry of a fireplace

Black iron and concrete blocks give dramatic modernity to this Swedish fireplace. Note how raised hearth incorporates bench

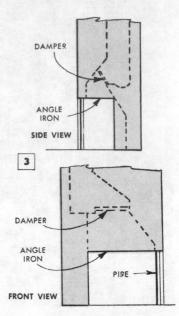

Above, two ways Swedish fireplaces can be built. Below, triangular-shaped back-wall forms smoke shelf to corner fireplace

Above, serving as a room divider, this variation of the Swedish fireplace gives firelight to both living and dining rooms. Flue must be extra large so cross drafts won't force smoke sidewise. Below, corner type takes little floor space

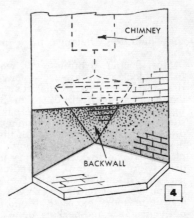

does give a saving in that there will be much less plaster and wood wall in the house to construct. When the fireplace is located along an interior wall, it also means that you can have brickwork in the kitchen or dining room as well as in the living room. Then, another or a barbecue fireplace can be added on the back side at considerably less cost than that of building two separate fireplaces. Fig. 2 and the photo show such a barbecue fireplace designed for a manufactured grill. As grills vary in size, it is always a good idea to obtain the size of the grill first and build the firebox accordingly. Because a barbecue

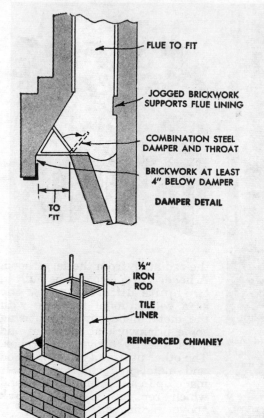

FLUE TO FIT

JOGGED BRICKWORK
SUPPORTS FLUE LINING

COMBINATION STEEL
DAMPER AND THROAT

BRICKWORK AT LEAST
4" BELOW DAMPER

DAMPER DETAIL

TO
FIT

½"
IRON
ROD

TILE
LINER

REINFORCED CHIMNEY

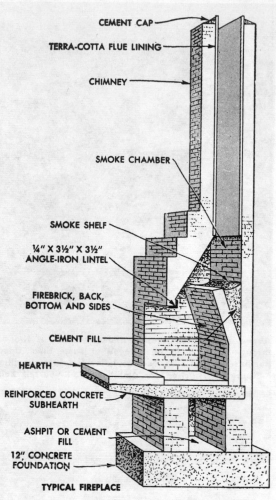

CEMENT CAP

TERRA-COTTA FLUE LINING

CHIMNEY

SMOKE CHAMBER

SMOKE SHELF

¼" X 3½" X 3½"
ANGLE-IRON LINTEL

FIREBRICK, BACK,
BOTTOM AND SIDES

CEMENT FILL

HEARTH

REINFORCED CONCRETE
SUBHEARTH

ASHPIT OR CEMENT
FILL

12" CONCRETE
FOUNDATION

TYPICAL FIREPLACE

fireplace is at counter height, there is usually a space below that can become a
handy wood box.

A Swedish or protruding corner fireplace is a somewhat different type very
popular today. These give a view of the
fire from two directions. They can nestle
into a corner of a room or accent the end
of a partition wall. As shown in Fig. 3,
the Swedish can be built with the conventional firebox design, having one side
left open back to the slanting rear wall.
Or the side can be fully open and the
rear wall vertical. Then the flue above
should be offset, as shown, to the rear or
the side to give a shelf to baffle downdrafts. On all Swedish designs, the angle-
iron lintel must extend around the corner
to support the side opening, and the corner
needs a 1 to 2-in. iron-pipe upright to support it. An attractive finish is obtained
here by sliding an equal length of thin-
wall brass or copper tubing over the pipe
before erecting.

Corner fireplaces are receiving deserved
popularity today because they can be seen
from any part of a room and because they
require little floor space for their hearths.
Slanting across a corner, they will also
break up the squareness of a room and will

The two details below show different ways of building a hood into a fireplace. In detail A the partial
hood replaces only part of the front and side brickwork, whereas in detail B, the complete hood and
iron-pipe chimney replaces all the brick above firebox

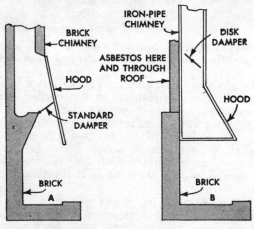

BRICK
CHIMNEY

HOOD

STANDARD
DAMPER

BRICK

A

IRON-PIPE
CHIMNEY

DISK
DAMPER

ASBESTOS HERE
AND THROUGH
ROOF

HOOD

BRICK

B

705

Above, this corner location allows warmth of fire and view through window to be enjoyed at same time. Upper right, purchased metal form for circulating fireplace simplifies actual masonry construction for ambitious do-it-yourself homeowner

This fireplace with its raised hearth was built around a metal form. Note warm and cold-air inlet and outlet in the masonry

the radiation from the large hood. A hooded fireplace can be built in two quite different ways, one as a conventional fireplace with the metal hood simply replacing some brickwork at the front and sides directly above the firebox. The other utilizes a complete hood and metal-pipe chimney that is made up in a sheet-metal shop and which replaces all brickwork above the firebox.

Not to be ignored are the circulating fireplaces. Their manufactured shells make these fireplaces fairly easy to build yourself and they are efficient heaters. Often considered objectionable is the warm-air grillwork exposed above the fireplace. A small hood can be made to cover the grillwork, to direct the heat upward. Or, the grillwork can be hidden in a mantel in the form of a shallow trough or planter box.

On almost any type of fireplace, a raised hearth can be an enjoyable feature. Built 12 to 16 in. above the floor and about 18 in. wide, the hearth will become a huge bench for serving guests and for placing decorations, as well as the best place to sit close by the fire. Many of today's fireplaces have the floor of the firebox lower than the hearth. Then, sparks cannot sneak out beneath a fire screen and ashes are much less noticeable.

Constructionwise, the first thing about the fireplace you choose is its foundation. Its foundation concrete should be at least 12 in. thick and the bottom must be below frost level of your climate to prevent movement in freezing weather. The foundation can be simply a thickening of a concrete

brighten a dark corner. Fig. 4 shows how a triangle of firebrick in the corner can protrude to give a smoke shelf. Or the chimney can be offset to the rear, as with a Swedish fireplace, to give the smoke shelf. The chimney above a corner fireplace can be square with the walls of the room or it may be built so it slants across the corner.

Most hooded fireplaces will give a very dramatic touch. Such a fireplace will also give considerably more heat, because of

Although of good size, this fireplace is kept subdued by incorporating it in a long Roman-brick wall

slab floor, or a separate slab in the crawl space or basement. The concrete subhearth detailed in the drawings on page 705 is the cantilever type. Note it is keyed into the rear brick wall and has the firebrick backwall resting on it. The cantilevering is done merely to simplify the wood-floor construction in a house. The hearth can also be built with a third brick wall supporting it on the front edge; that construction is best on a wide hearth. Either way, the concrete subhearth must be reinforced generously with wire mesh or rods.

To have a fireplace that works properly, there are several points to keep in mind. The height of most fireplace openings should not exceed 33 in. — the average height is 29 to 30 in. The bottom of the damper assembly should be placed at least 4 in. above the fireplace opening. Most dampers today come in a heavy metal box called the throat. These usually are the easiest to install and their metal throats are smoother than brickwork, giving best passage for the smoke through this important spot. The damper should extend the full width of the fireplace opening, if possible, and must have a cross-sectional area not less than that of the flue.

The smoke shelf behind the damper should be 6 to 12 in. deep and have a smooth concave surface. The smoke shelf should extend the full length of the throat or damper. The smoke chamber above the damper should have smoothly plastered sides that slope in at an angle of not more than 30 deg. from the vertical.

The most important thing is to have a chimney flue of adequate size. The cross-sectional area of your rectangular flue should be at least ⅒ the fireplace opening's area. For a fireplace 40 in. wide and 30 in. high, you thus would use an 11¼ x 11¼-in. (inside diameter) clay tile for the flue. Because round flue tile is more efficient, you can use ⅟₁₂ the area to compute for round. On a Swedish or hooded fireplace, add the area of any open side as well as the front opening of the fireplace to compute the flue size. The chimney should extend a good 2 ft. above the ridge of a pitched roof and 3 ft. above a flat roof.

In localities subject to high winds or earthquakes, reinforcing rods in a chimney are a good safeguard against expensive repairs. For winds, the rods can start at the bottom of the tile flue liner, extending to within 6 in. of top of chimney. For earthquakes, these rods are tied to other reinforcing rods that are anchored in the concrete foundation and are bent to extend up through the fireplace walls to the chimney. Along with the rods, a chimney on an outside wall of a house can be held securely against the house by two ⅛ x 1¼-in. iron straps, tied to two rods, passed through the brickwork and anchored to ceiling joists or upper plates of the house frame. The straps will give slightly when the house settles. Never key any rigid wood members of the house frame into the brickwork. That can give a fire hazard, and the difference in settling of the fireplace and house frame will cause cracks or other troubles. ★ ★ ★

FROM THE GROUND UP

brick by brick you can have the fireplace you have always wanted

By John O. Bull

WHAT WAS ONCE considered taboo for even the most capable handy man to touch, fireplace building is no longer a "hands off" project. Now, steel fireplace liners, which guarantee a proper-drawing fireplace, make it possible for the ambitious homeowner to do the job without fear of smoking himself out. The skill once required to brick

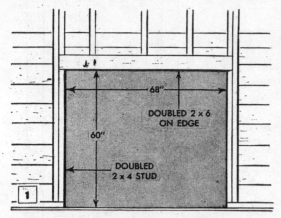

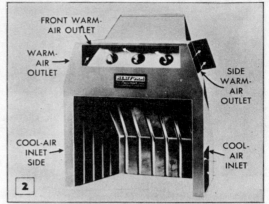

up the working innards of a fireplace has been lessened considerably by having this vital part (the smoke chamber) already preassembled within the liner itself. Essentially, you merely brick up around it. As for laying the bricks, it's not as difficult as you may think. By working slowly and carefully, and keeping the corners plumb, you'll wind up surprising yourself.

Here are all the steps of building a fireplace around a Heatform liner, Fig. 2. The steps are essentially the same even though you may prefer to change the interior hearth treatment used in the original. In this particular installation, the dwelling has a slab-type floor which affords ample support for the hearth. Where the structure has a crawl space or a basement, the flooring members should be strengthened by doubling the joists and adding crossheaders where necessary to safely carry the load.

Superior Fireplace Co. photo

This is the heart of the fireplace, the steel liner, which assures amateur builder a proper-drawing unit

Here the steel liner is being set in a bed of mortar on top of concrete, blocks and brick base. Note that liner is placed to bring front about ½ in. back from a line drawn flush across the inside wall

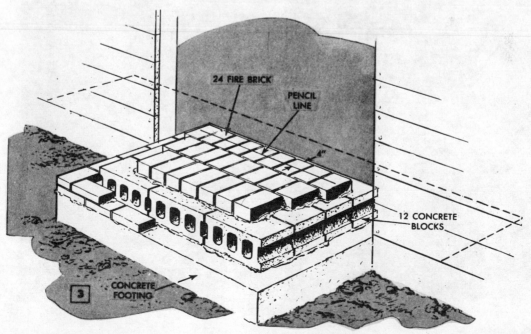

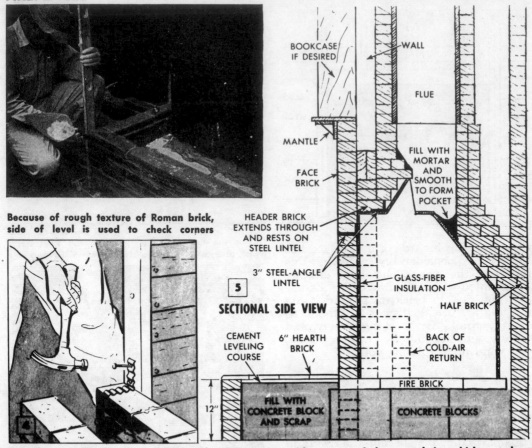

Because of rough texture of Roman brick, side of level is used to check corners

Sectional Side View labels:

BOOKCASE IF DESIRED

WALL

FLUE

MANTLE

FACE BRICK

FILL WITH MORTAR AND SMOOTH TO FORM POCKET

HEADER BRICK EXTENDS THROUGH AND RESTS ON STEEL LINTEL

3" STEEL-ANGLE LINTEL

GLASS-FIBER INSULATION

HALF BRICK

5 SECTIONAL SIDE VIEW

CEMENT LEVELING COURSE

6" HEARTH BRICK

BACK OF COLD-AIR RETURN

FIRE BRICK

12"

FILL WITH CONCRETE BLOCK AND SCRAP

CONCRETE BLOCKS

Outside wall of fireplace is anchored to framed opening with corrugated sheet-metal ties which are placed between every six or eight courses and nailed. Side-view drawing shows proper placement of common brick

Layer of glass-fiber insulation, which is added to steel liner, is held in place with coating of mortar

Besides acting as insulation, glass fiber also serves as spacer to keep common brick from touching liner

Left, steel liner is encased with common brick. Cross-row of brick in background forms back of cold-air duct. Center and right, brick is corbeled 30 deg. to form 12 x 12-in. flue opening. Inside is buttered with mortar

Fig. 1 shows the size of the rough opening required in the wall and the manner in which it should be framed. The outside chimney and the steel liner rest on a concrete foundation consisting of a concrete footing, concrete blocks and firebrick, mortared in the arrangement shown in Fig. 3. The steel liner sits on top of this in a bed of mortar. Footing for the concrete foundation should go to a depth of at least three feet and the overall size should be large enough to provide room for a wall of bricks on three sides. This outside wall is anchored to the house wall at each side with regular corrugated sheet-metal ties which are nailed to the framed opening and mortared between every six or eight courses. When the brick courses reach about a foot high, you should stop and cover the outside of the steel liner with glass-fiber insulation. This is held in place with mortar which is troweled on the liner and the insulation pressed into it. With this done, you begin to encase the liner itself with common brick, starting at the bottom on the sides, Fig. 7, and at the back 16 courses up, Fig. 5. Note the arrangement of these bricks at the front, which help support the flue tile and how the header bricks rest on a 3-in. steel lintel across the top of the liner. Notice, too, how a shelf is formed, Fig. 6, to provide a supporting ledge for the inner wall of Roman brick. In building up the corbel brick, plaster the inside to produce a smooth surface. An airspace of about 1 in. should be left between the common brick and the steel liner. Continue to work to the top, laying an inside and an outside wall as you go.

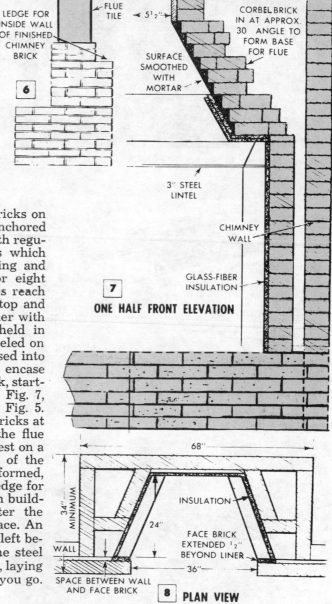

6 LEDGE FOR INSIDE WALL OF FINISHED CHIMNEY BRICK

FLUE TILE — 5½"

CORBEL BRICK IN AT APPROX. 30 ANGLE TO FORM BASE FOR FLUE

SURFACE SMOOTHED WITH MORTAR

3" STEEL LINTEL

CHIMNEY WALL

GLASS-FIBER INSULATION

7 ONE HALF FRONT ELEVATION

68"

34" MINIMUM

WALL

24"

INSULATION

FACE BRICK EXTENDED ½" BEYOND LINER

36"

SPACE BETWEEN WALL AND FACE BRICK

8 PLAN VIEW

Openings between bricks are filled with a grout made by mixing 1 part portland cement to 3 parts sand

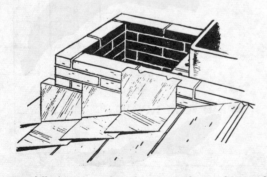

Metal flashing is anchored in mortar by notching with tin snips and then bending edge back at right angles

IN CONTINUING skyward with the chimney part of your fireplace, it is most important that you use a level frequently at the corners so you won't wind up with a leaning tower of Pisa. As described earlier, the chimney consists of an inner and outer wall of brick, the

Left, cross rods 6 to 8 in. down from the top support fill. Center, bricks rest on rods and on shoulders formed at ends by split bricks. Note notched brick. Right, scrap and common brick are utilized for fill

Top of chimney is reached with 18 courses above the ridge. Here fill is completed and ready to be grouted

Grout is forced down between bricks with short 2 x 4. Flue can be flush or left projecting a few inches

inner one being of common brick and encasing the flue tile. When you arrive at the roof line, copper flashing must be worked into the brick courses to keep roof water from running down between the chimney and the side of the house. The pieces of flashing are added as the courses rise and are bent and lapped in the manner shown. The top of the chimney is reached when you have gone about 18 courses above the roof ridge. However, while you are still three or four courses from the top, steel rods are mortared in place crosswise to support the bricks that cap the well on each side of the flue. These bricks are mortared in place, and as you continue to go up the remaining three or four courses, scrap and common brick are used as fill. When you have reached the top, your chimney should look like the photo in the upper left-hand corner. Notice that except at the four corners, the top course is laid with the bricks placed on edge. Finally, the voids between the bricks are filled with grout and sloped four ways from the flue. You have a choice of keeping the latter flush with the top or a few inches above it. This completes the chimney part.

Hearth tile is laid in thin layer of mortar. Note tile is ¾ in. above firebrick to form lip for ashes

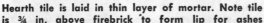

Above, scrap block and brick are used as hearth fill. Below, fill topped with grout, level with firebrick

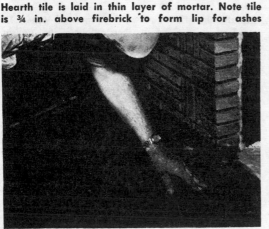

Grillelike openings for the air ducts are formed by cutting the bricks to size and standing them on end

A 10-percent solution of muriatic acid is used to clean brick of mortar stains, then rinsed with water

A grout of equal parts of white sand and white cement is used to fill voids between the hearth tile

Space across lintel is evenly divided by laying loose brick in place and cutting off where necessary

Whether you proceed as extensively as done originally, and face the entire wall with brick, or just face the steel liner itself, the same procedure is followed. In referring to the plan view shown in Fig. 8, you'll notice that a ½-in. airspace is left between the wall studs and the brick facing, and that the glass-fiber insulation that covers the liner is brought around to fill this space at the front. Do not attempt to mortar over this opening as it will only crack out later.

Start the brick facing even with the inner edges of the liner and carry it each way as far as you wish. Metal wall ties are used every few courses and duct openings are formed on each side, three courses high, by standing the bricks on end at the points where the cold-air ducts are located. A lintel of 3-in. steel angle is used to bridge the fire pit 14 courses up. See Fig. 5, page 710. Five courses up from the lintel a grille is formed of brick as before for the heat ducts. The raised hearth is made six courses high and is filled in with scraps of block and brick, after which it is grouted over and struck off level to provide a solid base for the hearth tile. ★ ★ ★

Hearth tile is cleaned with sponge and water. Thin coat of linseed oil is then applied and polished

FIREPLACE HOOD

Made of gleaming burnished copper, this attractive hood adds a Western touch to the front of a plain brick fireplace. Installation of the hood makes the opening appear lower and therefore wider, resulting in a more pleasing over-all appearance. Sheet copper is cut to the dimensions given in the detail. Note, however, that the length of the hood is not listed, as this must be determined by adding 16 in. to the width of the fireplace opening. The sheet is drilled for rivets and lag screws and then bent along the dotted lines. The top edge is rounded at the corners by brazing pieces of scrap copper to fill the notches opposite the bends, and then a ⅛ x 1-in. brass strip is riveted to the bottom edge. The completed unit is mounted on the fireplace by driving lag screws into lead shields inserted in the mortar joints as in the center detail. If desired, copper pilasters may be attached to the corners of the fireplace opening.

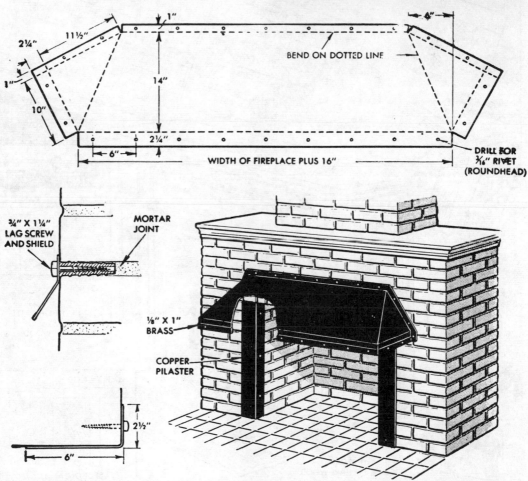

11½"

2¼"

1"

11½"

14"

BEND ON DOTTED LINE

10"

6"

2¼"

6"

WIDTH OF FIREPLACE PLUS 16"

DRILL FOR
3⁄16" RIVET
(ROUNDHEAD)

¾" X 1¼"
LAG SCREW
AND SHIELD

MORTAR
JOINT

⅛" X 1"
BRASS

COPPER
PILASTER

2½"

6"

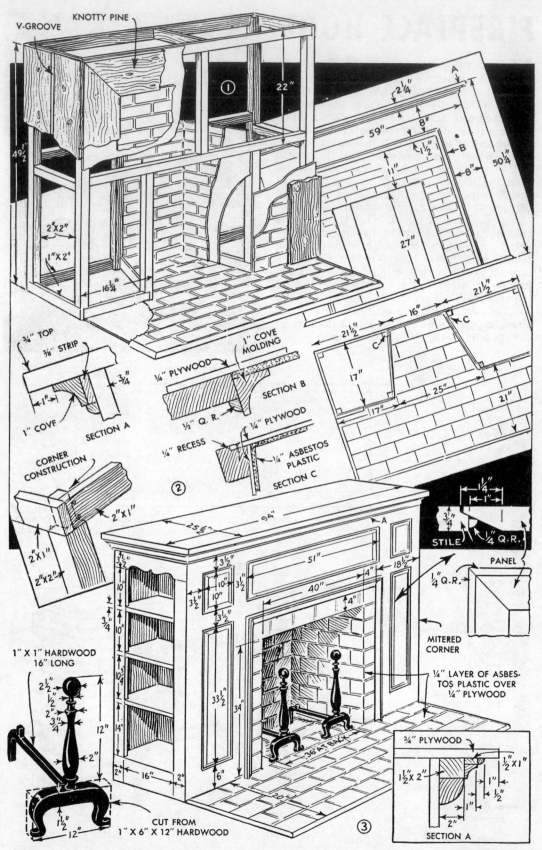

V-GROOVE

KNOTTY PINE

①

22"

49½"

2"x2"

1"X2"

16¼"

2¼"

8"

59"

1½"

B

50¼"

11"

8"

27"

21½"

16"

C

21½"

C

17"

25"

21"

17"

¾" TOP

3⁄8" STRIP

¾"

1"

1" COVE

SECTION A

CORNER CONSTRUCTION

2"X1"

2"X1"

2"X2"

1" COVE MOLDING

¼" PLYWOOD

SECTION B

½" Q. R.

¼" PLYWOOD

¼" RECESS

¼" ASBESTOS PLASTIC

SECTION C

②

¼"

1"

¾"

STILE

¼" Q.R.

PANEL

¼" Q.R.

MITERED CORNER

¼" LAYER OF ASBESTOS PLASTIC OVER ¼" PLYWOOD

1" X 1" HARDWOOD 16" LONG

2½"

½"

2"

¾"

12"

2"

94"

25½"

A

51"

3½"

10"

3½"

3½"

10"

40"

4"

18½"

4"

4"

3½"

33½"

34"

10"

¾"

10"

10¾"

14"

2"

16"

2"

6"

36" AT BACK

20"

③

¾" PLYWOOD

1½"X1"

1½"X2"

1"

½"

1"

2"

SECTION A

1½"

12"

CUT FROM 1" X 6" X 12" HARDWOOD

MANTELS AND IMITATION FIREPLACES

Four practical designs incorporating built-in book shelves and storage space. Plastic coating is applied and molded to imitate brick and stone

SO REALISTIC looking are these imitation fireplaces, you'll find it difficult to distinguish them from the real thing, especially when they are fitted with homemade wooden andirons and a "glowing" log. Among the four designs given there is one to suit practically any setting, from a modern living room to a den of knotty pine. The hearth of each is a separate unit from the rest of the fireplace for easy handling when moving.

Construction is basically the same for all, that is, a rough framework similar to the one shown in Fig. 1, is made first, which is covered with plywood before adding the finished trim and the imitation brick or stone. Slight variation of this procedure will be noted in the construction of the modern fireplace detailed in Figs. 4 and 5, as no inner plywood covering is necessary here. In case you are unable to obtain ¼-in. plywood, some of the bet-

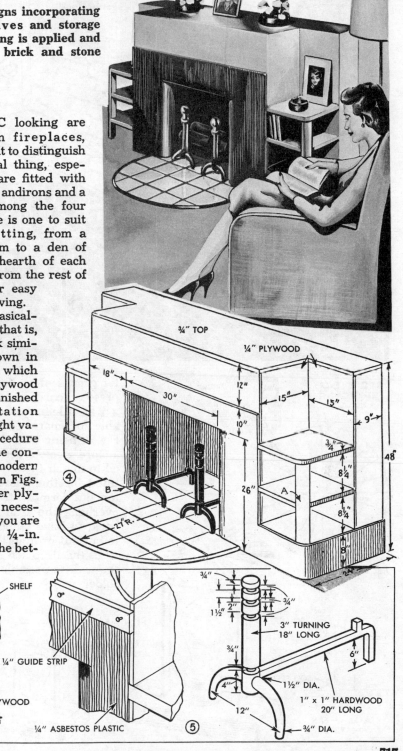

¾" TOP

¼" PLYWOOD

18" 30" 12" 15" 15" 9" 48"

¾" 8¼" A 8¼"

26" B 27" R. ④ 24" 18"

SHELF

SECTION A 3" x 3" ¼" GUIDE STRIP

SECTION B ¼" PLYWOOD ¼" ASBESTOS PLASTIC ⑤

¾" 2" 1½" ¾" 3" TURNING 18" LONG ¾" 6" 4" 12" 1½" DIA. ¾" DIA. 1" x 1" HARDWOOD 20" LONG

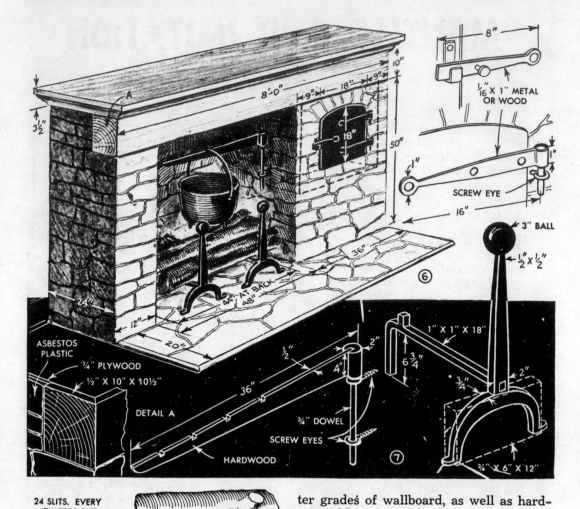

8'-0"

10"

3½"

9" 18" 9"

18"

50"

24"

12"

20"

36"

44" AT BACK

48"

ASBESTOS PLASTIC

¼" PLYWOOD

½" X 10" X 10½"

DETAIL A

⑥

8"

¹⁄₁₆" X 1" METAL OR WOOD

SCREW EYE

16"

1"

3" BALL

½" X ½"

1" X 1" X 18"

6¾"

2"

¾"

2"

½"

4"

36"

¾" DOWEL

SCREW EYES

HARDWOOD

⑦

¾" X 6" X 12"

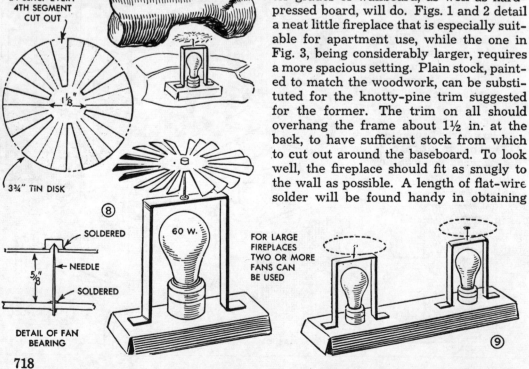

24 SLITS. EVERY 4TH SEGMENT CUT OUT

1⅛"

3¾" TIN DISK

⑧

SOLDERED

NEEDLE

⅝"

SOLDERED

DETAIL OF FAN BEARING

60 W.

FOR LARGE FIREPLACES TWO OR MORE FANS CAN BE USED

⑨

ter grades of wallboard, as well as hard-pressed board, will do. Figs. 1 and 2 detail a neat little fireplace that is especially suitable for apartment use, while the one in Fig. 3, being considerably larger, requires a more spacious setting. Plain stock, painted to match the woodwork, can be substituted for the knotty-pine trim suggested for the former. The trim on all should overhang the frame about 1½ in. at the back, to have sufficient stock from which to cut out around the baseboard. To look well, the fireplace should fit as snugly to the wall as possible. A length of flat-wire solder will be found handy in obtaining the shape of the baseboard for transferring to the end boards. Areas to be covered with plastic should have ¼-in. wire mesh tacked to them to make it adhere. However, if you are unable to obtain this material, another way to key the plastic is to groove the plywood deeply with a sharp tool, undercutting the grooves thus made, then size the wood with a coat of shellac.

Now to mix and apply the plastic: The ingredients of this are listed in the formula given in Fig. 13. Weigh and measure these carefully, and when adding the asbestos-whiting mixture, stir constantly and finally knead with the hands. Be careful not to add more water than is specified. A pail is a good container in which to mix and store the plastic. It can be kept for as long as a

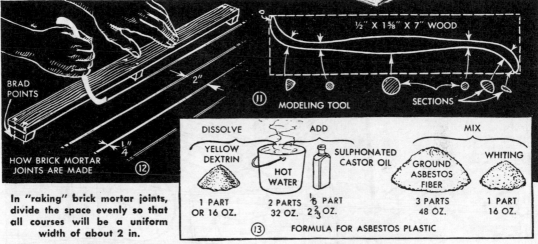

BRAD POINTS

2"

¼"

HOW BRICK MORTAR JOINTS ARE MADE ⑫

In "raking" brick mortar joints, divide the space evenly so that all courses will be a uniform width of about 2 in.

½" X 1⅝" X 7" WOOD

⑪ MODELING TOOL   SECTIONS

DISSOLVE   ADD   MIX

YELLOW DEXTRIN   HOT WATER   SULPHONATED CASTOR OIL   GROUND ASBESTOS FIBER   WHITING

1 PART OR 16 OZ.   2 PARTS 32 OZ.   ⅙ PART 2⅔ OZ.   3 PARTS 48 OZ.   1 PART 16 OZ.

⑬ FORMULA FOR ASBESTOS PLASTIC

month if covered with wet cloths to prevent it from drying out. Apply the plastic with the fingers or putty knife, pressing it into the wire-covered surface, and build up a layer about ¼ in. thick. Then smooth it lightly with a trowel dipped in water frequently. Avoid troweling the plastic too smoothly in order to have the texture resemble that of brickwork. To simulate stone as is used on the colonial fireplace detailed in Figs. 6 and 7, a wooden modeling tool like the one in Fig. 11 is needed to form the "mortar joints." This is used freehand as in Fig. 10 to produce irregular joints, but it is run along a straightedge as shown in Fig. 12 for producing brickwork effects. Where a rough stone effect is wanted, build up the thickness of the plastic by adding a second layer. The plastic dries hard in 48 hrs., the same color as cement.

Artists' oil colors, thinned with turpentine, are best to tint the plastic. Burnt sienna, Indian red or Venetian red, with or without lampblack added, will give practically any brick shade wanted. Apply a wash coat of this, leaving the mortar joints unpainted. Then tone individual bricks here and there a little darker than others. The back and sides of the fire pit should be given a coat of lampblack to make it look smoked. Stone surfaces require more care in coloring. Experiment with yellow, blue, green or orange colors mixed with sepia or raw umber to obtain the stone effect.

A log charred on the underside by applying a blowtorch or other flame to it, and placed over a hidden colored bulb as shown in Figs. 8 and 9, will give a flickering glow to further add realism. Also, by "peening" the wooden andirons and giving them a coat of flat-black paint, it will be hard to tell them from iron.

WOOD CHEST *and* BELLOWS

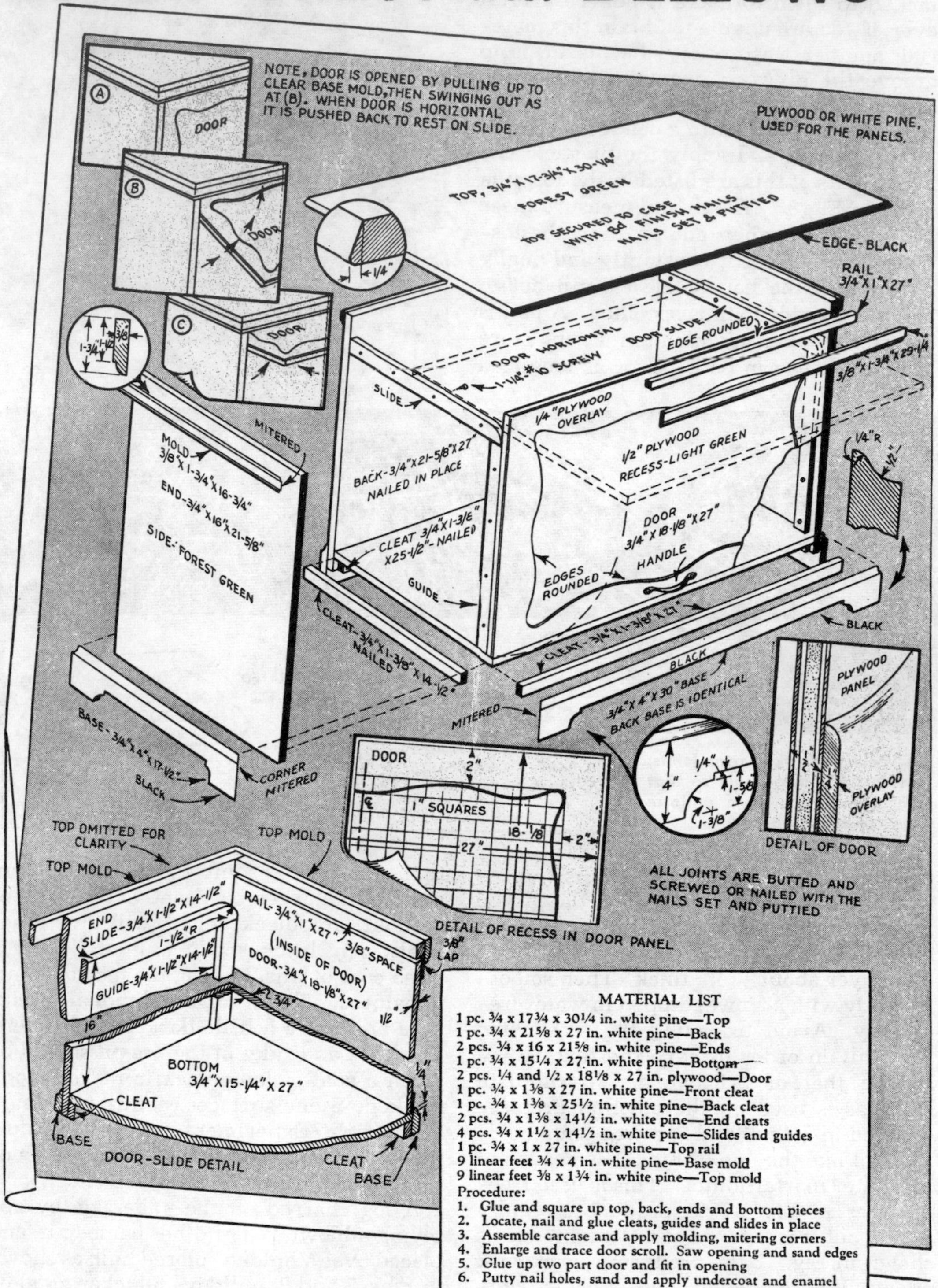

NOTE, DOOR IS OPENED BY PULLING UP TO CLEAR BASE MOLD, THEN SWINGING OUT AS AT (B). WHEN DOOR IS HORIZONTAL IT IS PUSHED BACK TO REST ON SLIDE.
A
DOOR
B
DOOR
C
DOOR
PLYWOOD OR WHITE PINE, USED FOR THE PANELS.
TOP, 3/4" X 17-3/4" X 30-1/4"
FOREST GREEN
TOP SECURED TO CASE WITH 8d FINISH NAILS NAILS SET & PUTTIED
1/4"
EDGE-BLACK
RAIL 3/4"X 1"X 27"
1-3/4"
1-1/2"
3/8"
DOOR HORIZONTAL
DOOR SLIDE
EDGE ROUNDED
1-1/4" #10 SCREW
3/8"X 1-3/4"X 29-1/4
SLIDE
1/4" PLYWOOD OVERLAY
MITERED
MOLD 3/8"X 1-3/4"X 16-3/4"
END-3/4"X 16"X 21-5/8"
SIDE-FOREST GREEN
BACK-3/4"X 21-5/8"X 27" NAILED IN PLACE
1/2" PLYWOOD RECESS-LIGHT GREEN
1/4"R
1/2"
CLEAT 3/4"X 1-3/8" X 25-1/2"-NAILED
DOOR 3/4"X 18-1/8"X 27"
HANDLE
EDGES ROUNDED
GUIDE
CLEAT-3/4"X 1-3/8"X 14-1/2" NAILED
CLEAT-3/4"X 1-3/8"X 27"
BLACK
BLACK
3/4"X 4"X 30" BASE BACK BASE IS IDENTICAL
MITERED
BASE-3/4"X 4"X 17-1/2"
BLACK
CORNER MITERED
DOOR
2"
℄
1" SQUARES
18-1/8
2"
27"
DETAIL OF RECESS IN DOOR PANEL
4"
1/4"
1-5/8
1-3/8"
PLYWOOD PANEL
PLYWOOD OVERLAY
DETAIL OF DOOR
ALL JOINTS ARE BUTTED AND SCREWED OR NAILED WITH THE NAILS SET AND PUTTIED
TOP OMITTED FOR CLARITY
TOP MOLD
TOP MOLD
END
SLIDE-3/4"X 1-1/2"X 14-1/2"
1-1/2"R
RAIL-3/4"X 1"X 27"
3/8" SPACE
3/8" LAP
(INSIDE OF DOOR)
DOOR-3/4"X 18-1/8"X 27"
GUIDE-3/4"X 1-1/2"X 14-1/2"
3/4"
1/2"
16"
BOTTOM 3/4"X 15-1/4"X 27"
1/4"
CLEAT
BASE
DOOR-SLIDE DETAIL
CLEAT
BASE

MATERIAL LIST

1 pc. 3/4 x 17 3/4 x 30 1/4 in. white pine—Top
1 pc. 3/4 x 21 5/8 x 27 in. white pine—Back
2 pcs. 3/4 x 16 x 21 5/8 in. white pine—Ends
1 pc. 3/4 x 15 1/4 x 27 in. white pine—Bottom
2 pcs. 1/4 and 1/2 x 18 1/8 x 27 in. plywood—Door
1 pc. 3/4 x 1 3/8 x 27 in. white pine—Front cleat
1 pc. 3/4 x 1 3/8 x 25 1/2 in. white pine—Back cleat
2 pcs. 3/4 x 1 3/8 x 14 1/2 in. white pine—End cleats
4 pcs. 3/4 x 1 1/2 x 14 1/2 in. white pine—Slides and guides
1 pc. 3/4 x 1 x 27 in. white pine—Top rail
9 linear feet 3/4 x 4 in. white pine—Base mold
9 linear feet 3/8 x 1 3/4 in. white pine—Top mold

Procedure:

1. Glue and square up top, back, ends and bottom pieces
2. Locate, nail and glue cleats, guides and slides in place
3. Assemble carcase and apply molding, mitering corners
4. Enlarge and trace door scroll. Saw opening and sand edges
5. Glue up two part door and fit in opening
6. Putty nail holes, sand and apply undercoat and enamel

for Your Fireplace

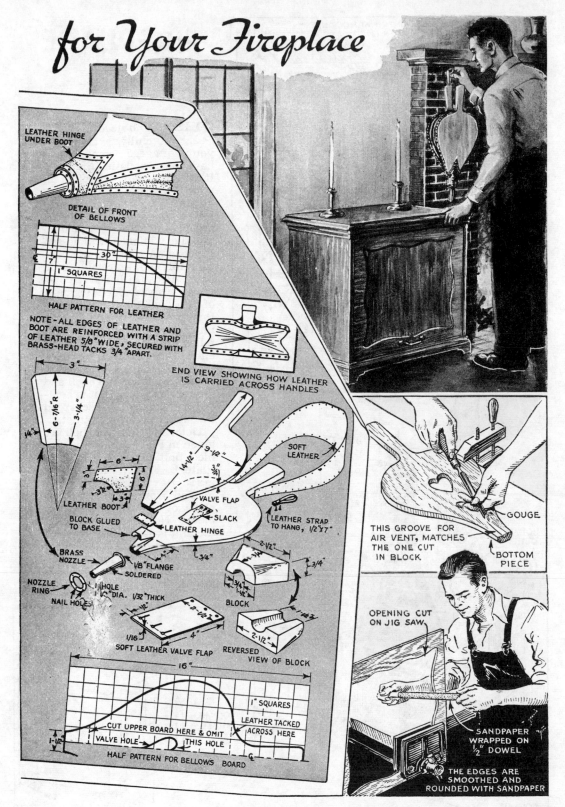

LEATHER HINGE UNDER BOOT

DETAIL OF FRONT OF BELLOWS

1" SQUARES

HALF PATTERN FOR LEATHER

NOTE - ALL EDGES OF LEATHER AND BOOT ARE REINFORCED WITH A STRIP OF LEATHER 5/8" WIDE, SECURED WITH BRASS-HEAD TACKS 3/4" APART.

END VIEW SHOWING HOW LEATHER IS CARRIED ACROSS HANDLES

3"

6-7/16" R

3-1/4"

1/4"

6"

LEATHER BOOT

BLOCK GLUED TO BASE

BRASS NOZZLE

NOZZLE RING

NAIL HOLES

HOLE 1/2" DIA.

1/8" FLANGE SOLDERED

1/32" THICK

SOFT LEATHER VALVE FLAP

1/16"

4"

2-1/2"

9-1/2"

14-1/2"

3/4"

VALVE FLAP

SLACK

LEATHER HINGE

SOFT LEATHER

LEATHER STRAP TO HANG, 1/2"x7"

2-1/2"

3/4"

3/4"

1-1/2"

BLOCK

2-1/2"

REVERSED VIEW OF BLOCK

16"

1" SQUARES

LEATHER TACKED ACROSS HERE

CUT UPPER BOARD HERE & OMIT THIS HOLE

VALVE HOLE

1-1/2"

HALF PATTERN FOR BELLOWS BOARD

THIS GROOVE FOR AIR VENT, MATCHES THE ONE CUT IN BLOCK

GOUGE

BOTTOM PIECE

OPENING CUT ON JIG SAW

SANDPAPER WRAPPED ON 1/2" DOWEL

THE EDGES ARE SMOOTHED AND ROUNDED WITH SANDPAPER

FIREPLACE

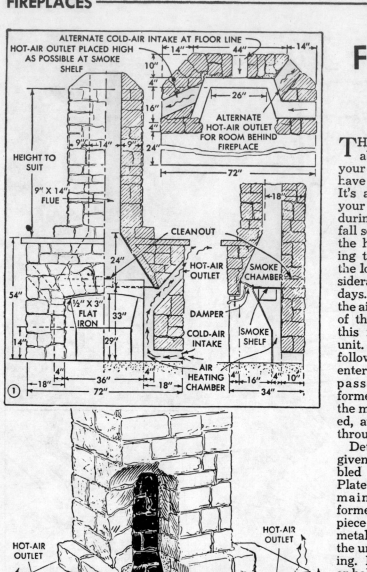

Fig. 1 labels:
ALTERNATE COLD-AIR INTAKE AT FLOOR LINE
HOT-AIR OUTLET PLACED HIGH AS POSSIBLE AT SMOKE SHELF

14"   44"   14"
10"
4"
26"
16"
ALTERNATE HOT-AIR OUTLET FOR ROOM BEHIND FIREPLACE
4"
24"
72"

18"

HEIGHT TO SUIT

9"   14"   9"

9" X 14" FLUE

CLEANOUT

HOT-AIR OUTLET

SMOKE CHAMBER

24"

1/2" X 3" FLAT IRON

54"

33"

DAMPER

COLD-AIR INTAKE

SMOKE SHELF

29"

14"

AIR HEATING CHAMBER

4"   18"   36"   4"   18"   4"   16"   4"   10"
72"   34"

①

HOT-AIR OUTLET

HOT-AIR OUTLET

COLD-AIR INTAKE

COLD-AIR INTAKE

②

THERE'S no need to worry about chilly evenings at your cottage or camp if you have this circulating fireplace. It's also equally effective in your home for cool evenings during late spring and early fall so you won't have to start the heating plant. And during the winter it will lessen the load on your furnace considerably on extremely cold days. Because it recirculates the air instead of sending most of the heat up the chimney, this fireplace is an efficient unit. The path which the air follows is shown in Fig. 2; it enters the cold-air intake, passes through the space formed by the metal shell and the masonry, where it is heated, and finally is discharged through the hot-air outlet.

Details of the steel shell are given in Fig. 4 and the assembled unit appears in Fig. 3. Plate E, Fig. 4, which is the main part of the unit, is formed from a 36 by 60-in. piece of No. 12-gauge sheet metal. No lap is required if the unit is assembled by welding. However, if it is riveted or bolted, the lap indicated by the dotted lines should be followed. These joints must be

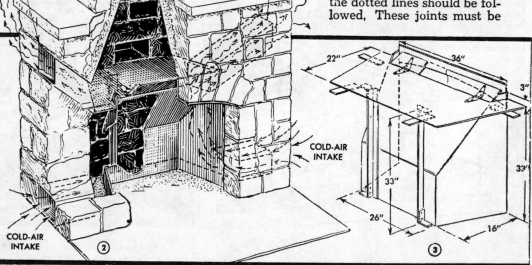

22"   36"   3"

COLD-AIR INTAKE

33"

33"

26"   16"

③

CIRCULATES WARM AIR

smoketight and may require the use of furnace cement. Plate A, Fig. 4, is cut from a 9 by 36-in. sheet and is hinged to the top front of the shell to act as a damper. The smoke shelf, Plate D, is a piece of No. 10-gauge metal 22 by 48 in. This is welded or bolted to the shell, Fig. 3, and supported at the rear by two 1/4 by 1 1/2 by 1 1/2-in. angles cut and assembled as shown in Plate C, Fig. 4. The edges of this plate are set into the masonry about 1 1/2 in., and, to give further support, flat-iron lugs are welded to the underside of the shelf.

The damper control, lower right-hand detail, Fig. 1, is a piece of flat iron cut in the shape of a gooseneck and hinged to the damper. Adjustment of the damper is obtained by engaging notches in the gooseneck with a catch set in the masonry. A 1/2 by 3 by 48-in. bar is used to make the arch, Plate B, Fig. 4.

A stone, rubble and concrete foundation is carried to solid ground below the frost line. If the house has a basement, the floor is broken up and the foundation carried down in the same manner. When the foun-

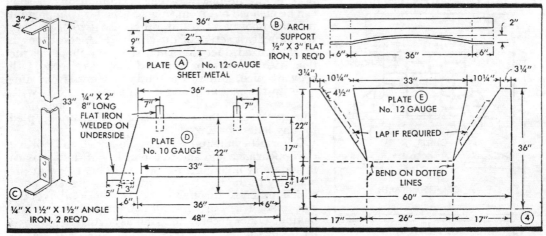

dation has been completed to the level of the hearth, the steel shell is set in place. The masonry is built up 4 in. away from the sides and the back of the shell, with the smoke shelf, as mentioned previously, sealed into the stonework. When building the masonry, allow for cold-air intakes at the bottom, Fig. 2. The hot-air outlets are slanted upward, beginning under the smoke shelf. These are either standard 6 by 8-in. ductwork or 7-in. stovepipes. Besides the outlets shown in Fig. 2, additional outlets are suggested in the upper right-hand detail of Fig. 1. This would apply when the fireplace is not against an outside wall and it is desirable to heat a room at the rear of the unit. For every outlet installed there is a cold-air intake.

However, before the outlets are completed, the arch bar, Plate B, Fig. 4, is installed. This is done when the masonry has been carried to the height of the damper. The smoke chamber part of the flue has a slope of about 60 degrees. It is built around a wooden frame which is knocked down and removed before the chimney is built. No attempt should be made to burn the frame out. The inside dimensions of the flue are given as 9 by 14 in., but these dimensions can be varied somewhat as long as the cross sectional area is over 100 sq. in.

Fig. 5 shows an alternate masonry design when it is desirable to have the chimney outside the house. This avoids cutting out a portion of the wall and roof of the house, but requires wider and heavier masonry at the base and a higher smoke chamber to obtain the proper bevels. In this case, since the chimney is not seen from inside the house, it can be built of brick.

There are many refinements and conveniences that may be added to this basic fireplace. A cleanout door can be located above the smoke shelf at the back of the fireplace so that accumulations of soot can be cleaned out from time to time. It is important that this door be a tight fit; otherwise it will interfere with the draft action of the chimney. A short length of galvanized duct the same size and shape as the flue, with a conical or pyramid-shaped rain cap, will prevent mice, squirrels and other rodents from running up the masonry and down the chimney. With this cap it also will be unnecessary to board the chimney over if the cottage is to be left unoccupied for any length of time.

Other attachments that may be added to improve the appearance and add to the utility of the fireplace include a swinging arm or crane. This is set in the masonry at the front of the fireplace. A metal oven which extends through the stonework above the smoke shelf will provide for some Dutch oven style baking. Other accessories such as revolving spits for barbecues and hot-water heating coils will add to the usefulness of the fireplace.

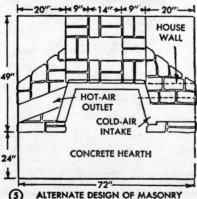

⑤ ALTERNATE DESIGN OF MASONRY FOR CHIMNEY OUTSIDE OF HOUSE

LIGHTWEIGHT ICE-FISHING SHELTER

LIGHTWEIGHT AND COMPACT, this portable ice-fishing shelter can be set up in a matter of minutes and offers maximum protection against wind and weather. The upright sections of the frame are 1-in. aluminum tubing, 72 in. high. The cross members are ¾-in. aluminum tubing, 48 in. long. The ends of the cross members are closed with wooden plugs into which are inserted 3/16-in. machine screws. Two ¼ x ½-in. slots which receive the screw heads are cut in one end of the uprights. The canvas is a piece of water-repellent khaki drill measuring 75 x 156 in. A 1½-in. seam is sewn along the top and 2-in. seams along the tent wall as indicated in the diagram. The roof is a triangular section of canvas measuring 50 in. on each side, one side being stitched to the back tent wall. A grommet and rope placed opposite this sewn edge will allow you to secure the roof tightly. To set the tent up, measure off and mark three points on the ice at the proper intervals and drill holes here 2 in. deep. Slip the canvas over the uprights and place the uprights in the holes. Now install the cross members and pull the roof down. The 5-in. overlap at the bottom can be pulled in and weighted down to keep the wind out.

Anchored to the ice, and set facing prevailing winds, the tent offers sturdy and comfortable shelter for one or two-man fishing expeditions. Ventilation is through top joint openings

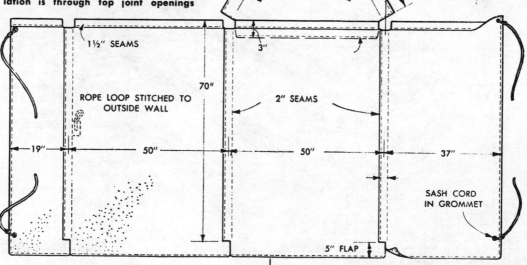

3/16" MACHINE SCREWS

WOODEN PLUG

¼ x ½" SLOT

60°

TOP VIEW

¾" ALUMINUM TUBING

48"

1" TUBING

72"

25"

50"

4"   4"

1½" SEAMS

3"

70"

ROPE LOOP STITCHED TO OUTSIDE WALL

2" SEAMS

19"   50"   50"   37"

SASH CORD IN GROMMET

5" FLAP

Wooden BAIT BOX
has cantilever action trays

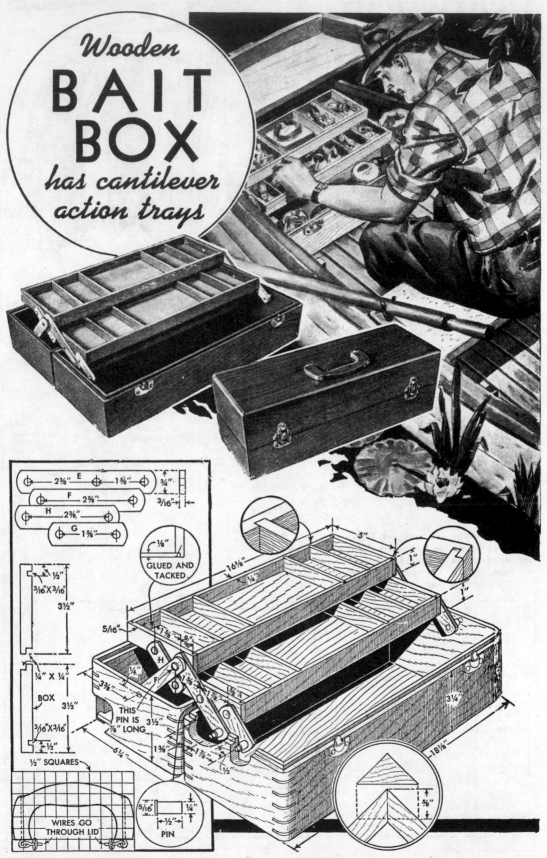

GLUED AND TACKED

1/2" SQUARES

WIRES GO THROUGH LID

PIN

THIS PIN IS 7/8" LONG

BOX

You Will Be Proud Of This Bait Box

You'll never regret being unable to obtain a metal bait box if you make this fine wooden one, which also affords a very interesting woodworking project. The original box was made of ½-in. walnut, but any available hardwood will do. A careful study of the drawings will show you how the box is assembled. The upper and lower halves are identical in size and shape, the top of the box being rabbeted into the upper half and the bottom dadoed into the lower half. Notice in one of the lower left-hand details how the abutting edges, when the box is closed, are rabbeted on opposite edges to form an interlocking joint that excludes water and dirt. The box is put together with simple glued miter corners. When the glue has dried, the corners are slotted horizontally and reinforcing splines are glued in place, after which all corners and top edges are carefully rounded. Two five-compartment trays of ¼-in. stock are made as shown and pivoted to the box with cantilever arms of hard maple. The attaching or pivoting pins are simply pieces of 5⁄16-in. dowel having narrow shoulders or heads turned on the ends as shown in one of the lower details. The pins are inserted through the levers and then glued into holes in the trays, the heads on the pins keeping the levers from slipping off. Hinges and snap locks taken from an old suitcase may be used on the box. A handle is jigsawed from matching wood and is attached by means of wire "hinges" as shown in the lower left-hand detail. After a careful and thorough sanding, the box is given a weatherproof finish by applying three coats of spar varnish inside and outside.

Bait Carrier Fastened to Shirt Keeps Tackle at Hand

When wading in midstream or fishing along the shore, it's difficult to carry a tackle box with a supply of extra baits. However, with this canvas carrier, three or four lures can be carried with no inconvenience. The carrier is made of light khaki cloth and each pocket is about 2 by 4 in., the number of pockets being determined by the number of lures you wish to carry.

Bait Net Made From Umbrella

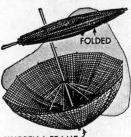

UMBRELLA FRAME COVERED WITH BOBBINET

An easily carried minnow net that will fit into a small space can be made from a discarded umbrella frame. Cut fine-meshed bobbinette to fit the ribs of the frame, using linen fish line as thread to sew the net to the frame. The handle is removed and a fairly heavy cord is tied to the shaft of the umbrella when seining for minnows.

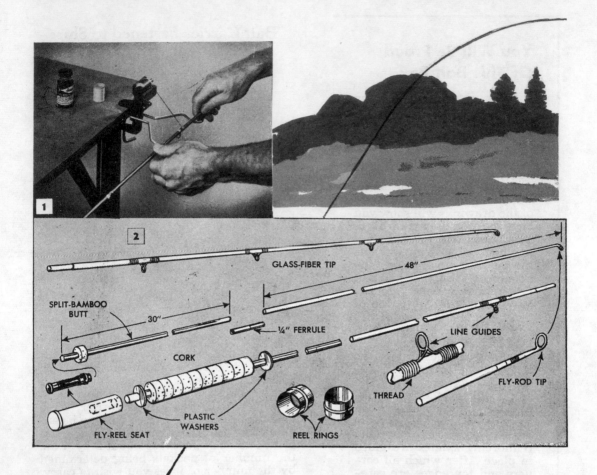

"TAILOR MADE" CASTING ROD

By Joe Ott

CONTROLLED flexibility is the added advantage I now include in the design of tailor-made casting rods made for my own use. The secret is to use a combination of a bamboo butt and a glass-fiber tip. Weight and length of the bamboo determine the weight and balance of the rod, the glass fiber controls flexibility. If more spring is desired, the bamboo butt is shortened and the glass-fiber tip is made longer in relation to the over-all length of the rod. Reversing the ratio will proportionately stiffen the rod.

Parts for assembling the rod are shown in Figs. 2 and 7, and are available at the shops of custom-rod makers and some sports stores. As with any custom-made rod, type and number of fittings are left to the discretion of the individual. Lengths given for the glass-fiber and bamboo sections of the rod are only suggested and can be changed to suit. Remember that the top end of the butt and lower end of the tip must fit in the same size ferrule. Average

handle length is about 11 in., requiring 22 cork rings ½ in. thick.

Assemble the rings on the bamboo butt, attach all line guides, ferrules and fittings with masking tape, Figs. 3 and 4, and tape on a reel. Check the rod now for flexibility and balance and shorten the bamboo or glass-fiber sections to suit your personal requirements. Keep in mind that the finished length of the rod should be somewhere between 6 and 7 ft. The rod will be long enough for a fly rod and light enough for a spinning outfit. If a fly-reel seat is to be used, glue the end of the butt in a length of dowel drilled to receive it. The dowel can be turned or filed down to provide a snug fit for the reel seat. Drive a 1/16-in. rustproof-metal pin through the seat, dowel and into the bamboo.

When making the handle, glue on all but two of the cork rings. Turn the handle to size and shape so the reel rings fit snugly on the center portion but cannot slip off the end. Slip on the rings, then glue on

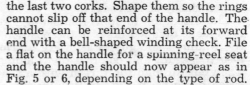

the last two corks. Shape them so the rings cannot slip off that end of the handle. The handle can be reinforced at its forward end with a bell-shaped winding check. File a flat on the handle for a spinning-reel seat and the handle should now appear as in Fig. 5 or 6, depending on the type of rod.

If a fly-reel seat is not used, a butt plate is screwed to the end of the handle. To prevent the butt from splitting when the butt-plate screw is driven into it, the bamboo is wrapped with thread, then wiped with glue. Two contrasting colors of thread are used to bind the guides, ferrules and winding check with a rod winder, Fig. 1. If the guides have thick bases, file them to a slight taper. Attach the guides to the rod with masking tape, then wind tape on the rod at each end, so it can be filed down, continuing taper of guide base. ★ ★ ★

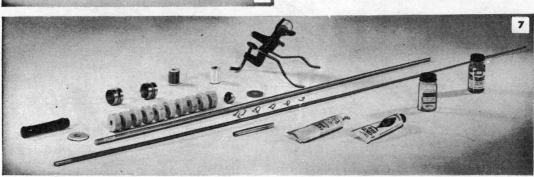

REPAIRING FISHING RODS

WHEN fighting trout or bass take the fly, or when the deep-sea heavyweights hit the lure, from there on out everything depends on your skill as a fisherman and on the strength and reliability of your tackle.

After several seasons of hard usage a bamboo rod may appear rather shabby and unkempt. Perhaps the tip section has taken a "set" or bend; likely the varnish is chipped or cracked badly, and probably the guides are worn and the windings are beginning to fray at the edges. If allowed to go without repair these defects will affect the efficiency of the rod.

The first thing to do in refinishing a rod is to make detailed notes of the position of the windings and guides as in Fig. 1. Note also the width and color of the windings. Then cut through the thread with a sharp razor blade as in Fig. 2. Usually the old varnish can be removed quite easily by scraping with either a razor blade or a sharp knife as in Fig. 3 but be careful not to round the corners of the hexagon section or to cut any deeper than the varnish coating. Don't use a varnish remover; however, nail-polish remover can be used

very sparingly to clean off what remains of the varnish, after a thorough, careful scraping. If the ferrules are loose, remove them as in Fig. 6. Then scrape off the old cement, melt new cement, which comes in stick form, and apply in an even coating. Force the ferrule back in place, Fig. 9, and give it a quarter turn to spread the adhesive uniformly. Wipe off all surplus which may be forced out. Sometimes on old rods the bamboo segments will be separated at places along the length, especially near the ferrules. Treat this condition as in Figs. 7 and 8, and be sure to allow plenty of time

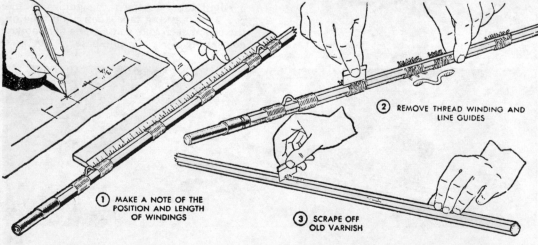

① MAKE A NOTE OF THE POSITION AND LENGTH OF WINDINGS

② REMOVE THREAD WINDING AND LINE GUIDES

③ SCRAPE OFF OLD VARNISH

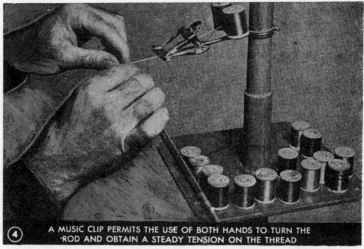

A MUSIC CLIP PERMITS THE USE OF BOTH HANDS TO TURN THE ROD AND OBTAIN A STEADY TENSION ON THE THREAD

for the glue to dry before unwinding the "clamping" thread. Wipe off surplus glue with a damp cloth before it dries. In this operation, it's important that the segments fit true, otherwise that section of the rod may show up a bend or "kink" which will affect its usefulness.

Now's the time to make sure that the ferrules fit properly. Often old ferrules tend to stick due to accumulated dirt and corrosion of the sliding surfaces. A buffing wheel will polish the parts to a velvety fit, but you have to be careful that the metal is not heated to the point where the cement will be softened. Badly roughened or corroded ferrules will have to be smoothed with very fine emery or "crocus" cloth, Fig. 11, before buffing. It's necessary to be careful that you don't polish away the metal to the point where the parts fit loosely. With the work completed to this stage, check the location of the guides from the reference sketch previously made as in Fig. 1, and mark lightly on the rod the position of each. If there is a set or bend in either or both of the rod tips—most fly rods are provided with two

tips—the bend can be worked out by gently straightening the tip against the original set, using both hands. This takes a bit of patience, but the method is effective. Another way is to hang the tip from the ceiling with a weight attached to the lower end. Guides should be replaced on the underside of the bend. Many rods are fitted with the so-called "snake" guides, and any of these that show undue wear or other damage should be replaced with new parts. This also is particularly true of the reel guide and the tip-top guide. If these are worn or grooved they will damage the line.

Fig. 5, details A to D inclusive, shows how to tie an invisible knot when making the new windings. First give the rod a thinned coat of special rod varnish and allow this to dry thoroughly. You'll note in Fig. 4 an arrangement for maintaining a uniform tension on the thread when making the windings, the thread being pulled through a music clip attached to a standard. Jaws of the clip should be smoothed so that they do not tear the strands of the silk thread. Use the same color and size of thread as the

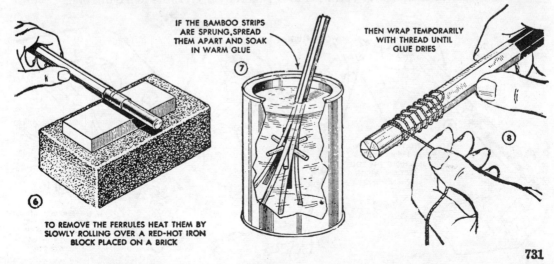

IF THE BAMBOO STRIPS ARE SPRUNG, SPREAD THEM APART AND SOAK IN WARM GLUE

THEN WRAP TEMPORARILY WITH THREAD UNTIL GLUE DRIES

TO REMOVE THE FERRULES HEAT THEM BY SLOWLY ROLLING OVER A RED-HOT IRON BLOCK PLACED ON A BRICK

Making the Invisible Knot

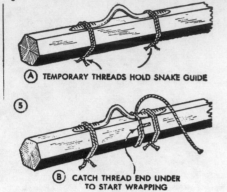

Ⓐ TEMPORARY THREADS HOLD SNAKE GUIDE

⑤

Ⓑ CATCH THREAD END UNDER
TO START WRAPPING

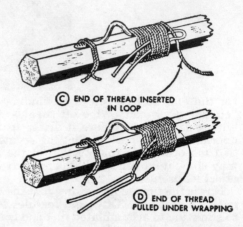

Ⓒ END OF THREAD INSERTED
IN LOOP

Ⓓ END OF THREAD
PULLED UNDER WRAPPING

original windings. It should be remembered that the windings add "tension" to the rod and that's why it's important to duplicate the position of the originals. Although the number of turns may vary, 25 turns per winding is a good average. Some refinishers space in an extra winding to stiffen an old rod, but usually this is not necessary.

Apply thinned white shellac to the windings and when dry follow with several coats of clear collodion or a special silk-thread color preservative. Use your finger for these applications as a brush picks up too much of the finishing material. Follow with three to five coats of rod varnish applied with a small brush as in Fig. 10. Hang the sections of the rod by fitting a wood plug and screw eye in the ferrules. Allow the varnish to dry several days between coats. Rub down the last coat with fine pumice stone and water and finish with dry rotten-stone rubbed with chamois. If you wish to

produce an exceptionally fine finish rub down each coat after a thorough drying, using pumice stone only. This leaves the surface slightly rough so that succeeding coats will bond properly. However, the principal purpose of rubbing down each coat is to level the varnish to a film of uniform thickness. After each rubbing clean the rod thoroughly with a damp rag and allow to dry before applying fresh varnish. When not in use the rod should be kept in a case to protect it from breakage, scratches or other damage. A tubular metal case is generally preferable to a cloth one.

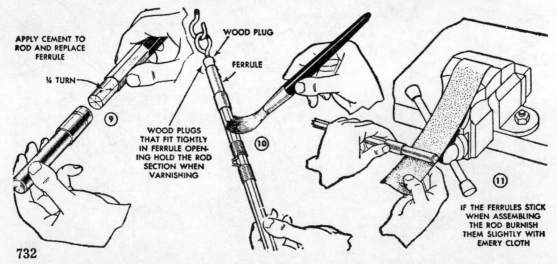

APPLY CEMENT TO
ROD AND REPLACE
FERRULE

¼ TURN

⑨

WOOD PLUG

FERRULE

WOOD PLUGS
THAT FIT TIGHTLY
IN FERRULE OPEN-
ING HOLD THE ROD
SECTION WHEN
VARNISHING

⑩

⑪

IF THE FERRULES STICK
WHEN ASSEMBLING
THE ROD BURNISH
THEM SLIGHTLY WITH
EMERY CLOTH

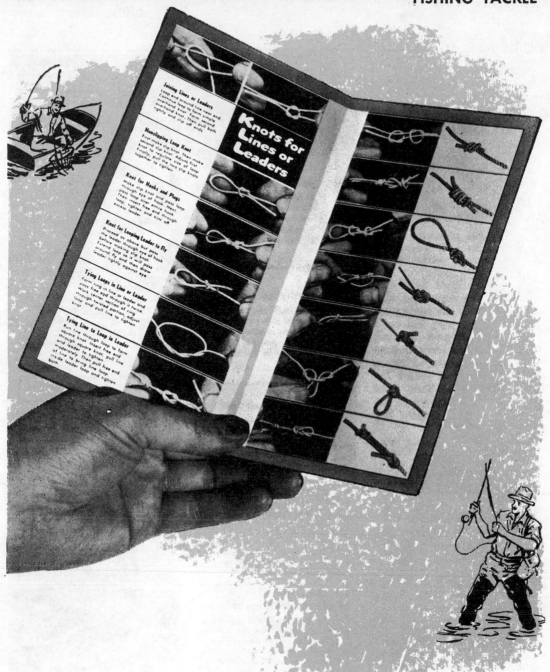

FISHERMAN'S KNOT BOOK

NEED A BRIEF refresher course on how to tie certain fishline knots?

The three photos across the top of the book show successive steps in tying a common fisherman's knot which is widely used to join lines or leaders. First, form a simple overhand knot near the end of one line. Then insert the end of the second line through the center of the overhand knot, loop the end around the first line and tie a second overhand knot. When this is done,

733

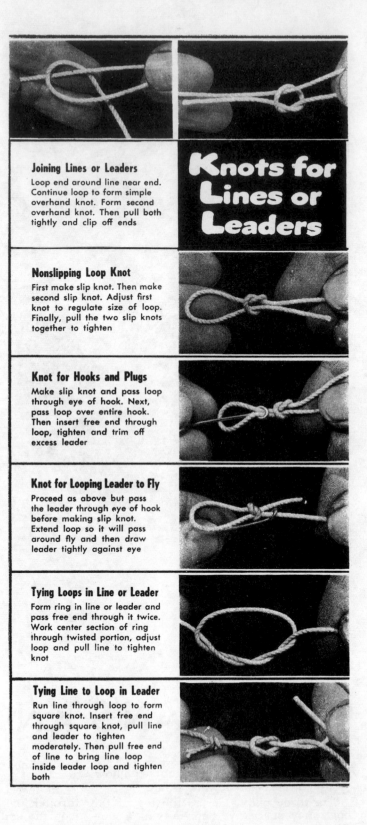

Knots for Lines or Leaders

Joining Lines or Leaders
Loop end around line near end. Continue loop to form simple overhand knot. Form second overhand knot. Then pull both tightly and clip off ends

Nonslipping Loop Knot
First make slip knot. Then make second slip knot. Adjust first knot to regulate size of loop. Finally, pull the two slip knots together to tighten

Knot for Hooks and Plugs
Make slip knot and pass loop through eye of hook. Next, pass loop over entire hook. Then insert free end through loop, tighten and trim off excess leader

Knot for Looping Leader to Fly
Proceed as above but pass the leader through eye of hook before making slip knot. Extend loop so it will pass around fly and then draw leader tightly against eye

Tying Loops in Line or Leader
Form ring in line or leader and pass free end through it twice. Work center section of ring through twisted portion, adjust loop and pull line to tighten knot

Tying Line to Loop in Leader
Run line through loop to form square knot. Insert free end through square knot, pull line and leader to tighten moderately. Then pull free end of line to bring line loop inside leader loop and tighten both

pull the two lines tightly to complete the knot and clip off the ends. If the same procedure is followed but each line is wrapped around three or four times before forming the overhand knots, you can make a splice for joining leaders. This particular knot is shown in the photo directly below the fisherman's knot.

To tie a nonslipping loop, or "fisherman's eye," first form a common slip knot in one end of the line. Continue with the free end of the line and tie a second knot by looping the end of the line around the standing portion of the line. Then adjust the first knot to regulate the size of the loop and finally pull the two knots together.

To attach a leader to a hook or plug, make a simple slip knot, pass the loop through the hook eye and pull enough leader through so the loop can pass over the entire hook. Note the photos captioned "Knot for Hooks and Plugs." Then draw up the slack to the point shown. Before pulling the loop tight, insert the free end of the leader through it, pull tight and trim off any excess. Many fishermen use this knot to tie nylon leaders.

To loop a leader to a dry or wet fly, proceed as in the next row of photos. Pass the leader through the hook eye

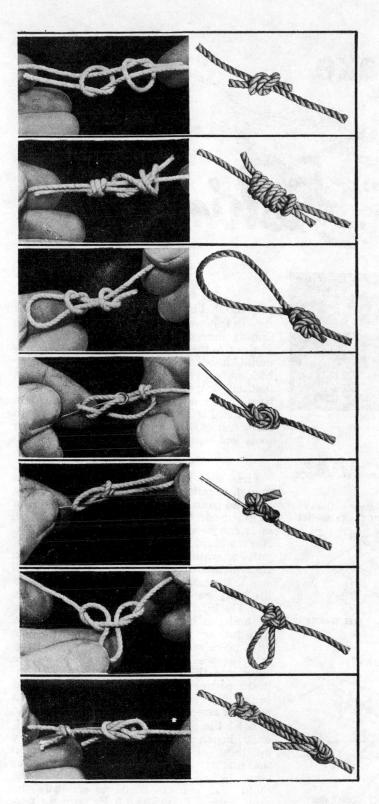

before tying the slip knot. Then extend the loop so it will pass around the fly and draw it tightly against the eye.

Forming loops, sometimes called blood-drop loops, in a line or leader is done by making a ring in the line and passing the free end through it twice. Next, work the center of the untwisted section of the ring through the center of the twisted portion and adjust the resulting loop to the desired size. Then pull the line to tighten the knot. This knot is shown in the second row of photos from the bottom of the page.

To attach a line to a leader or to another line, run the line through a loop to form a square, or reef, knot and bring the end of the line around the remainder as in the bottom row of photos. Insert the end through the square knot, pull line and looped leader to tighten the knot moderately and then pull the free end of the line to bring its loop inside the leader loop. Finally, tighten the knot by pulling again on the line and leader. The resulting knot should look like the accompanying drawing when tied properly. ★ ★ ★

How to make *Fishing Jigs*

ONE OF THE MOST effective lures used in salt-water fishing, and which now is finding increasing favor with fresh-water anglers, is the "jig." This lure consists of a metal "head" in which a single hook is embedded, and a "body" of bucktail hair, feathers or nylon. The most attractive feature of jigs is that any fishing enthusiast who ties his own flies or makes his own lures can cast the jigs with a minimum of tools and equipment.

Making the Molds

First step in making jigs is to have a model, or pattern. The pattern can be a jig on hand from which the feathers have been stripped and the hook and eyelet removed, or it can be carved from softwood, Fig. 1. Next, a mold is made by pouring plaster of paris or water putty into a cardboard box. As indicated in Fig. 2, the box should be a size that permits a space of 3/8 in. between the body end of the jig and the box side, and 1½ in. from the opposite end of the jig and the box side. First, pour the box half full of plaster, coat the jig pattern with petroleum jelly and press it halfway into the wet plaster. Two nails then are sunk into the plaster near diagonally opposite corners and allowed to project about ¼ in., Fig. 3. They will act as locating pins when reassembling jig halves for casting.

After the first half of the mold has hardened, brush its entire surface with heavy oil, then fill the box with plaster. When the plaster sets, which usually requires about ½ hr., break the box away from the mold. Use a knife blade to separate the mold halves, Figs. 5 and 6. Pry out the pattern, which will remain in one of the mold halves, and set the mold aside to season at room temperature for about two weeks.

1 MODEL JIG HEAD CARVED FROM WOOD

SUNK HALFWAY INTO WET PLASTER

2 3/8"

1½"

CARDBOARD BOXES

WET PLASTER

3 NAILS

4 COAT FIRST HALF OF MOLD BEFORE POURING SECOND HALF

When the plaster mold has thoroughly seasoned, use the point of a knife to cut eyelet grooves and hook slots, Fig. 8, which are determined by placing hooks and eyelets on the mold and tracing around them with a pencil. Eyelets, Fig. 7, are formed from brass or copper wire. Also carve a funnel-shaped pouring hole in each mold half.

Casting the Jigs

Metal for casting the jigs should be lead or tin, which often can be purchased as scrap metal. A combination of the two metals, such as bar solder, also is good. The greater the proportion of tin, the lighter the jig will be. Melt the metal in a ladle and pour some into each half of the mold, both to warm it and to remove any moisture. Next, place the hook and eyelet in position, Fig. 9, hold the mold halves together and quickly pour the mold full of metal, Fig. 10. When the surface of the metal indicates that it is hardening, lay the mold on its side until the metal has cooled completely. Wear heavy gloves for this operation, as the mold quickly becomes too hot to hold, and there is the risk of splashing molten metal on the hands.

In a minute or two the mold halves can be separated and the jig removed. Cut off the excess metal, Fig. 11, and drop it back into the ladle. A mold made as described will permit casting up to two dozen jigs. Chips or holes in the mold can be patched, but when the mold gets rough it should be remade. For a permanent mold, take a freshly cast plaster mold to a foundry and have it cast in bronze or aluminum. The cost should not be more than a few dollars, and the mold can be used for a lifetime.

Finishing the Jigs

After a number of jigs have been cast, file them smooth, then polish with sandpaper or emery cloth. Feathers or hair now are applied in several steps. First, wrap a few turns of heavy thread around the jig where the feathers will be attached, and cover this wrapping with quick-drying cement. Place a pinch of feathers against the cement, then wrap a few more turns of thread over them. Again apply the cement and a few more feathers. Repeat this operation until the hook is well concealed. Finally, wrap a few extra turns of thread around the assembly and coat them with cement. If the metal used for casting the jig had a high tin content, it probably will stay shiny. Metal containing more lead will quickly oxidize and turn dark, so it should be painted in colors that are compatible with the colors of the feathers used. Eyes may be painted on the jig to give it a more professional look. ★ ★ ★

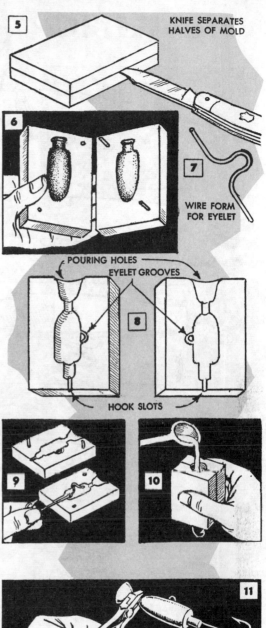

5 KNIFE SEPARATES HALVES OF MOLD

6

7 WIRE FORM FOR EYELET

POURING HOLES
EYELET GROOVES
8
HOOK SLOTS

9

10

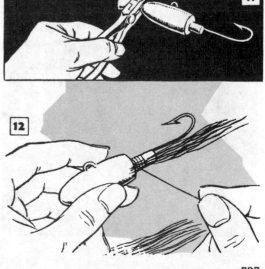

11

12

MAKING *fresh-Water*

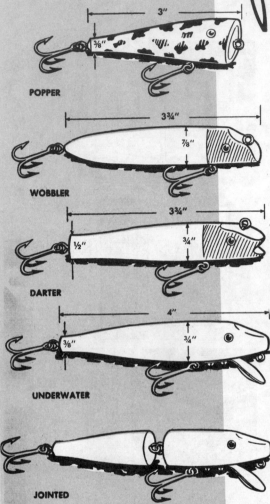

POPPER

3"

3/8"

WOBBLER

3¾"

7/8"

DARTER

3¾"

½" ¾"

UNDERWATER

4"

3/8" ¾"

JOINTED

Above, body shapes for fishing plugs. Below, spray-painting through cloth net produces "scale" effect

THERE IS NO GREATER THRILL for a real fishing enthusiast than to hook into a big one with a lure that he has made himself. Trout fishermen know this, and have made fly tying a popular hobby. What many freshwater fishermen do not know is that making plugs is just as simple, and just as personally rewarding when going after fighting game fish.

Most wooden fishing plugs are made of red or white cedar. Bass and birch also can be used, but the cedars are best, as they are worked easily and stand up well in water. If you have a wood-turning lathe, the plugs can be "mass produced," but you can do as well with a sharp knife and hand tools and each plug you make will be even more individual.

There are several basic body types used in making fresh-water fishing plugs, detail at left. The first is the popper type. This plug is about 3 in. long and has a 1-in. diameter at the large end. The tail end of the plug tapers to a diameter of 3/8 in. A slight depression is carved in the squared-off face of the plug. All dimensions given for the plugs are approximate, none being critical. The second type plug is the wobbler, with a diameter of 7/8 in. and tapers to a point at the tail. The diagonally cut forward end of this plug is slightly concave. Next is the darter-type plug. It is ¾ in. at the large diameter, tapering to ½ in. A notch is cut at the head end to form a "fish mouth" and the upper surface of the head is flattened. Both the under-water and the jointed plugs are made from the same body shape, which is ¾ in. at the larger diameter, tapering to 3/8 in. at the tail The upper portion of the head is cupped and a metal "lip" is screwed to the underside of the body. Dimensions for the lip are shown in the lower, right-hand detail on the facing page. It is cut from aluminum, copper, brass or stainless steel. A ball-peen hammer is used to give the lip a cupped shape. The jointed-type plug is made by cutting the under-water body in two and rejoining the parts with brass screw eyes. After all the plug bodies have

FISHING PLUGS

been shaped and sanded smooth, they should be dipped in white lacquer, then allowed to dry thoroughly. Cans of pressurized spray paint then can be used to make the plugs "two toned" by masking the area not to be painted. For a natural-fish-look, spray the top and sides of a plug with blue, green or brown, leaving the lower portion white. When the color has dried, hold the plug against a piece of cloth netting tacked to a wood frame and spray through the netting with aluminum paint to provide a glittering scale effect. The cloth netting can be obtained from the Netcraft Co., 3101 Sylvania Ave., Toledo 13, Ohio. They also have preshaped plug bodies for those who prefer assembling plugs from a kit. ★★★

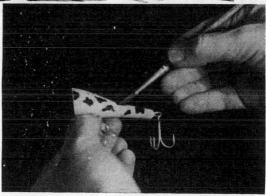

Above, brush applies "dappled" look. Below, left, spray cans are fast, convenient. Below, metal lip

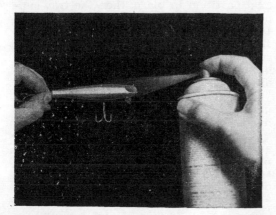

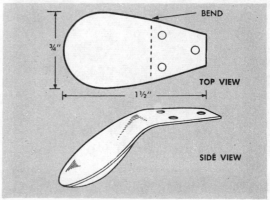

BEND

¾"

1½"

TOP VIEW

SIDE VIEW

TACKLE BOX of Plywood

By George X. Sand

This lightweight tackle box can be carried either by side handles or an adjustable leather carrying strap

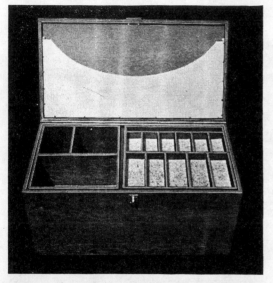

Ample storage space is provided in the lid and trays for a good selection of lures, leaders, line, camera and film. Fishing reels, two vacuum bottles and miscellaneous gear are easily stowed in the bottom

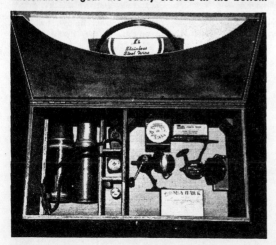

WANT an inexpensive tackle box that will remain dry inside under most conditions and provide adequate storage space for all your fishing accessories, a camera and a hearty lunch? This marine-plywood box will do the job. The bottom is partitioned to provide compartments for two vacuum bottles, reels and similar equipment. Above these compartments are trays for lures, camera, etc., and a large pocket inside the lid stores flat articles such as line, leaders and snelled hooks. Two brass handles and a leather carrying strap offer alternative means of carrying it.

Constructing the Box

First step is to build the box of ⅜-in. plywood. Cut the plywood according to the dimensions given in the diagram. Be sure to allow 1⅜ in. for the lid in the over-all height. Sand all members smooth, apply waterproof glue along each surface to be joined, and nail the top, side and end pieces together with 1-in. brass brads. You now have a box that is enclosed on all sides but the bottom. The top will be cut off later to make the lid. This will assure a perfect fit between box and lid.

Next, turn the box over and glue the vertical partition in place, then the tray-support members in both compartments, each 1½ in. up from the bottom. For added strength use 1-in. brads and allow the glued surfaces to set overnight. Wood clamps can be used to advantage here, although they are not a must.

After the bottom of the box is glued and nailed in place, the top is sawed off to make the lid, which will provide storage space for miscellaneous flat items when an aluminum sheet is screwed to ¾ x ½-in. wood spacer strips to form a pocket between the lid and metal, as indicated in the detail. The lid is attached to the box with a 23-in. strip of brass piano hinge.

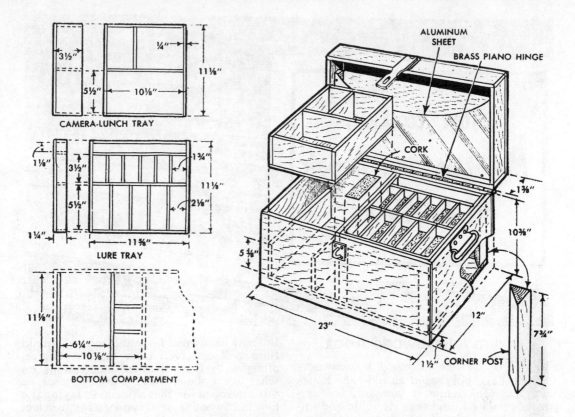

CAMERA-LUNCH TRAY

LURE TRAY

BOTTOM COMPARTMENT

ALUMINUM SHEET

BRASS PIANO HINGE

CORK

CORNER POST

Next, a carrying handle is bolted to each end of the box. Use small brass bolts and countersink the heads to fit flush on the inside. The same procedure applies for mounting the lock hasp and staple, which are centered at the front of the box. Two lengths of doubled ¾-in. leather strap fitted with adjustable buckles and snap hooks can be snapped on the handles for one-hand carrying.

Trays

The lure tray and the camera-lunch tray are made from ¼-in. plywood. These may be partitioned as suggested or modified to suit individual requirements. After the partitions have been glued and nailed in posi-

tion, glue thin sheet cork in the bottom of each lure compartment to protect the finish of the lures.

Under the camera-lunch tray, and acting as a support for one side of it, are the vacuum-bottle and miscellaneous equipment storage compartments (lead sinkers, first-aid equipment, etc.). The longest member is cut from ⅜-in. plywood while ¼-in. material is used for the short partitions. All three pieces are glued and nailed to the bottom and sides of the box to complete construction of the tackle box. Additional hooks, brackets and pockets can be installed in the box where desired to accommodate some special gadget or extra tackle. ★ ★ ★

Rod Holder Made From Spools Is Fisherman's "Third Hand"

When still fishing from a small boat, there are times when a "third hand," like the one shown, is helpful for holding a rod or fishing pole, as when eating lunch, or rowing to change fishing locations. The holder is made from two large thread spools which are screwed to the inside of the boat at the gunwale. The angle and spacing of the spools depends upon individual preference and the rod or pole to be accommodated. For some boats a spacer block may be necessary to bring the lower spool in line with the upper one.

How to Lay, Maintain and Repair Wood Floors

LAYING A HARDWOOD FLOOR

IF YOU are one of many homeowners who have purchased an old-type house and are remodeling it yourself, few improvements will increase its value and improve its interior appearance more than beautiful hardwood floors. Whether the condition of present floors is beyond refinishing and requires resurfacing with thin flooring, or whether an old softwood floor is to be covered, almost anyone who is handy with a hammer and saw can do the job with excellent results. Most of the tools required are common ones. Besides a hammer, you'll need handsaws for ripping and crosscutting, a nailset, a pair of dividers or a compass and a can of plastic wood putty to cover exposed nailheads where the flooring must be surface-nailed.

Complete instructions on how to finish the new hardwood floor and refinish an old floor will be given later in this chapter, along with fully detailed suggestions on what to do about floors that creak, sag or vibrate and stairs that squeak. In laying the new hardwood floor, it is necessary to select a type of flooring that will suit your particular needs and add beauty to your home.

Types of flooring: The attractive grain of quarter-sawed flooring makes a beautiful job when waxed or varnished and, when available, is to be preferred to the plain or "flash sawed" type shown in Fig. 3. Quarter-sawed flooring is recognized by the wavy pattern of surface grain and by the slant of the growth rings in the end grain. It is somewhat more expensive than plain-sawed flooring, but has less tendency to curl and surface splinter. Flooring is usually sold in bundles of strips ranging in length from 2 to 12 ft. or more and end-

This is how the last strip of each row is marked for length with a try square by placing it end for end against the wall and parallel with adjoining strip

Flooring is sold in bundles of strips of random lengths up to 12 ft., which are end and edge-matched with a tongue and groove, and cup-molded on the underside

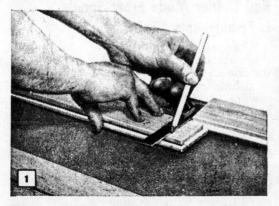

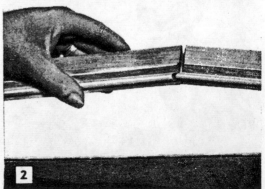

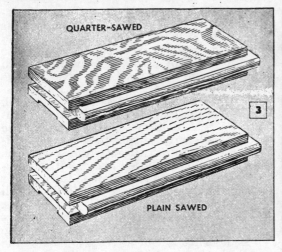

matched, Fig. 2, as well as edge-matched by a tongue and groove in the edge. The underside face of the strips is hollowed or cupped so that any unevenness of the subfloor will not interfere with their laying flat. Flooring can be had in four hardwoods: oak (white and red), maple, beech and birch. Oak flooring is available in strips of two standard widths and thicknesses. One measures ⅜ by 1½ in., the other 1³⁄₁₆ by 2¼ in. The condition of the subfloor or nailing base determines largely the size and type of flooring to use. Some homeowners prefer a floor laid of narrow strips which are used in resurfacing an old hardwood floor and when the nailing base is solid. The 1³⁄₁₆-in. flooring generally is used over a rough subfloor or one that is not thick enough or properly reinforced to give adequate support to thin-type flooring.

Ready-finished flooring recently has been introduced which saves the work of finishing and the inconvenience encountered in waiting for the floor to dry. This feature is especially desirable when laying a new floor in an occupied house. It differs from regular flooring in that it has

Starting strip should be laid at right angles to side walls. If corners of room are not square, mark grooved edge of strip with compass to match wall

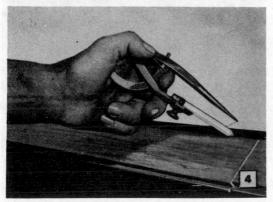

Finished with two coats of durable varnish, a hardwood floor will withstand rough usage by youngsters

a V-joint instead of a tongue and groove and, of course, it is stained, sealed or otherwise finished, ready for use as soon as it is laid. However, being prefinished, it requires great care in laying to avoid marring. To help reduce possible damage from hammer marks, the flooring is factory drilled for nails and is packaged for further protection. It naturally is considerably more expensive, as in addition to being finished, it is specially selected for straightness and uniform grain.

Keep flooring dry: Due to its low moisture content when kiln dried, flooring is highly subject to dampness and, until it is laid and completely finished, it is very important that it be kept *dry* at all times. This is especially so if the flooring is stored for any length of time prior to laying. It also is important that if laid during damp weather, the building be heated. If allowed to absorb moisture, a tightly laid floor will shrink when it dries out, leaving objectionable openings between the strips. In new construction, flooring should not be laid until the plaster has dried completely as it will absorb moisture from the walls.

Preliminary steps: The first step in laying a new floor is to inspect the old floor, or subfloor if it is new construction, for loose boards, ridges and any other high places that might prevent the new flooring from lying flat. Nail such places thoroughly to pull the boards down flush. This is important to assure a squeakless floor and prevent movement in the finished floor. In resurfacing a previously laid hard or softwood floor, it is advisable to remove the baseboard. This can be done without damaging the baseboard by locating the nails and driving them completely through and into the studs with a pin punch. Following this, the floor should be swept clean and covered with a good grade of building paper, lapped at the sides and ends. Old softwood floors that are worn badly sometimes are covered first with plywood and special long nails used to apply the flooring. On new floors, the paper liner serves as a dust-and-draft barrier between the subfloor and finish floor, while on an old floor, which without doubt was originally laid over a paper covering, the new paper simply provides a smooth, clean, working surface.

How flooring is nailed: Flooring is nailed blind, in other words toenailed, so that the nailheads are hidden. This is done by driving the nails into the angle between the tongue and front edge of the strip as shown in Fig. 6. Use 8-penny wire flooring nails or special cut-steel flooring nails and drive them at an angle of 45 deg. Experience will enable you to drive the nails practically all the way with a hammer, as in Fig. 9. However, it is advisable at first to drive them part way and finish with a nailset to avoid the possibility of accidentally damaging the edge of the flooring. If cut nails

are used, they can be driven home by using the side of the head of another nail as shown in Fig. 7. The important thing is to drive the head flush or slightly below the surface so that it will not interfere with drawing up the subsequent strip. In the case of very hard woods, such as maple or birch, it may be necessary to first drill holes for the nails to avoid splitting, especially if wire nails are used. The blunt nose of cut nails will not split the wood as readily, as they punch through the wood. The nails should be spaced about 8 in. in laying ⅜-in. flooring and from 10 to 16 in. for thick flooring. It pays to nail a floor well to avoid later squeaks and loose boards.

Laying the starting strip: If you are covering a badly worn hardwood floor, the new flooring is laid at right angles to the old. The first strip is selected for straightness and is laid with the grooved edge facing the wall and close enough so that the baseboard, if used, will cover any small opening. If the corners of the room are not square, the starting strip should be placed at a 90-deg. angle to the side wall, marked

When waste portion of the last strip in each row is a foot or more in length it is used to start next row

Blind-nail each strip by nailing in angle of tongue and edge. Use 8-penny nails driven at 45-deg. angle

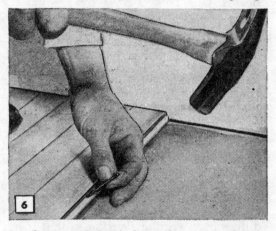

Each nailhead must be set flush or slightly below surface. Side of cut nail or regular nailset will do

Pencil compass is handy for marking strips when fitting flooring neatly around or under a doorcasing

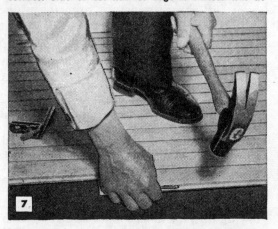

with a compass as in Fig. 4 and ripped to conform to the adjacent wall. This starting strip generally is face-nailed along the rear edge and sometimes it also is toenailed in the tongue. While it is best to have the starting strip in one piece, the size of the room may require several pieces laid end to end. In the latter case, if the piece cut off is greater than a foot in length, it usually is used to start the next row, Fig. 5. The last strip in each row is marked for length with a try square as in Fig. 1, after placing it end for end and against the wall. From here on it is a case of drawing the flooring strips of each row tightly against those of the preceding row to assure tight-fitting joints. For this purpose cut a scrap of flooring and use it to drive against. This will prevent damaging the tongue and will be found helpful in drawing up stubborn joints. Strips of flooring that are slightly bowed can be forced tightly against the preceding row by prying with a wooden block placed against a 2 by 4-in. lever and block temporarily nailed to the floor. The joints in each subsequent row always

Abutting strips are placed crosswise to the door opening when ending the floor at bathroom or kitchen

9

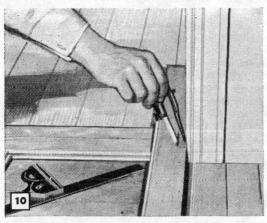

10

Final fill-in strip is marked to conform to wall by wedging full-width strip and marking with compass

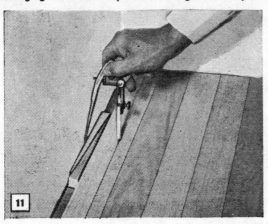

11

Practice will enable you to drive nails rapidly from standing position. Heads are set later with nailset

should be staggered at least 6 in. or more.

Notching around doorcasing: When you must fit the flooring around or under the casing of a doorway leading to an adjacent room or closet, a pair of dividers or a compass is used to mark the depth of the required notch. Fig. 8 illustrates how this is done, the flooring in this case being fitted to butt against the casing. If you are resurfacing an old floor and wish the flooring to run under the casing and jamb, it will be necessary to saw off these two pieces to allow for the extra thickness. As shown in Fig. 8, the strip to be marked is not nailed but is simply tapped temporarily in position and butted against the end of the adjoining strip in the same row. Note that the joint of the adjoining strip ends flush with the face of the jamb. Now, measure the space between the loose strip and the face of the casing and set the compass so that this distance is marked on the strip when one leg of the compass is held in contact with the casing. Any slight cant or irregularity of the casing will be transferred to the strip assuring a perfect-fitting butt joint. The loose strip is removed and replaced with a full-width strip, the two strips being laid at the same time to enable wedging snugly in place. When the direction of the flooring runs through a doorway and you wish the new floor to end in

Drive nails part way and bend them over to support narrow fill-in strip flush with the rest of the flooring

Bowed fill-in strip is forced in place tightly for marking by prying against wall with board and block

the center of the opening as in Fig. 10, the compass method is used as before to mark the strip to fit the jamb. Note here that one or two strips of flooring are first nailed down parallel with the opening and serve as header strips against which the flooring is butted. This generally applies when a hardwood floor is butted against a bathroom or kitchen floor which is to be built up flush and covered with linoleum.

Fitting final strips: If no baseboards are to be used and only a shoe mold, the steps in fitting the last remaining strips are shown in Figs. 11 to 15 inclusive. When the space remaining along the wall is less than a full width of flooring, the strip next to

the final one is set in place temporarily and wedged either with tapered blocks as shown in Fig. 11, or forced in place by prying as shown in Fig. 12. After this it is marked, as before, with a compass to transfer the contour of the wall, then ripped and used as a fill-in strip. Due to the fact that flooring is cupped or hollowed on the underside and ripping removes one supporting edge, a few nails should be driven part way into the subfloor and bent over, as shown in Fig. 13, to support the fill-in strip flush with the others. Actual laying of the fill-in strip and the last few strips is done at the same time, as in Fig. 14, so that the matched edges will go in place. Tapping with a hammer and wooden block will drive them into position as shown in Fig. 15. As the fill-in strip cannot be toenailed, it is face-nailed so that the heads will be covered by the shoe mold. Fitting the fill-in strip tightly is not so important when both baseboard and shoe mold are used, as together they will cover any slight gap that may remain along the wall.

To permit inserting the fill-in strip, last few strips are laid at same time to engage the matched edges

Fill-in strips and others are gradually forced down with hammer and block. Then the strip is face-nailed

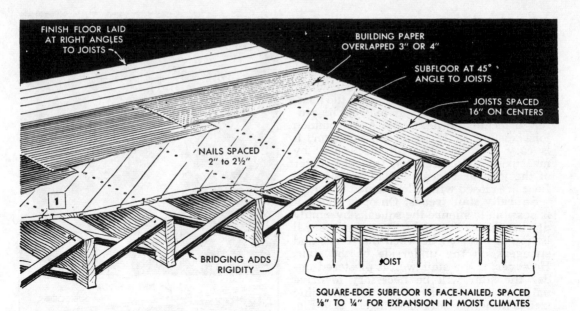

FINISH FLOOR LAID AT RIGHT ANGLES TO JOISTS

BUILDING PAPER OVERLAPPED 3" OR 4"

SUBFLOOR AT 45° ANGLE TO JOISTS

JOISTS SPACED 16" ON CENTERS

NAILS SPACED 2" to 2½"

1

BRIDGING ADDS RIGIDITY

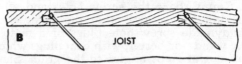

A JOIST

SQUARE-EDGE SUBFLOOR IS FACE-NAILED; SPACED ⅛" TO ¼" FOR EXPANSION IN MOIST CLIMATES

B JOIST

2 TONGUE-AND-GROOVE FLOORING BLIND-NAILED WITH 8d FLOORING NAILS DRIVEN AT 45° ANGLE

FLOOR CARE AND REPAIR

As floors are subjected to more wear and all-around harder usage than any other structural part of the home, they should be given proportionally more care. The common wood used in laying floors in private houses has been so satisfactory and inexpensive that no substitute is available or desired. Many different woods are available as prepared floor boards, either square-edges or tongue-and-groove. The common woods are whitewood, maple, oak, birch and walnut. The boards should not be more than 5 in. wide, to avoid open joints through shrinkage. Stock sizes are from ½ to 1¼ in. thick and from 2¼ to 4 in. wide. It is common to have a rough floor of whitewood and to cover it with thinner hardwood boards, forming geometric designs. Wood floors are distinguished as single or double. Single floors consist of one layer of flooring only. Double floors have two layers of flooring, the subflooring being of rough lumber and topped with a finished floor.

Fig. 1 shows the common construction of a wooden floor. In the best type of work, the subfloor is laid diagonally and the finish floor at right angles to the joists, with a layer of building paper between the subfloor and the top floor. In new construction, plywood also is extensively used for subflooring. It is important that the subfloor be nailed securely to the joists and that the wood be thoroughly dry. Square-edged subfloors, spaced ⅛ to ¼ in., are used frequently in humid climates and where buildings are unheated. In laying this type of subfloor, 8 or 10d nails are driven straight as in Fig. 2 A. Tongue-and-groove subflooring, as well as finish flooring, is nailed with 8d flooring nails driven through the tongue at a 45-deg. angle, and spaced from 8 to 12 in. apart as in Fig. 2 B. Rabbeted subflooring, or shiplap, is nailed straight with 10d flat-headed nails spaced 2 to 2½ in. apart.

Squeaking floors: Shrinkage of wood often causes flooring to loosen slightly so that the boards rub on the nails and against each other, causing the floor to squeak when walked on. If the trouble is in the first floor, thin wedges driven between the top of the joists and the subfloor, as in Fig. 3, usually will stop the squeaks in that particular area. Where the tendency to squeak extends over a wide surface, strips of hardwood forced tightly against the underside of the subfloor and fastened with nails or screws will help, Fig. 4. A squeaky second floor over a ceiling is a different problem. The simplest remedy is to drive flooring nails through both the finish floor and the subfloor into the joists. Fig. 5, details A, B and C, shows how to locate concealed joists. Slide a hardwood block along the floor at right angles to the joists, tapping it continuously with a hammer. When the block is directly over a joist the tapping gives off a solid sound, but anywhere between joists a hollow sound results. Determine the exact position of a joist by drilling a small hole close to the joist as in detail B. Bend a wire feeler as in detail C and insert this through the hole, turning it until the bent end contacts the joist under the floor. Mark the angle of the handle on the floor to locate the side of the joist. It is then easy to cross-nail the floor to the joist as in detail D. Avoid hammer marks on the floor by driving the nails only part way in, and sinking the heads below the surface with a nailset. After locating one joist in the manner described, measure 16 in. from its center to locate the next one. As a common joist spacing is 16 in. center-to-center, it is easy to drive the nails accurately by measuring 16 in. each way from the center of the joist first located. Nail holes in the floor are closed with filler stained to match.

Squeaky stair treads: On open stairs, it is possible to silence the squeaks by simply driving the wedges tight. These wedges will be found inserted between the treads and stringers on the underside of the stair. However, if the stair well is plastered under the stair will be necessary to drive nails or screws through the offending treads into the risers or stringers as in Fig. 6. Counterbore the screw holes and after driving the screws, plug the holes with readymade screw-hole plugs of a matching wood—or better, with boat plugs which are cut at right angles to the grain. Sand the plugs flush, stain and refinish.

Raising sagged floors: Undue settling of floors at the center of the house often is due to rotting of wooden girder posts. In some cases uneven floors are caused by sagging of the girder between posts. To replace a post, first set up temporary supports on each side of the girder joint as in Fig. 7, with the lower ends of the supports resting on jackscrews. Make sure that the supporting posts are perpendicular, and raise the jackscrews until the weight is fully supported. Spike a 4 x 6-in. bridge block to the underside of the girder across the girder joint as in Fig. 8 and place a steel jack post as indicated, with its lower end bearing squarely on the concrete footing and its upper end centered against the underside of the bridge block. Now, being sure that the supporting jack post is perpendicular, tighten the jack at the top end to take the weight. The steel post is left in place permanently. Where additional supporting posts are required to straighten a sagging girder, it will be necessary to break up a portion of the concrete floor and pour a substantial footing for each post as in Fig. 9. After placing the jack post under a sagging girder, turn the jack up so that it takes the weight, and then raise the girder ⅛ in. at intervals over a period of time. In this way, loosening of framing nails and excessive cracking of plaster will be avoided.

Vibrating floors: Floors that vibrate when walked upon result from inadequate support, such as the use of joists which are too small in cross-sectional area, too long a

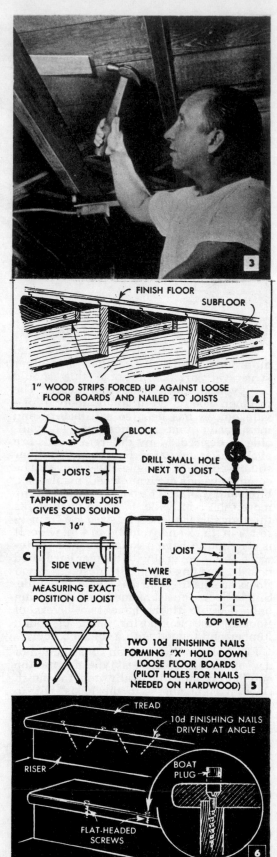

FINISH FLOOR
SUBFLOOR
1" WOOD STRIPS FORCED UP AGAINST LOOSE FLOOR BOARDS AND NAILED TO JOISTS **4**

BLOCK
A JOISTS
TAPPING OVER JOIST GIVES SOLID SOUND
DRILL SMALL HOLE NEXT TO JOIST
B
16"
C SIDE VIEW
MEASURING EXACT POSITION OF JOIST
WIRE FEELER
JOIST
TOP VIEW
D
TWO 10d FINISHING NAILS FORMING "X" HOLD DOWN LOOSE FLOOR BOARDS (PILOT HOLES FOR NAILS NEEDED ON HARDWOOD) **5**

TREAD
10d FINISHING NAILS DRIVEN AT ANGLE
RISER
BOAT PLUG
FLAT-HEADED SCREWS
6

Above, to correct sagging of first floor, one or more temporary supports are placed under girder with the lower ends bearing on jackscrews. Below, the old post is then removed and replaced with a new-type steel post having a built-in jack for raising the girder

TEMPORARY 6".X 6" SUPPORTING POSTS

BASE PIECES TO DISTRIBUTE WEIGHT ON FLOOR

7

COMBINATION STEEL POST AND JACK

8

span between supporting girders, and insufficient or improperly located bridging between the joists, Fig. 1. There are several simple remedies that can be applied where the floor is open on the underside. Doubling the joists by nailing or bolting an additional member to each of those already installed often is practical and effective. Jacking up the floor from underneath and installing additional lines of bridging is nearly always a sure remedy. When vibration occurs in the second floor, the ceiling of the first floor may have to be opened to install bridging or extra joists.

Gap at shoe mold: Settling and shrinkage of wood often cause unsightly gaps between the baseboard and the shoe mold. Details A and B of Fig. 11 show what happens when the shoe mold is nailed either to the baseboard or to the finish floor. To make it easy to close these openings when they occur, the nails holding the shoe mold should be driven diagonally between the baseboard and the finish floor and into the subfloor as in detail C. This latter method of nailing can be used only if there is space equal to the width of the baseboard between the floor and wall. Otherwise, the only way to eliminate the gap is to renail or replace the shoe mold periodically, Fig. 10.

Refinishing wooden floors: When hardwood floors are in good condition and the finish is not excessively marred or worn down to the bare wood in spots, refinishing without resurfacing, Fig. 12, is entirely practical. The floor should be thoroughly cleaned before refinishing, and all wax must be removed with turpentine. On ordinary work there is a choice of two types of floor finishes: (1) Floor sealers which penetrate into the wood, and (2) Floor varnish, shellac and paint, the latter three forming a coating on the surface. Floors treated with a sealer do not show scratches or streaks as readily as do varnished or shellacked floors. However, the sealers used alone are not as durable. The finish must be cleaned and renewed more frequently. Cleaning can be done with a me-

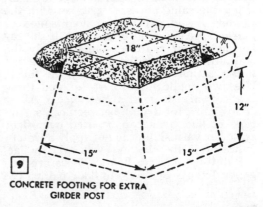

18"

12"

15"

15"

9

CONCRETE FOOTING FOR EXTRA GIRDER POST

dium solution of trisodium phosphate. After washing the floor, there may be some discoloration and, if so, the wood can be bleached to a uniform color with a mild solution of oxalic-acid crystals (poison) and water. This is applied to the floor with a cloth swab and then rinsed off with clear water. Usually a single application is sufficient. Water in the solution will raise the grain of the wood, so, the floor should be sanded lightly before a finish is applied. (*Caution*: When sanding a floor on which a bleach has been used, wear a dust respirator.) Floor sealer must be laid on quickly, either with a wool applicator or with a wide-bristle brush, first working across and then with the grain. Allow the sealer to set for a few minutes and then wipe off the excess. When the sealer is dry, smooth the floor with No. 2 steel wool. When finishing a floor, start at the corner farthest from the door and cover the floor in strips 4 to 6 boards wide, ending up at the door opening. Clean up the dust as you go with a painters' tack rag and leave the window sash open at the top and bottom and the door slightly ajar until the finish is dry. White shellac is quite extensively used as a wax base on hardwood floors because it dries so quickly that the floor can be back in service within a day's time.

Resurfacing wooden floors: When a floor is uneven and its surface has become badly worn, resurfacing with a sanding machine, Fig. 13, will be necessary. These machines can be rented from most hardware and paint stores. Removal of varnish or paint will require the use of a No. 4 open-coat abrasive. After the finish is removed down to bare wood, use a No. 2 abrasive for reducing the deep scratches made by the coarse abrasive. Do not stop the machine while the sanding drum is in contact with the floor, but rather allow the machine to pull itself across the floor. After high spots and the old finish have been removed with the two coarser grades of abrasives, finish a hardwood floor with No. ½ or No. 0 abrasive. Most floor sanders will not run closer than 2 or 3 in. from the baseboard. This strip is finished with an electric edger, using the same abrasive grits as with the sander. Avoid getting the floor soiled or marked during or after sanding. If the resurfaced floor is to be stained, apply the stain first and then the filler, and after the latter is thoroughly dry, apply the finish. Use two applications of sealer and three coats of varnish on resurfaced floors. Allow 36 to 48 hrs. for drying between coats. Any type of floor wax can be used over floor sealer or varnish but do not apply a water-emulsion (self-polishing) wax over shellac.

Painting concrete floors: There are two general types of concrete floor paints, the

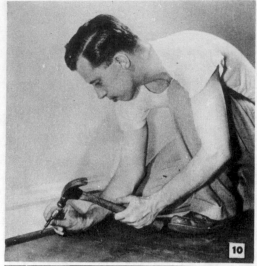

10

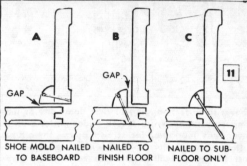

A	B	C
SHOE MOLD NAILED TO BASEBOARD	NAILED TO FINISH FLOOR	NAILED TO SUBFLOOR ONLY

11

Shoe molds commonly are nailed to the baseboard or to the finish floor. Undue settling and shrinkage of wood in the framing often causes a gap to show under the shoes as at A, or, when nailed to the floor, as at B. To avoid these faults, the shoe mold should be nailed as in detail C. Then, when settling causes a gap to show in either position, it can be closed by simply driving the nails down as shown.

12

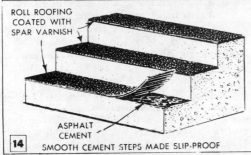

ROLL ROOFING COATED WITH SPAR VARNISH

ASPHALT CEMENT

SMOOTH CEMENT STEPS MADE SLIP-PROOF

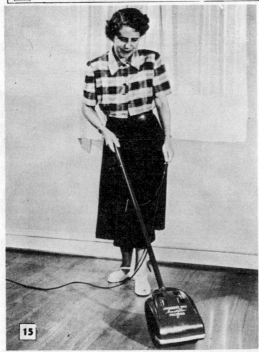

varnish-base enamel type and the rubber-base type. Use the former on concrete floors that are above grade and uniformly dry. The rubber-base concrete paints are suitable only for use on concrete floors below grade which are protected from direct sunlight. Rubber-base paints can be applied only to unpainted concrete floors, and should not be applied over any other type of paint. There also are combination concrete sealers and stains. These do not have the color brilliance of the others but do have an advantage in that worn spots can be finished to match other areas of the floor without producing a spotty appearance. In any case, new concrete should age for a year before being painted. Before painting, apply a neutralizer consisting of zinc-sulphate crystals, 3 lbs., dissolved in water, 1 gal. Concrete floors that have been troweled smooth should be etched to assure good adhesion of paint. An etching solution is made by slowly adding muriatic acid, 1 pint, to water, 1 gal., while stirring constantly. (*Caution:* Do not allow the acid or solution to touch the clothing or skin as it can cause severe burns. Avoid inhaling the fumes.) Apply the solution with a cloth swab, and allow to stand for 10 to 20 minutes. Then wash off with a soda solution to remove the acid and also to neutralize any remaining on the surface. Finally, flush off the floor with a quantity of clear water. To minimize dusting of unpainted concrete floors apply a hardener made by dissolving magnesium fluosilicate crystals, 2 lbs., in water, 1 gal. Allow the first application to dry 24 hrs. and then follow with a second application. This treatment may be followed by painting. Smoothly troweled concrete steps which are slippery when wet can be made slip-proof by etching as described, or by covering the treads with pieces of roll roofing laid on asphalt cement as in Fig. 14. The surface of the roofing is given three coats of spar varnish or enamel to bind the slate surfacing. Oil or grease spots on driveways and concrete floors can be removed by scrubbing with a solution of trisodium phosphate, 4 oz., and water, 1 gal. After scrubbing, sprinkle hydrated lime over the stained area and allow it to remain for several hours before sweeping it up. This will remove the oil, and generally most, if not all, of the stain.

Floor coverings: A common trouble with new floor coverings is lack of complete adhesion. When single tiles or blocks loosen, it will be necessary to remove the block entirely and replace it over new adhesive. To cement asphalt tile, use asphalt emulsion and spread it very thinly, as excess cement oozing up between the tiles may cause discoloration. The cement is allowed to set until tacky (unless instructions.

direct otherwise) and then the tile is laid carefully in place. Asphalt tile can be cemented directly to smooth concrete floors above grade. On wooden floors, asphalt tile must be laid on an asphalt-impregnated felt cemented to the floor with lignin paste. Edges of the felt are butted, not lapped. Wooden flooring blocks can be easily cemented directly to concrete or wood with a hot asphalt cement specially made for the purpose. Lignin paste is used to cement cork and linoleum floor coverings. If the floor covering must be cleaned frequently by mopping or flushing with water, it is best to use resin cement and asphalt-impregnated felt as a base. For bonding rubber tile, lignin paste, rubber cement or latex cement may be used.

Cleaning and waxing floors: Varnished or shellacked floors which are not waxed should be cleaned with an oiled mop. Floors coated with a sealer can be washed with a slightly soapy water, rinsed with a wet cloth and then wiped dry. Clean waxed floors with a soft floor brush. Do not use an oiled mop as oil softens the wax. To remove embedded grime, rub lightly with a soft cloth wrung out in warm, soapy water. Clean painted concrete floors with plain water. Linoleum floors that are not waxed or lacquered are washed with a mild solution of trisodium phosphate, care being taken that water does not seep under the edges to loosen the adhesive bond. Rubber-tile floors should not be cleaned with hot water. Use a solution of household ammonia in cold water. Most common stains on rubber floor coverings can be removed by rubbing the stained area with No. 00 steel wool. Cork flooring is ordinarily cleaned with a floor brush or a dry mop. If it is very dirty and soiled, use warm, soapy water applied with a cloth or sponge. Rinse and dry the floor immediately. Cleaners and polishes containing oils should not be used on asphalt tile. The common floor waxes are of two kinds: (1) The paste and liquid waxes having volatile organic solvents, and (2) the water-emulsion waxes which are known as nonrubbing or self-polishing. The former require polishing either by hand or with an electric polisher, Fig. 15. Apply wax in thin coatings, each coat being wiped on at right angles to the previous one.

Hints on filler application: Sufficient filler for a room 12 x 14 ft. can be prepared inexpensively. Mix the filler in a large pan that can be discarded afterwards, and mix only enough for one room at a time, as shown below. The filler will stain the floor slightly. You can vary the amount of sienna to get darker or lighter effects. If still darker tones are desired, substitute burnt sienna or burnt umber for the raw sienna. Use pure benzine, not the kerosene-and-gasoline mixture sometimes sold. Apply the filler with a brush or a wad of cotton waste, first with and then across the grain as illustrated, lower left. Burlap sacking can be folded into useful four-ply pads, as illustrated in the picture above.

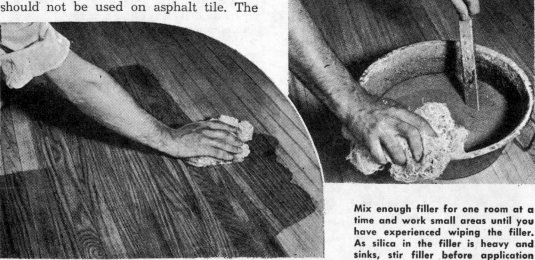

Mix enough filler for one room at a time and work small areas until you have experienced wiping the filler. As silica in the filler is heavy and sinks, stir filler before application

How to Lay Linoleum and Floor Tile

FLOORS HAVE character and personality. They can be warm and friendly or harsh and unattractive. They can be clean and easy to keep that way, or marred and scuffed no matter how much time the housewife spends in scrubbing and waxing them.

Even the worst of floors, gouged and stained, can become bright and cheerful through the magic of modern floor coverings. Laying a new floor is one of the most satisfying of all home projects, for almost overnight you can finish a project that makes an old room spanking new. Furthermore it's a project a beginner can handle (provided he knows what he's going to do before he starts) and one that can save him enough money to make it well worth his time.

You probably can't lay a new floor from scratch in a single evening (despite those beautiful advertisements), but it's literally true that if you have prepared the old floor in advance, if you have already marked off the room, and if you select one of the easy-to-lay floorings, you can floor the average-size room in a few hours.

And what a selection of materials the homeowner has today! Asphalt tile and vinyl sheets, rectangles of cork and inlaid linoleum.

Which Floor Goes Where

Regardless of which type you eventually select — tile or sheet — you should know what *kinds* of flooring can be installed in the various parts of your home.

The deciding factor in selecting any flooring is the amount of moisture in the subfloor. This, in a large part, is determined by the kind of subfloor and what is under it. For most homes this means the *grade* of the floor—that is, the relation of the floor to the outdoor ground level.

Below-grade floors are any floors which are beneath the ground level around the foundation. In most homes, the only below-grade floors are basement floors. Very few types of floor coverings can be laid below grade because moisture from the ground penetrates through the concrete and attacks first the adhesive and then the floor covering itself. Regardless of how dry your basement floor may feel, it has moisture in it and on its surface. Furthermore this moisture, as it penetrates the concrete, becomes very alkaline. Only an asphaltic adhesive, or one especially compounded for use below grade, can withstand this highly alkaline moisture. (And of course it's foolish to lay any type of flooring over a below-grade floor which is subject to water seepage or standing water.)

On-grade floors are slab floors poured directly on the earth's surface. These floors have become quite common in recent years because of the large number of homes built without basements. For on-grade floors, use only a flooring which is recommended for below-grade installation. The one exception to this rule is the case of on-grade floors which are radiant-heated by pipes in the concrete. A special type of linoleum tile is made for such installations. This is perhaps the only case where the job should be done with professional help. The heat of the home depends upon the amount of heat which rises through the flooring, and a delicate balance between the flooring and the heat must be maintained. If you decide to install a floor covering on a radiant-heated floor yourself, get the advice of both your flooring dealer and the contractor who installed your heating plant.

Above-grade floors are any floors which are not directly in contact with the earth. With the exception of basement floors, most residential floors are above-grade wooden floors, and virtually any type of floor covering can be applied to them.

The diagrams below show which floorings can be installed below grade, on grade and above grade in your home.

BELOW GRADE →

ASPHALT TILE
VINYL TILE
VINYL SHEET
VINYL-ASBESTOS TILE

← ON GRADE

ASPHALT TILE   VINYL-ASBESTOS TILE
VINYL TILE   VINYL SHEET
ON GRADE WITH RADIANT HEAT—
SPECIAL LINOLEUM TILE

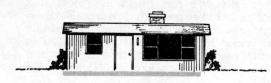

ABOVE GRADE →

ASPHALT TILE
CORK TILE
VINYL TILE AND SHEET
RUBBER TILE AND SHEET
LINOLEUM TILE AND SHEET

Which Kind of Flooring?

Sheet floorings: Until a few years ago almost all floorings were of the sheet type and there was little from which to choose except the various linoleums. Today, despite the fact that sheet floorings are not as popular for home installation as they were a few years ago, there are more types of sheet floorings available to the homeowner that he can lay himself.

Sheet floor coverings have some advantages over tile. There are very few seams in the entire floor when sheet floorings are used. They are somewhat lower in price than the corresponding types of floor tile.

To be sure of getting a good fit when installing linoleum, push the piece into position along the wall, leaving the ends to run slightly up room's end walls

Large pattern effects are possible with sheet floorings, whereas tile floorings are limited to the designs which can be worked out with contrasting colors of tile.

The major disadvantage of sheet floorings—and it's a big one—is that they are more difficult for the inexperienced man to lay than tile. Another disadvantage is that if a floor becomes damaged it is more difficult to patch.

There is no significant difference in wearing quality between a sheet flooring and a tile flooring of the same type.

Sheet floorings are almost always preferred over tile for wall and counter-top installations in the home.

Floor tiles: Why take a perfectly good sheet of flooring and cut it up into small squares? In effect, that is what is done in the manufacture of floor tile. There's only one reason: to make the material easier to lay. A novice may have trouble maneuvering a 20-foot strip of linoleum and cutting it precisely. He'll have little difficulty in handling a 9 by 9-in. tile of the same material. Around borders and in doorways he can mark each tile and then remove it for cutting, but if he's trying to handle sheet flooring he must cut it in place. This ease of installation is the reason for the development of floor tiles and the reason they have become so popular with homeowners. Certain types of floor tiles such as asphalt and cork (those that are easily damaged before installation) are not available in sheet form.

Types of Tile

Each type of tile has its advantages and disadvantages. The major types are asphalt, linoleum, rubber, vinyl and cork.

Asphalt tile: Asphalt is the lowest cost tile you can select. It is a tough, wear-resistant material, colorful and easy to keep clean. It resists abrasion better than most other materials and for that reason is better suited to areas subject to sand and dirt. Asphalt tiles are made of a compound of asphalt and asbestos, two materials that are fire resistant and will not rot. These materials also are little affected by moisture, so asphalt tile is one of the few materials recommended for below-grade installation. It is odorless and is easily cleaned with a mop. Most manufacturers of asphalt tile polish and wax one surface before the tiles are packed. Asphalt tiles are available in a wide range of colors and, contrary to some other types of floorings, are priced by color. The lighter colors are more expensive than the darker ones. All manufacturers use the same numbering system to designate colors. The "A" colors, for example, are the least expensive. Other classifications run through a "D" group which includes the lightest colors. Prices vary significantly between groups. Thus the "D" colors are as much as 2½ times as expensive as the "A" colors. The standard size of asphalt tile is 9 by 9 in. by ⅛ in. A ³⁄₁₆-in. tile is also available for heavy-duty service. Asphalt tiles are brittle to handle and easily chipped or cracked until actually bedded in the adhesive. Once they are in place, however, they are not likely to be damaged.

Linoleum tile: Linoleum is made by bonding a mixture of oxidized linseed oil, resins, pigments and fillers to a burlap or felt backing. Modern linoleums are far superior to those of 20 years ago, and a floor tiled with a high-quality linoleum will last virtually a lifetime with proper care. Linoleum is flexible. This makes it somewhat easier to handle before and during laying than asphalt tile, and slightly more resilient underfoot. Linoleum tile is available in richer colors than asphalt, and the pattern effects (swirls and mottles) are somewhat larger. Two gauges or thicknesses are available: light and standard. The relatively low-cost standard gauge has 75 percent more wearing surface than the light gauge and thus is much to be preferred. The size usually installed in homes is 9 by 9-in., but some manufacturers also make 6 by 6, 12 by 12, and 18 by 36-in. sizes.

Rubber tile: In the manufacturing process, a sheet of high-grade synthetic rubber is cured under high-pressure plates that make the surface almost as smooth as glass. Rubber floors are the quietest and most resilient of all tile floors with the exception of thick cork tile. Because the surface is nonporous, dirt can't work its way into the flooring. More brilliant colors are possible with rubber flooring than with almost any other type. Rubber, on the other hand, is not as resistant to grease, oil and some household solvents as asphalt or linoleum. The ⅛-in. thickness is standard for home installations but a ³⁄₁₆-in. gauge is also available for heavy-duty areas. The sizes are 9 by 9-in. and 6 by 6-in.

Vinyl tile: Vinyl is a flexible plastic which will not crack under repeated flexing. It recovers more quickly from denting than most types of tile and is more resistant to household acids, cooking greases, oils, solvents, detergents, soaps and cleaning agents than any other type. It adjusts more quickly to room temperature than linoleum—a factor to be considered for underfoot warmth. It never needs waxing, though it can be waxed if desired. It is less slippery even when wet than linoleum or asphalt tile. Vinyl tile can be installed below grade over concrete in direct contact with the ground. The standard gauge is ³⁄₃₂ in. thick, but it is also made in a ⅛-in. gauge. Most manufacturers make it only in the 9 by 9-in. size.

Cork tile: Cork has an appearance all its own which can't be duplicated in any other type of tile. Cork varies in color from light tan to deep rich brown, and it is this variegated effect which imparts a unique beauty to a cork floor. This is the most resilient flooring made and for this reason is easiest on the feet. It also has greater heat insulation value than any other type of tile, and is quieter underfoot. Its disadvantages include: It absorbs liquid and therefore should never be laid in kitchens, baths or laundries; it is damaged by greases and quite easily stained; and it is the most expensive type of tile. Cork is available in sizes measuring 9 by 9 inches, 6 by 12 inches and 12 by 12 inches.

Comparative costs: Costs, of course, vary from store to store, manufacturer to manufacturer and from year to year. The following cost comparisons are general.

Asphalt tile is the cheapest of all tiles. Linoleum tile is slightly more expensive than asphalt. Rubber is about twice as expensive as linoleum, vinyl slightly more expensive than rubber, and cork somewhat more expensive than vinyl, or about three times as expensive as linoleum.

Tile Inserts and Accessories

Before you plan your job, decide whether you want to take advantage of the many inserts and accessories available. These vary with the type of tile, but accessories are available in most materials except cork.

A striking effect is offered by "theme" tiles—individual tiles inlaid at the factory with a wide range of designs. The center areas actually are cut out like a jigsaw puzzle, and contrasting color inserts pressed into place to depict the theme. There is no cutting or altering to be done on the theme tile itself or on the adjoining tiles when the floor is laid.

You can find a pattern in theme tile to match virtually any theme you wish to carry out in the room. There are plain geometric designs, ivies, flowers, teakettles, spoons and forks, dogs, musical notes, champagne glasses, and birds. For children's rooms there are humorous animals and bucking broncos.

Don't make the mistake of laying too many theme tiles into a single room. Two, or at the most four, of these tiles can make a striking difference in the appearance of a room and set the theme immediately, but a dozen of them can create a hodge-podge.

Similar to theme tiles are feature inserts, usually laid in the center of the room or one at each end of a large room. A single insert usually occupies the space of four ordinary field tiles. Intricate designs in several colors are possible in this larger area—clowns and card hands, sailfish and compasses.

Letters, numbers and punctuation marks are also available so you can write your own theme into the floor. If you plan to use them, keep in mind that the inserts are the standard 9 inches long, but vary in width so that the letters automatically space themselves right. The "M," for example, is considerably wider than the "I." For this reason you'll have to measure the total width of the "message" before you start, so you can center it or position it exactly as you want it.

One of the most popular of inserts is a complete shuffleboard court.

Feature strips can be laid around a room or used to mark off areas for various purposes (foul lines for playing darts and other games). Most manufacturers make a feature strip 1 in. wide, and some make strips from 1 in. to 3 in. wide in multiples of ½ in. If you plan to lay a feature strip into your own floor, don't forget that unless the strip runs all the way across the room you'll have to trim off each tile adjoining the strip. For this reason, if you plan to run the strip around the room without using the special border tile, it is easiest to cross the intersection of two strips and run them both all the way to the wall, rather than forming a mitered corner.

Most manufacturers make a special border tile wider and longer than the standard field tile. The usual size is 18 in. by 24 in. This special border goes down fast and eliminates the need for cutting field tile when a feature strip is used, as the border width can vary slightly around the room.

Another product that fills a special need is a tile edging. Most installations have a raw edge exposed, usually in a doorway. Although the surface of most tiles is highly resistant to wear, an exposed edge can easily crumble or chip off. Such an edge can be covered with a strip of metal molding, but a special edging made of tile is also available. It has one edge tapered so that it looks like a wedge in cross section. The usual size is 1 in. wide by 18 in. long.

To finish off your job you may want to install a cove base which in effect is a shoe mold around the room. The cove flares down over the tile and usually is 4 in. to 6 in. high. Most manufacturers make it in 24-in. lengths. The colors here are restricted. Black is always available, and usually one or two other colors. Cove bases are installed with special cement, so check with your flooring dealer as to the type and amount you'll need for your installation.

A few manufacturers make both floor tiles and plastic wall tiles. In this case the two may be color-matched, so borders, inserts or feature strips laid into the floor can be matched exactly to wall tiles. If you are planning a bath or kitchen installation and plan to do both walls and floor, you can produce an integrated color design with these matching tiles.

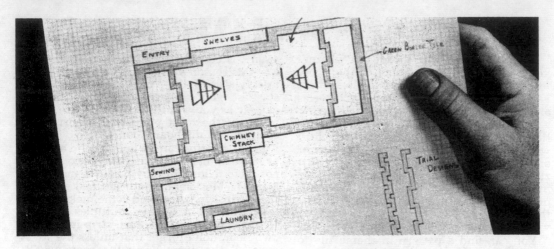

Planning the Tile Job

Floor designs in tile are limited only by your own imagination. Three possible designs are shown below. By using three or more colors you can work out basketweaves and other pleasing patterns.

You'll find that the design can have a marked effect on the size and shape of the room. Poorly-proportioned rooms can be greatly improved through the careful choice of a good design. A room that is too narrow for its length, for example, can be made to appear considerably wider by running a design across it. A diagonal pattern will make the entire room seem larger. Any long, straight lines in a pattern will give the appearance of added length.

Your choice of colors can also have an effect on the apparent size and "feeling" of the room. Bright, warm colors are best installed on the north side of a home, while in general the subdued and cooler colors usually look best in a sunlit room.

In selecting colors, consider the dirt problem, too. The deciding factor is the type of dirt to which the floor will be subjected. Lighter colors show dust the least, but scuff and heel marks the most. The reverse is true of the darker shades of tile.

The easiest way to plan your installation is to use a sheet of graph paper. Measure the room accurately, and then draw it to scale on the paper, letting each little square represent a 9 by 9-in. tile. To do this you'll have to convert the room measurements into inches, but the time spent will be well worth while.

After you have drawn the room to scale, measure and draw in any permanent installations such as sinks, washing machines and work counters. Now, using colored pencils, draw your preferred design on the floor plan. If you want to experiment you can try out several different designs.

Next mark the location of any theme tiles, feature strips and borders. (The photo above shows a shuffleboard court sketched into a floor plan.) Run borders around, rather than behind, any permanent fixtures such as ranges and refrigerators.

If you do this work precisely, you not only can use your drawing as a guide while laying the tile, but you can actually count every tile of each color that you'll need in the entire room.

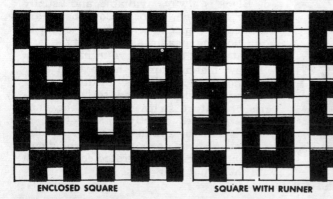

ENCLOSED SQUARE   SQUARE WITH RUNNER

PINWHEEL (9" X 18" TILES)

What You'll Need

If you use the graph-paper system of planning your installation you can count exactly the number of tile of each color you'll need. However, this takes time, and if you are planning a simple one-color floor you can use the chart below to determine the number of tiles you'll need to cover a room of a given size.

Regardless of whether you use the table below or count your needs to the exact tile, you should allow for trimming and waste. The following figures are recommended waste allowances based on hundreds of installations: for 5 to 50 sq. ft. add 15 percent; for 50 to 200 sq. ft. add 10 percent; for 200 to 500 sq. ft. add 5 percent. The waste on asphalt and cork tile is usually slightly higher than on the other types, because these tiles are more likely to be damaged before installation than the others. Most dealers will give you a refund for clean, unused tile, but better check when you buy. If your dealer will take back unused tile, slightly overestimate your needs so you'll have plenty on hand when you start.

Some types of tile require an underlayment of hardboard or plywood, or a lining felt. Asphalt tile laid on concrete requires neither. On page 765 you'll find information on preparing subfloors for installations other than asphalt tile.

Though most brands of adhesives for the same kind of tile are similar, play safe and order an adhesive of the same brand as your tile. The label on the can will tell you the approximate coverage.

The figure at which the readings cross in the table gives the number of tiles for a floor of that size

FEET	1	2	3	4	5	6	7	8	9	10	11	12	13	14	15	16	17	18	19	20
1	2	4	6	8	9	11	13	15	16	18	20	22	24	25	27	29	31	32	34	36
2	4	8	11	15	18	22	25	29	32	36	39	43	47	50	54	57	61	64	68	72
3	6	11	16	22	27	32	38	43	48	54	59	64	70	75	80	86	91	96	102	107
4	8	15	22	29	36	43	50	57	64	72	78	86	93	100	107	114	121	128	136	143
5	9	18	27	36	45	54	63	72	80	90	98	107	116	125	134	143	152	160	169	178
6	11	22	32	43	54	64	75	86	96	107	118	128	139	150	160	171	182	192	203	214
7	13	25	38	50	63	75	88	100	112	125	137	150	162	174	187	200	212	224	237	249
8	15	29	43	57	72	86	100	114	128	143	157	171	185	200	214	228	242	256	271	285
9	16	32	48	64	80	96	112	128	144	160	176	192	208	224	240	256	272	288	305	320
10	18	36	54	72	90	107	125	143	160	178	196	214	232	249	267	285	303	320	338	356
11	20	39	59	78	98	118	137	157	176	196	214	235	255	274	294	313	333	353	372	391
12	22	43	64	86	107	128	150	171	192	214	235	256	278	299	320	342	363	384	405	427
13	24	47	70	93	116	139	162	185	208	232	255	278	301	324	347	370	393	416	440	463
14	25	50	75	100	125	150	174	200	224	249	274	299	324	349	374	399	424	448	474	498
15	27	54	80	107	134	160	187	214	240	267	294	320	347	374	400	427	454	480	507	534
16	29	57	86	114	143	171	200	228	256	285	313	342	370	399	427	456	484	512	541	569
17	31	61	91	121	152	182	212	242	272	303	333	363	393	424	454	484	514	545	574	604
18	32	64	96	128	160	192	224	256	288	320	353	384	416	448	480	512	545	576	609	640
19	34	68	102	136	169	203	237	271	305	338	372	405	440	474	507	541	574	609	642	676
20	36	72	107	143	178	214	249	285	320	356	391	427	463	498	534	569	604	640	676	712
21	38	75	112	150	187	224	262	299	336	374	411	448	487	523	560	598	636	672	710	747
22	40	78	118	157	196	235	274	313	352	391	431	470	509	548	587	627	665	704	764	783
23	41	82	123	164	205	246	287	327	368	409	450	491	532	573	614	655	696	736	777	818
24	43	86	128	171	214	256	299	342	384	427	470	512	556	598	640	683	726	768	812	854

Laying Asphalt Tile

Asphalt tile is perhaps the most widely used of the various types of tile because it can be installed below grade. For that reason this section on laying tile describes the technique of laying asphalt tile. However, all other types of tile are laid in exactly the same way except for two steps: the preparation of the subfloor and the spreading of the adhesive. Be sure to check these two steps on page 765 before starting to lay other types of tile, but otherwise follow these instructions.

Concrete floor under asphalt tile must be smooth, dry, clean and free from grease, wax and paint. Fill all cracks and holes with a good concrete patching compound. If there is paint on the concrete it must be removed. *Don't use an inflammable paint remover.* The easiest and safest way to remove this paint is to rent a floor-sanding machine at your local hardware store. This is relatively inexpensive and will do the job quite fast.

All old floor coverings must be removed before the installation of any kind of tile.

You can install asphalt tile over double wooden floors with boards no more than three inches wide. Don't install tile over wood floors that are in bad condition. First nail down all loose boards, replace any broken ones and, if the floor boards are over 3 in. wide, badly worn or there is no subfloor under the boards, apply an underlayer of plywood or special hardboard over

Snapping chalk line through center points of room, above, forms guide lines for tile. Below, measuring to make sure border will be over a half tile wide

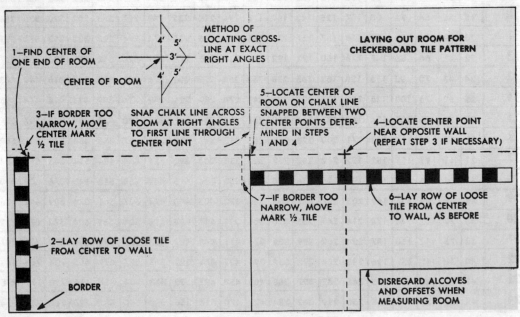

METHOD OF LOCATING CROSS-LINE AT EXACT RIGHT ANGLES

LAYING OUT ROOM FOR CHECKERBOARD TILE PATTERN

1—FIND CENTER OF ONE END OF ROOM

CENTER OF ROOM

3—IF BORDER TOO NARROW, MOVE CENTER MARK ½ TILE

SNAP CHALK LINE ACROSS ROOM AT RIGHT ANGLES TO FIRST LINE THROUGH CENTER POINT

5—LOCATE CENTER OF ROOM ON CHALK LINE SNAPPED BETWEEN TWO CENTER POINTS DETERMINED IN STEPS 1 AND 4

4—LOCATE CENTER POINT NEAR OPPOSITE WALL (REPEAT STEP 3 IF NECESSARY)

7—IF BORDER TOO NARROW, MOVE MARK ½ TILE

6—LAY ROW OF LOOSE TILE FROM CENTER TO WALL, AS BEFORE

2—LAY ROW OF LOOSE TILE FROM CENTER TO WALL

BORDER

DISREGARD ALCOVES AND OFFSETS WHEN MEASURING ROOM

Edge of tile is held firmly against adjacent piece, as shown above, and tile is lowered into adhesive

the floor. These underlayers are available at lumberyards in sheets 4 ft. square. They should be nailed every 3 in. along the seams, making sure that the seams do not coincide with the joints in the boards. The tile is applied directly to this underlayer.

In the case of new wood floors, apply a layer of felt paper first. The paper is cemented to the floor with its own type of adhesive.

Remove the quarter-round around the room. This can best be done by pulling off the quarter-round, letting the heads of the finishing nails pull on through the molding. In this way damage to the board itself is minimized. When the job is finished, replace the quarter-round, but don't use the old nail holes. Drive the nail heads beneath the surface and fill both the new and old holes with wood putty or water-mixed patching putty.

Give the floor, whether it's concrete or wood, a final wipe-up with a cloth that is *barely* damp. If the surface gets wet you'll have to wait some time for it to dry thoroughly. From this point on it is important that you minimize the amount of dust that collects on the floor, both before and after you apply the adhesive.

After preparing the floor, the next step is to mark off the room so that the tile can be laid true regardless of any irregularity in the walls. Don't trust that the walls are square with each other.

The manner of squaring up the room is shown in Fig. 1, which describes the checkerboard pattern. This method is basic for all patterns in which the tile runs parallel with the walls.

Note in Fig. 1 that test rows of loose tile are laid from the center point of the walls to check the width of the border. If the test indicates that the border will be less than a half-tile wide, the point should be relocated a half tile. This will leave you with more than a half tile all around the room. When you have located the two points lengthwise of the room, pull a chalk line taut between them and snap it.

Now find the center point of this chalk line and mark it. Use the "3-4-5" method of calculating a precise right angle. The importance of this right angle can't be overemphasized. If the two chalk lines aren't snapped at exact right angles you'll find yourself in trouble as soon as you start laying the tile.

Now spread adhesive over the chalk lines with a notched trowel, leaving the intersection of the two lines and the ends of each line exposed as reference points. When the adhesive becomes tacky (about ½ hour) resnap the chalk lines, using the reference points. Now without covering the chalk lines, spread adhesive over half the room, lengthwise. Use a swirling motion with the trowel and hold it almost at right angles to the surface so the ridges of adhesive are the proper depth. The adhesive should be at a temperature of at least 70 degrees when it is applied. Let the adhesive dry ½ to 4 hours before starting to lay the tile. You can tell when it's dry enough by pressing it with your finger. If the adhesive does not stick to the finger you can begin laying the tile. There's no hurry, as the adhesive can remain on the floor for two or three days, if necessary, before the tile is laid. (Important—this does not apply to adhesive for types of tile other than asphalt.) Spreading the adhesive evenly over the floor is extremely important. The adhesive never completely hardens, and if it is too thick in spots it will ooze up through the tile seams. In addition, a layer of adhesive that is spread evenly but too thickly will produce a cushion under the tile so that furniture legs and casters will cause depressions in the tiled floor. On the other hand, a tile which is not cemented completely may crack after it is on the floor only a short time. For best results use the notched trowel specified by your flooring dealer and bear down hard on it when spreading the adhesive.

Start laying the tile at the intersection of the chalk lines and work outward in a semicircle from the center line toward the walls. Be sure that each course of tile is started exactly on the chalk line to keep the rows straight. In laying the tiles, alternate the direction of the marbleized pattern, and carefully place each succeeding tile firmly in the angle formed by the two adjacent tiles. Don't slide the tile in place as this will cause the adhesive to ooze up from the joint. Instead, place the tile firmly against the edge of the adjacent tile and lower it into position. After finishing the field tile on half the room, spread the adhesive over the other half. While the adhesive is drying, you can lay the border tile around the first half of the room.

Fig. 2 illustrates the method of installing 18 by 24-in. border tile when 9 by 9-in. field tile is used. Score the border tile with the grain, as in the upper illustration, and snap the tile apart, starting at one end of the score line. Then sand off the burr along the snapped edge and lay the tile in the adhesive. Fitting border tile around door trim is done by using a second piece of border tile as a straightedge for transferring the irregular contour to the tile being fitted. Keep the straightedge parallel with the tile being marked, and score the tile at the widest point marked. Snap off the tile along the straight score line, heat the back of the tile with a blowtorch until pliable (you can also heat it in the oven if you wish) and then cut the tile with a sharp knife, following the contour marks. If you are using field tile instead of the larger tile for the border, place the tile to be marked atop the last field tile instead of the next-to-last one.

Asphalt tile can be cut easily *with* the grain by scoring it deeply with a sharp awl and, starting at one end, snapping it in two. Against the grain, you must score both sides of the tile deeply. Irregular shapes can be cut on a jigsaw, or by heating the tile and using a sharp knife.

To fit the tile around pipes and radiator legs, mark the tile, heat it and cut to fit. If a radiator can be raised, slip the tile under the legs, first reinforcing the tile with a nut, washer or ball bearing as shown in the lower detail, Fig. 2. Otherwise the heat from the radiator will soften the tile and the weight will crack the tile around the legs.

A good thing to remember when laying asphalt floor tiling is that it can be ironed into place. Set the iron for medium heat (not too hot) and press it slowly and lightly across the tile. Not only does the weight of the iron help to make a better bond between the tile and the adhesive, but the heat softens the tile and permits pressing down any curled edges. *Never* roll an asphalt tile floor with a heavy roller.

To remove adhesive smudges from the face of the tile, wipe the tile with a wet cloth dipped in scouring powder and follow with a rinse of clear water.

Because asphalt tile is brittle, it should be allowed to stand 10 days or more with as little wear as possible. This, of course, is impossible in a kitchen or bathroom installation, but don't subject it to any more hard wear than necessary. This gives the tile time to "relax" down into the bed of adhesive so there is firm support under the entire tile.

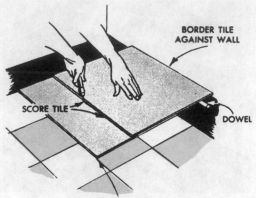

BORDER TILE AGAINST WALL

SCORE TILE

DOWEL

BORDER TILE PLACED ALONG SECOND SEAM OF FIELD TILE

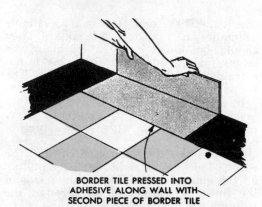

BORDER TILE PRESSED INTO ADHESIVE ALONG WALL WITH SECOND PIECE OF BORDER TILE

INSTALLING BORDER TILE

DOWEL

MARKING BORDER TILE TO FIT AROUND DOOR CASING

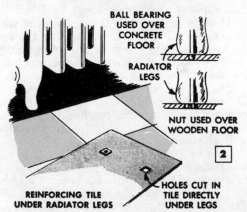

BALL BEARING USED OVER CONCRETE FLOOR

RADIATOR LEGS

NUT USED OVER WOODEN FLOOR

2

REINFORCING TILE UNDER RADIATOR LEGS

HOLES CUT IN TILE DIRECTLY UNDER LEGS

Installation photos courtesy Congoleum-Nairn, Inc.

Laying Diagonal Tile Pattern

For a distinctive effect, lay your floor tile in the diagonal pattern. Though this pattern is sometimes seen in large buildings, it is rather unusual in homes. It makes a strikingly different floor that will draw a good many comments.

Actually, laying the diagonal pattern is not much more difficult than laying the checkerboard pattern described in the preceding section, but it takes a little more planning and more time in laying out the

4 SQUARING THE BORDER IS FIRST OPERATION

(labels in figure 4:) BORDER IS NOT CEMENTED — CUT ON THIS LINE — TRIMMED EDGE — NOT TRIMMED — 4' — 3' — 5' — A — B — C — LINING-FELT SEAM — STRIKE ARCS FROM A AND B TO LOCATE POINT C

(labels in lower figure:) QUARTER TILE IN CORNER — BORDER

DIAGONAL CHECKERBOARD STARTS WITH QUARTER TILE

installation before you actually start applying the tile.

Snap a straight chalk line the length of the room. Now lay loose tiles, fitting them corner to corner, along the line from wall to wall. Pick up the end tiles and readjust the row of tiles until you have determined the border width you desire.

Now start in the corner of the room which is most frequently seen. Usually this will be in the corner nearest the entry door. Cut one strip of border tile this width and lay it in place but don't cement it down.

The second piece is left overwidth and is fitted to the wall at right angles to the first piece. However the width of the first piece is marked on the second at point A, Fig. 4.

At this point the room is squared up, again using the "3-4-5" method. Measure 4 ft. out from point A along the first border piece installed. Then from point A strike an arc of 3 ft. along the second piece of border tile. From point B strike a 5-ft. arc to the second piece. A line drawn from the intersection of these two arcs to point A is precisely at right angles to the edge of the first border tile you installed. This line becomes the trim line for the second border piece.

It's most important that you make these calculations to be certain that the first two pieces of border are exactly at right angles. Never trust a room to be square. Otherwise you will be in trouble by the time you're a few feet out from the first corner.

After cutting the second border piece, apply cement to the corner of the room, coming out no farther than you can reach easily. Wait for the adhesive to become tacky and then carefully position the two border pieces you have cut.

The first field tile you lay should be a quarter tile. Cut a tile diagonally, then locate the exact center point of the long side of one of the two parts. Cut again from the corner to obtain the quarter tile. Smooth off the cut edges with a file or by running them across the cut edge of another tile. Place the quarter tile in position in the adhesive.

The next tile you lay will be a full tile just in front of the quarter tile. Be especially careful in positioning the first dozen tiles as these will determine the neatness of the entire installation.

Each of the tiles adjoining the border tile is a half-tile, made by cutting a full tile on the diagonal.

Be sure that wall variations do not interfere with the correct alignment of the border tiles as you progress. Each border tile must be laid precisely in a straight line from the last. Use a long straightedge as a guide.

Laying the diagonal pattern takes somewhat more time than laying the checkerboard pattern because you are limited in the amount of area you can cover with adhesive. Never apply adhesive to an area larger than you can easily reach to position the tile, until you have laid enough tile so you can work from the floor you've already covered.

If the room is very large, divide it into smaller areas by laying single rows of tile at 5 or 6-ft. intervals as shown in Fig. 3.

Figures 5 and 6 show an alternate method of laying out the diagonal pattern. In this method you locate the center point of the room exactly as you do in laying the checkerboard pattern. Snap right-angle chalk lines through this point as previously described. Then, using a measurement of 4 ft. or more, locate the diagonal points and snap diagonal chalk lines as indicated in Fig. 5. Lay loose tiles across the room to determine the borders and relocate the diagonal lines if necessary. Cover the chalk lines with adhesive except for the intersection and ends. Using these reference points, resnap the lines and, starting in the middle of the room, lay the tiles to the walls. Borders should be laid last.

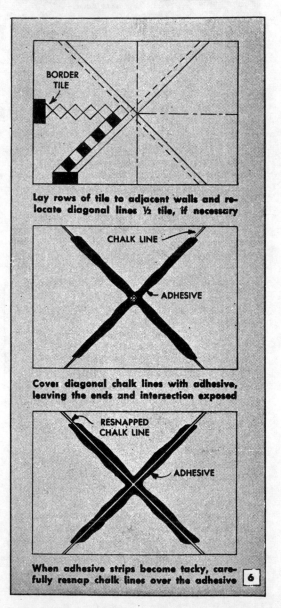

Lay rows of tile to adjacent walls and relocate diagonal lines ½ tile, if necessary

Cover diagonal chalk lines with adhesive, leaving the ends and intersection exposed

When adhesive strips become tacky, carefully resnap chalk lines over the adhesive | 6

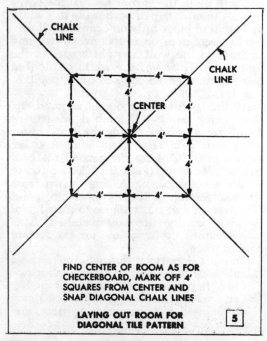

FIND CENTER OF ROOM AS FOR CHECKERBOARD, MARK OFF 4' SQUARES FROM CENTER AND SNAP DIAGONAL CHALK LINES

LAYING OUT ROOM FOR DIAGONAL TILE PATTERN | 5

Laying Other Types of Tile

Linoleum Tile

Linoleum tile, made of sheet linoleum, is flexible and therefore more easily handled without damage prior to installation than asphalt tile.

The floor for linoleum tile must be smooth and firm. If there is much "give" to the floor it must be covered with a layer of plywood or hardboard. Plywood underlayment panels should be at least ¼ in. thick and hardboard panels at least ³⁄₁₆ in. thick. These panels should be nailed with special underlayment nails around the edges and in the center. No point on the panel should be more than 9 in. from a nail.

If the floor is firm enough that no underlayment is required, plane or sand all the high spots and renail any loose boards. Even the slightest ridge in the floor will soon show up after the tile is laid. Fill any cracks or holes with tight-fitting strips of wood or plastic wood. If the floor is new or freshly sanded, apply one coat of wall size to prevent the wood from absorbing moisture from the paste and warping.

Floors without underlayment should be covered with a layer of lining felt (available at your flooring dealer). The strips of felt should run across the floor boards. The seams are butted tightly, not overlapped. When the felt has been cut to fit, lap the strips back and apply the special lining-felt paste to one half the floor. Smooth the felt back firmly over the paste. Then lap the felt back again and paste down the other half of the room.

After laying out the installation as described on preceding pages, spread the linoleum-tile paste over an area approximately three feet square, bounded by two of the chalk lines. Linoleum paste dries hard in a fairly short time, so you can spread no more adhesive than you can conveniently cover before it dries. When excess paste gets on the surface of a tile, wipe it up immediately with a damp cloth.

Because the paste becomes extremely hard when it dries, be sure that every tile is bedded firmly as soon as it is laid. It will never settle into the paste. Press the entire surface of each tile with your hand and rub the seams with a hammer head. Wipe up excess paste as you go. Once it dries you'll have to chip it away from the edges.

Rubber Tile

To prepare subfloors for rubber tile, cover any rough wood subfloors with ¼-in. plywood. Make sure the nailheads are driven flush with the surface. No lining felt is needed over plywood. Otherwise, always apply a layer of 15-lb. asphalt-saturated felt lining as described above. Always lay the felt face up as it unrolls. If you turn it over you may create air pockets between the felt and the subfloor.

Apply the rubber-tile adhesive to no more than 6 or 8 sq. ft. of area at one time and then lay the tile immediately. If it is possible to obtain a floor roller, roll the tile before spreading the adhesive over another area. If a roller is not available, use a wooden rolling pin and press down as firmly as possible. While still wet, rubber-tile adhesive can be removed from the surface of the tile with a damp cloth. After it has hardened, use a cloth moistened with alcohol.

Vinyl Tile

The installation of vinyl tile depends upon the type of adhesive recommended by the manufacturer. Some vinyl-tile adhesives are similar to asphalt-tile adhesive, while others are fast-setting cements. The area you can cover at one time will vary with the adhesive, so be sure to check the drying-time as indicated on the label. Otherwise prepare subfloors for vinyl tile the same as for linoleum tile. If vinyl tile is laid below grade be sure the concrete is dry and dust-free.

Cork Tile

Prepare wood subfloors as indicated above, using either an underlayment or a pasted-down asphalt-saturated felt. Do not spread adhesive over more than 6 or 8 sq. ft. at a time as it will film over and the cork will not stick. In installing cork tile it's important that you roll an area immediately after covering it with tile. As soon as you've finished the entire job (or at the end of a day's work), tap each tile. If any cork sounds hollow, drive a headless brad through the center of it, or apply a sandbag and let it lay overnight. Any adhesive on the tile surface should be cleaned off immediately with a cloth moistened with alcohol. Cork tile is more easily stained than other types of tile.

Only a razor-sharp knife can be used in cutting cork tile, as a dull knife will cause the cut edge to crumble. Cork floor covering is not available in sheet form because it is difficult to roll and is easily damaged before installation.

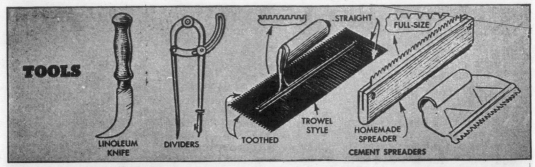

TOOLS

LINOLEUM KNIFE   DIVIDERS   STRAIGHT   FULL-SIZE

TOOTHED   TROWEL STYLE   HOMEMADE SPREADER   CEMENT SPREADERS

LINOLEUM
(STANDARD SIZES AND TYPES OF BASES)

BORDER

PLAIN-FELT BASE
SHOULD BE APPLIED "LOOSE-LAY"
NO LINER IS USED . SHOULD
NOT BE CEMENTED

DUPLEX-FELT BASE
IS A DOUBLE TYPE OF BACKING
AND IS INTENDED FOR
DIRECT CEMENTING TO FLOOR

BURLAP BASE
IS CEMENTED TO
A FELT LINER

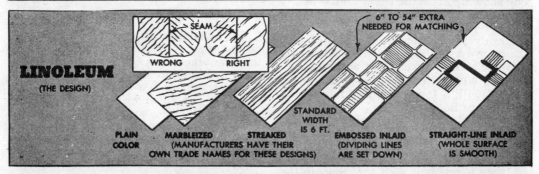

LINOLEUM
(THE DESIGN)

SEAM
WRONG   RIGHT

6" TO 54" EXTRA
NEEDED FOR MATCHING

STANDARD
WIDTH
IS 6 FT.

PLAIN COLOR

MARBLEIZED
(MANUFACTURERS HAVE THEIR
OWN TRADE NAMES FOR THESE DESIGNS)

STREAKED

EMBOSSED INLAID
(DIVIDING LINES
ARE SET DOWN)

STRAIGHT-LINE INLAID
(WHOLE SURFACE
IS SMOOTH)

FIRST POINTERS IN LAYING

LINOLEUM IS USUALLY
EXTENDED HALFWAY
THROUGH DOORWAYS

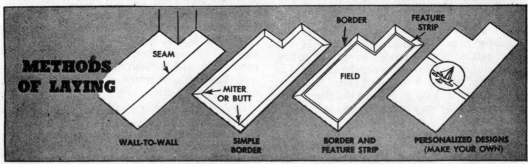

METHODS OF LAYING

SEAM

BORDER   FEATURE STRIP

MITER OR BUTT

FIELD

WALL-TO-WALL

SIMPLE BORDER

BORDER AND
FEATURE STRIP

PERSONALIZED DESIGNS
(MAKE YOUR OWN)

Linoleum and Other Sheet Floorings

Linoleum, vinyl and rubber sheet floorings are the most common types, with linoleum laid more often in homes than the other two kinds. Linoleum has less flexibility than rubber or vinyl and therefore must be handled somewhat more carefully during installation to prevent damage.

The information in this section covers the normal installation of linoleum, but other sheet floorings are laid in a similar manner.

Estimating your needs: The best way to figure your needs in sheet flooring is to make a simple scale drawing of the room, including all the cutouts. If you plan a border or feature strip, mark it on your drawing. Next mark in the strips of sheet flooring, using the width of the particular type you have chosen. Make as few seams as possible. Never estimate your flooring on the basis of square yards (even though it may be priced this way) but on the basis of the number of strips required and the length of each strip. Allow at least 3 in. for trimming all around. And don't forget to figure the pattern in your flooring in your estimate. Patterned sheet floorings must be matched the same as you match wallpaper. If the room is 15 ft. long, you can't necessarily order two or three strips 15 ft. 6 in. long, but must consider the way the pattern will match at the seams. If the pattern is repeated every 12 in., add this amount to every strip except one (which represents the first strip you will lay).

Prepare the subfloor with underlayment or felt in the same way you would prepare it for the corresponding type of floor tile.

Types of linoleum: First of all, study the sketches on the opposite page which cover the fundamental procedure. Then decide what kind of linoleum you want. The cheapest material has a plain felt base and the pattern is usually a printed enamel. This type of floor covering must always be applied "loose lay," that is, not cemented or tacked to the floor, because it must be free to expand. A better grade comes with a duplex felt back and can be applied either loose-lay or cemented directly to the floor. The best grade of linoleum is built up on a burlap base and is always cemented over a lining felt. All linoleum is stiff and brittle when cold and should not be unrolled until warmed to a temperature of 70 deg. for at least 24 hours. When it is practical to do so, it also is a good idea to allow the linoleum to lie flat for another 24 hrs. after unrolling. In this way, all danger of breaks in the surface of the linoleum will be avoided.

Laying wall-to-wall: This is the most common application and is illustrated by the details on the following page, which also explain the basic operation of scribing. Scribing simply means marking the linoleum to a shape and size to fit the room in which it is to be laid. It is done with a pair of dividers of the type used in woodworking, or with special dividers made for linoleum work. The latter tool is called an overscriber. In laying linoleum floor covering wall-to-wall, begin by removing the shoe mold at the bottom of the baseboard. If the floor is rough, with offsets at the joints, it should either be sanded or planed smooth. Then, cut the first sheet of linoleum about 4 in. larger than needed and fit it in place against one wall, letting the ends ride up on the baseboard. Follow through with the procedure pictured in Figs. 1 to 4 inclusive, which show the methods of scribing quite clearly. A close fit against the baseboards is not advisable in ordinary wall-to-wall installation. It is best to allow at least ⅛ in., or better, ¼ in. all around. The gap will be covered when the shoe mold is replaced. If the doorway is of the arched type or if it is fitted with a swinging door, it is common practice to extend the linoleum halfway through. Otherwise, the linoleum is ended at the doorstop, Fig. 2. The edge should be protected with a metal molding of the type shown in the upper detail, Fig. 2. This can be fitted before or after laying the linoleum, as desired. As suggested in Fig. 1, fasten the mold with two screws and then scribe to it. If required, it then can be shifted easily.

Laying second sheet: The second sheet is fitted as shown in Figs. 5 and 6. When rough trimming the second sheet, be sure to scribe and make the cut parallel with the opposite edge. When fitted in place, the edge at the seam should be parallel with the wall. After fitting the second sheet, there will be an overlap where the two pieces come together, Fig. 6. A neat butt joint, or seam, is made by double cutting as in Fig. 5. A recommended alternate method involves the use of a special tool called an under-scriber, Fig. 7. This tool speeds the scribing job and assures accuracy. When the under-scriber is pulled along with the round boss riding against the edge of the under sheet, the pointer scribes a mark on the top sheet directly above the edge of the under sheet. The top sheet is then cut on the scribed line for a perfect fit. The seam-cutting method used will affect the manner of applying the

SCRIBING IS BASIC OPERATION ON ALL JOBS

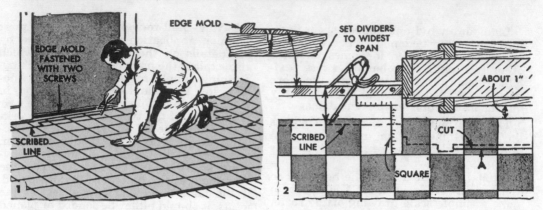

Cut linoleum 4 in. over required length. Lay on the floor with one side about 1 in. from wall and let both ends ride over baseboard. Set dividers at the required opening (Fig. 2) and, with one point of the dividers in contact with baseboard, scribe the line

When scribing to fit a doorway, metal edge molding can be temporarily fastened in place with two screws to serve as a guide. Shoe mold will cover the cut at A, so linoleum can be cut from 1/8 to 1/4 in. beyond the scribed-to-wall mark, making piece easy to fit

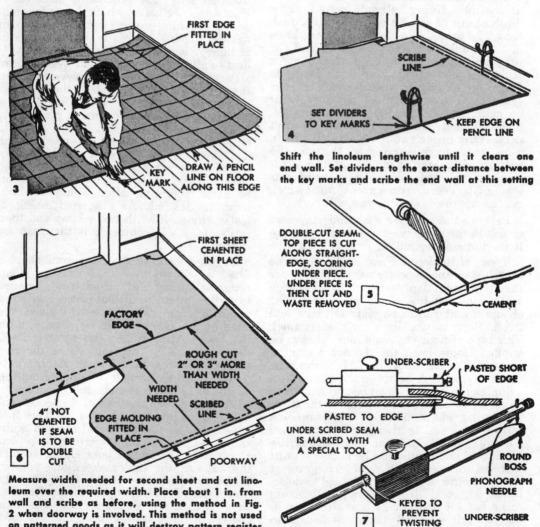

Shift the linoleum lengthwise until it clears one end wall. Set dividers to the exact distance between the key marks and scribe the end wall at this setting

Measure width needed for second sheet and cut linoleum over the required width. Place about 1 in. from wall and scribe as before, using the method in Fig. 2 when doorway is involved. This method is not used on patterned goods as it will destroy pattern register

cement. If the seam is made by double cutting, both edges are left uncemented for a distance of about 4 in. from the edges. After cutting, cement is spread under the projections to complete the job. If an under-scriber is used, the first sheet is cemented to the edge as in Fig. 7. When using either method of cutting, avoid fitting the seam too tightly. It is better to leave them a little loose to prevent ridging or buckling. Then, after cleaning up the surplus cement with a damp cloth, press the edges down to a perfect fit by rubbing with a hammer head covered with a soft cloth.

Fitting with paper pattern: Sometimes you will run into a job that is difficult or impractical to scribe by ordinary methods. In this case, use of a paper pattern probably will be the solution. To build up the pattern, cut and paste pieces of heavy paper or cardboard together to form the exact shape you want the linoleum to be. Then apply rubber cement or linoleum cement to the face of the pattern and roll the linoleum onto it so that the two stick together firmly, Fig. 8. Then turn the linoleum over and you have the required cutting pattern cemented to the back. This method also works out well when fitting linoleum having a figure or design imprinted or inlaid. In this case, you cannot cut to form a seam in the usual way as this may destroy the design register. Using the paper pattern, the linoleum is cut a little over the required width; the second sheet is butted against the first sheet and then rolled to the wall where it picks up the paper pattern.

Fitting simple border: In nearly all border jobs, you have the choice of laying either the field or the border first. Figs. 9, 10 and 11 show the border laid first. Chalk a line all around the room an equal distance from the walls. Use either the scribing or paper-pattern method for marking

Paper pattern is used for transferring odd shapes

Above, border is scribed to fit contour of the wall. Below, joint is double-cut to produce a perfect fit

LAYING BORDER AND FEATURE STRIP

the border pieces at doorways. After the pieces have been cut out, place them in position and check for fit. Then remove the pieces, one at a time, and spread cement under each one out to the chalk line. Replace all pieces and double-cut the corner seams, using either a miter or plain butt joint at the corners. Although the miter joint wastes more material, it is by far the neatest and most attractive. After the border has been cemented down, clean up all excess cement and then rough-cut the field material 1 to 2 in. oversize, except, if desired, one factory edge, which can be butted to the border. On the remaining edges use the under-scriber, Fig. 10, to mark a line for the cut above the border. Cut on the scribed lines and finish cementing at the edges of the field. Clean up with a damp cloth and then rub down all joints with a hammer head.

Border and feature strip: This attractive style, Fig. 17, requires only a little more time to lay than does the simple border. The method pictured in Figs. 15 to 20 inclusive calls for laying the field first, a procedure which many workers prefer for this installation. Chalk a line around the room a distance from the walls equal to the combined width of the border and strip. Butt one factory edge of the field to the line and trim the other edges about 1 in. oversize. Roll the material back and spread the cement, first on one half of the floor, then on the other, Fig. 12. Be sure to keep the cement inside the line. Bed the linoleum in the cement, pick up the chalk marks with a straightedge and cut the field

Cement for linoleum field is spread to the chalk line

Above, a straightedge is used to trim field linoleum. Below, scriber is set to exact width of feature strip

Place the border against field and scribe to wall, making sure strip does not buckle while being scribed

THIS IS THE MOST ATTRACTIVE OF THE FLAT-LAY STYLES AND IS EASY TO DO WITH READY-CUT STRIPS AND BORDERS

to the required net size, Fig. 13. Then sandbag the field and clamp the edges with wooden strips nailed to the floor, Fig. 19. Allow to stand for 24 hrs. Border pieces are now trimmed to a width of about ½ in. less than the distance between the edge of the field and the wall, Fig. 18. Set the scriber (dividers) to the width of the feature strip, Fig. 14, and, with the border pressed tightly against the field, scribe as in Fig. 20. If all measurements have been made correctly, the border and feature strip will fit neatly into the opening as in Fig. 16. It should be noted that in border work, the border itself is scribed net to the wall without a gap. The slight pressure fit thus obtained helps to get a good, tight joint between the border and feature strip and between the strip and the field. In some jobs involving a border of the same pattern and color as the field, the linoleum is laid wall-to-wall and the feature strip is cut in. This procedure is sometimes advantageous, depending on the size of the room and the distance from the wall to the strip. Make suitable allowances at the baseboard for a prominent feature strip.

Tips on matching patterns: You may find that the pattern in two strips of linoleum doesnt' match precisely. Due to the nature of linoleum (and some other sheet floorings) the material at the ends of a roll will stretch more than those cut from the middle of the roll.

To make two strips match perfectly, line them up and determine which one has been stretched. Roll it into a fairly tight roll (be careful not to crack it) with the face *inside* the roll. To stretch the other piece slightly,

If essential measurements have been properly made, border and feature strip will fit opening accurately

roll it *face out.* If the linoleum is quite warm when this is done, the one piece will stretch slightly and the other will shrink. They then should match much more closely.

If you discover that one end of a strip is not going to match the adjoining strip because the pattern runs long, place a very thin strip of wood under the linoleum at a point about halfway through the mismatched area. Paste down the strip and roll it on each side of the thin stick. Then slide out the stick and carefully roll down the buckled area. This will tend to shrink as it sinks into the paste, and the pattern should match much better. The strip of linoleum can be kept pliable by ironing the edges with an electric iron set at medium.

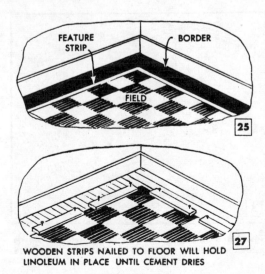

WOODEN STRIPS NAILED TO FLOOR WILL HOLD LINOLEUM IN PLACE UNTIL CEMENT DRIES

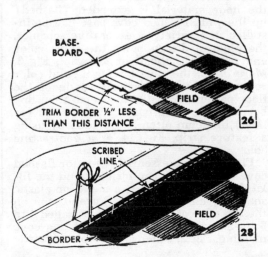

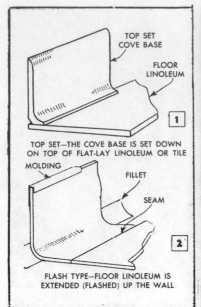

TOP SET
COVE BASE

FLOOR
LINOLEUM

1

TOP SET—THE COVE BASE IS SET DOWN
ON TOP OF FLAT-LAY LINOLEUM OR TILE

MOLDING

FILLET

SEAM

2

FLASH TYPE—FLOOR LINOLEUM IS
EXTENDED (FLASHED) UP THE WALL

3

Lay Your Own
LINOLEUM COVE BASE

By Sam Brown

EXTREMELY NEAT and colorful, the cove-base linoleum floor has the added advantage of forming a smooth, easily cleaned joint between floor and walls, an especially desirable feature in kitchens, laundry and utility rooms. Although the simplest installation is top set, Fig. 1, the true cove base is the style in which the floor material is extended (flashed) up the wall. Flashed cove base can be installed in a variety of decorative schemes, the plainest design being the same color and pattern as the floor material, Fig 3. More often, the cove base is a solid color repeating the predominant shade of the floor pattern. A distinctive separation line between the cove base and the floor (or field) linoleum often is provided by using a feature strip, Fig. 14, of a contrasting color.

Fittings: Two essential items for flashed cove base are the cap molding and the fillet. The cap molding is a metal or plastic shape which provides a trim and stop on the top edge of the cove, and is nailed 4 to 6 in. above the floor. The fillet is a cove molding, Fig. 2, which is available in plastic

Above, simplest installation of cove base uses same color and pattern of linoleum as the floor, or field

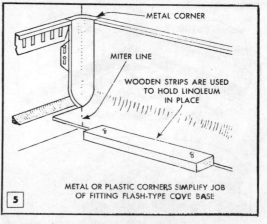

METAL CORNER

MITER LINE

WOODEN STRIPS ARE USED
TO HOLD LINOLEUM
IN PLACE

5

METAL OR PLASTIC CORNERS SIMPLIFY JOB
OF FITTING FLASH-TYPE COVE BASE

Figs. 4 and 5 show method of using metal or plastic inside and outside corners to fit flash-type cove base

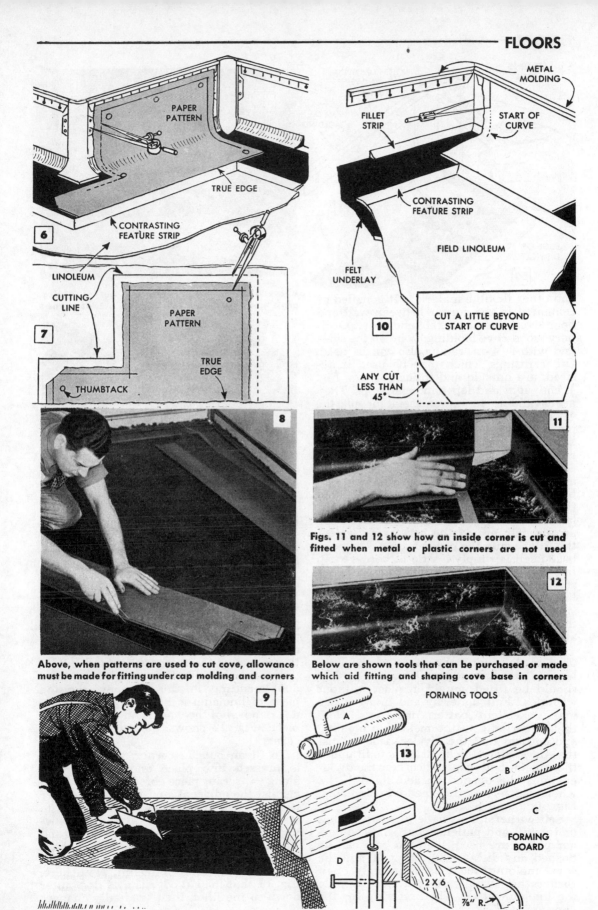

6

PAPER PATTERN

TRUE EDGE

CONTRASTING FEATURE STRIP

LINOLEUM

CUTTING LINE

7

PAPER PATTERN

TRUE EDGE

THUMBTACK

METAL MOLDING

FILLET STRIP

START OF CURVE

CONTRASTING FEATURE STRIP

FIELD LINOLEUM

FELT UNDERLAY

10

CUT A LITTLE BEYOND START OF CURVE

ANY CUT LESS THAN 45°

8

11

Figs. 11 and 12 show how an inside corner is cut and fitted when metal or plastic corners are not used

Above, when patterns are used to cut cove, allowance must be made for fitting under cap molding and corners

12

Below are shown tools that can be purchased or made which aid fitting and shaping cove base in corners

9

FORMING TOOLS

A

13

B

C

D

FORMING BOARD

2 X 6

⅞" R.

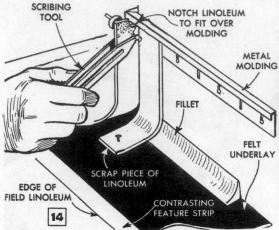

SCRIBING TOOL

NOTCH LINOLEUM TO FIT OVER MOLDING

METAL MOLDING

FILLET

FELT UNDERLAY

SCRAP PIECE OF LINOLEUM

EDGE OF FIELD LINOLEUM

CONTRASTING FEATURE STRIP

14

15

Above, linoleum on self corner is cut at 45-deg. angle down to middle of fillet on outside corners

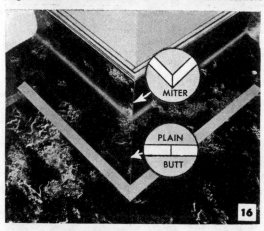

MITER

PLAIN

BUTT

16

Above, from center of fillet to corner of field linoleum edge is cut at right angle to form plain butt

and other flexible materials. It is nailed or cemented in the corner between wall and floor over the usual felt underlay. Ordinary wood-cove molding, ⅞ in. on the sides and with a ⅞-in. radius also can be used. Other fittings which may be used if desired, are outside and inside corners, Fig. 4, and right and left-hand end stops. They are available in either metal or plastic, 4½ or 6 in. high. In all cases, when installing cove-base floor, the conventional wood baseboard and base shoe, if present, are removed.

Installation with corner pieces: As with a flat-lay floor, either border or field can be laid first. Fig. 9 shows the field laid first, while Fig. 5 shows the cove border laid first. Wood strips nailed to the floor are used to crowd the cove strip against the fillet while the cement dries. The cove base itself is simply a strip of border-strip linoleum trimmed to the desired width and shaped to fit into the corner. The miter line on the floor in the corner can be cut singly as each piece is applied, Fig. 5, or the two corner pieces can be overlapped and cut together.

Either direct or pattern scribing can be used to determine the shape of the linoleum. If a paper pattern is used, Fig. 6, it should be fitted snugly in place without wrinkles. Felt underlay and lining paper make excellent pattern materials. Note that in scribing to the metal cap molding and corners that the dividers ride against the edges. Since the linoleum is to fit under the edge of both cap and corner, the dividers must be opened an additional ⅛ in. when transferring this line to the linoleum, Figs. 6, 7 and 8.

Self corners: This style of corner takes more skill and patience, but since no corner pieces are used, the cove base can be flashed any distance up the wall, and the cove molding located accordingly. Self corners are usually scribed directly onto the linoleum itself. The first strip for the

corner is pressed into place and scribed from the top down to about halfway across the fillet, Fig. 10. The second strip then is pushed into position, Fig. 11, and scribed and cut in the same manner. Both strips are cemented in place, then the cut is continued down across the fillet and out to the corner of the floor linoleum. After double-cutting in this manner, the top piece of linoleum is lifted slightly to permit removal of the waste end of the underpiece. Fig. 12 shows the finished inside corner.

To fit an outside corner, the first strip is pressed into place and underscribed along a scrap piece of linoleum fitted against the adjacent surface, Fig. 14. After it is marked the corner is cut down to about halfway across the fillet, the cut being a 45-deg. miter, as shown in Figs. 15 and 16. After the linoleum is cemented in place, the cut is continued across the fillet to the corner of the floor linoleum. Note here, Fig. 16, that the cut edge is a 45-deg. miter down to the fillet, then gradually changes

Above, asphalt tile used for top-set cove is notched, heated and bent to form inside corner as shown below

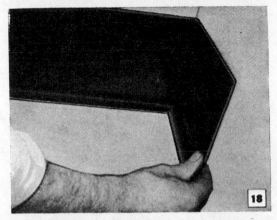

Below, score back of asphalt tile and heat to form outside corner. Also cut slit in the surface on floor

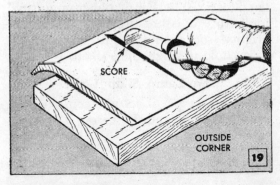

Below, close-coupled inside and outside corners present neat appearance when shaped from one piece

across the fillet to become a right-angle cut to form a plain butt the rest of the way across the cove.

Whether you use metal or self corners, the most difficult part of laying a base cove is shaping the linoleum to the required bend. The linoleum must be warm. If the room is cool, use a heat lamp to warm the linoleum before bending it. Form the bend as well as possible by hand before fitting. A better method is to use a forming board, shown in detail C, Fig. 13. Be sure the linoleum fits snugly against the fillet before scribing it. Also, double-check your cementing job; a few sandbags will help keep the linoleum in place while the cement is drying. Detail A in Fig. 13 shows a manufactured metal tool that is used to press the linoleum firmly against the fillet strip. Detail B is an easily made wooden tool used for the same job. Detail D shows a simple scribing tool that can be made if you do not have a regular one.

Top-set cove base: This style is easy to lay, being the same as the flashed type, except that the cove base is merely set on top of the floor covering, Fig. 1. If an asphalt material is used, corners are made by heating the spot with a blowtorch or heat lamp. To make an inside corner, notch the front of the molding, Fig. 17, apply heat and bend, Fig. 18. For an outside corner, score the back, heat and bend, Figs. 19 and 20. If the corner breaks slightly when bent, apply heat and mold shut with a hot knife, Fig. 21. Dust scraped from a scrap piece of asphalt can be used to fill in and "weld" a wider gap.

Rubber cove base must be cut and fitted the same as linoleum. Rubber does not cut as easily as linoleum and is usually fitted by using a special deep miter box and a fine-toothed saw. Some types of rubber tile are obtainable in preformed inside and outside corners, thus eliminating the problems of mitering. Preformed corners are cemented in place first and base strips are installed and fitted between them.   ★ ★ ★

Scrap piece of asphalt tile is welded into opening left when outside corner is bent. Hot knife is used

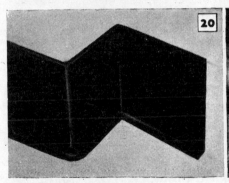

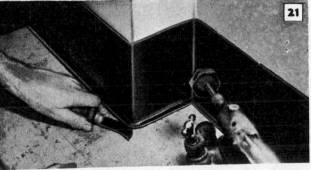

Assemble Your Own Fluorescent Lamps

Although fluorescent lighting is not a new subject, it did not find widespread application until recently, and originally its uses were largely industrial and commercial. Today, however, this type of lighting is becoming increasingly popular in the home and workshop as a source of superior, low-cost illumination.

Assembled from standard parts, fluorescent fixtures are not difficult to build for almost any lighting condition. Like ordinary filament lamps, the simplest installation of the fluorescent tube is a surface mounting. Bare as this is, it does the trick in certain locations.

The basic wiring consists of two circuits, one of which supplies current to start the lamp or tube and then plays no further part in operation, while the second circuit supplies the operating current. This line must carry a suitable ballast to limit the current to the amount needed for any particular lamp.

A two-or-more lamp circuit requires either a separate ballast for each lamp, or two ballasts mounted in one case.

Parts

Parts include ballasts having the proper capacity, and lamp holders, the latter consisting of one lamp holder and one combination lamp holder and starter socket. Also, either automatic starting switches, or one of the manual types which are for push, turn and pull operation and control of one or two lamps, are needed. Always be sure the ballast is for the proper wattage, frequency and voltage range.

All-Wood Fixtures

Fluorescent lamps generally are considered to radiate less than one half the heat of filament lamps, and can be mounted satisfactorily in all-wood fixtures. Fixtures in the detailed drawings of "All Wood Utility Fixtures" include one with a simple light strip using a plug-in type of ballast and two using standard ballasts mounted inside the fixture (B and C). These units can be made up to 40-watt size, the lamp length determining the length of fixture (see the "Fluorescent Lamp Sizes and Electrical Data" table for lamp sizes). The lamp-holder mounting for fixture C is not provided for in the original socket and requires drilling a screw hole through the socket.

Two-Lamp Shop Light

A better type of fixture construction combines wood and sheet iron. This type

Fluorescent lamps can be wired separately or two can be combined on one circuit.

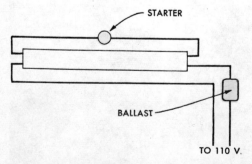

WIRING DIAGRAM (ONE LAMP)

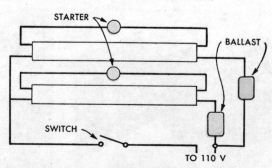

WIRING DIAGRAM (TWO LAMPS)

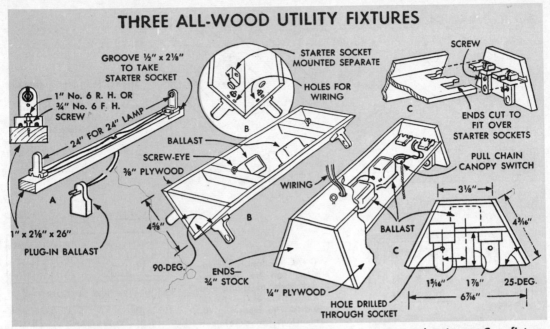

THREE ALL-WOOD UTILITY FIXTURES

Fluorescent lamps can be mounted in either: A—a simple light strip; B—an inverted casing; or C—a fixture combining two lamps.

of construction with two 20-watt lamps makes an excellent bench light, while with two 40s it will serve nicely for general illumination. This same general construction can be used for fixtures B and C. All two-lamp fixtures can also be made up for only one lamp by narrowing the width of the base.

Channel Strips

Channel strips are basic fluorescent-light units used extensively as fixture

A two-lamp shop light is best constructed with a combination of wood and sheet metal.

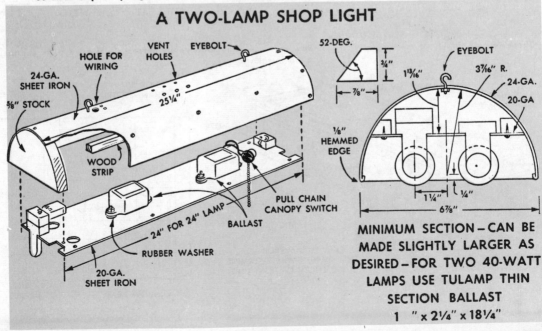

A TWO-LAMP SHOP LIGHT

MINIMUM SECTION—CAN BE MADE SLIGHTLY LARGER AS DESIRED—FOR TWO 40-WATT LAMPS USE TULAMP THIN SECTION BALLAST 1 " x 2¼" x 18¼"

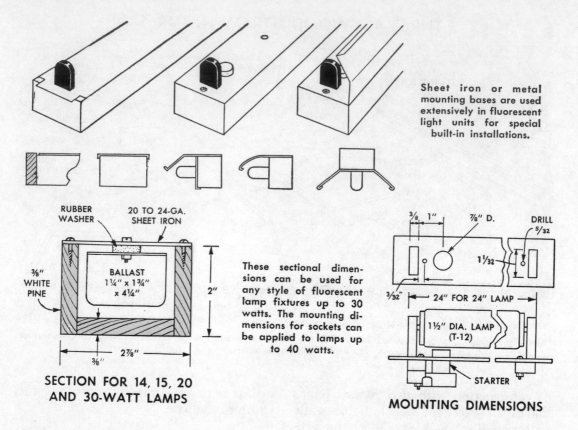

Sheet iron or metal mounting bases are used extensively in fluorescent light units for special built-in installations.

RUBBER WASHER   20 TO 24-GA. SHEET IRON

3/8" WHITE PINE

BALLAST 1¼" x 1¾" x 4¼"

2"

2⅞"

3/8"

SECTION FOR 14, 15, 20 AND 30-WATT LAMPS

These sectional dimensions can be used for any style of fluorescent lamp fixtures up to 30 watts. The mounting dimensions for sockets can be applied to lamps up to 40 watts.

3/8" 1"   7/8" D.   DRILL 5/32

1 1/32

3/32   24" FOR 24" LAMP

1½" DIA. LAMP (T-12)

STARTER

MOUNTING DIMENSIONS

bases or for special built-in installations. The strips can be made up of wood boxes with sheet iron or metal mounting bases. Sectional dimensions will accommodate lamps up to 30 watts. The 40-watt size will require a slightly larger box to suit the larger size ballast. Mounting dimen-

sions for sockets, as given in the detailed drawing, apply to any style of fixture using 14, 15, 20, 30 or 40-watt lamps.

Cove Lighting

The two examples of cove lighting are typical channel strip installations. The

These two examples of cove lighting for window cornices (right) and vanity mirrors (left) are typical channel strip installations.

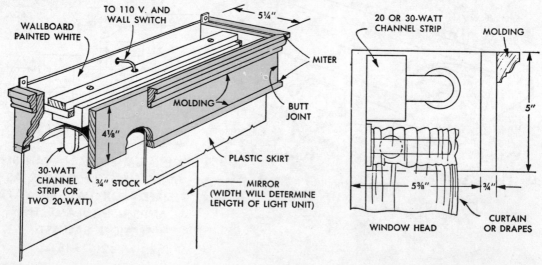

WALLBOARD PAINTED WHITE

TO 110 V. AND WALL SWITCH

5¼"

MITER

MOLDING

BUTT JOINT

4⅛"

30-WATT CHANNEL STRIP (OR TWO 20-WATT)

¾" STOCK

PLASTIC SKIRT

MIRROR (WIDTH WILL DETERMINE LENGTH OF LIGHT UNIT)

20 OR 30-WATT CHANNEL STRIP

MOLDING

5"

5⅜"   ¾"

WINDOW HEAD

CURTAIN OR DRAPES

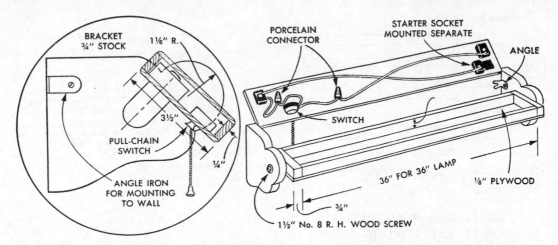

All wood construction can be used for the housing of fluorescent lights for bed lamps.

general construction details in the illustrations can be altered to fit individual requirements. If possible, the power line should be concealed in the wall, with control from a wall switch. However, the simpler method of tacking the wiring along woodwork and then to a receptacle can be used.

Bed Lamps

Bed lamps introduce the problem of magnetic ballast hum. All fluorescent-lamp ballasts make a low humming sound, which is inaudible in most locations but like a bee in flight in the quiet of a bedroom. Fortunately, it is practical to cut the ballast in at some remote point in the power line, and the noisemaker thus can be shifted to a far corner of the room or, even better, to some distant location like the basement or attic.

However, for successful operation, the voltage drop must not be too great, and this may occur when the ballast is located too far from the lamp. As a general rule, do not locate the ballast more than 50 ft. from the lamp and avoid locations where there is extreme moisture or where the surrounding air temperature is higher than 120 deg. F.

Without the ballast, the basic light unit takes the form of a flat box housing

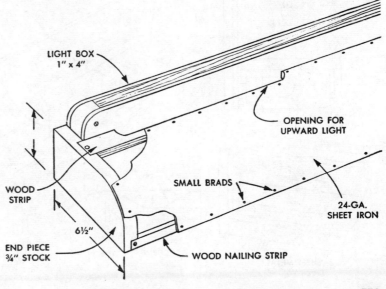

A wood housing with a metal shade extending outward can be used for a fixed headboard style bedlamp. In this unit the lamp housing box is flat against the wall.

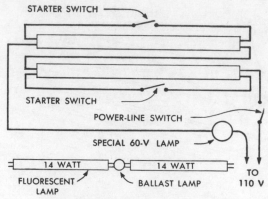

STARTER SWITCH

STARTER SWITCH

POWER-LINE SWITCH

SPECIAL 60-V LAMP

14 WATT 14 WATT

FLUORESCENT LAMP BALLAST LAMP TO 110 V

ARRANGEMENT AND WIRING FOR 14-WATT—TWO IN SERIES

Two 14-watt lamps can be connected in series and operated from one switch. In order to prevent confusion, this diagram for such a series shows three switches; however, one manual switch—of a special type—can be used.

the lamp holders and starting switch. All-wood construction can be used for the 1-in.-dia. tubes (15 and 30 watts) and the housing can be held to 1-in. thickness. This tiltboard style makes a very practical bed lamp allowing rotation of the light to any desired position. The fixed head-board style uses the lamp-housing box flat against the wall with a combination wood and metal shade extending outward.

Series Hookup

Two 14-watt lamps (this one size only) can be connected in series and operated with a small 60-volt lamp as a resistance ballast. Total wattage of lamps and ballast is about 45 watts. This circuit can be used on alternating or direct current. It has no ballast hum, making it ideal for bed lamp use. The detailed wiring diagram shows three separate switches in order to prevent confusion, but actually the three switching operations (two starters and one power line) are combined in one manual fluorescent switch. The switch must be the type designed to op-

A shelf-type fluorescent lamp holder can be constructed for either living room or kitchen installation.

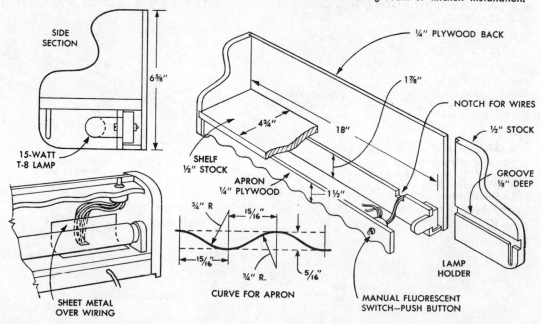

SIDE SECTION

6⅝"

15-WATT T-8 LAMP

SHEET METAL OVER WIRING

¼" PLYWOOD BACK

1⅞"

NOTCH FOR WIRES

½" STOCK

4¾"

18"

GROOVE ⅛" DEEP

SHELF ½" STOCK

APRON ¼" PLYWOOD

1½"

¾" R.

15/16"

15/16"

¾" R.

5/16"

CURVE FOR APRON

MANUAL FLUORESCENT SWITCH—PUSH BUTTON

LAMP HOLDER

Fluorescent Lamp Sizes[1] and Electrical Data

Lamp	Diameter	Length (2)	Lamp Holder	Total (3) Watts	Filament (4) Lamp Equal	Lamp Life (Hrs.)	Ballast Size (5)
6-Watt	⅝"	9"	Miniature Bipin	8	20-Watt	2500	1¼" X 1¾" X 4¼" (1 Lamp)
8-Watt	⅝"	12"	Miniature Bipin	11	25-Watt	2500	
13-Watt	⅝"	21"	Miniature Bipin	20	40-Watt	2500	
14-Watt	1½"	15"	Medium Bipin	18	30-Watt	2000	1¼" X 1¾" X 4¼" (1 Lamp)
15-Watt	1"	18"	Medium Bipin	20	40-Watt	2500	
15-Watt	1½"	18"	Medium Bipin	20	40-Watt	2500	1¼" X 1¾" X 6½" (2 Lamps)
20-Watt	1½"	24"	Medium Bipin	25	50-Watt	2500	
30-Watt	1"	36"	Medium Bipin	40	75-Watt	2500	1¼" X 1¾" X 6½" (1 Lamp)
40-Watt	1½"	48"	Medium Bipin	50	100-Watt	2500	1⅜" X 2¼" X 8¾" (1 Lamp) 2⅜" X 3⅛" X 9½" (2 Lamps)
100-Watt	2⅛"	60"	Mogul Bipin	125	200-Watt	3000	2⅜" X 3⅛" X 14⅜" (1 lamp)

(1) Lists all common sizes — some other sizes and styles also available.
(2) Over-all mounted length of one-lamp and two-lamp holders.
(3) Lamp watts plus watts lost at ballast.
(4) Filament lamp which gives same approximate light as fluorescent lamp listed.
(5) Smallest size — some other sizes available.

erate two lamps—a manual fluorescent switch for one lamp will not work.

Wall Shelves

Illuminated wall shelves are attractive and practical—one of the best applications of fluorescent lighting in the home. The lamp in the wall sleeve pictured is a 15-watt T-8 (T means tubular and the number gives the diameter of the tube in eighths of an inch, in this case 8/8 in.). Such a size is easier to conceal than the larger T-12. The switch is a manual type, push button, for one lamp. This switch is operated by pushing it in, holding for a few seconds until the lamp lights, and then releasing. It combines a starting switch and power-line switch in one unit, and has four lead wires.

Power leads usually are black and are wired into the power circuit, while the second pair of wires is cut in on the starting circuit. The ballast is mounted apart from the shelf, using a plug-in type or running wiring to the regular ballast which can be mounted in the basement or on a wall. A modification of the shelf-type holder can be constructed in the living room.

T-5 Lamps

T-5 lamps are available in 6, 8 and 13 watts. These lamps are excellent for shelves, picture lighting, portable trouble lamps, etc., where their small dimensions and low wattage are important considerations. Wiring is standard, and switching can be done with automatic starters or manually—the same as with the larger-diameter lamps. When connecting starters, ballasts, etc., if wiring diagrams are included with the equipment, refer to these as a double check.

Installation Applications

Don't use a one-lamp fixture as a lathe light or for illuminating any revolving machinery; the best unit for such installations is a two-lamp unit and, further, ballasted with a two-lamp high power-factor ballast. Don't overrate the light value of fluorescent lamps; a sound conservative rating is twice the illumination of a similar wattage filament lamp. Use fluorescent lighting with one or two simple units, and then, as an appreciation of this new and better lighting grows, make other installations as dictated by experience.

HOW TO SERVICE FLUORESCENT LAMPS

The three units requiring service in fluorescent-lighting installations are the ballast, the tube and the starter switch.

Ballast Hum

The ballast, itself, is relatively trouble free, however, a hum occasionally occurs. Correction for this ballast hum often is made by simply tightening loose screws holding the ballast. A rubber shim under the ballast will give a more positive reduction of noise. For complete elimination of noise, the ballast can be moved any reasonable distance from the lamp without affecting its performance. As a general rule, keep the ballast within 50 ft. of the lamp; avoid damp locations as well as air temperatures of 120 deg. F. and above.

The Tube

Both ends of the tube are alike. The electrode or filament furnishes a terminal for the arc and originally is covered with an electron-emissive material. This is dissipated during the life of the lamp, and is deposited inside the tube; causing the familiar end blackening; which is a fair index of the "life expectancy" of the lamp. Early end blackening indicates faulty starting.

Starter Switch

When the starter switch is closed, power is supplied to the tube filaments, and they heat and become a dull red. Modern fixtures are fitted with an automatic starter, commonest of which is the glow lamp. When the fluorescent fixture is turned on, the glow switch receives a full supply of current, causing the movable metal strip to heat and make contact. When the arc strikes, voltage to the glow switch is lowered and the metal strip cools and opens the circuit. Because the glow switch must heat on a certain voltage and not heat on a slightly lower voltage, it is impractical to test the switch electrically by any method other than placing it in the fixture.

Other considerations in the maintenance of fluorescent lamps are:

Lamp Blinking

Near the end of life, the electron-emissive deposit on tube filaments is exhausted, the filaments are no longer self-sustaining and a cycle of blinking continues until either lamp or starter ceases to function. To prevent blinking, auxiliary equipment was added to the glow switch —making a double switch, with the second switch turning off the first when the fixture is not functioning correctly.

When a fluorescent lamp is turned on the starter (center) causes metal to expand and make contact. This results in the lighting of the filament (left).

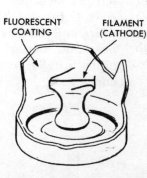

FLUORESCENT COATING

FILAMENT (CATHODE)

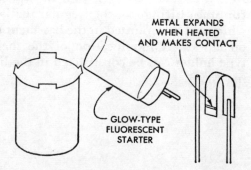

METAL EXPANDS WHEN HEATED AND MAKES CONTACT

GLOW-TYPE FLUORESCENT STARTER

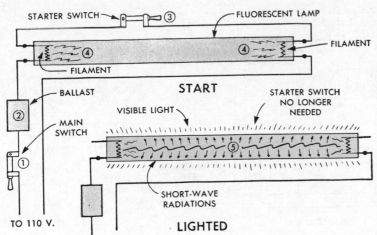

STARTER SWITCH
FLUORESCENT LAMP
FILAMENT
FILAMENT
BALLAST
MAIN SWITCH
START
VISIBLE LIGHT
STARTER SWITCH NO LONGER NEEDED
SHORT-WAVE RADIATIONS
TO 110 V.
LIGHTED

The operation of a fluorescent lamp is as follows:
Main switch 1, is turned on. Ballast 2, limits current to amount required by lamp. Starter switch 3, is closed (usually automatic) to complete circuit. Lamp filaments become heated and send out electrons 4, and in a few seconds the arc 5, strikes. Starter switch then is opened automatically or manually and plays no further part in operation. Arc 5, sends out short-wave invisible light, which activates fluorescent coating on inside of tube causing it to glow and produce visible light.

Testing Lamps

Use an extension cord with the ends scraped clean. Connect a socket in one of the power lines. When the test wires are touched to the prongs of the tube, the test lamp should light. If it does not, a broken filament is usually indicated. If the tube glows red, the filament is operating correctly but the activating material has been burned off. When the lamp lights and the end of the tube glows, that end of the tube is good. If both ends test, the tube is satisfactory. For accurate results, and also to avoid overloading the tube filament, the test lamp should be 60 watts for 14, 15, 20 and 30-w. tubes. Use a 100-w. test lamp for 40-w. tube; 20-w. test lamp for 65 and 100-w. tubes; 25-w. test lamp for the small miniature tubes.

Radio Interference

Direct radiation from the tube is eliminated easily by simply moving the lamp or radio. Line feed-back can be cut to a very low level by connecting a small condenser across the line. Special condensers are made for this purpose. Ground the free end of each condenser to some part of the fixture and most of the feedback will be eliminated.

Circuit Testing

If both lamp and starter check correctly, the fault is in the circuit. Test with an electrical tester or a 220-v., 100-w. lamp. If the test lamp does not light, the fault is farther along the line and the whole wiring system must be systematically checked.

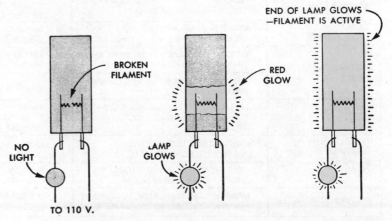

When test wires are touched to the prongs of the tube, a good lamp will glow bright. If it glows red, the activating material has been worn off; and, if it doesn't glow at all, there is a broken filament.

BROKEN FILAMENT
NO LIGHT
TO 110 V.
RED GLOW
LAMP GLOWS
END OF LAMP GLOWS —FILAMENT IS ACTIVE

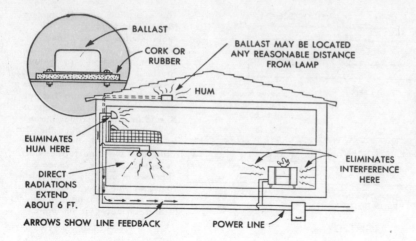

BALLAST

CORK OR RUBBER

BALLAST MAY BE LOCATED ANY REASONABLE DISTANCE FROM LAMP

HUM

ELIMINATES HUM HERE

DIRECT RADIATIONS EXTEND ABOUT 6 FT.

ARROWS SHOW LINE FEEDBACK

POWER LINE

ELIMINATES INTERFERENCE HERE

To completely eliminate ballast hum, move the ballast any reasonable distance from the lamp. This should not affect the performance of the lamp.

Power Factor

This means that the line must carry an over-supply of current in order to transmit a smaller amount of current which is actually used. Thus, if a ballast requires twice as much current in the line as it actually uses, it has a low power factor of 50 percent. Power factor does not affect lamp performance. Its only effect is that heavier wiring is needed.

Fluorescent-Lamp Trouble-Shooting Chart

FAULT	POSSIBLE CAUSE	REMEDY
LAMP BLINKS	END OF LIFE (Normal life is 2500 hours)	INSTALL NEW LAMP
	DEFECTIVE STARTER	TEST WITH NEW STARTER
	LOOSE CONTACTS	CHECK CONTACTS AT LAMP ENDS
	WITH NEW LAMP: MAY BE CAUSED BY DEFECTIVE LAMP	CHECK WITH A LAMP KNOWN TO BE SATISFACTORY
	WITH PLUG-IN FIXTURES: LOOSE CONNECTION AT PLUG	CHECK PLUG. TRY NEW PLUG-IN. TEST FROM DIFFERENT OUTLET
POOR OR SLOW START	USUALLY DEFECTIVE STARTER	REPLACE STARTER
	COLD WEATHER (Fluorescent lamps are unsatisfactory below 50° F.)	SHIELD LAMP (A special lamp for low-temperature operation is available)
NO START	LAMP OR STARTER OR CIRCUIT DEFECTIVE	CHECK LAMP, STARTER AND CIRCUIT IN ORDER NAMED
ENDS OF LAMP REMAIN LIGHTED	DEFECTIVE STARTER	REPLACE STARTER
BALLAST HUM	NORMAL. MOST PRONOUNCED IN CHEAP SINGLE-LAMP BALLAST	INSULATE WITH RUBBER BASE. TIGHTEN SCREWS. BE SURE BALLAST HAS SOME MEANS OF VENTILATION.
RADIO INTERFERENCE	DIRECT RADIATION FROM LAMP OR LINE FEEDBACK	MOVE RADIO AWAY FROM LAMP. CONNECT CONDENSER ACROSS POWER LINE
STROBOSCOPIC EFFECT	NORMAL TO SOME EXTENT WITH ALL SINGLE-LAMP BALLASTS	REPLACE FIXTURE WITH TWO-LAMP UNIT USING TWO-LAMP BALLAST
	MOST PRONOUNCED WITH BLUE AND DAYLIGHT LAMPS	CHANGE TO WHITE LAMPS
FLICKER OR SWIRL	NORMAL, ESPECIALLY WHEN LAMP IS FIRST USED, BUT MAY OCCUR AT ANY TIME	SWITCH LAMP ON OR OFF A FEW TIMES OR LET IT ALONE AND IT WILL CLEAR UP ITSELF
DECREASE IN LIGHT OUTPUT	LIGHT OUTPUT DURING FIRST 100 HRS. IS ABOVE NORMAL	LAMPS ARE RATED AT 100 HR. VALUE (About 10% above normal)
	COLD WEATHER. A LIGHT LOSS OF ABOUT 1% PER DEGREE BELOW 65° F.	ENCLOSE OR PROTECT LAMP. USE SPECIAL COLD-WEATHER LAMP
END BLACKENING	NORMAL NEAR END OF LIFE. CAUSED BY BURNING OF COATING ON FILAMENT	IF OCCURRING EARLY IN LIFE, CAREFUL CHECK OF ENTIRE FIXTURE SHOULD BE MADE

FURNITURE REPAIR

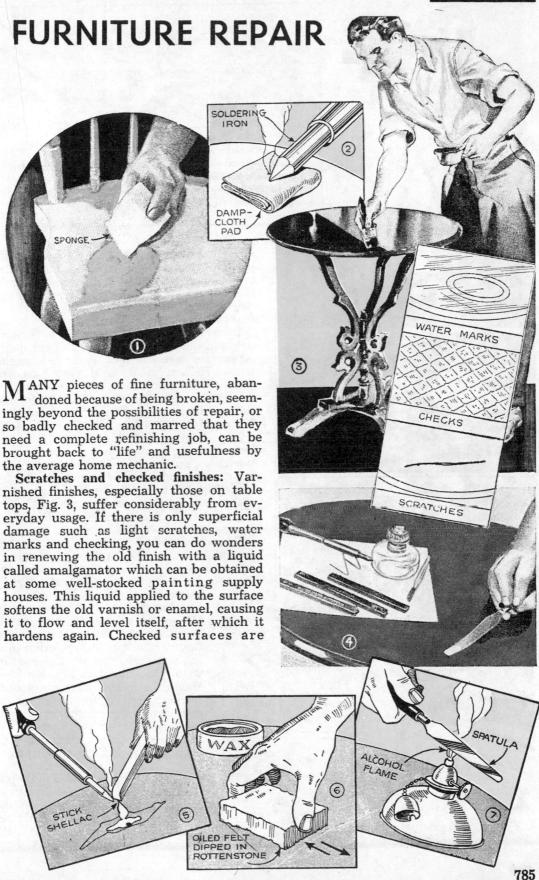

SPONGE

SOLDERING IRON

DAMP-CLOTH PAD

WATER MARKS

CHECKS

SCRATCHES

WAX

STICK SHELLAC

OILED FELT DIPPED IN ROTTENSTONE

ALCOHOL FLAME

SPATULA

MANY pieces of fine furniture, abandoned because of being broken, seemingly beyond the possibilities of repair, or so badly checked and marred that they need a complete refinishing job, can be brought back to "life" and usefulness by the average home mechanic.

Scratches and checked finishes: Varnished finishes, especially those on table tops, Fig. 3, suffer considerably from everyday usage. If there is only superficial damage such as light scratches, water marks and checking, you can do wonders in renewing the old finish with a liquid called amalgamator which can be obtained at some well-stocked painting supply houses. This liquid applied to the surface softens the old varnish or enamel, causing it to flow and level itself, after which it hardens again. Checked surfaces are

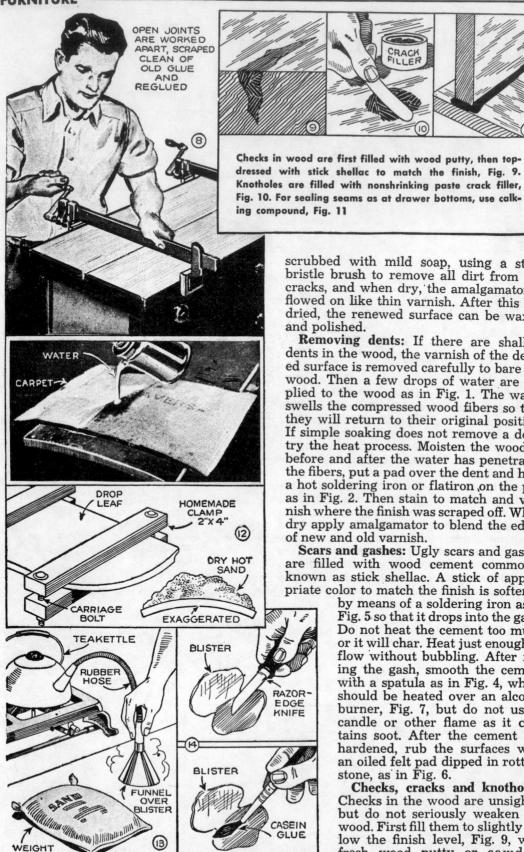

OPEN JOINTS ARE WORKED APART, SCRAPED CLEAN OF OLD GLUE AND REGLUED

Checks in wood are first filled with wood putty, then top-dressed with stick shellac to match the finish, Fig. 9. Knotholes are filled with nonshrinking paste crack filler, Fig. 10. For sealing seams as at drawer bottoms, use calking compound, Fig. 11

scrubbed with mild soap, using a stiff-bristle brush to remove all dirt from the cracks, and when dry, the amalgamator is flowed on like thin varnish. After this has dried, the renewed surface can be waxed and polished.

Removing dents: If there are shallow dents in the wood, the varnish of the dented surface is removed carefully to bare the wood. Then a few drops of water are applied to the wood as in Fig. 1. The water swells the compressed wood fibers so that they will return to their original position. If simple soaking does not remove a dent, try the heat process. Moisten the wood as before and after the water has penetrated the fibers, put a pad over the dent and hold a hot soldering iron or flatiron on the pad as in Fig. 2. Then stain to match and varnish where the finish was scraped off. When dry apply amalgamator to blend the edges of new and old varnish.

Scars and gashes: Ugly scars and gashes are filled with wood cement commonly known as stick shellac. A stick of appropriate color to match the finish is softened by means of a soldering iron as in Fig. 5 so that it drops into the gash. Do not heat the cement too much or it will char. Heat just enough to flow without bubbling. After filling the gash, smooth the cement with a spatula as in Fig. 4, which should be heated over an alcohol burner, Fig. 7, but do not use a candle or other flame as it contains soot. After the cement has hardened, rub the surfaces with an oiled felt pad dipped in rottenstone, as in Fig. 6.

Checks, cracks and knotholes: Checks in the wood are unsightly but do not seriously weaken the wood. First fill them to slightly below the finish level, Fig. 9, with fresh wood putty or sawdust

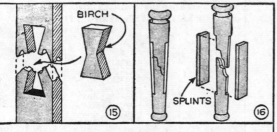

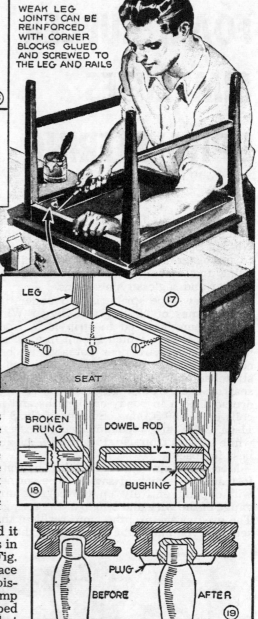

Fractures of legs may be repaired with a double wedge as shown in Fig. 15, but if the legs are too slender you can apply splints as in Fig. 16. Repair pieces should be same kind of wood. Often, corner blocks, glued and screwed in place will hold legs rigidly, Fig. 17

WEAK LEG JOINTS CAN BE REINFORCED WITH CORNER BLOCKS GLUED AND SCREWED TO THE LEG AND RAILS

mixed with casein glue. When dry, apply stick shellac to match the finish. Cracks and knotholes not in highly polished surfaces can best be filled with a nonshrinking paste crack filler applied with a spatula as in Fig. 10.

Regluing and filling seams: On a job involving extensive repairs, pieces should be reglued and clamped as in Fig. 8. The edges should be scraped clean of old glue before applying fresh glue. Calking compound settles the old problem of shrunken drawer backs, Fig. 11, as it never gets hard but remains elastic, yet keeps the gap plugged.

Warping: Curved pieces of wood such as found on drum tables and circular-table aprons can be returned to their original shape if you make use of the natural tendency of the wood to warp. As shown in the photo above Fig. 12 a piece of carpet is laid on the convex side and hot water is applied, while the other side is kept dry, allowing free circulation of air. When the wood has reached the desired curvature, place it in clamps or forms to hold it in position until dry. The same method works in reverse to take the warp out of table leaves, Fig. 12. Here a wet pad is put on the concave surface so that wood fibers on this side will absorb moisture and expand. Watch the progress and clamp the leaf when it is straight, leaving it clamped overnight. Should the leaf be bent too far so that it is warped in the opposite direction, hot, dry sand will bring it back as shown in Fig. 12.

Blisters on veneer: If loose or blistered, the wood must be steamed to a pliable state before it can be worked, taking care not to soften the glue that is still holding. A simple steamer can be improvised as shown in Fig. 13. Then a sharp knife is used to cut the blister open as in Fig. 14, after which glue is applied and the wood pressed down in place again, working fast to get the job done before the wood dries out and breaks. Excess glue squeezed out at the edges is wiped away and a bag of sand is placed on the spot as a weight.

Repairing fractures: Fractures often need reinforcing. In Fig. 15, a double wedge of hardwood is glued in a mortise cut out to make a snug fit. Dress down when dry. Splints such as shown in Fig. 16 are set in pieces that are too slender for a double wedge.

Leg joints and chair rungs: When a leg of a chair or table is weak and needs reinforcement, corner blocks glued and screwed in place, Fig. 17, are sometimes the best solution. If the chair has a rung broken at the tenon, refit with a dowel tenon, as shown in Fig. 18. A repair for an enlarged socket is shown in Fig. 19.

FOAM RUBBER SIMPLIFIES UPHOLSTERING

TABLE OF GAUGES AND SIZES OF SAGLESS-TYPE SPRINGS FOR SEATS

Inside-Seat Dimension	Gauge	1¼" Arc	1½" Arc	1¾" Arc	2" Arc
12"	11	11¾"	12"	12½"	
13"	11	12¾"	13"	13½"	
14"	10½	13¾"	14"	14½"	
15"	10½	14¾"	15"	15¼"	
16"	10	15¾"	16"	16¼"	
17"	10	16¼"	16½"	16¾"	
18"	9½	17"	17½"	18"	
19"	9½	18¼"	18½"	18¾"	
20"	9	19"	19½"	19¾"	20"
21"	9	20"	20½"	20¾"	21"
22"	8½	21"	21¼"	21¾"	22"
23"	8½	22"	22½"	22¾"	23"
24"	8½	23"	23¼"	23½"	24"
25"	8	24"	24¼"	24½"	25"
26"	8	25"	25¼"	25½"	26"
27"	8	26"	26¼"	26½"	27"

Inside-seat dimension is the distance between the inside of the front and back rails. Sagless springs cut to this exact length will give you the normal arc. It varies from 1¼" to 2" increasing with the length of the spring as shown above. When clip is not attached to inside edges of frame, clip-to-clip dimensions can be used instead of inside dimensions.

In this article John Bergen, in cooperation with the U. S. Rubber Co. and the No-Sag Spring Co., shows how simple it is to upholster both old and new furniture using two new products—resilient foam rubber and sagless-type springs.

This new-type spring is sold under the trade names of No-Sag and Zigger Wire and is manufactured in strip form from spring-steel wire which is bent in a zigzag pattern. The wire does not actually become a spring until it is uncoiled and stretched and anchored at each end to the seat or back frame. Sagless-type springs are sold both in ready-cut lengths and in coils up to 160 ft. long. Springs of No. 8 to 11-ga. wire are recommended for seats, while springs from No. 10½ to 12½ ga. are best for backs.

Measuring springs for length: The comfort and resiliency of sagless-type springs will depend entirely on the correct arc, gauge of the wire and length of the springs. The greater the arc, the more resilient the seat. Never make the arc greater than 2

in. high without using a hinge link, which is a U-shape wire connector applied to the end of the spring at the back seat rail. To measure sagless-type springs for length, hold one end of the uncoiled spring on one end of a yardstick. Then roll back the other end of the spring until it lies flat on the yardstick. The distance between the extreme outside edges of the bent ends is the correct length of the spring. Avoid measuring with a flexible-steel tape around the curve shape of the spring as this will give an incorrect measurement. Springs that are sold already cut are measured by the yardstick method.

Cutting and bending ends of springs: When the spring wire is purchased in coils, it must be cut into individual springs of the proper length, after which the ends must be bent back slightly. The wire can be cut either with a file or fine-tooth hacksaw blade. With a file, a notch is made in

the wire while it is clamped in a vise and then the wire is bent back sharply to snap it off. Bending back of the ends is done by clamping the spring in a vise and hammering the end back. Bending the ends back is necessary to prevent the springs from slipping out of the clips which are used to anchor them to the wooden frame. When the springs are purchased ready-cut to length, they come with the ends already bent.

How springs are installed: The special metal clips which hold the spring ends securely to the frame are nailed in place first. The chart given on this page recommends the number of springs needed in the seats and backs of certain size frames and also gives the correct spacing of the clips. Mark the location of the clips on the rails of the frame. When the seat tapers to the back, the outside clips on the back rail should be placed the same distance in from the sides as they are placed at the front. The other clips for the back seat rail are spaced evenly between the outside clips. On large seats, the second clip from the outside on the back seat rail is spaced evenly between the outside clip and the normal position of the third clip. The springs are always installed between the front and the back seat rails in the case of the seat, and from the top rail to the back liner when springing the back of a chair. The only exception is when the seat and the back are upholstered together in one continuous form. Then the springs are installed between the side seat rails and between the back posts.

When nailing the clips in place, be sure each clip overhangs the inside edge of the frame at least ⅛ in. This allows the spring to swivel freely inside the clip and prevents noise that might otherwise result from restricted spring movement. It is best to install all clips in their respective positions with one nail before hooking the springs in place. In placing the springs, it is important to alternate the direction of

Threadbare occasional chair, above, becomes like new with foam-rubber padding and red plastic upholstery

TABLE FOR DETERMINING
NUMBER OF SAGLESS STRANDS, PROPER
SPACING OF CLIPS AND CORRECT SIZE OF SEAT
HELICALS, EXTENSION SPRINGS FOR CHAIR AND SOFA SEATS

Distance Between Arms Along Front Rail	Number of Sagless Strand	Center-to-Center Spacing for Clips	Center Spacing of Two Outside Clips From Inside Arm Posts	Seat, Helical and Extension Spring Size
21″ Chair	5	4¼″	2″	2″
22″ Chair	5	4½″	2″	2″
23″ Chair	5	4¾″	2″	3″
24″ Chair	5	5″	2″	3″
24″ Chair	6	4″	2″	2″
25″ Chair	6	4¼″	1⅞″	2″
58″ Sofa	12	5″	1½″	3″
59″ Sofa	12	5″	2″	3″
60″ Sofa	13	4¾″	1½″	3″
61″ Sofa	13	4¾″	2″	3″
62″ Sofa	13	4¾″	2½″	3″
63″ Sofa	13	5″	1½″	3″
63″ Sofa	14	4½″	2¼″	2″
64″ Sofa	14	4½″	2¾″	2″
65″ Sofa	14	4¾″	1⅝″	3″
66″ Sofa	14	4¾″	2⅛″	3″
67″ Sofa	15	4½″	2″	2″

Where distance between arms is in half inches use table for next smaller or larger size and set each outside clip ¼″ farther away from arm post (if table for smaller size is used) or ¼″ closer to arm post (if table for larger size is used).

Sagless-type springs are installed in back by nailing lower clips closed and drawing springs upward

First step is to nail spring clips to frame. Note wire hinge links along back rail. Links plus clips are used at rear rail when greater spring arc is desired

the bent ends. For example, if the bent end of the first spring points to the right, the bent end of the adjacent spring should point to the left. Alternating the direction of the bent ends of the springs brings closed loops opposite each other, thus permitting helical and retainer springs to be applied to the sagless-type springs in a straight line. Alternating the bent ends of the springs also is necessary to permit installing edge springs.

Installing springs in seat: When all the clips have been nailed to the frame, you are ready to install the springs. To determine the gauge and length of the springs needed for the particular frame at hand,

measure the frame from the inside of the front rail to the inside of the back rail. Then consult the chart on page **788** to find the length and the gauge of the springs needed. Keep the arc about 2 in. high. This will make the most resilient seat.

Each spring is installed individually by first hooking it in the open clip at the back seat rail and then nailing the clip shut. After this the spring is pulled forward, hooked in the clip at the front rail and the clip is nailed shut as before. As sagless-type springs are quite stiff and thus require a good deal of pull to stretch them, you should make sure that the clips are well nailed and that you have a good hold

Next, the springs are covered with burlap. Long running stitches are used in sewing it to the springs

Tacking strips of muslin, cemented to edges of foam-rubber pad, serve to secure rubber in place on seat

Above, small helical springs tie sagless-type springs together crosswise in both seat and back. Below, foam rubber, covering arms of chair, is cemented at seams

Above, chair arms are covered on inside with furniture webbing. Back and seat have already been covered with burlap. Below, photo shows chair padded with foam rubber and ready for fabric cover. Cotton is used to pad arms on outside

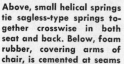

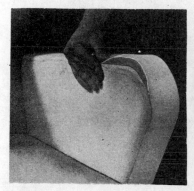

Below, fabric cover is applied to outside face of arms last. First, welting is tacked all around outer edge of arm. Then fabric is blind-tacked along top edge by tacking through cardboard strip and rear side of fabric. Cardboard is concealed when fabric is pulled down

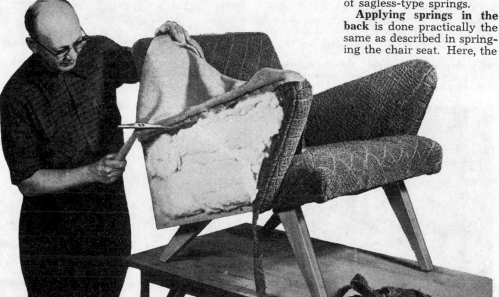

on the spring. One of the best ways to stretch the springs is to grip the free end with the claw of a hammer. With the hammer held in the right hand, left hand is used to press downward on the crown of the spring as it is pulled forward and hooked in the clip. As each spring is stretched in place, remember to alternate the direction of the bent ends.

Helical springs installed next: Helical springs are used to connect the sagless-type springs together crosswise so they will function as a unit and spread the seating load evenly over all the springs. When installing the helical springs, be sure the open hook of the coil is placed downward so that the hook will not snag the burlap covering and foam-rubber padding. At least two rows of helical springs should be used, three are better. These are anchored to the side seat rails with retainer plates which are sheet-metal hooks that are nailed vertically to the outside face of the rails. The plates should be spaced evenly three or four spring loops apart along each rail, and should be nailed at a height on the rail that will permit a straight sideward pull against the outside row of sagless-type springs.

Applying springs in the back is done practically the same as described in springing the chair seat. Here, the

After foam rubber is applied to bolster, the rubber is cut with scissors all the way through to burlap. This allows the bolster to be deeply tufted when it is covered

Above, wooden frame to which sagless springs are applied and then covered with burlap, is designed to take standard, cored foam-rubber mattress. Below, helical springs are added to sagless springs of bolster

springs are stretched from the back liner (lower crossrail) of the frame to the top rail. Two or three rows of helical springs are installed across the back as was done in the seat. However, the springs at the ends of the rows are held to the frame with staples instead of retainer plates. After all the springs are installed in both the back and seat, the springs are covered with burlap which is drawn taut and tacked to

Below, bolster is "wrapped" with fabric which is brought around and tacked to ends of frame. Separate plywood panels, covered with fabric, cap each end

Below, before foam rubber is applied, edge roll is tacked all around each end of bolster to soften the hard edges of frame and produce recess for end panels

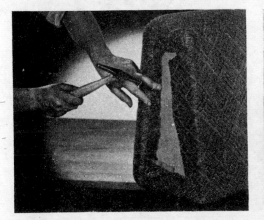

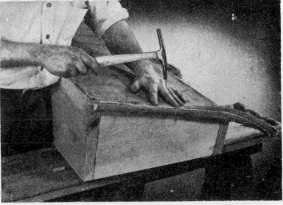

Above, this photo of the Davenette shows it ready for the foam-rubber padding. Note the spring edge wire that is required across front of T-type seat

the top edges of the wooden chair frame.

Adding foam-rubber padding: Padding the springs with foam rubber is much simpler than padding them with loose stuffing, as the rubber is of uniform thickness and density. Foam rubber comes in cored and plain slab stock of various densities. Rubber of extra-soft density is recommended as a topping over back springs. Rubber of medium density is best for soft seats, with or without springs. Rubber of soft density is used for both back and seat padding. Plain slab stock (not cored) of

UPHOLSTERY ALLOWANCE	
0 to 6"—Allow ¼" over-all	36 to 48"—Allow 1¼" over-all
6 to 12"—Allow ½" over-all	48 to 60"—Allow 1½" over-all
12 to 24"—Allow 1" over-all	60 to 72"—Allow 2" over-all

These allowances can be varied slightly when extra soft or very firm foam rubber or rubberized fiber is used. When using extra-soft stock add more to these allowances and when using very firm stock less allowance can be made.

Above, edge roll is tacked around the front of each arm to soften hard edge and prevent excessive cover wear. Notice torsion spring and how edge wire is tied

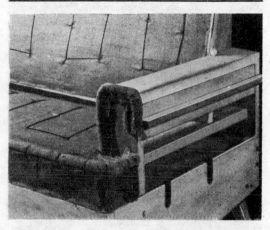

Above, close-up view of arm and corner of seat show how edge roll should look. Roll is tacked to arm and sewed to seat. Long stitches fasten burlap to springs

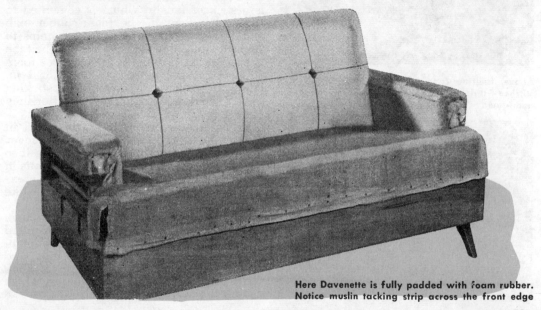

Here Davenette is fully padded with foam rubber. Notice muslin tacking strip across the front edge

Making a Foam-Rubber Cushion

Above, solid slab stock is sandwiched between two cored slabs and then all three are cemented together

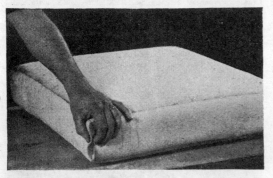

Above, strips of solid slab rubber are cemented to edges and at four corners of built-up center portion

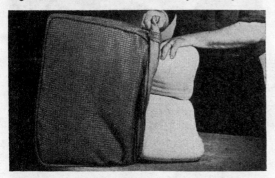

Above, built-up foam-rubber pad is inserted in a stitched-fabric cover and then open side of cover is hand-sewn shut along welt edge of the cushion

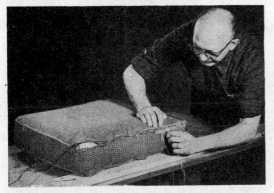

medium density is used for padding the top and inside surfaces of arms, slip seats, benches, shaped seats and thinly padded chair backs.

A paper pattern should be made of all parts that are to be padded with foam rubber. To assure that the fabric cover will fit snugly, the foam rubber should be cut slightly larger than the pattern. Consult the chart on page **793** for proper allowance. The pattern can be traced on the foam rubber with an indelible pencil, ball-point pen or colored pencil. A few pins will hold the pattern in place while tracing. Any thickness of solid-slab foam rubber can be cut completely through with scissors. The same applies to cored stock up to 2 in. thick. In the case of heavier stock, it is best to make the first cut through the smooth top surface deep enough to sever the top of each core. Then cut through each core well. The scissors should be dipped in water frequently to lubricate them and make cutting easier.

Cementing foam rubber: Foam rubber is cemented to the burlap over the springs to hold it in place. Both the burlap and foam rubber is given a coat of special cement made for the purpose and allowed to become tacky before placing the foam-rubber slab in position. In the case of cored stock, the cores should first be dusted with talcum powder to prevent any cement from sticking that might run down inside the cores. Slabs of foam rubber may be cemented together edgewise in the same way when building up several pieces for width. After several hours, the bonded seams will be stronger than the foam rubber itself.

Applying tacking tape: Foam rubber is held to the frame with tacking tape. This is a strip of muslin which is cemented to the outer edges of the foam-rubber slab and tacked to the frame. It also helps to reinforce the edges of the rubber. The tape is applied by coating the edges of the foam rubber and the tape, a distance of 1 in. along the edge with cement, and sticking the two coated surfaces together after they have dried a minute or two.

From here on the job is completed in the normal way, pulling the fabric cover on over the foam rubber and tacking it to the frame. As a rule, a conventional muslin cover is not required over foam rubber, except where the cover is a pile fabric like cut velour.

While the steps described here have been presented briefly due to limited space, a much more detailed explanation of working with sagless-type springs and foam rubber may be found in a book written by the author, John Bergen, which covers the subject completely.   ★ ★ ★

First Aid for Furniture Legs

By Walter E. Burton

Pencil clamped to length of wood scrap is handy gauge for marking chair legs for uniform cutting

UNSIGHTLY SCRATCHES or other damage to the legs of your favorite chair or table needn't be the cause for discarding the piece, or paying a small fortune for refinishing it. To restore the original beauty of the damaged piece simply follow the repair suggestions illustrated in this article. Even broken legs can be made to appear like new by anyone familiar with common tools as indicated in Fig. 5.

Surface scratches can be made less noticeable by applying furniture wax or scratch remover. Another way of concealing scratches is to rub boiled linseed oil on the damaged finish with the fingers. Then,

After sanding damaged finish on furniture leg, varnish of matching color is applied with artist's paintbrush to blend touched-up areas with old finish

rub the area with a turpentine-dampened cloth and polish it with a dry cloth. To darken and refinish worn areas that appear bleached, sand the areas, and apply varnish stain to match the finish, Fig. 2. Dark spots on blond-finished wood may be lightened with dry-cleaning fluid rubbed on with a cloth. If this doesn't do the job, try rubbing the spots with tooth powder mixed with water to make a paste. After removing the abrasive material, the wood is waxed or varnished as necessary.

For accurate trimming of uneven chair legs, clamp a pencil to a length of wood and mark the legs as in Fig. 1. Then, trim each leg with a rasp. Most chairs have front legs that are of a different length than the rear ones and must be trimmed proportionately. An easy remedy for leveling uneven table legs is to place caster cups under each leg with cardboard disks inserted in each cup that requires shims, as shown in Fig. 3.

A good way of protecting legs from scratching is to install metal ferrules on each leg as in Fig. 4. The ferrules are cut from metal tubing of the desired diameter and then are driven onto the legs with a mallet. A furniture glider tapped on the end of each leg protects the floor.

Casters that drop from chair legs are repaired by replacing the worn sleeves, Figs. 7 and 8. To prevent a leg from splitting when driving in a new sleeve, the hole is enlarged and a length of copper tubing inserted to receive the sleeve.

Disks cut from sheet of heavy cardboard are placed in caster cup to provide inconspicuous shim for furniture leg that is slightly shorter than others

To repair broken chair leg saw off damaged part and join extension piece to leg with dowel. Folded sandpaper on dowel aids dressing surfaces of joint

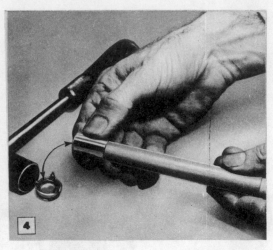

Ferrule for small furniture leg is cut from length of brass tubing and driven on leg. Furniture glider installed on end of leg protects floor from damage

Cracked chair leg is repaired by applying glue to contacting surfaces of break and wrapping strong rubber band around leg to clamp pieces securely

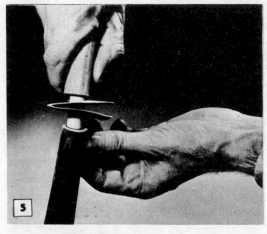

To prevent caster from falling out of socket, worn sleeve is replaced by new one. Length of copper tubing inserted in hole prevents leg from splitting

When installing caster in socket, center punch should be used for driving stem into sleeve. Striking caster wheel with hammer might damage the wheel

1

⅝" DOWEL

METAL
CORNER ←
BRACE

CASTER →

THE SWING IS TO
DOOR FURNITURE

By Tom Riley

THERE WAS A TIME when a door was just a door. Now it can be anything from a bed headboard to a patio screen. These thick, smooth panels, called flush doors, are making craftsmen out of everyone since in many cases they require merely finishing the edges and the job's practically done. The suggestions given here are but a few of the many ways that standard flush doors can be utilized to produce modern pieces of furniture that are both inexpensive and practical.

Types of Doors

Flush doors are available with solid or hollow cores. If they are to be used as is, hollow-core doors, which are lighter and cheaper than the solid-core type, will do. However, where it is necessary to cut the door in several sections, it is best to select a solid-core door. When a hollow core is cut crosswise, other than at the center, it exposes a series of core strips which must be cut back and a strip of solid wood inserted, as in Fig. 12, to fill in the open end. Rather than rip a door lengthwise, it is best to select a door of the approximate width desired. You'll find that most flush doors are available in widths ranging from 18 in. to 36 in. wide in 2-in. multiples. The average interior-type door measures 1⅜ in. thick and 80 in. long. And, of course, you can get them faced in either common or fancy wood grains.

To stretch the budget on a sofa, purchase two cushions with matching bolsters and a flush door of the right width. Attach ready-made legs to the door and center the cushions as shown. Let the ends of the door serve as end tables. You'll wind up with a smart sofa for a song

Right, a 30-in. flush door with the edges taped makes a simple Hollywood headboard for a double bed. The space at the projecting ends can serve to support small shelves or an attractive pedestal storage cabinet as shown below

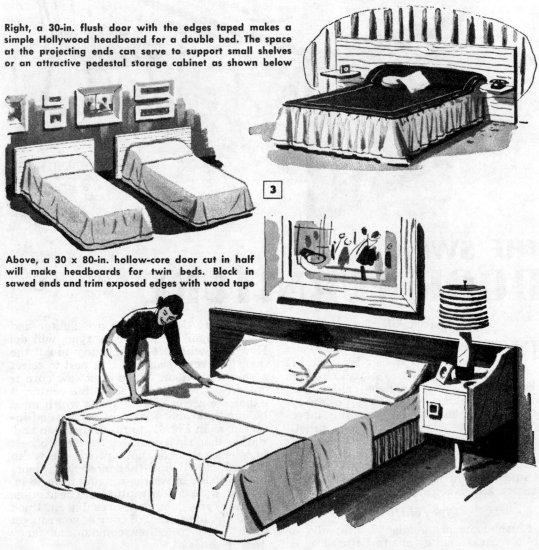

Above, a 30 x 80-in. hollow-core door cut in half will make headboards for twin beds. Block in sawed ends and trim exposed edges with wood tape

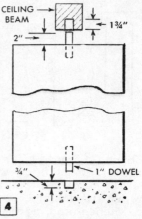

Blind holes in floor and ceiling for dowel pivot pins allow doors to be removed by lifting up to free lower pin at the bottom

Two or more doors pivoted at top and bottom can be used like a vertical Venetian blind to keep out sun

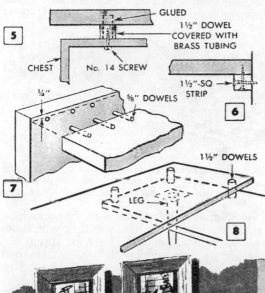

The edges of flush doors vary considerably. Some have softwood showing, others have hardwood. Some are quite rough, others very smooth. Often you can cull a stack and find a door with edges that need only to be varnished or lacquered. The new hardwood tape in ribbon form offers an easy way to conceal the edges and make them match the surface. The tape is applied with contact cement, which bonds instantly and without clamping. Another way of treating the edges is to rip ¾-in. strips of matching stock and use as trim to form a rim around the door as in Fig. 9.

Novel Applications

The pass-through table idea shown in Fig. 1 is a novel and practical answer to the

"Tudor" corner desk is two doors resting on two-drawer file cabinets. New handles and paint camouflage files, leg supports doors at the corner

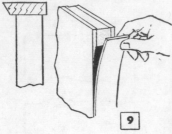

problem of space. Here a table of doors fitted with casters and extended through an opening between the kitchen and a dinette permits one table to serve both rooms by pulling it from one to the other. A simple two-piece screen that raises and lowers like a window can be used to close off the opening.

Another novel use for flush doors is pictured in Fig. 4. A series of doors pivoted vertically on a porch or roofed patio so they may be adjusted make a vertical "Venetian blind" that affords both privacy and ventilation.

The "tudor" king-size desk, pictured and detailed in Figs. 5, 6, 7 and 8, shows how a double desk can be arranged in a corner of a room without undue crowding. Twin two-drawer cabinets support the door tops at the ends and a tapered leg supports them at the corner. Short dowels raise one door above the other to bring it to regulation desk height. The other should be 24 to 26 in. to provide the best working height for a typewriter. Cleats screwed to the wall can be used instead of the leg to support

A 24-in. closet door supported at the ends 29 to 30 in. off the floor and equipped with several padded stools makes a quickie breakfast bar

Infinite variety of coffee tables can be made from flush doors, king-size and otherwise. Add custom or ready-made legs

the doors at the corner. Fig. 7 shows how door stock can be joined together with dowels to form a simple desk that is supported at the opposite end with a cleat attached to the wall. ★ ★ ★

When hollow-core doors are cut, open-core end is filled with hardwood strip glued and clamped

Solid-core door requires no filling of edge after cutting. This is true of hollow door when cut at center

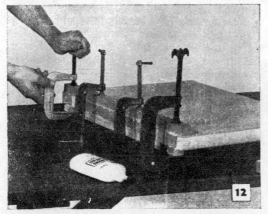

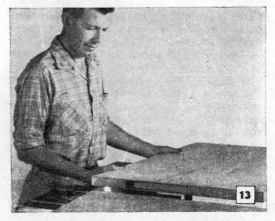

YOUTH BED

Inexpensive and easy to build, this Hollywood-type youth bed is just the thing for baby when he begins to outgrow his crib. Except for a headboard panel of ¼-in. plywood, the bed is made entirely of solid stock. Over-all dimensions of the bed and the length of the guard rails are not given in the detail as these are determined by the size of the mattress, the guard rails being approximately half the length of the bed. Note that the bed rails are fastened permanently to the headboard and the footboard by mitering the ends and gluing and nailing them into mortises in the tapered legs. After the bed is assembled, a rope spring (clothesline will do) is laced through notched strips of 1 x 1-in. stock screwed to the sides of the bed rails as well as to the headboard and the footboard. After all nails are set and puttied over, the bed is enameled, using either a two-tone effect or a color to harmonize with the bedroom.

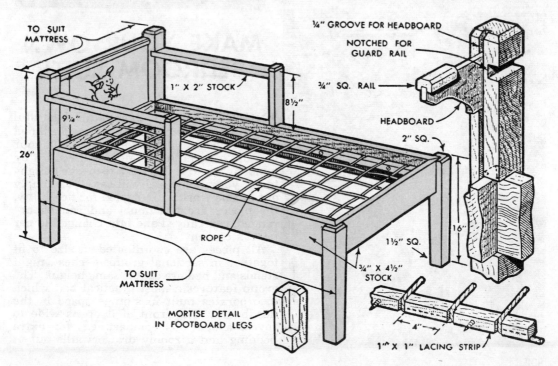

TO SUIT MATTRESS

1" X 2" STOCK

9¼"

26"

8½"

ROPE

TO SUIT MATTRESS

MORTISE DETAIL IN FOOTBOARD LEGS

¼" GROOVE FOR HEADBOARD

NOTCHED FOR GUARD RAIL

¾" SQ. RAIL

HEADBOARD

2" SQ.

1½" SQ.

16"

¾" X 4½" STOCK

4"

1" X 1" LACING STRIP

Here is a bedroom suite whose beauty lies in modern lines matched by simplified construction appealing to any craftsman

MAKE YOUR OWN BEDROOM SUITE

PICTURE in your home this beautiful bedroom ensemble in honey maple, limed oak or rich walnut and then try to talk your way out of building it. Mom will want it by tomorrow, and if there is a teen-age daughter in your home she will say, "It's simply out of this world." Designed for flexibility, the pieces are functional and can be arranged, rearranged and interchanged to her heart's content.

All pieces are coordinated in size to fit together in sectional groups — chest, night stands and bed are all the same height. The group features a most practical bed which incorporates built-in storage space in the headboard. The front of it opens wide to reveal a spacious compartment for extra bedding and a roomy drawer pulls out at

each end of the headboard to provide storage for shoes. The chest-on-chest unit can be stacked to serve as a five-drawer highboy, or a pair of base units can be built and placed end-to-end under a large mirror to obtain the popular Mr. and Mrs. dresser. A novel three-piece vanity consists of two twin end units bridged with a separate top unit which opens to expose a cosmetic compartment and make-up mirror.

A product of a basement shop, the original furniture was built with the power tools shown. Only two tools, a saw and a jointer, actually are required as the construction involves just simple,

Right, edges of the plywood are mitered with the saw table tilted at a 45-deg. angle and planed accurately on the jointer to obtain a perfect fit

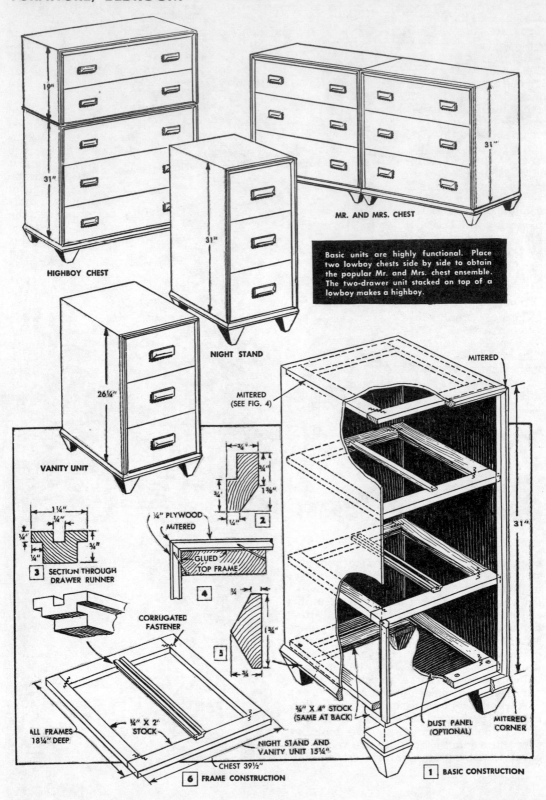

HIGHBOY CHEST

19"

31"

MR. AND MRS. CHEST

31"

31"

NIGHT STAND

Basic units are highly functional. Place two lowboy chests side by side to obtain the popular Mr. and Mrs. chest ensemble. The two-drawer unit stacked on top of a lowboy makes a highboy.

26¼"

VANITY UNIT

MITERED (SEE FIG. 4)

MITERED

¼" PLYWOOD
MITERED

GLUED
TOP FRAME

4

31"

1¼"
¼"
¼"
¼"
¾"

3 SECTION THROUGH DRAWER RUNNER

¾"
¾"
¾"
1⅜"
¼"

2

¼
1¾"
¾"

5

CORRUGATED FASTENER

¼" X 2" STOCK

ALL FRAMES 18¼" DEEP

NIGHT STAND AND VANITY UNIT 15¼"

CHEST 39½"

6 FRAME CONSTRUCTION

¾" X 4" STOCK (SAME AT BACK)

DUST PANEL (OPTIONAL)

MITERED CORNER

1 BASIC CONSTRUCTION

straight cuts in dimensional stock and incorporates the use of plywood to simplify the work.

Basic construction of the night stands, chests and vanity units is exactly the same. It's merely a case of increasing the over-all height and width as given for each respective cabinet. Fig. 1 shows the extreme simplicity of construction. Each unit, with the exception of the two-drawer chest, requires three drawer frames and a top frame, four in all, which are made exactly alike as detailed in Fig. 6. Pine or other softwood will do for the frames, although the front rail of each frame can be of hardwood, if you wish. The top frame is of ½-in. stock while the others are ¾-in., and if the bottom frame is to be fitted with a dust panel, a groove is centered in the edge of the members to take a ¼-in. plywood panel. Otherwise, the frame pieces are merely butted, glued and joined together with corrugated fasteners.

The next step is to glue and screw the bottom frame to two ¾ x 4-in. base pieces. These pieces, which are placed across the front and back, are made the same length as the frame. Note that at the front the frame is placed 1⅛ in. in from the edge, while at the back the frame is glued flush with the edge of the base piece. Now, a 1¾-in. molding, Fig. 5, is mitered and glued to the edges of the base pieces so that it is flush with their top surfaces. The molding along the sides is cut ¼ in. longer than the depth of the base to allow for a ¼-in. plywood back. Glue blocks along the sides, plus screws driven at an angle through the edges of the base pieces from the inside, are used to anchor the molding.

The edging which conceals the laminated edges of the plywood at the front is ripped from ¾-in. stock according to Fig. 2. This is mitered and glued together as a separate assembly. The top piece of the edging is cut ½ in. longer than the width of the frame to allow for the side panels. Glue the pieces together on a flat surface and place a temporary brace across the bottom. Next, the top frame is glued to the edging. The frame is kept flush with the rabbeted edge and is fastened with long screws driven through the edge of the frame from the inside. Now, you are ready to attach the edging-and-frame assembly to the base, but first the back panel should be made ready as this is installed at the same time. The plywood back panel is made the same width as the frames and is cut ¼ in. less than the length of the edging. Nail the panel to the back edges of the top and bottom frames and then coat the ends of the edging strips with glue and clamp to the base with bar clamps. After the glue has dried, drill a pilot hole up into the end of each strip and drive a 1½-in. No. 9 flat-headed screw. The re-

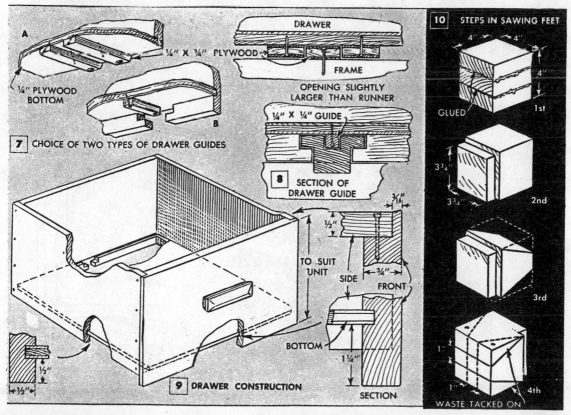

¼" PLYWOOD BOTTOM

¼" X ¾" PLYWOOD

7 CHOICE OF TWO TYPES OF DRAWER GUIDES

DRAWER

FRAME

OPENING SLIGHTLY LARGER THAN RUNNER

¼" X ¼" GUIDE

8 SECTION OF DRAWER GUIDE

TO SUIT UNIT

SIDE

FRONT

¾"

½"

BOTTOM

SECTION

1¼"

½"

½"

9 DRAWER CONSTRUCTION

10 STEPS IN SAWING FEET

4"

4"

4"

GLUED

1st

3¾"

3¾"

2nd

3rd

1"

1"

4th

WASTE TACKED ON

maining two frames are spaced equally between the top and bottom ones. These are
fastened to the inside of the edging strips
with small screws. Pockets are formed for
the screws by drilling and counterboring
holes through the frame at an angle.

Now, the framework is ready to be covered with ¼-in. plywood. Fit and install
the top piece first. In addition to obtaining
a well-fitting mitered joint, it also is important to get a tight fit where the plywood
abuts the rabbet of the front edging. Use
bar clamps to draw this joint tightly and
C-clamps to clamp the plywood firmly to
the frame. Brads can be used here, as indicated in Fig. 4, although a good resin-type
glue will hold sufficiently. Like the top
piece, the sides fit flush with the outer face
of the edging and the molding at the bottom. Clamps should be used to draw the
mitered joint together. Brads can be used
to reinforce the joint and to nail the plywood to the edge of the frames.

Steps in sawing the feet are given in Fig.
10. In most cases, the blocks for these will
have to be glued up using three or more
pieces. The front feet require a ¼ x 1-in.
rabbet on two adjacent edges, while the
rear ones need a rabbet only along one side.
The feet taper to 1 in. square at the bottom.
After sawing two sides, the waste is replaced and held with either brads or cellulose tape so that a flat surface will be had
to complete the sawing.

Typical drawer construction is detailed
in Fig. 9. The method of fitting the bottom
differs somewhat with the type of drawer
runner used. Note that the lower edge of
each drawer extends to cover the drawer
frame. Drawer handles are detailed in Fig.
11. A choice of two types of drawer guides
is given. One features a T-shaped runner,
Fig. 3, over which the back of the drawer
hooks to prevent the drawer from dropping
down when all the way open. The runner
is grooved for a ¼-in.-square guide, which
is nailed to the underside of the drawer
bottom as shown in Fig. 7, detail B. Note
that the T-slot in the drawer, Fig. 8, is
made slightly larger than the cross section
of the runner. A more simple guide is pictured in Fig. 7, detail A. This is formed
merely by nailing two strips of plywood to
the drawer bottom to form a track for a
plywood runner nailed to the frame. Fig. 1
shows both types of runners in place.

Construction of the highboy (two-drawer) chest unit, Fig. 12, differs from the other
units in one respect; the bottom drawer
frame is screwed to a mitered base frame
which is beveled to match the edging.

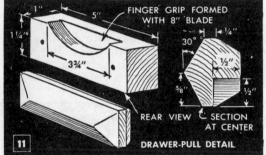

FINGER GRIP FORMED WITH 8" BLADE

REAR VIEW — SECTION AT CENTER

11 | **DRAWER-PULL DETAIL**

12 CONSTRUCTION OF HIGHBOY-CHEST UNIT

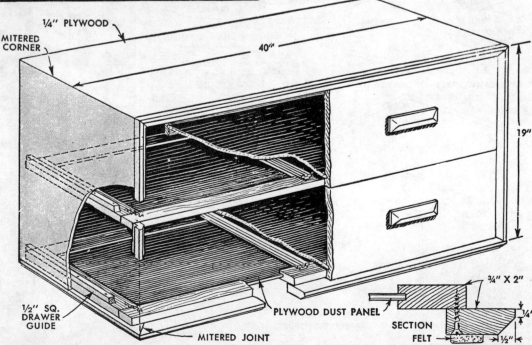

¼" PLYWOOD

MITERED CORNER

40"

19"

½" SQ. DRAWER GUIDE

MITERED JOINT

PLYWOOD DUST PANEL

¾" X 2"

SECTION

FELT

¼"

½"

WITH THE night stands, chests and vanity units completed as described earlier, you can tackle the bed. In addition to its pleasing simplicity, it features a built-in storage compartment in the headboard for bedding and two roomy drawers for shoes. If twin beds are preferred to a full bed, the basic construction is the same. It would be merely a matter of making the bed narrower, installing only one drawer and eliminating the center partition in the storage compartment. Most of the bed is made of ¼-in. plywood. On the original bed, the lid of the storage compartment was a ¾-in.-plywood panel, but to save cost, this too can be of ¼-in. material by gluing it to a half-lapped frame as shown in Figs. 13 and 14.

The bed footboard consists of a ¼-in. plywood panel which is framed on three sides with a ¾ x 2-in. molding. The latter is chamfered and grooved

Right, a jointer plus a bench saw are the only power tools needed. Here, base molding is being run on jointer after being ripped on saw

A roomy drawer opens at each end of the bed headboard to provide storage space for seasonal footwear. Being concealed when the headboard is flanked with night stands, the drawers also provide a safe place for personal papers and jewelry

Another feature of this headboard is a convenient built-in storage compartment for bedding. If you wish, the compartment can be lined with aromatic, red cedar to protect woolen blankets from moths. Open, the lid rests on the bed

⅜ in. deep on its inside face to fit over the edge of the plywood. The panel is faced across the bottom with a ¾ x 1¾-in. molding which matches the molding on the night stands, chests and other pieces. This molding is glued to the plywood so that it overlaps the bottom edge ½ in., sectional detail Fig. 16, and then five rabbeted cleats, 6 in. long, are spaced along the inside and screwed to the molding. Note that the molding is mitered at the ends and returned at the corners for a distance of 4 in., Fig. 16. Note also that the lower ends of the grooved molding, which covers the edges of the plywood, are chamfered on two adjacent outside edges to fit flush with the bottom molding and the upper ends are mitered. The feet are made the same as detailed in Part I, except that here the shoulder must measure 1¼ in. long instead of 1 in. The feet are rabbeted on two adjacent sides and glued into the corners formed by the molding to bring them flush.

The headboard is built around a framework of scrap wood, Fig. 15. Start each end assembly with a ¾ x 4 x 11½-in. base piece and screw a ¾ x 2½ x 15-in. upright piece to it, ¼-in. in from the front edge. Note that the upper end of this piece is notched for a cross member. Another piece, ¾ x 1½ x 30¾ in., is attached vertically to the base piece, ¼ in. in from the rear edge. This piece is joined to the front piece with a cross member located 10 in. up from the top surface of the base, forming the drawer opening. Both end assemblies of the framework are joined together as shown, fitting a ¾ x 1-

13

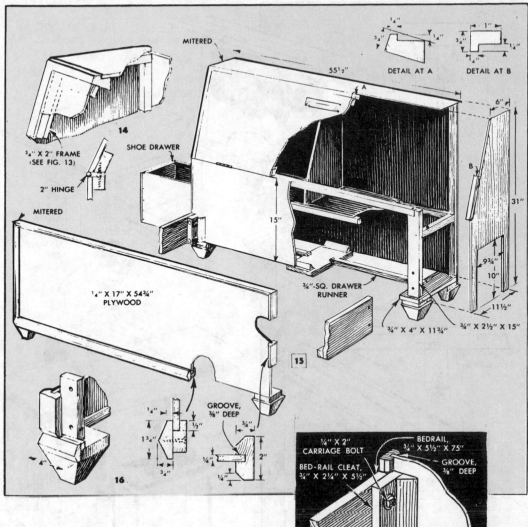

DETAIL AT A

DETAIL AT B

MITERED

55½"

SHOE DRAWER

14

¾" X 2" FRAME
(SEE FIG. 13)

2" HINGE

MITERED

¼" X 17" X 54¾"
PLYWOOD

15"

A

B

6"

31"

¾"-SQ. DRAWER
RUNNER

9¾"

10"

11½"

¾" X 4" X 11¾"

¾" X 2½" X 15"

15

GROOVE,
⅜" DEEP

¼"

½"

¾"

1¾"

¼"

¾"

2"

¼"

4"

16

¼" X 2"
CARRIAGE BOLT

BEDRAIL,
¾" X 5½" X 75"

BED-RAIL CLEAT,
¾" X 2¼" X 5½"

GROOVE,
⅜" DEEP

¾"-SQ. BED-
SLAT CLEAT

¾" X 1½" X 6"
CLEAT (5 REQD.)

INSIDE CORNER AT FOOTBOARD 17

BED RAIL

½"

1¼"

4½"

GLUE
BLOCK

¼" X 4"
CARRIAGE BOLTS

18

INSIDE CORNER AT HEADBOARD

in. strip into the notched front uprights, another
one below it at a point flush with the member at
the top of the drawer opening and a third piece at
the same height at the rear. These two latter
strips form a ledge for the bottom of the compartment which is of plywood.

Now, cover the back of the framework. This
requires a fir-plywood panel, ¼ x 30¾ x 55 in.,
which is nailed and glued so that the edges are
flush with the framework. Next, fit the front
panel, cutting it 15 x 55 in. The plywood pieces
covering the ends of the headboard taper to 6 in.
at the top from a point 15 in. up from the bottom.
These are made right and left hand, selecting the
best face of the plywood for the outside, and mitered at the top. After the ends are glued in
place, the drawer-runner assembly is installed.
The runners are simply ¾-in.-square strips,
notched at each end to hook over the base pieces
and a center piece fastened to the plywood with
glue blocks.

Fit the panel forming the bottom of the bedding

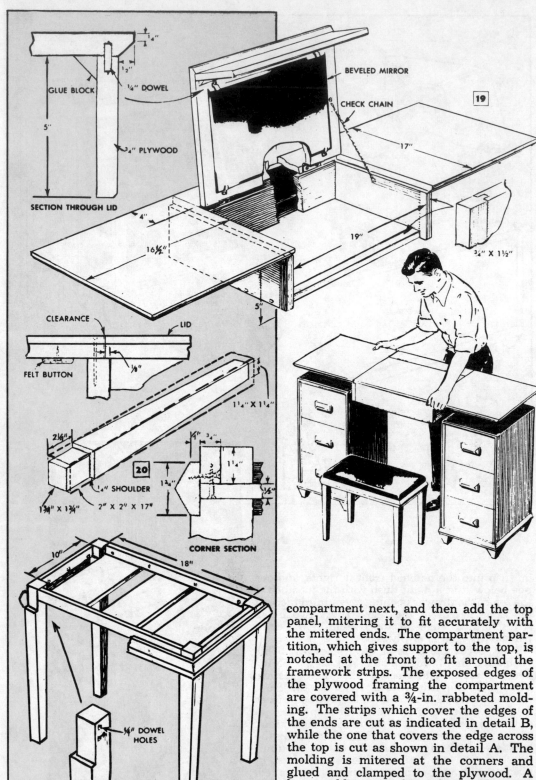

GLUE BLOCK

5"

¼" DOWEL

¾" PLYWOOD

½"

¼"

SECTION THROUGH LID

BEVELED MIRROR

CHECK CHAIN

19

17"

4"

16½"

19"

5"

¾" X 1½"

CLEARANCE

LID

FELT BUTTON

⅛"

1¼" X 1¼"

2½"

¼" SHOULDER

20

1¼"

1⅜"

½"

1¾" X 1¾"

2" X 2" X 17"

CORNER SECTION

10"

18"

¼" DOWEL HOLES

21   ASSEMBLY OF VANITY STOOL

compartment next, and then add the top panel, mitering it to fit accurately with the mitered ends. The compartment partition, which gives support to the top, is notched at the front to fit around the framework strips. The exposed edges of the plywood framing the compartment are covered with a ¾-in. rabbeted molding. The strips which cover the edges of the ends are cut as indicated in detail B, while the one that covers the edge across the top is cut as shown in detail A. The molding is mitered at the corners and glued and clamped to the plywood. A base molding, matching that used on the footboard, is fitted around the outside corners, gluing and clamping it to the edges of the base pieces of the framework.

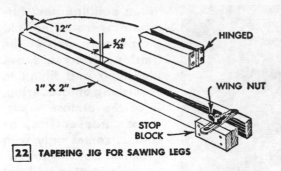

22 TAPERING JIG FOR SAWING LEGS

The compartment lid is hinged as shown in the sectional detail, Fig. 14, and drawers and handles are made as described earlier.

Bedrails are attached to the head and footboard as detailed in Figs. 17 and 18.

The separate top, Fig. 19, which merely rests on two base units to form a vanity, is made of ¾-in. plywood and solid stock. The top requires a panel 17 x 52½ in. Three edges are chamfered on the underside and then the panel is cut into four pieces. The cosmetic compartment is made like a box. The sides and back are screwed to a plywood bottom and a fourth piece is installed to support the narrow fill-in piece to which the lid is hinged. Note how end grain of the side and bottom members of the compartment is concealed with edging strips, tongued and grooved. The outboard panels are nailed and glued to the top edges of the compartment ⅛ in. in from the inner faces to provide a shoulder for the lid. This is shown in the detail above Fig. 20. The front apron is attached to the lid with dowels and a triangular glue block is placed on the inside. The lid can be leaned against the wall when opened or a check chain can be used to hold it at the right angle.

Assembly of the vanity stool is detailed in Fig. 21. First make the legs by cutting a ¼ x 2¼-in. rabbet on two adjacent faces of each one. The legs taper from 2 in. square at the shoulder to 1¼ in. square at the bottom, Fig. 20. Before tapering the legs, bore holes in adjacent inner faces as shown for doweling ¾ x 1¼-in. rails flush with the face of the rabbets. A jig like the one shown in Fig. 22 may be used to rip the taper on each face, after which the cut is dressed smooth on a jointer. The corner-section detail at the right of Fig. 20 shows how a mitered face molding is attached to the rails with screws from the inside. A choice of two methods for upholstering the stool is given in Fig. 23. If tow or hair is used, the seat is supported by three ½-in. pieces spaced as in Fig. 21. If foam rubber is used, the bottom of the stool is covered with a piece of ¼-in. plywood held by cleats screwed to the rails.

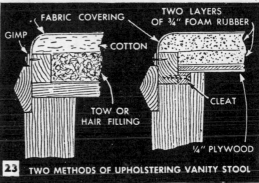

23 TWO METHODS OF UPHOLSTERING VANITY STOOL

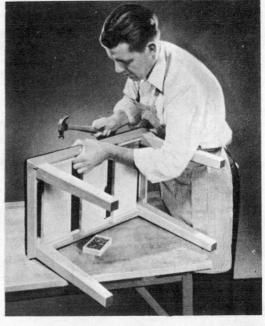

When building new furniture or restoring old pieces, each step of the finishing process, from bleaching and filling to varnishing or lacquering, is of the utmost importance. Perfection, of course, comes only with practice, but the following information will get you off to a good start

AFTER COMPLETING the bedroom furniture described in the previous two pages it's time for the all-important job of finishing it, because right here you can either flatter or ruin the appearance of the furniture.

No doubt, you have built the furniture of a wood suitable to take the particular finish desired, whether it be harvest wheat or heather mahogany, ambered walnut or limed oak. Naturally, the kind of wood used is a determining factor as, for instance, one cannot expect to obtain a limed-oak finish on birch. The finishing schedules presented below give a condensed procedure to follow in producing a number of the popular, modern finishes, but, if the final results are to compare with finishes seen on store furniture, the finishing operation demands the same careful attention that you put into the cabinet work. Brushes and materials, as well as the room where the work is done, must be clean. Finishing should not be attempted in a cold room and the materials should not be cold. These precautions are important.

Sanding: Perhaps the most important

FINISHING SCHEDULES

FINISH	APPLICATION
Ambered walnut	Bleach. Stain with amber stain. Apply sealer coat of thin lacquer. Fill with natural filler. Finish with clear lacquer.
Old-World walnut	Bleach. Seal. Fill with natural filler lightly tinted with burnt umber. Seal. Shade with brown wiping stain. Finish with clear lacquer.
Honeytone maple or birch	Tone with blond toner, using 1 part white lacquer to 4 parts clear, flat lacquer. Finish with water-white lacquer.
Pickled pine	Bleach. Stain with gray stain for pine. Finish with water-white lacquer or clear varnish.
Limed oak	Bleach. Seal. Fill pores with white paste wood filler. Finish with water-white lacquer.
Harvest-wheat mahogany	Bleaching will give required wheat color. Fill with natural filler lightly tinted with raw-sienna color in oil. Finish with lacquer.
Tweed mahogany	Bleach. Seal. Fill pores with red paste wood filler. Finish with water-white lacquer or clear varnish.
Heather mahogany	Bleach. Seal. Fill pores with white paste wood filler. Finish with water-white lacquer or clear varnish.

step in producing a beautiful, flawless finish is the sanding of the wood. Application of any number of finishing coats will not compensate for a careless job of sanding, but only tends to emphasize defects. Power sanders of the oscillating or belt types take the work out of sanding; however, if these are not available, you can do a satisfactory job of sanding by hand, wrapping the paper around a flat, felt-covered block and working with progressively finer grades of garnet paper from medium down to 5-0 grade.

Bleaching: Practically all of the so-called blond finishes are produced by first bleaching the wood to remove its natural color. This is done to obtain such popular mahogany finishes as harvest wheat, heather and tweed, and limed oak, and ambered walnut. Mahogany, when bleached and filled with white filler, is known as heather mahogany. When filled with red filler (natural filler with red oil

Above, a piano or draftsman's stool provides an excellent turntable when spraying lacquer on the smaller units. Below, a power sander makes play of sanding the broad, flat surfaces, but care must be used to avoid cutting through the top veneer

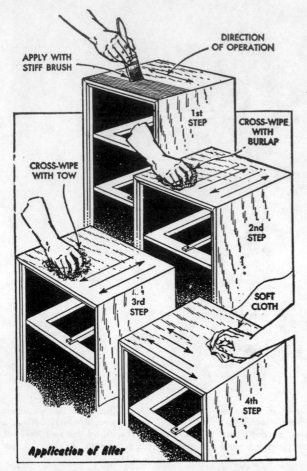

APPLY WITH STIFF BRUSH

DIRECTION OF OPERATION

1st STEP

CROSS-WIPE WITH BURLAP

CROSS-WIPE WITH TOW

2nd STEP

3rd STEP

SOFT CLOTH

4th STEP

Application of filler

the filler is applied liberally in the direction of the grain, preferably with a short-bristled brush. Do not cover more than 6 or 8 sq. ft. of surface at one time or you will get ahead of the wiping and cleaning-up operations that follow. As soon as the filler flattens, it is wiped off. This is done by wiping across the grain with a coarse cloth such as burlap, or excelsior, using a circular motion.

This is followed by cross-wiping with a fine material called tow, commonly used for upholstering purposes. This second wiping across the grain cuts the surplus filler flush with the surface of the wood.

A third cross-wiping with a soft cloth wrapped around a felt block is excellent practice. A second application of filler, somewhat thinner than the first, is sometimes required when filling mahogany or other wood having a very open grain. This is determined by noting whether the pores are completely filled.

Finally, the work is wiped lightly with the grain, using a soft cloth. This serves to remove any traces of filler missed in the towing-off operation. The filler should be allowed to dry 24 to 48 hrs. and then sanded very lightly with 5-0 waterproof garnet paper.

Toning: Toning is not successful on dark wood such as walnut, but very much so on naturally light-colored woods such as birch and maple. Toning, to some extent, takes the place of the bleaching process and is accomplished by spraying the bare wood with a semitransparent undercoat to further lighten the wood.

Toning is recommended for all extremely light finishes, as it does not obscure the grain, being almost as clear as water. Toner is made by adding white lacquer, 1 part, to clear flat lacquer, 4 or 5 parts. In the case of oak and mahogany, the toner should be made with tan-colored lacquer instead of white.

Sealing: Whether or not the bleached wood has been toned or stained, the surface must be sealed with a wash coat of shellac or lacquer before the work is filled. The wash sealer is made by cutting 1 part of clear shellac or lacquer with 6 parts of thinner. This coat is sanded lightly when dry, and then, after the grain is filled, a second sealer coat is applied. This is likewise sanded when dry, and followed with a coat of varnish or lacquer sealer. The latter coat, which fills any tiny open pores remaining, also is sanded. From here on, varnish or lacquer coats are applied, using a rubbed-effect or full-gloss type.

color added), it is called tweed, because of its pleasing pink tone. Bleached and filled with natural filler, it's called harvest-wheat mahogany. After bleaching, almost any color desired can be had by giving the wood a coat of diluted stain.

Bleaching is done with a commercial chemical solution consisting of two separate solutions which are mixed together and used immediately. As all bleaching solutions are highly corrosive, they should be handled carefully. You should wear rubber gloves. Use a sponge to swab the solution on the wood and see that you wet the entire surface evenly.

One application of bleach is usually sufficient although, in any case, it is good practice to make a test on a wood sample. Let the bleach stand and dry for at least 48 hrs.

Filling: Open-grained woods, such as oak, walnut, mahogany, etc., must be filled, that is, the pores of the surface and end grain must be packed level with a prepared paste filler. Fillers are available for either lacquer or varnish finishes and require cutting with benzine or turpentine to the consistency of thick cream before applying, so that they will sink into the pores.

Original vanity was framed in inexpensive woods and finished as you see it here with plastic veneer. Matching chairs and mirrors are made in duplicate

DOUBLE VANITY DESK

By John Bergen

FINE WOODS and conservative modern lines fit this double vanity desk into almost any arrangement of room furnishings. The simplest type of frame construction and drawer joinery make it easy to build, even with a small shop and limited equipment. At the start you have a choice of materials. You can use fine cabinet woods, such as cherry, birch, or primavera in solid stock or plywood faced with any of these three. The selection of wood depends on the color desired. Or you can use a less expensive wood, such as white pine or poplar, and face all exposed parts with a plastic veneer. The original vanity, pictured above, was made by the latter method.

Details of the cabinet-frame construction, also the top and drawers, are given in Figs. 1 and 2. Note first that the upper three drawers are of the flush type and are exposed, while those below in the cabinet, or pedestal, are housed behind doors. Build the lower part of the cabinet first. This unit consists of the base, bottom, side panels, back panel and drawer framing. These parts assemble into the unit pictured in the photo in Fig. 1. All parts except the drawer framing are cut from plywood. Note that the base is inset on three sides the thickness of the plywood panels and doors. The top section, Fig. 2, consists of the top proper, a full-length back rail, end rails, and the drawer framing. Note especially in the perspective view in Fig. 2 how these parts are joined and that the top is flush at the back, ends and front. The top on the original piece was made from a 5/8-in.-plywood panel and covered with linoleum. The edges are finished with a strip of solid stock rabbeted and mitered as in a lower right-hand detail, Fig. 2. An alternate method of finishing the top, using a plastic laminate with edgings of the same material, also is shown. The sides of the drawers in the lower cabinet are grooved before assembly. Each drawer slides on a strip attached to the inner face of the end panel and on the center guide which is attached to the center stile. The slide grooves engage the guides as in the lower left-hand detail, Fig. 1. A clearance of 1/8 in. is provided between the drawers as in the lower right-hand detail, Fig. 1.

The drawers in the top section slide on flat rails and center guides which are a part of the top-section framing. The cutaway view, Fig. 2, shows how this framing is assembled into a unit and then attached to the lower cabinet, or pedestal. Assemble the top section completely before making and fitting the drawers.

The legs which support the overhang at

Upper edge of all panels must be sanded or planed flush with the frame so top section will fit

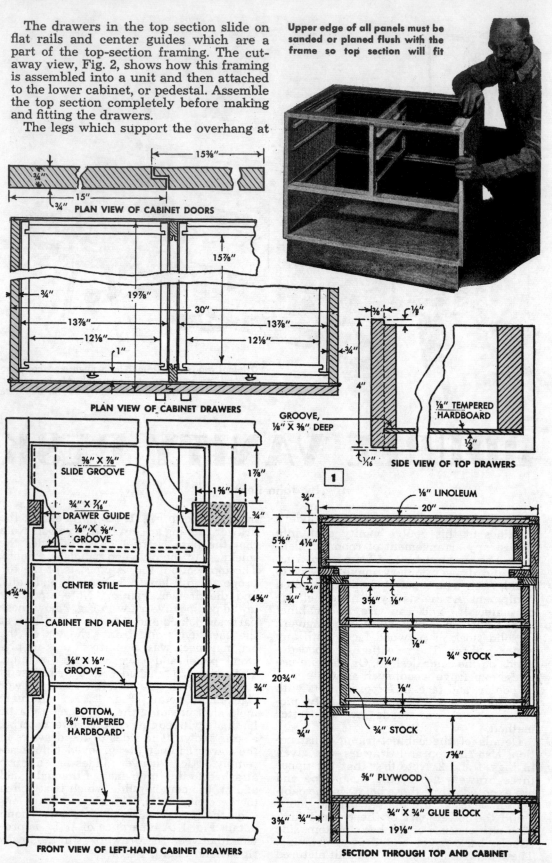

PLAN VIEW OF CABINET DOORS

PLAN VIEW OF CABINET DRAWERS

SIDE VIEW OF TOP DRAWERS

GROOVE, ⅛" X ⅜" DEEP

⅛" TEMPERED HARDBOARD

1

⅜" X ⅞" SLIDE GROOVE

¾" X ⅞/₁₆" DRAWER GUIDE

⅛" X ⅜" GROOVE

CENTER STILE

CABINET END PANEL

⅛" X ⅛" GROOVE

BOTTOM, ⅛" TEMPERED HARDBOARD

FRONT VIEW OF LEFT-HAND CABINET DRAWERS

⅛" LINOLEUM

¾" STOCK

¾" STOCK

⅝" PLYWOOD

¾" X ¾" GLUE BLOCK

SECTION THROUGH TOP AND CABINET

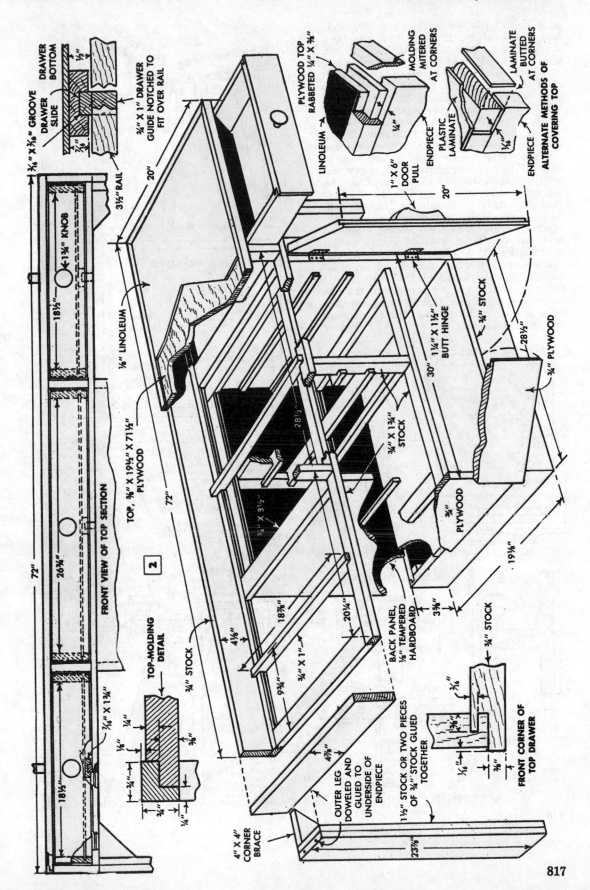

¾₆" X ⅜₆" GROOVE

DRAWER BOTTOM

½"

DRAWER SLIDE

¾" X 1" DRAWER GUIDE NOTCHED TO FIT OVER RAIL

LINOLEUM

PLYWOOD TOP RABBETED ¼" X ⅜"

MOLDING MITERED AT CORNERS

LAMINATE BUTTED AT CORNERS

¼"

ENDPIECE

PLASTIC LAMINATE

ENDPIECE

1/16"

ALTERNATE METHODS OF COVERING TOP

1" X 6" DOOR PULL

20"

¾" STOCK

¾₆" RAIL

3½" RAIL

20"

1¾" KNOB

18½"

26¾"

72"

FRONT VIEW OF TOP SECTION

18½"

⅛" LINOLEUM

TOP, ⅞" X 19¾" X 71½" PLYWOOD

2

TOP-MOLDING DETAIL

¾" STOCK

⅛"   ¼"

¾"   ⅜"

¼"

¾"

72"

18⅞"

9¾"

4⅞"

¾" X 1"

20¼"

OUTER LEG DOWELED AND GLUED TO UNDERSIDE OF ENDPIECE

1½" STOCK OR TWO PIECES OF ¾" STOCK GLUED TOGETHER

4" X 4" CORNER BRACE

4⅞"

23⅞"

BACK PANEL, ⅛" TEMPERED HARDBOARD

¾" X 1¾" STOCK

28½"

30"

1½" X 1½" BUTT HINGE

¾" STOCK

¾" PLYWOOD

¾" PLYWOOD

19⅞"

3⅝"

28½"

¾" STOCK

⅜₆"

⅜"

1/16"

⅜"

½"

FRONT CORNER OF TOP DRAWER

each end of the top section are 5 in. wide and 1½ in. thick. If solid stock has been used in the construction of the cabinet, then the legs should be cut from one piece of 1½-in. material. However, if the cabinet is to be finished with plastic veneer, then each leg can be built up to the required thickness by gluing two pieces of ¾-in. stock face to face as indicated.

Figs. 3 and 4 detail the twin mirrors and matching chairs. These units, of course, are optional. The mirrors may be attached to the wall as pictured on page 815, or pivoted on brackets attached to the back of the top cabinet section as in Fig. 3. In either case, the mirrors should be backed with ⅝-in. plywood. The chairs are of the swiveling type, the seat frame being mounted on a ball-bearing swivel, or fixture, as detailed in Fig. 4. The exposed legs and back braces are cut from wood that can be natural-finished to match the cabinet. All other parts of wood are covered by the upholstering materials. Upholstering consists of a simple padding and outer covering welted and tacked. ★ ★ ★

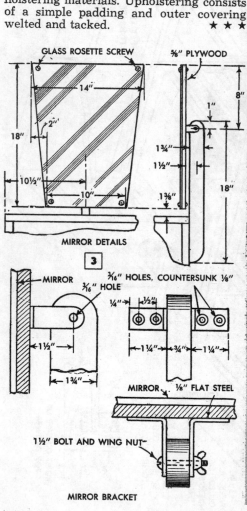

MIRROR DETAILS

3

MIRROR BRACKET

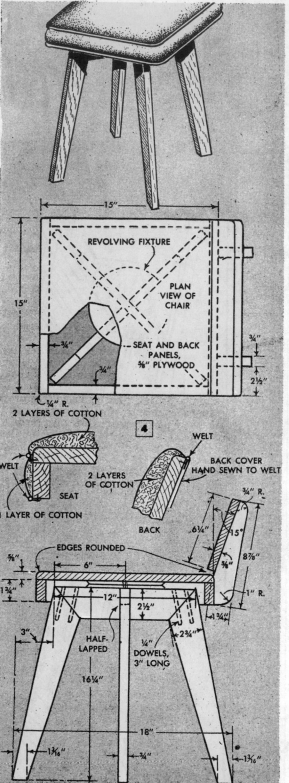

PLAN VIEW OF CHAIR

4

CHILD'S CHIFFOROBE

DESIGNED to complete the furnishings of a child's room, this attractive chifforobe offers generous wardrobe space, a chest of drawers with a full-width storage drawer and a special compartment for toys or linens. It looks its best when made from a close-grained wood such as poplar or birch, and finished in ivory enamel with the interior drawer fronts finished in the natural color of the wood. As the first step in the construction, build up the top to the required width by edge-gluing four to six strips of selected stock. Allow ½ in. all around for trimming to finish size. Although the detail on page 820 shows the edge of the top molded, this can be omitted if no shaper is available. While the glued-up top is drying, cut selected stock for the drawer fronts, corner posts and the scrolled front and back aprons. Bandsaw the edges of the drawer fronts and the aprons, laying out the curves full size from the patterns given below. Round the bandsawed edges and sand smooth. Groove and rabbet the front and back posts. Frame the ends by fitting top and bottom rails and then glue and clamp the parts together. Note that the front posts are cut off square at the lower ends, flush with the scrolled edge of the apron, and are fitted with turned feet. Drill a hole in the lower end of each front post to take a ½ x 1¼-in. tenon. After turning out the feet, glue the parts together.

Note the assembly of parts in sections A-A and B-B, then build up the top and bottom frames, using grooved stretchers

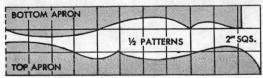

BOTTOM APRON
½ PATTERNS   2" SQS.
TOP APRON

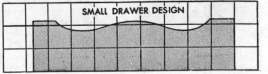

SMALL DRAWER DESIGN

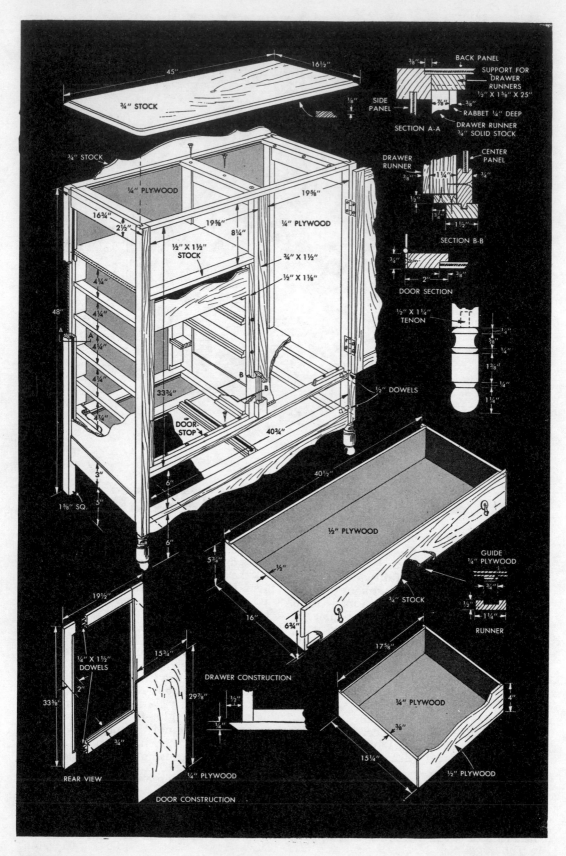

45"

16½"

¾" STOCK

⅛"

¾" STOCK

¼" PLYWOOD

16¾"

2½"

19⅝"

19⅜"

8¼"

¼" PLYWOOD

½" X 1½" STOCK

¾" X 1½"

½" X 1⅛"

4¼"

4¼"

48"

4¼"

4¼"

4¼"

33¾"

DOOR STOP

40¾"

½" DOWELS

3"

6"

1⅜" SQ.

5"

6"

BACK PANEL

⅜"

SUPPORT FOR DRAWER RUNNERS ½" X 1⅜" X 25"

SIDE PANEL

⅞"

⅜"

RABBET ¼" DEEP

DRAWER RUNNER ¾" SOLID STOCK

SECTION A-A

DRAWER RUNNER

CENTER PANEL

⅜"

1¼"

¾"

½"

¾"

1½"

SECTION B-B

¾"

⅜"

2"

DOOR SECTION

½" X 1¼" TENON

¼"

⅝"

¼"

1⅜"

¼"

1¼"

40½"

½" PLYWOOD

5¾"

½"

GUIDE ¼" PLYWOOD

¾"

½"

¾" STOCK

1¼"

16"

6¾"

RUNNER

19½"

17⅞"

¼" X 1½" DOWELS

15¾"

DRAWER CONSTRUCTION

½"

¼"

29⅞"

¼" PLYWOOD

4"

33⅝"

2"

¾"

REAR VIEW

¼" PLYWOOD

DOOR CONSTRUCTION

15¼"

3⅜"

½" PLYWOOD

above are formed by a paneled partition supported on the intermediate frame. Make up this paneled partition first and join to the top and intermediate frames with screws and glue. Now, groove the back drawer-runner supports and screw them in place. The front-runner supports are ripped to the same width but are not grooved, the front ends of the runners being attached with screws as in the detail and section B-B. Rabbet the runners and glue and screw them in place. Attach the top, then fit plywood bottoms in the storage and wardrobe compartments. Now all that remains is the making and fitting of the drawers and doors. Construction of the drawers is clearly shown in the details, but note that the large drawer is fitted with a ½-in.-plywood bottom for added rigidity and also is fitted with a center guide. Doors can be paneled in the manner shown or the panels can be housed in grooves cut in the stiles and rails. The doors are hinged to close flush, but the lower drawer front is rabbeted all around and the outer edges are beveled to give a raised-panel effect. After the cabinet has been completely assembled, sand all exposed surfaces and apply a coat of sanding sealer. When this is dry, sand lightly and finish with two coats of ivory enamel. Apply a sanding sealer to the inside drawer fronts, sand lightly when dry, and finish in the natural color with two coats of varnish or one coat of water-white lacquer. The exposed center upright and the front drawer-runner supports also can be finished in the natural color if desired. Attach two pulls to the lower drawer.

and the tenoned rails. Note that the bottom frame is paneled to provide dustproof construction, and that the back stretchers are rabbeted to take the back panel. Build up the intermediate frame, then drill blind holes for ½ or ¼-in. dowels which join the frames to the posts. After making a trial assembly of the parts to check the fit, apply glue to the doweled joints and clamp the parts together. Check the assembly for square corners before the glue dries, and cut and fit the back panel while the assembly is in the clamps. Attach the panel with screws, but do not use glue in the joints. Now, note that the back ends of the inside drawer runners are housed in grooves cut in uprights fitted into the corners of the drawer compartment, and that this compartment and the special storage space

Simple Bed Tray You Can Make in One Evening

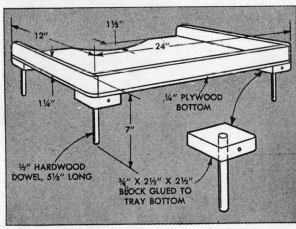

12"
1½"
24"
1¼"
¼" PLYWOOD BOTTOM
7"
½" HARDWOOD DOWEL, 5½" LONG
¾" X 2½" X 2½" BLOCK GLUED TO TRAY BOTTOM

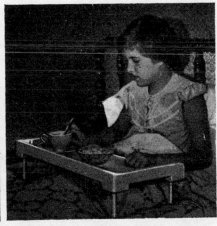

This simple and attractive lap tray will help mother in a dozen ways around the house to save time and eliminate extra cleaning, especially in the sickroom. Complete meals can be placed on the tray and carried to a bedridden child or adult, then placed on the bed over the patient's lap. Between meals, the cleared tray can be used as a play surface for a youngster or as a card or writing table for an adult.

The suggested dimensions for the tray can be varied to suit the individual needs, but care should be taken to see that it is not so large as to be awkward to handle the tray nor so small that it is impractical. The cutout at the back of the table top, which allows the tray to fit closer to the person using it, was cut with 1½-in. radius on the original. This size is all right for a child, but might have to be increased for an adult. For purposes of storage, the dowel legs of the tray could be removable.

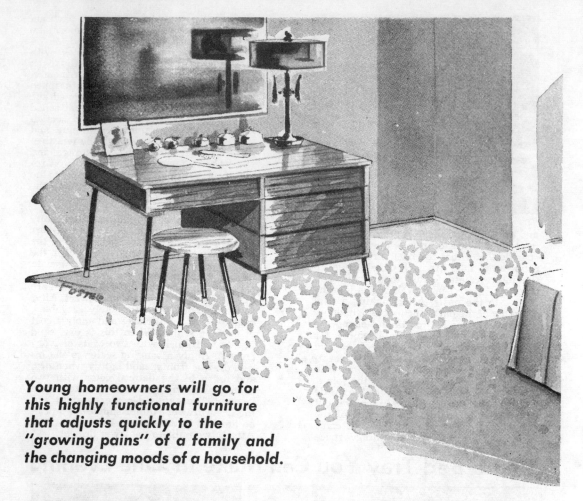

Young homeowners will go for this highly functional furniture that adjusts quickly to the "growing pains" of a family and the changing moods of a household.

Stacked-Drawer

By Tom Riley

HERE IS build-it-yourself furniture that is ideal for the young couple who have little cash, but own a circular saw and have the desire for fine furnishings. The furniture is easy to make and yet has all the eye appeal and quality look of expensive purchased furniture. You assemble the pieces by stacking two or more individual drawer units, attaching ready-made legs and adding a simple top. This assembly method makes the furniture completely functional. When you tire of one grouping, you can unstack the drawer units and rearrange them to make completely new-appearing pieces. And when more storage space is needed, you simply add another

BEDROOM FURNITURE

drawer to the stack, or make a double chest from a single one by adding a stack alongside. To provide both shallow and deep drawers, the units are built in two heights, 5 in. and 8 in. These two dimensions also allow you to assemble vanity bases and other pieces that will work out to the proper height when using ready-made legs of standard lengths. Fig. 9 shows how legs of various lengths are used on different pieces of furniture and, also, how the drawer units can be assembled to produce a variety of furniture.

Drawer Units

Building the drawers and their outer frames can be a production job. In other words, you can cut all similar pieces at the same time with the same setting of your circular saw, simplifying the job and assuring greater accuracy. Only the drawer front and the two sides of the drawer frame need to be hardwood. And these can be either solid stock, or hardwood-faced ¾-in. plywood. When plywood is used, cover the end grain with plywood-veneer tape. Figs. 2, 3 and 4 give construction details of both the 5-in. and the 8-in. drawers. Note in the right-hand detail in Fig. 2 that the top of the drawer is offset ¾ in. To maintain this offset on both the 5 and 8-in. drawers, different angles must be cut on the drawer sides. On the 5-in. drawers, the sides are cut at an 8-deg. angle; on the 8-in. drawers the sides are cut at 5 deg.

In Fig. 3 a ³⁄₁₆ x ³⁄₁₆-in. rabbet is indicated along the bottom edges, as well as the front and back of the frame sides. This

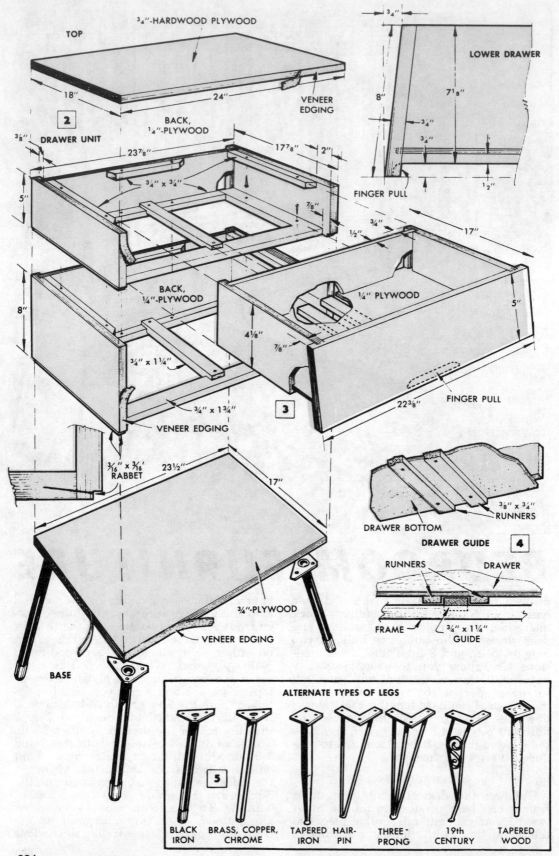

TOP

¾"-HARDWOOD PLYWOOD

VENEER EDGING

18"

24"

2

DRAWER UNIT

⅜"

BACK, ¼"-PLYWOOD

23⅞"

17⅞"

2"

¾" x ¾"

5"

⅞"

LOWER DRAWER

¾"

8"

7⅛"

¾"

¾"

FINGER PULL

½"

¾"

½"

17"

BACK, ¼"-PLYWOOD

8"

¼" PLYWOOD

5"

4⅛"

⅞"

¾" x 1¼"

3

VENEER EDGING

¾" x 1¾"

22⅜"

FINGER PULL

3/16" x 3/16" RABBET

23½"

17"

DRAWER BOTTOM

⅜" x ¾" RUNNERS

DRAWER GUIDE

4

RUNNERS

DRAWER

¾"-PLYWOOD

FRAME

¾" x 1¼" GUIDE

VENEER EDGING

BASE

ALTERNATE TYPES OF LEGS

5

BLACK IRON

BRASS, COPPER, CHROME

TAPERED IRON

HAIR-PIN

THREE-PRONG

19th CENTURY

TAPERED WOOD

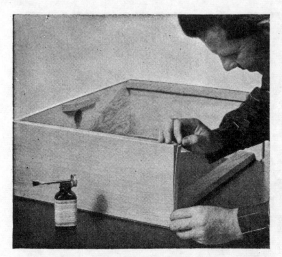

Above, veneer tape is applied to the edges of all plywood. Above right, rabbet is cut along bottom edges, front and back of drawer-frame assemblies

rabbet becomes a decorative groove when the drawers are stacked, and hides any small variation in the width or lengths of the drawers. Handles can be installed on the drawers or they can have hidden finger pulls cut on the inner edge of the bottom of the drawer fronts, as indicated in Figs. 2 and 3. There need be no exposed nails or screws showing on the drawers or frames. Glue and clamp all components of drawers and frames. Use nails on the drawer back only. To attach the inner pieces of the drawer frames, glue and nail or screw from the inside. Where it might seem imperative to nail the front framing into the side pieces, small finishing nails can be hidden by being driven through the rabbet, as indicated in the left-hand detail, Fig. 3. Notch the center drawer guide into the framing so it projects only ½ in. above the frame. Then turn the assembled drawer-and-frame unit upside down and position the two runners on the drawer bottom.

Tops and Bases

The simple tops for the stacked-drawer furniture are sheets of ¾-in. plywood, and will be 24, 48 or 72 in. long to cover a single, double or triple side-by-side assembly. Use hardwood-faced plywood and tape the exposed edges. With all tops 18 in. wide, the dimensions will provide a slight overhang all around to cover any variation in the sizes of individual units. Fig. 1 illustrates the effect of this overhang.

Bases for single or multiple units are cut from sheets of ¾-in. fir plywood, and should be slightly smaller in dimensions than the bottom of the piece of furniture. This keeps it clear of the drawers and the

One above the other, or side-by-side, drawer units are held together by screws driven through frames

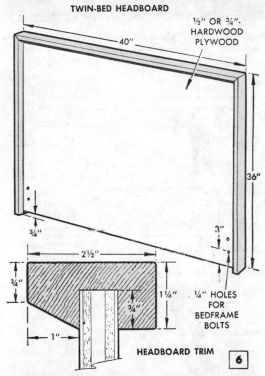

TWIN-BED HEADBOARD

40″

½″ OR ¾″-HARDWOOD PLYWOOD

36″

¾″

3″

2½″

¾″

1¼″

¾″

1″

¼″ HOLES FOR BEDFRAME BOLTS

HEADBOARD TRIM

6

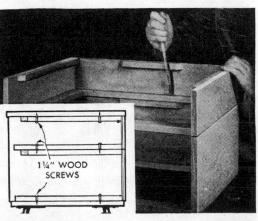

1¼″ WOOD SCREWS

Upper right-hand photo, "chopping block" vanity stool is made by gluing together strips of hardwood of contrasting grain and color. Left-hand photo shows how bevel is turned on bottom of seat for leg angle

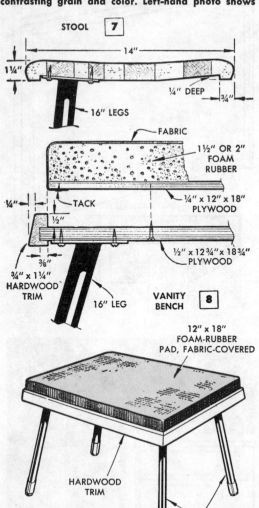

STOOL **7**

14″

1¼″

¼″ DEEP

¾″

16″ LEGS

FABRIC

1½″ OR 2″ FOAM RUBBER

¼″

TACK

¼″ x 12″ x 18″ PLYWOOD

½″

½″ x 12¾″ x 18¾″ PLYWOOD

⅜″

¾″ x 1¼″ HARDWOOD TRIM

16″ LEG

VANITY BENCH **8**

12″ x 18″ FOAM-RUBBER PAD, FABRIC-COVERED

HARDWOOD TRIM

16″ LEGS

rabbet on the lower edges of the drawer frame. The edges of the base can be taped, or strips of ¾ x 1-in. hardwood can be used. The latter extend ¼ in. below the base to cover the edges of the leg plates.

Matching headboards, Fig. 6, are easy to make. Simply cut a ¾-in. groove in lengths of trim stock to fit on three sides of a sheet of ¾-in. hardwood-faced plywood. Miter the two corners of the trim. For a single bed the headboard is 40 in. wide, for a double bed it is 65 in. wide.

Vanity Stools and Benches

The latest idea in vanity seats is a lightweight three-legged stool. The top can be turned from a single piece of hardwood and ready-made legs attached. Less expensive is the "chopping block" stool, Fig. 7. Scrap lengths of hardwood are glued and clamped together to form the seat which is turned on a lathe. The bottom side of the seat is beveled as indicated, both to hide the leg plates and to give the legs a greater angle. The legs of a three-legged stool must be angled as much as possible to provide stability when sitting near the edge. Detailed in Fig. 8 is a vanity bench, which is preferred for a large vanity. The seat consists of a piece of ½-in. plywood to which four legs are screwed. A piece of foam rubber 12 x 18 in. then is cemented to a piece of ¼-in. plywood and it is covered with fabric that is folded under and tacked to the plywood. This assembly is dropped onto the bench and attached with screws.

Although all furniture described in this article is for a bedroom, stacked-drawer construction also could be used for dining-room and living-room furniture. ★ ★ ★

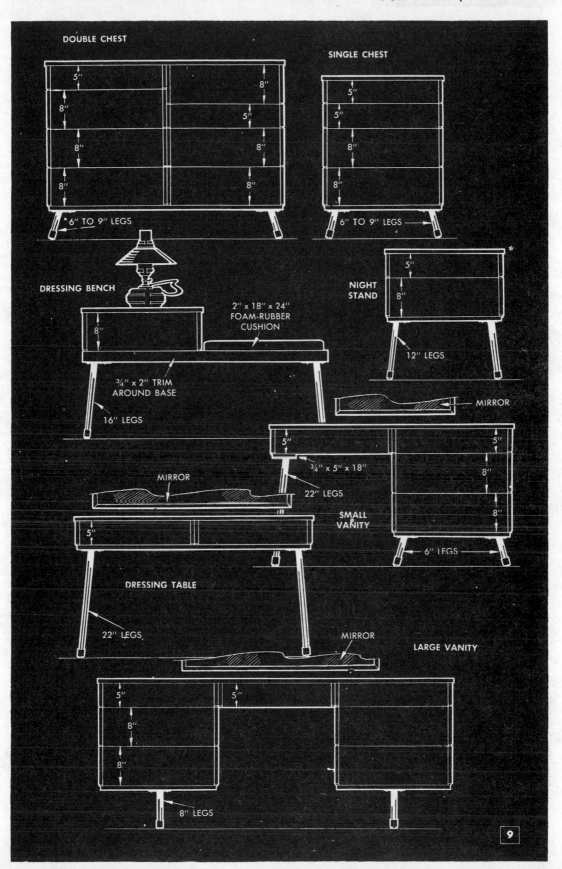

DOUBLE CHEST

5"
8"
8"
8"
8"
5"
8"
8"

6" TO 9" LEGS

SINGLE CHEST

5"
5"
8"
8"

6" TO 9" LEGS

DRESSING BENCH

8"

2" x 18" x 24"
FOAM-RUBBER
CUSHION

¾" x 2" TRIM
AROUND BASE

16" LEGS

NIGHT STAND

5"
8"

12" LEGS

MIRROR

MIRROR

5"
¾" x 5" x 18"
22" LEGS

SMALL VANITY

5"
8"
8"

6" LEGS

DRESSING TABLE

22" LEGS

MIRROR

LARGE VANITY

5"
5"
8"
8"

8" LEGS

9

Desk-Chair

WITH ONE SIMPLE MOTION, this novel youth-size chair can be converted into a neat little desk that is just right for play or school homework. When used as a chair, the back locks firmly in place. By sitting astraddle the chair backwards and pushing the back up and outward, the chair is changed into a desk. A small metal clip locks the desk top securely in place. Releasing this clip permits the desk top to be returned to its original position as a chair back. A small drawer that opens at one side is handy for pencils, crayons and paper.

Any Wood Will Do

The drawings show how the parts are made and fitted together. Dowels, screws and glue are used in assembling the parts. Hardwood is best for this project but any clear, straight-grained wood can be used. All screwheads are deeply sunk and the holes plugged wherever they show.

A spring clip on the underside holds the desk top in place. It is placed so that it locks over the upper dowel rung at the top of the legs. The recess at this point is to allow space for the clip to operate freely. The clip is released by pressing upward on it if you want to change from desk to chair.

Drawer Under the Seat

Standard drawer construction is used in making the drawer. It is mounted on guide strips fastened to the inside face of the seat rails and the drawer sides are grooved to fit the guides. Glue and nails are used in assembling the drawer, and a small knob is attached to the front.

Each back leg is cut from a piece 4 x 25 in. Follow the side-view drawing in laying them out. Where possible it is best to bandsaw or jigsaw them as a pair to assure identical shape and also sand and bore the holes for the dowel rungs while the two

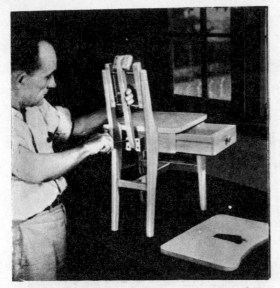

back-leg pieces are still tacked together.

Dowel pins and screws are used in assembling the chair frame. Glue is applied to all joints at the time of final assembly. Three rails are all that are used in the chair, one side being left open for the drawer. Screws for attaching the seat board are placed in counterbored holes in the rails. Corners of both the seat board and back board are rounded as shown. The arm should be made of ¾-in. plywood for strength and to prevent splitting at the ends.

The desk action of the chair back is easy to see in the side view. The holes for the countersunk screws are plugged with plugs made of ⅜-in. dowel. These are glued and sanded down smooth. Holes and moving parts may have to be filed or sanded a little to make the parts work freely. The completed project can be finished with wood stain and varnished or painted. ★ ★ ★

Pivot blocks for the lower end of the desk-top brace are attached securely with screws to side of chair seat rail. Brace must work freely to fold properly

The combination desk-top-and-chair-back is attached with screws to slotted cleats that ride on dowel rungs. Notice how notched ends of cleats hook over lower rung to lock desk top in chair-back position

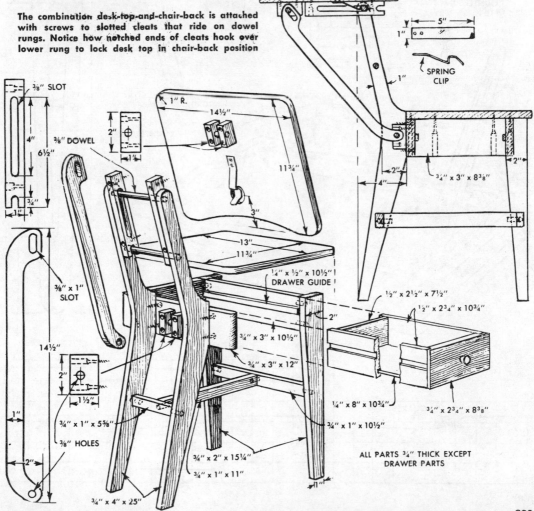

ALL PARTS ¾" THICK EXCEPT DRAWER PARTS

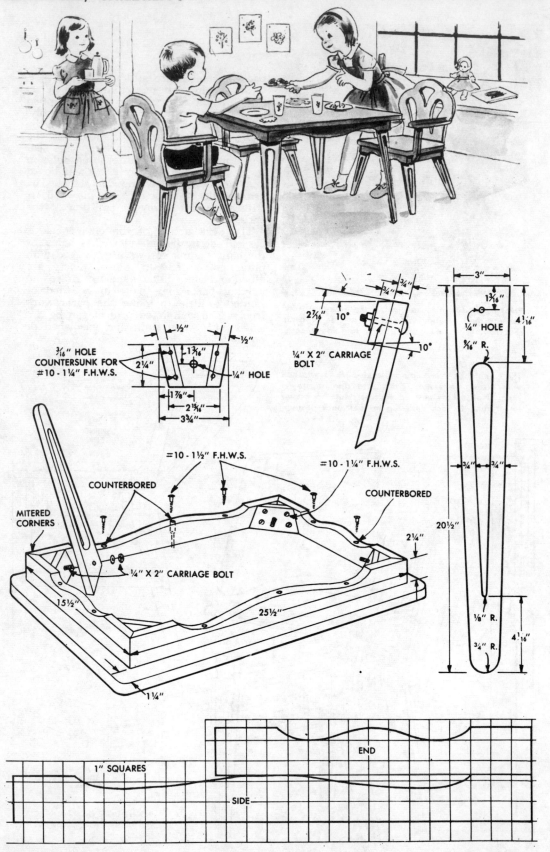

3/16" HOLE COUNTERSUNK FOR #10 - 1¼" F.H.W.S.

2¼"

½"   1³/₁₆"   ½"

¼" HOLE

1⅞"
2¹⁵/₁₆"
3¾"

2⁷/₁₆"   10°   ¾"   ¾"

10°

¼" X 2" CARRIAGE BOLT

3"

1³/₁₆"

¼" HOLE

⁵/₁₆" R.

4¹/₁₆"

=10 - 1½" F.H.W.S.

=10 - 1¼" F.H.W.S.

COUNTERBORED

COUNTERBORED

MITERED CORNERS

¼" X 2" CARRIAGE BOLT

2¼"

15½"

25½"

1¼"

¾"   ¾"

20½"

⅛" R.

¾" R.

4¹/₁₆"

END

1" SQUARES

SIDE

Children's Dinette Set

Always appealing to little girls and boys, a pint-sized dinette set means tea parties in style as well as a fine place for drawing and playing games. The table top may be a 20 x 28-in. piece of ¾-in. plywood or the sink-cutout blank from a plastic-laminated counter top. Rails and legs are made of ¾-in. lumber and assembled as in the details. If ordinary ¾-in. plywood is used for the table top, it may be covered easily with plastic laminate. Make as many chairs as you like, using the patterns shown below. The back and seat are of ¾-in. plywood, with legs, rails and arms of ¾-in. lumber. When assembling both chairs and table, apply glue to all joints before fastening them together with wood screws. Then simply bolt the legs to the corner blocks. The exposed surfaces of the wood can be enameled or stained and varnished

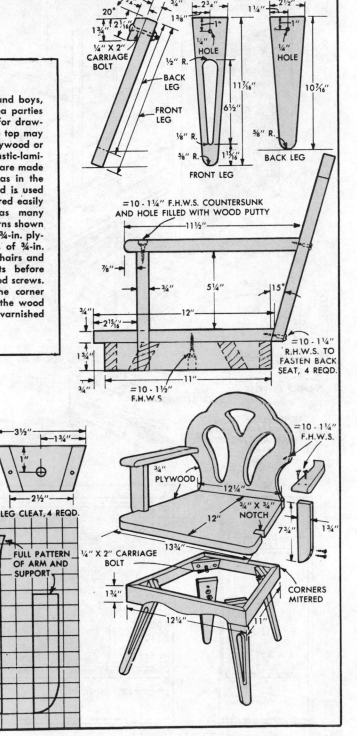

20° ¾" ¾" 2¾" 1¼" 2½"

1¾" 2¹/₁₆" 1⅜" 1" 1"

¼" X 2" CARRIAGE BOLT

¼" HOLE   ¼" HOLE

BACK LEG

FRONT LEG

½" R.   11⁷/₁₆"   10⁷/₁₆"

6½"

⅛" R.   ⅝" R.

⅝" R.   1¹⁵/₁₆"

FRONT LEG   BACK LEG

=10 - 1¼" F.H.W.S. COUNTERSUNK AND HOLE FILLED WITH WOOD PUTTY

11½"

⅞"   ¾"   5¼"   15°

¾"   12"   =10 - 1¼" R.H.W.S. TO FASTEN BACK SEAT, 4 REQD.

2¹⁵/₁₆"

1¾"

¾"   11"

=10 - 1½" F.H.W.S

1" SQUARES

ONE-HALF PATTERN OF BACK

ONE-HALF PATTERN OF FRONT

3½"   1¾"

1"

2½"

LEG CLEAT, 4 REQD.

FULL PATTERN OF ARM AND SUPPORT

¼" X 2" CARRIAGE BOLT

¾" PLYWOOD

=10 - 1¼" F.H.W.S.

12¼"

¾" X ¾" NOTCH

12"

7¾"   1¾"

13¾"

1¾"

12¼"   11"

CORNERS MITERED

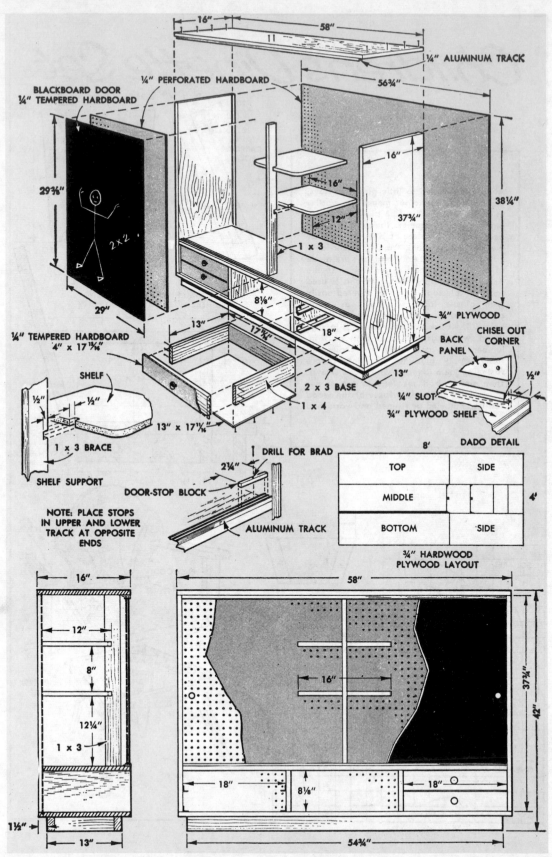

16"

58"

¼" ALUMINUM TRACK

¼" PERFORATED HARDBOARD

56¾"

BLACKBOARD DOOR
¼" TEMPERED HARDBOARD

29⅜"

2 x 2

16"

16"

12"

1 x 3

37¾"

38¼"

29"

¼" TEMPERED HARDBOARD
4" x 17¹³⁄₁₆"

8⅛"

¾" PLYWOOD

BACK
PANEL

CHISEL OUT
CORNER

½"

SHELF

½"   ½"

13"

17¾"

18"

13"

¼" SLOT

¾" PLYWOOD SHELF

1 x 3 BRACE

13" x 17¹³⁄₁₆"

2 x 3 BASE

DADO DETAIL

SHELF SUPPORT

1 x 4

NOTE: PLACE STOPS
IN UPPER AND LOWER
TRACK AT OPPOSITE
ENDS

DRILL FOR BRAD

2¼"

DOOR-STOP BLOCK

ALUMINUM TRACK

8'

TOP	SIDE
MIDDLE	
BOTTOM	SIDE

4'

¾" HARDWOOD
PLYWOOD LAYOUT

16"

58"

12"

8"

12¼"

1 x 3

16"

37¾"

42"

18"

8⅛"

18"

1½"

13"

54¾"

By Dave Swartwout

REAR VIEW

CHILD'S WARDROBE
Is Island of Storage and Play

GROWING FAMILIES having a shortage of wardrobe space can relieve some of the "bulging-at-the-seams" by building one or more wardrobes like this one. Designed as a child's wardrobe, it may be backed against a wall, or located as above so as to project into the room like a divider.

The upper three-fourths of the wardrobe-divider has two shelves and two clothes hanging compartments, while the lower part has four good-sized drawers and a shoe compartment. Two sliding doors enclose the front, one of which is perforated hardboard. The other is tempered hardboard that may be painted flat black or green to serve as a blackboard. The back of the unit is covered with a panel of ¼-in. perforated hardboard, providing a pin-up surface for play, inset above, or for hanging things on utility hooks such as are available for this purpose. Sides, top, middle and bottom shelves, plus drawer partitions and center

shelves of the wardrobe are cut from a 4 x 8-ft. panel of ¾-in. solid-core hardwood plywood as indicated in the layout detail. Drawer sides, backs and fronts are made of 1 x 4-in. lumber. Bottoms and drawer-front facings are ¼-in. tempered hardboard. The drawers slide on ⅛ x ¾ x ¾-in. aluminum angles screwed to the wardrobe as shown in the drawings.

After cutting out all wardrobe parts, begin assembly with the base, which consists of 2 x 3s nailed on edge to the ¾-in. plywood bottom. Then install the drawer slides and dado the wardrobe sides, top and bottom to take the hardboard panel at the back, which is glued and nailed in place. Drawer partitions, drawers and shelf assembly are installed next, followed by the sliding doors, which are fitted in a double aluminum track as shown in the track detail. Installation of pull-out-type clothes hanger or brackets and a coat or two of paint, completes the wardrobe. ★ ★ ★

YOUNGSTER'S

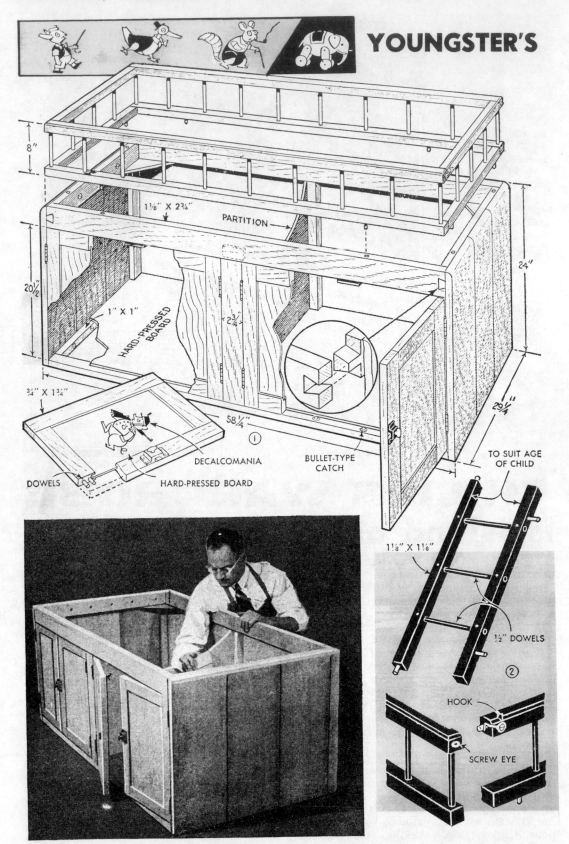

8"

$1\frac{1}{8}'' \times 2\frac{3}{4}''$

PARTITION

$20\frac{1}{2}''$

1" X 1"

HARD-PRESSED BOARD

$2\frac{3}{4}''$

24"

$\frac{3}{4}'' \times 1\frac{3}{4}''$

58½"

①

DECALCOMANIA

HARD-PRESSED BOARD

DOWELS

BULLET-TYPE CATCH

29¾"

TO SUIT AGE OF CHILD

$1\frac{1}{8}'' \times 1\frac{1}{8}''$

½" DOWELS

②

HOOK

SCREW EYE

CHEST-BED

IN SMALL homes and apartments where it is impossible to furnish a room for the child, this combination bed and chest will be of real value, as it serves as a comfortable bed at night and provides storage space for extra blankets, toys and other household items. In daytime, removing the railings and covering the chest with an appropriate drapery converts it into a useful couch. If made higher than shown in Fig. 1, the railings can be removed and set up separately to form a child's play pen. When used in this way, however, a floor for the pen must be assembled and drilled for pegs to keep the railings in place.

Before assembling the frame, have the springs at hand so they can be measured, as the exact size of the chest depends upon these dimensions. Corners of the frame are dovetailed and glued, with triangular blocks glued and screwed to the underside of the top members at each corner to support the springs. Note that the ends of the chest are built up of tongue-and-groove stock, glued and screwed to the frame. To improve the appearance, the outer edges of these boards are rounded at the top.

Note that the chest is fitted with a partition which is curved at the top to prevent

the springs hitting it when they are pressed down by weight of a person sitting or lying on them. Railings are assembled quickly by clamping the upper and lower members together and drilling them both at the same time. The holes should be just large enough to provide a sliding fit for the dowels, these being held in place by glue and small finishing nails driven in from the sides. To prevent shifting of the railings, tapered pegs are fitted in the lower members to correspond with holes drilled at the top of the chest frame as shown in Fig. 2. End railings are also fitted with pegs which slip into holes drilled in the side railings. Hooks and screw eyes lock the railings together.

Doors are hung with hinges having removable pins for convenience in detaching them, in case the edges need planing to make them fit accurately. A stop block at the top and bullet-type catches in the bottom rail hold the doors shut. Or, you can fit them with elbow catches and cabinet latches, if desired. Although the bed is somewhat higher than cribs in general, this gives the advantages of adding to the storage space, Fig. 3, and facilitating making the bed with a minimum of stooping for the housewife. Low railings are also a convenience where the bed is made without removing them. Decalcomania transfers are applied in the center of each door.

YOUNGSTER'S 4-IN-1

H ERE'S A DESK youngsters won't out-grow. Preschoolers will have fun with it as a play center, and then continue to find it useful as a homework desk all through the grades and even high school. It makes good use of the small space it takes, for it not only provides storage galore for books and toys, but incorporates a king-size blackboard on the underside of the desk. Best of all, the desk part swings up out of the way so the unit takes even less space when closed.

Most of It Is Hardboard

The complete unit consists of two separate cabinets (a base and a top) both of which are assembled from simple wooden frames faced with tempered and perforated hardboard. The latter is used for facing of ends on the inside and, in turn, to hold the hangers that are used to support the shelves. With the exception of the frame for the writing desk, which is made of 1 x 4s, all frames are cut from 1 x 2s. Glue and corrugated fasteners are used to join the frame members.

Both upper and lower units are simple boxlike assemblies. The end frames can be faced with perforated hardboard at this time, but the outside, as well as the entire assembly, is not covered with hardboard until after the frames are glued and nailed together. You'll notice in the case of the base unit, Fig. 4, that the top frame differs from the bottom one in that wider end members are used, and that the bottom frame fits inside the ends, whereas the top frame laps the latter. In the case of the top unit, Fig. 3, identical pairs of frames are made and, in turn, lapped and nailed to the ends of the end frames. Only the bottom and ends are covered both sides.

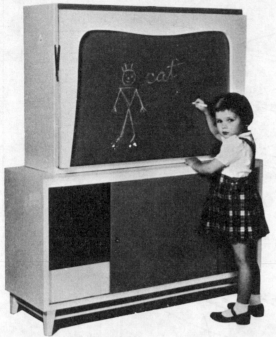

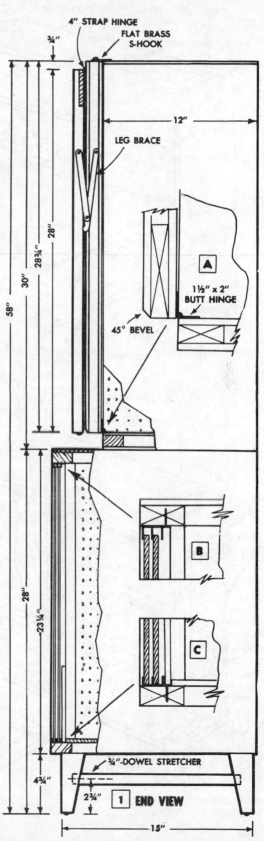

It's a blackboard, desk, bookcase and toy box all in one. Makes compact play center for preschool tot and future home-study desk for teen

PLAY DESK

"Veneering" the Outside

In gluing the hardboard panels to the framework, a better job will result if you have a few C-clamps on hand to clamp the work. Start by adding the back panels first. These are kept flush all around and will add rigidity to the units. Both units are covered in much the same manner, the main difference being that both sides of the bottom frame of the upper unit are covered with hardboard, whereas just one side of the bottom frame of the base unit is covered. The panels covering the tops of both units lap the panels covering the ends, and all panels lap the edges of the back panels. When facing the sides of the writing-desk frame, apply both panels at one time to avoid unequal stress and possible warping. The three shelf frames, one for the toy chest and two for the bookcase, can be faced on just one side, although if

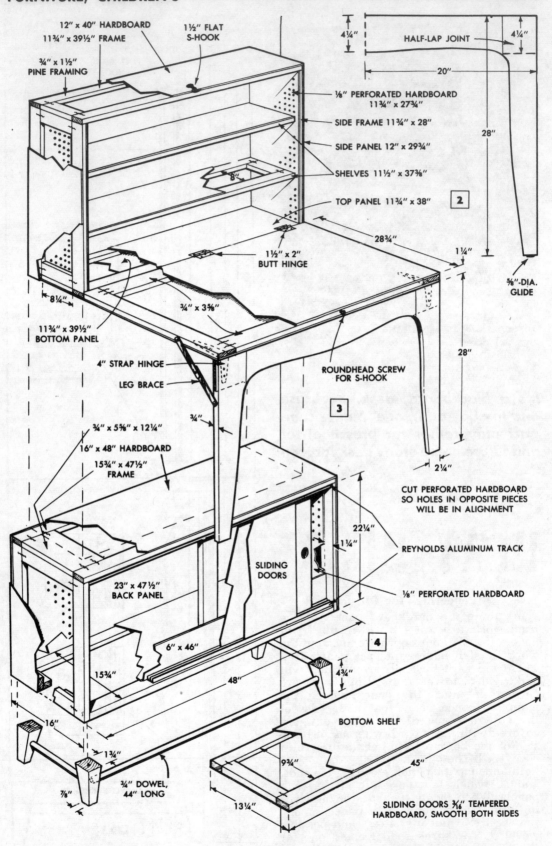

12" x 40" HARDBOARD
11¾" x 39½" FRAME

1½" FLAT S-HOOK

¾" x 1½" PINE FRAMING

HALF-LAP JOINT

4¼"

4¼"

20"

28"

⅛" PERFORATED HARDBOARD 11¾" x 27¾"

SIDE FRAME 11¾" x 28"

SIDE PANEL 12" x 29¾"

SHELVES 11½" x 37⅜"

TOP PANEL 11¾" x 38"

2

8"

28¾"

1¼"

1½" x 2" BUTT HINGE

⅝"-DIA. GLIDE

8¼"

¾" x 3⅝"

11¾" x 39½" BOTTOM PANEL

4" STRAP HINGE

LEG BRACE

ROUNDHEAD SCREW FOR S-HOOK

28"

3

¾"

2¼"

¾" x 5⅝" x 12¼"

16" x 48" HARDBOARD

15¾" x 47½" FRAME

CUT PERFORATED HARDBOARD SO HOLES IN OPPOSITE PIECES WILL BE IN ALIGNMENT

22¼"

1¼"

REYNOLDS ALUMINUM TRACK

SLIDING DOORS

⅛" PERFORATED HARDBOARD

23" x 47½" BACK PANEL

6" x 46"

4

15¾"

48"

4¾"

16"

BOTTOM SHELF

1¾"

¾" DOWEL, 44" LONG

9¾"

45"

⅞"

13¼"

SLIDING DOORS 3/16" TEMPERED HARDBOARD, SMOOTH BOTH SIDES

faced on both sides they will hold a lot of books without bowing.

Adding Legs and Doors

Holes for the dowel stretchers that join the legs are bored before the legs are tapered. If you should find it difficult to buy a dowel 44 in. long, thin-wall conduit can be used for the stretchers. In tapering the legs from 1¾ in. square at the top to ⅞ in. square at the bottom, note that only the inside adjacent faces are tapered, the outside faces are left straight. The legs are fastened to the corners of the base with 2-in. No. 10 flathead screws driven down through the hardboard and frame members. Use glue in addition to screws and set the legs ⅞ in. in from the corners. Both the legs for the base and those that support the writing desk should be made of hardwood to withstand years of use.

The bypassing hardboard doors for the toy chest slide in aluminum tracks which can be purchased at hardware stores. Details B and C, Fig. 1, show where the tracks are located, top and bottom. They are set about ⅛ in. in from the front edges and fastened with small nails. A 1 x 2 center post gives support to the base unit, and this is installed next, gluing and nailing it top and bottom, and positioning it at the very edge of the bottom hardboard panel.

Finally, a 6 x 46-in. hardboard strip is fitted across the front, gluing it to the post and to the edges of the hardboard bottom and perforated side panels. The sliding doors measure 20⅞ in. high and 23¾ in. wide and are fitted with regular brass finger grips pressed into ¾-in. holes bored 1¼ in. from the outer edges. It should be mentioned that when installing the tracks, the track with the wide flange is placed at the top, otherwise the doors will not engage the upper track and will appear to be too short.

Cutting Desk Legs

Fig. 2 gives a half pattern for the scroll-cut desk legs. This is a one piece unit which is assembled from three members that are half-lapped at the corners and later bandsawed, after gluing. Strap hinges are used to attach the legs to the writing desk and three butt hinges are used to pivot the writing desk to the upper cabinet. In both cases, the hinges are surface mounted. Card-table leg braces hold the legs in the open position, and a round-headed screw and a flat brass S-hook are used to hold the desk when swung up. Green blackboard paint is applied to the hardboard; the rest is painted to suit.

Any nails exposed in the hardboard surfaces should be set below the surface and puttied over before painting. ★ ★ ★

MAKE THIS COMPLETE
DINING SET

This smart-looking seven-piece dining-room group—one of a special series of fine furniture for the entire house— is our answer to the tremendous response received for more home-built furniture of good, practical design

Designed expressly for the craftsman working with small home-workshop tools, this complete dining ensemble, which is sufficient to furnish a full-size dining room, consists of seven pieces, including an extension table for eight, four chairs, a credenza and a china cabinet. However, if you haven't room for the entire group, you can eliminate the china cabinet or, in the case of an exceptionally small dinette or dining alcove, the base section of the two-piece china cabinet can be built and used alone as a server to take the place of the large credenza. The table is designed to take an extra leaf which permits serving as many as eight persons, and the seats of the upholstered chairs are spring-filled for real added comfort, a feature not found in all commercial suites.

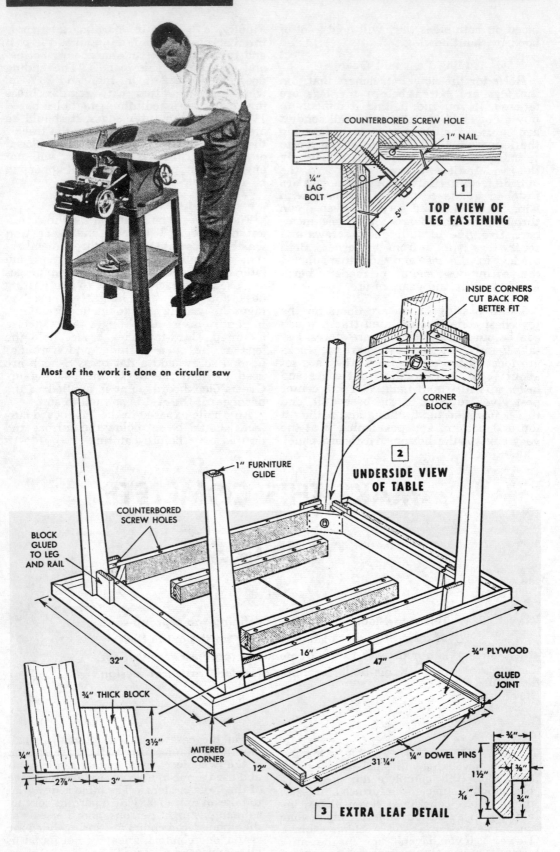

COUNTERBORED SCREW HOLE

1" NAIL

¼" LAG BOLT

5"

1 TOP VIEW OF LEG FASTENING

Most of the work is done on circular saw

INSIDE CORNERS CUT BACK FOR BETTER FIT

CORNER BLOCK

2 UNDERSIDE VIEW OF TABLE

1" FURNITURE GLIDE

COUNTERBORED SCREW HOLES

BLOCK GLUED TO LEG AND RAIL

16"

47"

¾" PLYWOOD

GLUED JOINT

32"

¾" THICK BLOCK

3½"

¼"

2⅞"

3"

MITERED CORNER

12"

31¼"

¼" DOWEL PINS

¾"

⅜"

1½"

¾"

3 EXTRA LEAF DETAIL

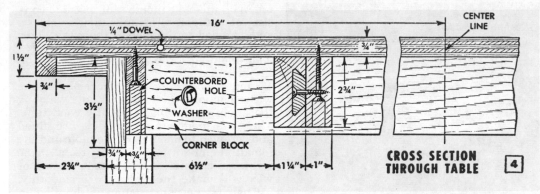

CROSS SECTION THROUGH TABLE [4]

Construction of the table is detailed in Figs. 1 to 7 inclusive. Like the living-room suite, which incorporated the use of both plywood and solid stock, the table top and extra leaf are cut from ¾-in. plywood to save the work of gluing up solid stock. All the rest of the table is made of solid material. A ¾ x 1½-in. facing or edging strip, mitered at the corners and rabbeted on the back, is glued and nailed to the edge of the plywood to conceal the laminations. The top, of course, consists of two separate sections having the conventional aligning pins and holes in the edges at the joint. The sectional view in Fig. 4 indicates the position of the legs and the slides and also shows how the 3-in. aprons, or rails, are screwed to the underside of the top. The ends of the end aprons are cut off squarely, while the two-piece side ones, which butt together at the joint, are cut at an angle to match the slant of the tapered legs. Locate the side aprons 3½ in. in from the edge of the top and the end ones 6 in. inward. Then glue and screw them securely to the plywood.

The tapered legs, Fig. 7, are cut from 1¾-in. stock. Note in the detail at the left of Fig. 3, that the tops of the legs are cut at a ¼-in. angle. Each leg is placed in the corner formed by the aprons and drawn up rigidly with lag screws. Corner blocks are drilled for the screws and then glued and nailed to the aprons as shown in Fig. 1. The lag screws are the only fastenings the legs require and, if the legs loosen with use, it is easy to make them rigid simply by drawing the lag screws tighter. Additional rigidity is had by the eight overlay blocks which are applied to the face of the aprons at the corners. Note that the blocks at the sides of the table are fitted flush with the face of the legs.

Figs. 4, 5 and 6 show how the dovetail joint is formed in the table slide. The

[5] **METHOD OF CUTTING DOVETAIL**

[6] **TABLE SLIDE**

[7] **TABLE LEG**

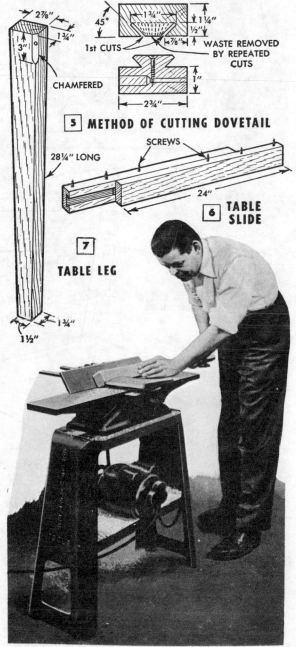

tenon on the male member of the slide consists of a separate strip shaped as shown and screwed to the face of the piece. This strip engages a matching groove in the female member. The groove can be cut on the circular saw by first making the two 45-deg. outside cuts and then removing the waste portion with repeated cuts, varying the angle of the blade slightly each time. The male members of the slide are glued and screwed to one half of the table and the female members to the other, using three screws in counterbored holes. A coating of wax will make the slides work smoothly.

Chair-frame construction is detailed in Figs. 9 to 12 inclusive. Whether four or more chairs are built, at least one should be made a guest, or host, chair by adding arms as shown in Fig. 8 and increasing the width of the front and back, Fig. 11. The over-all height and depth remain the same. Identical parts can be mass-produced to save time by using stops and jigs on the saw. As the legs are the only part of the

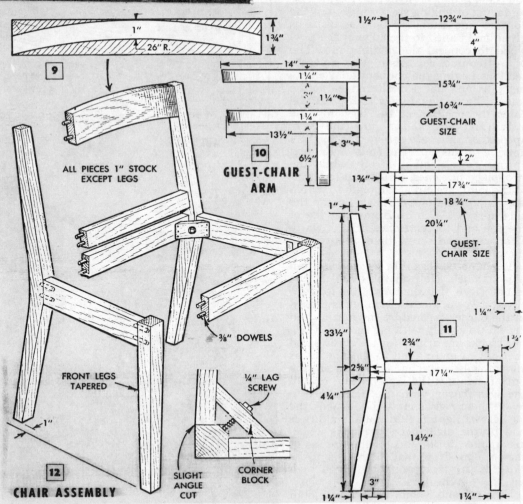

13 WEBBING ENDS DOUBLE-TACKED

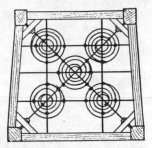

14 SPRINGS CROSSTIED LIKE THIS

15 BURLAP IS TACKED OVER SPRINGS

16 THEN WELT IS TACKED TO EDGE

frame exposed, the rest of the assembly can be rough. Note in Fig. 12 that all members are doweled and each corner of the seat is braced with lag screws the same as the table. The curved back rail is bandsawed from a piece 1¾ x 4 in., Fig. 9, while the front legs are tapered on all four faces from a point 2¾ in. from the top. The exposed part of the legs should be finished before upholstering.

Upholstering the chairs: The first step is to tack furniture webbing to the seat bottom, Fig. 13. Six strips are interlaced and stretched tautly in the manner indicated in the detail to the right of Fig. 16. The ends of the webbing are left about 1 in. long for folding back and double-tacking. Five No. 1 plain-end coil springs are used in the seat. These are placed in position, tack-sewed to the webbing, and then tied and crosstied to the bottom of the seat rails as shown in Fig. 14. The dots in the drawing indicate knots. The springs are compressed so that the center one is about 1½ in. above the top of the seat. The spring twine is brought down through holes punched in the webbing and tacked securely to the underside of the rails. Next, the springs are covered with burlap, Fig. 15. The edges are tacked, folded over and retacked, and then a welt edging is tacked around the outer edge on three sides, Fig. 16. The welt used here is the same as used later on the back, Fig. 25, except that being hidden it can be made up of scrap material wrapped around a length of ¼-in. rope. Hair, tow or moss filling is added next, Fig. 17. This is held in place by tack-sewing it to the burlap. A layer of cotton is applied over the filling so it covers the sides of the seat rails, Fig. 18. After this, the whole job is covered with the finished fabric, and the completed seat should look like Fig. 19. Patterns for the seat covering as well as the rest of the chair are given in Fig. 24. When completed, the underside of the seat is covered with black cambric, the edges being folded under.

Two strips of webbing are tacked to the back, Fig. 20, and then it is covered with burlap, moss and finally cotton. The cotton is brought around the sides and over the top

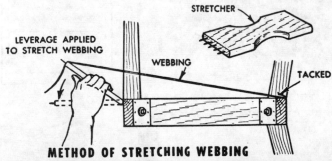

STRETCHER

LEVERAGE APPLIED TO STRETCH WEBBING

WEBBING

TACKED

METHOD OF STRETCHING WEBBING

17 MOSS FILLING COMES NEXT **18** THEN IS COVERED WITH COTTON **19** AND HERE'S THE COMPLETED SEAT

20 FIRST, WEBBING IS APPLIED TO THE BACK

21 THEN WEBBING IS COVERED WITH BURLAP

22 LAYER OF MOSS IS TACK-SEWED TO BURLAP

23 COTTON IS ADDED NEXT, THEN THE FABRIC

and the lower edge is folded up under the moss. Note in applying the covering to the front of the back that the fabric is first pulled through and tacked to the face of the rear seat rail, Fig. 25. Before the back covering is applied, a welt made of the finished fabric is tacked to three sides. Then a strip of cardboard, ½-in. wide, is cut to fit across the top between the welt at the sides. The fabric is tacked at the top first, driving the tacks through the cardboard strip as in Fig. 25. With the top tacked, the fabric is brought down over the back, the edges folded under and hand-stitched to the welt. Blued gimp nails are used in tacking the covering where it passes over the exposed surface of the legs. This method is called blind tacking. In addition to concealing the tacks, the cardboard strip provides a firm edge which avoids irregular pleats when the cloth is pulled taut.

(Note—Traditional methods of upholstering are shown here. For instructions on foam rubber upholstering, see page 788.)

24 **PATTERNS**

These fabric patterns were taken from the actual covering on one of the chairs and are somewhat approximate in size. While over-all measurements are ample, the various cuts and folds indicated should be made while fitting to avoid an error

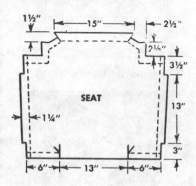

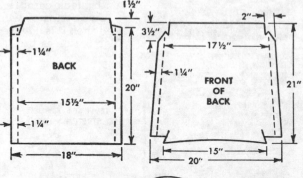

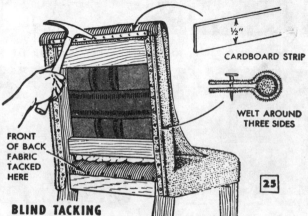

CARDBOARD STRIP

WELT AROUND THREE SIDES

FRONT OF BACK FABRIC TACKED HERE

BLIND TACKING

25

WITH THE table and chairs completed as detailed **earlier**, you should be ready to tackle the more pretentious pieces of the dining-room group — the credenza and the china cabinet. Construction of the credenza is fairly simple as revealed in the cutaway drawing in Fig. 28. Over-all dimensions for this piece are given in Fig. 26, and a view of the interior, Fig. 27, shows how the doors are hinged, where friction catches are installed and how finger pockets in the rails are provided to facilitate

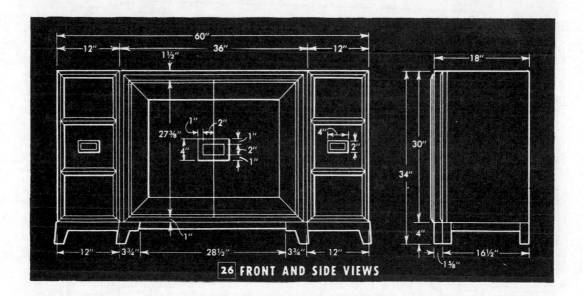

26 FRONT AND SIDE VIEWS

removal of the two silverware drawers.

Start the credenza by making the base framework. Each end is made up exactly the same, right and left hand, and then joined together with front and rear members. Section A-A in Fig. 28 gives the sizes of these members and shows how they are screwed together. Note that the ¾ x 1½-in. strip placed on edge runs the full length of the base and is glued and doweled to the two rear legs. All legs are the same size and shape, six being required, three of which are made for the right side and three for the left. All are doweled to the rails. Note that the outside faces of the end rails are beveled to match the flare of the legs. Section D-D shows how intermediate rails are rabbeted along one edge to receive ¼-in. plywood bottoms. Cleats are fitted on the three other rails to support the plywood. Center legs of the credenza are doweled to the face of the front rails 12 in. in from the corner. Then, the 1 x 1⅛-in. strip is screwed to the projecting ends of the rails and small overlay blocks are used to conceal the screwheads. Section A-A shows how the back rail is built up of two additional pieces, both being the same length and set between the intermediate rails.

Next, the side members of the end compartments are installed. These are cut to size from ¾-in. plywood. The upper ends of the outside panels are mitered 45 deg. while the lower ends are trimmed off squarely and bored for three ¼-in. dowels, which are located in the base to bring the outer panels flush with the rail. The rear edges of the two outer panels are rabbeted for a ¼-in. plywood back. The inner panels of each compartment are made ¾

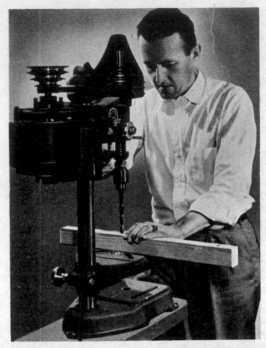

in. shorter than the outer ones and narrower to permit covering the plies of the wood with a ¾ x 1⅝-in. strip of solid stock as detailed in section B-B. This strip is edge-glued and may be doweled for additional strength. The two panels of each unit are held together at the top with a frame of ¾ x 1½-in. stock. Front and rear pieces of the frame are grooved on the inside edges for tenons on the sidepieces. The frame is screwed in place through the edge so it is even with the bottom of the miter and flush with the top of the inner

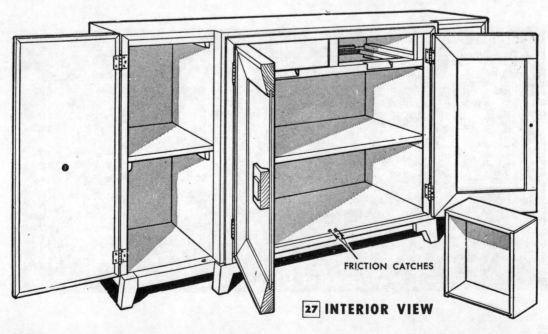

FRICTION CATCHES

27 INTERIOR VIEW

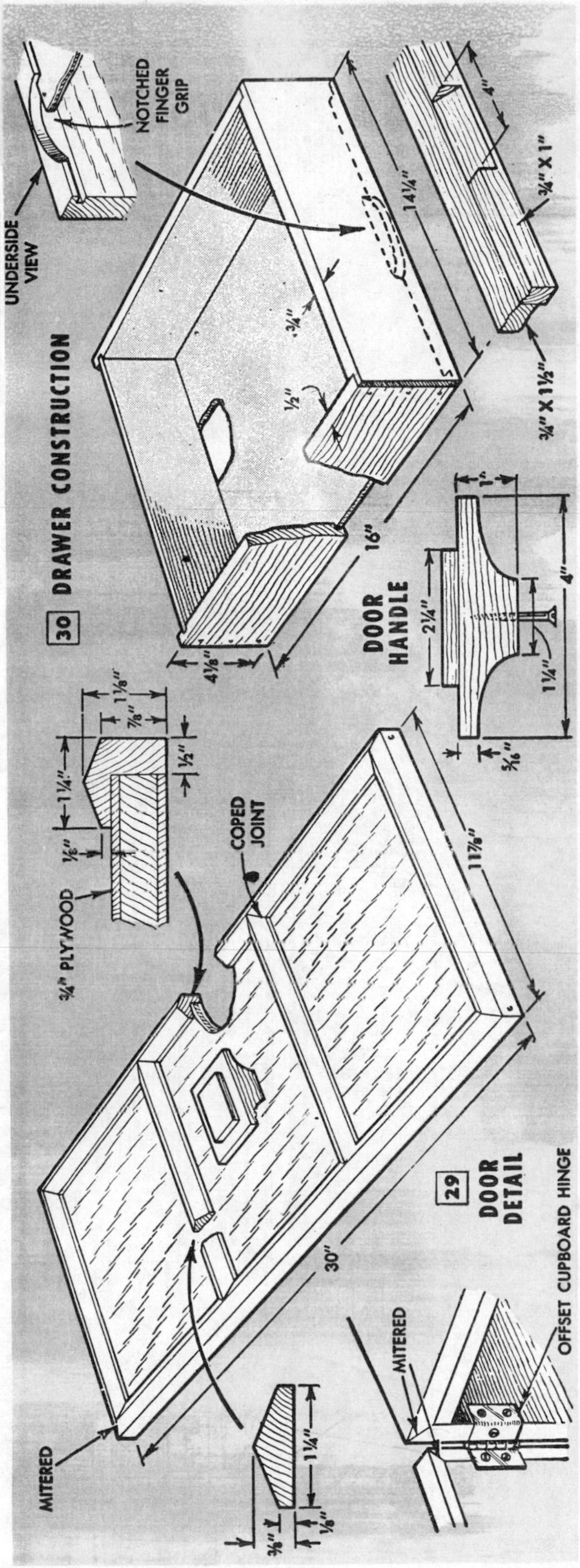
30 DRAWER CONSTRUCTION
UNDERSIDE VIEW
NOTCHED FINGER GRIP
14¼"
¾" X 1"
¾" X 1½"
¾"
½"
16"
4⅛"
DOOR HANDLE
1"
2¼"
4"
1¼"
5/16"
¾" PLYWOOD
1¼"
1⅛"
⅞"
½"
⅛"
COPED JOINT
11⅞"
29 DOOR DETAIL
30"
MITERED
OFFSET CUPBOARD HINGE
1¼"
⅜"
⅛"

panel. The plywood back is added next to strengthen the assembly. This is nailed into the rabbets of the outer panels, to the edge of the inner panels and to the framing at the top and bottom.

Next comes the top. This is cut 15¾ in. wide and is mitered at each end to make a perfectly fitting joint with the end panels. As in the case of the inner panels, a ¾ x 1⅝-in. strip of solid stock is edge-glued to the top to build it out flush with the sides. With this done, the center door molding is applied. Sections A-A and B-B give the size of the molding. The side and top members are rabbeted on the outer edge to fit over the edge of the top and inner panels, while the bottom member is rabbeted to take a ¼-in. plywood bottom panel. Facing edges of the molding are beveled according to the sectional views and mitered to fit perfectly at the corners. Note, however, that the center shelf and the drawer frame should be installed before the molding is applied.

The drawer frame is made similarly to the frames at the top of the end units. Drawer runners are installed in the center and at each side after the frame is in place. Note that the front edge of the frame is faced with a hardwood strip which is notched at a 45-deg. angle to provide a finger pocket for each drawer. While the dimension for this is missing in Fig. 28, it is included in Fig. 30. The center doors are built up according to section C-C. They can be made in one piece by framing ¼-in. plywood with a heavy molding grooved to fit over the edge and then sawing in half. A ⅜ x 1½ in. strip is used to reinforce the plywood along each side of the saw cut. Construction of the doors for the end units is detailed in Fig. 29. Plywood is framed with a rabbeted molding to conceal the laminations, and overlay strips, coped at the ends, are surface-glued to the plywood to divide the doors into three equal panels. Regular offset cupboard hinges are used on the end doors, while 3-in., loose-pin hinges are used on the center doors.

The china cabinet consists of two separate units which are held together at the back with a cleat. If space is so limited that you can accommodate neither the large credenza nor the complete china cabinet, just the base of the latter can be built and used as a small server. Fig. 31 shows the general construction of both units of the cabinet. Top, sides, back and dust panels of the lower unit are ¼-in. plywood. Top and bottom frames are joined at the back with ¾ x 1¾-in. posts which are notched for the shelves and two drawer frames. Fig. 32

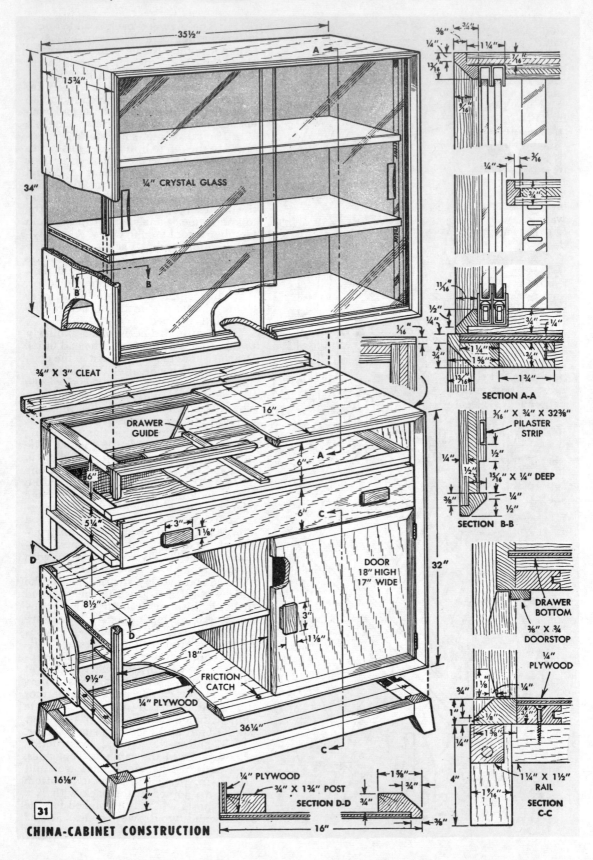

¾" X 3" CLEAT

DRAWER GUIDE

¼" CRYSTAL GLASS

35½"

15¾"

34"

16"

6" A

6"

5¼"

6" C

3" 1⅛"

D

8½"

D

3

18" 1⅛"

9½"

18"

¼" PLYWOOD

FRICTION CATCH

DOOR 18" HIGH 17" WIDE

32"

36¼"

16½"

4"

¼" PLYWOOD

¾" X 1¾" POST

SECTION D-D

16"

C

SECTION A-A

³⁄₁₆" X ¾" X 32⅝" PILASTER STRIP

¼"

½"

¹⁵⁄₁₆" X ¼" DEEP

⅜"

¼"

½"

SECTION B-B

DRAWER BOTTOM

⅜" X ¾ DOORSTOP

¼" PLYWOOD

¾"

1"

¼"

4"

1¼" X 1½" RAIL

SECTION C-C

31

CHINA-CABINET CONSTRUCTION

shows how the drawer frames are assembled. The top and bottom frames are supported at the front by a rabbeted molding which is mitered and assembled as a picture frame and then glued to the front edges of the frames at top and bottom. Side and top panels fit the rabbeted molding as shown in section D-D. Section C-C shows how the bottom frame is screwed to the base. Note that the top panel is rabbeted at each end to overlap the side panels. Drawers are assembled as in Fig. 30 and made to fit the openings. A grooved runner which rides on the guide is nailed to the underside of each drawer. Fig. 34 shows the simple wooden drawer pull. If desired, a silverware drawer can be included, Fig. 33. A bevel is run around the outer edges of the doors ¼ in. deep and 1⅛ in. wide to give a raised panel effect.

The top unit of the cabinet is made like a box from ¾-in. plywood. Sections A-A and B-B show how the pieces are rabbeted at the front edge to receive a molding which covers the laminations. Note that the rabbets at the top and bottom are made wide enough to house a standard showcase door track (see section A-A) and that rabbets also are made along the sidepieces to provide end grooves for the sliding glass doors. Note in section B-B that a groove is run at the front and back edges of the sidepieces for a standard adjustable shelf pilaster. In ordering glass panels for the doors, notice in section A-A that they must be short enough to permit inserting in the top track and then down into the lower one. Use crystal glass as it is less expensive. Any glass shop can grind the finger grips.

The china cabinet makes the seven-piece group complete. Featuring sliding glass doors, it's designed as two separate units to simplify moving and to permit base alone to be built and used as dinette server

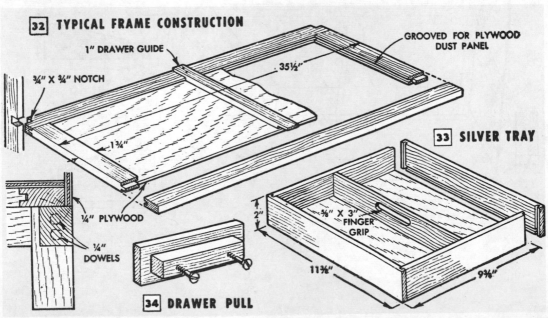

32 TYPICAL FRAME CONSTRUCTION

1" DRAWER GUIDE

GROOVED FOR PLYWOOD DUST PANEL

¾" X ¾" NOTCH

35½"

1¾"

¼" PLYWOOD

¼" DOWELS

33 SILVER TRAY

2"

⅝" X 3" FINGER GRIP

11⅜"

9⅜"

34 DRAWER PULL

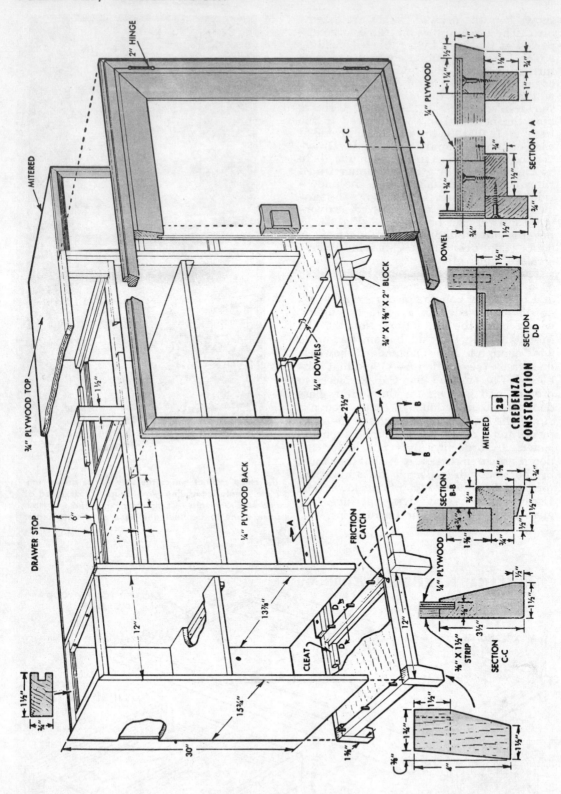

CREDENZA CONSTRUCTION

Dining Table

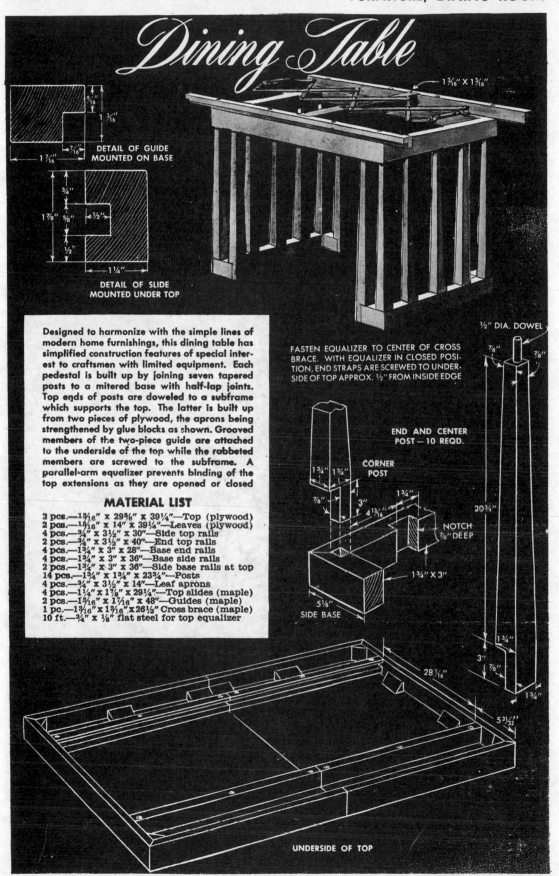

DETAIL OF GUIDE MOUNTED ON BASE

DETAIL OF SLIDE MOUNTED UNDER TOP

$1\frac{3}{16}'' \times 1\frac{3}{16}''$

Designed to harmonize with the simple lines of modern home furnishings, this dining table has simplified construction features of special interest to craftsmen with limited equipment. Each pedestal is built up by joining seven tapered posts to a mitered base with half-lap joints. Top ends of posts are doweled to a subframe which supports the top. The latter is built up from two pieces of plywood, the aprons being strengthened by glue blocks as shown. Grooved members of the two-piece guide are attached to the underside of the top while the rabbeted members are screwed to the subframe. A parallel-arm equalizer prevents binding of the top extensions as they are opened or closed

MATERIAL LIST

2 pcs.—$1\frac{3}{16}''$ x $29\frac{5}{8}''$ x $39\frac{1}{4}''$—Top (plywood)
2 pcs.—$1\frac{3}{16}''$ x 14" x $39\frac{1}{4}''$—Leaves (plywood)
4 pcs.—$\frac{3}{4}''$ x $3\frac{1}{2}''$ x 30"—Side top rails
2 pcs.—$\frac{3}{4}''$ x $3\frac{1}{2}''$ x 40"—End top rails
4 pcs.—$1\frac{3}{4}''$ x 3" x 28"—Base end rails
4 pcs.—$1\frac{3}{4}''$ x 3" x 36"—Base side rails
2 pcs.—$1\frac{3}{4}''$ x 3" x 36"—Side base rails at top
14 pcs.—$1\frac{3}{4}''$ x $1\frac{3}{4}''$ x $23\frac{3}{4}''$—Posts
4 pcs.—$\frac{3}{4}''$ x $3\frac{1}{2}''$ x 14"—Leaf aprons
4 pcs.—$1\frac{1}{4}''$ x $1\frac{7}{8}''$ x $29\frac{1}{4}''$—Top slides (maple)
2 pcs.—$1\frac{3}{16}''$ x $1\frac{7}{16}''$ x 48"—Guides (maple)
1 pc.—$1\frac{3}{16}''$ x $1\frac{3}{16}''$ x $26\frac{1}{2}''$ Cross brace (maple)
10 ft.—$\frac{3}{4}''$ x $\frac{1}{8}''$ flat steel for top equalizer

FASTEN EQUALIZER TO CENTER OF CROSS BRACE. WITH EQUALIZER IN CLOSED POSITION, END STRAPS ARE SCREWED TO UNDERSIDE OF TOP APPROX. $\frac{1}{2}''$ FROM INSIDE EDGE

½" DIA. DOWEL

END AND CENTER POST — 10 REQD.

CORNER POST

NOTCH $\frac{7}{8}''$ DEEP

SIDE BASE

UNDERSIDE OF TOP

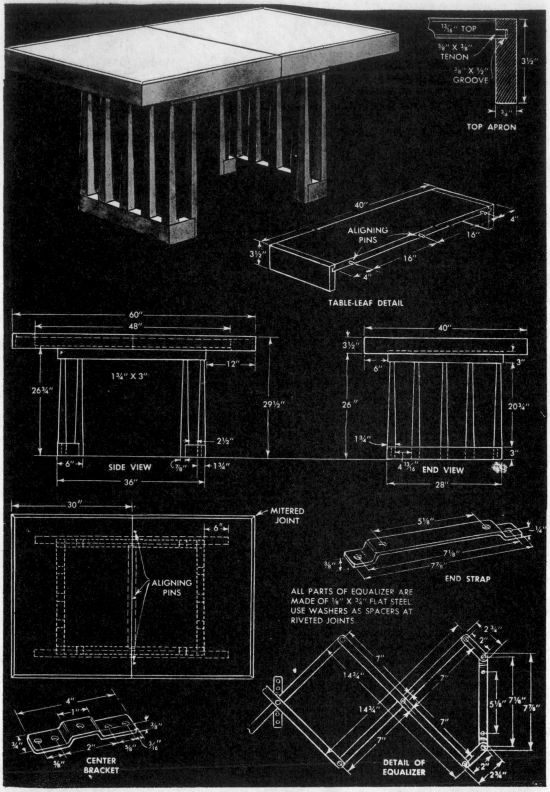

TOP APRON

$1\frac{13}{16}$" TOP
$\frac{3}{8}$" X $\frac{3}{8}$" TENON
$\frac{3}{8}$" X $\frac{1}{2}$" GROOVE
$3\frac{1}{2}$"
$\frac{3}{4}$"

TABLE-LEAF DETAIL

40"
ALIGNING PINS
16"
16"
4"
$3\frac{1}{2}$"
4"

SIDE VIEW

60"
48"
12"
$1\frac{3}{4}$" X 3"
$26\frac{3}{4}$"
$29\frac{1}{2}$"
$2\frac{1}{2}$"
6"
$\frac{7}{8}$"
$1\frac{3}{4}$"
36"

END VIEW

40"
$3\frac{1}{2}$"
6"
3"
26"
$20\frac{3}{4}$"
$1\frac{3}{4}$"
3"
$4\frac{13}{16}$"
28"

MITERED JOINT

30"
6"
ALIGNING PINS

END STRAP

$5\frac{1}{8}$"
$\frac{1}{4}$"
$7\frac{1}{8}$"
$7\frac{7}{8}$"
$\frac{3}{8}$"

ALL PARTS OF EQUALIZER ARE
MADE OF $\frac{1}{8}$" X $\frac{3}{4}$" FLAT STEEL.
USE WASHERS AS SPACERS AT
RIVETED JOINTS

CENTER BRACKET

4"
1"
$\frac{3}{8}$"
$\frac{3}{4}$"
2"
$\frac{5}{8}$"
$\frac{3}{16}$"
$\frac{5}{8}$"

DETAIL OF EQUALIZER

$2\frac{3}{4}$"
2"
7"
$14\frac{3}{4}$"
7"
$14\frac{3}{4}$"
7"
$5\frac{1}{8}$"
$7\frac{1}{8}$"
$7\frac{7}{8}$"
7"
2"
$2\frac{3}{4}$"

Dining Table Commode

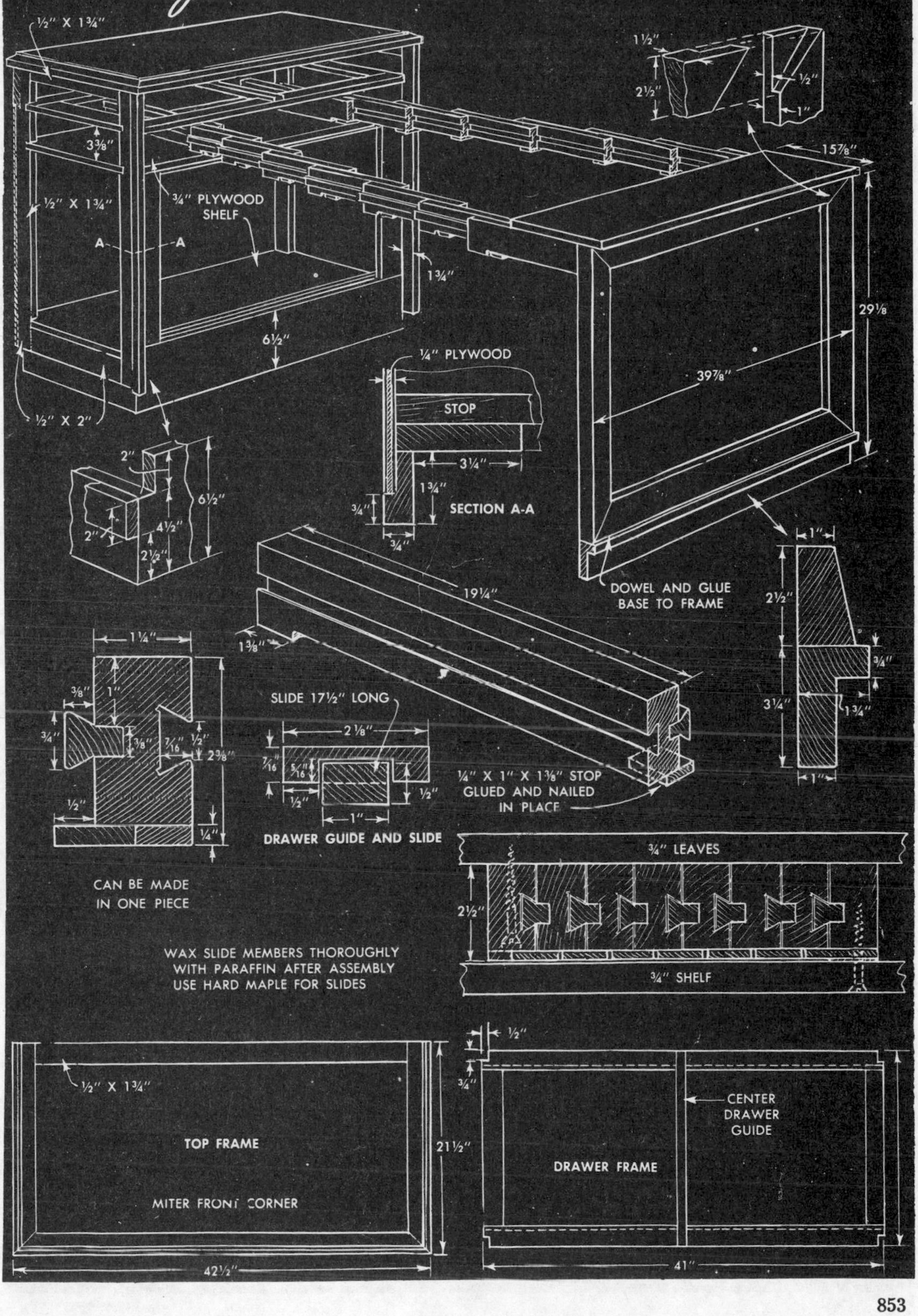
½" X 1¾"
3⅜"
½" X 1¾"
¾" PLYWOOD SHELF
A—A
1¾"
6½"
½" X 2"
1½"
2½"
½"
1"
15⅞"
29⅛
39⅞"
¼" PLYWOOD
STOP
3¼"
1¾"
¾"
¾"
SECTION A-A
2"
6½"
2"
4½"
2½"
DOWEL AND GLUE BASE TO FRAME
1"
2½"
¾"
3¼"
1¾"
1"
19¼"
1⅜"
1¼"
⅜"
1"
¾"
⅜"
7⁄16"
½"
2⅜"
½"
¼"
SLIDE 17½" LONG
2⅛"
7⁄16
5⁄16
½"
½"
1"
DRAWER GUIDE AND SLIDE
¼" X 1" X 1⅜" STOP GLUED AND NAILED IN PLACE
CAN BE MADE IN ONE PIECE
WAX SLIDE MEMBERS THOROUGHLY WITH PARAFFIN AFTER ASSEMBLY USE HARD MAPLE FOR SLIDES
¾" LEAVES
2½"
¾" SHELF
½" X 1¾"
TOP FRAME
MITER FRONT CORNER
21½"
42½"
½"
¾"
CENTER DRAWER GUIDE
DRAWER FRAME
41"

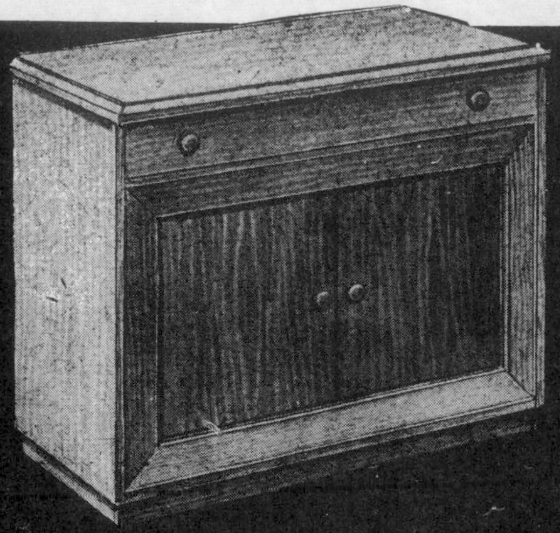

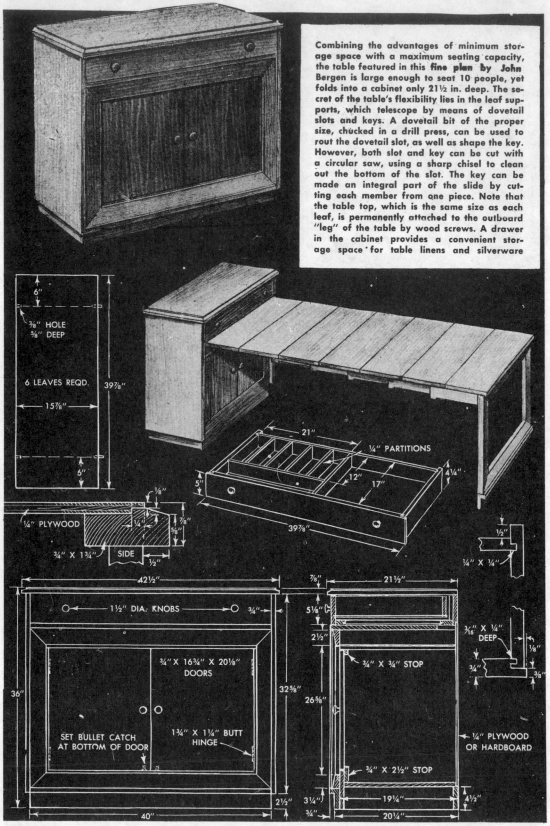

Combining the advantages of minimum storage space with a maximum seating capacity, the table featured in this **fine plan by John** Bergen is large enough to seat 10 people, yet folds into a cabinet only 21½ in. deep. The secret of the table's flexibility lies in the leaf supports, which telescope by means of dovetail slots and keys. A dovetail bit of the proper size, chucked in a drill press, can be used to rout the dovetail slot, as well as shape the key. However, both slot and key can be cut with a circular saw, using a sharp chisel to clean out the bottom of the slot. The key can be made an integral part of the slide by cutting each member from one piece. Note that the table top, which is the same size as each leaf, is permanently attached to the outboard "leg" of the table by wood screws. A drawer in the cabinet provides a convenient storage space for table linens and silverware

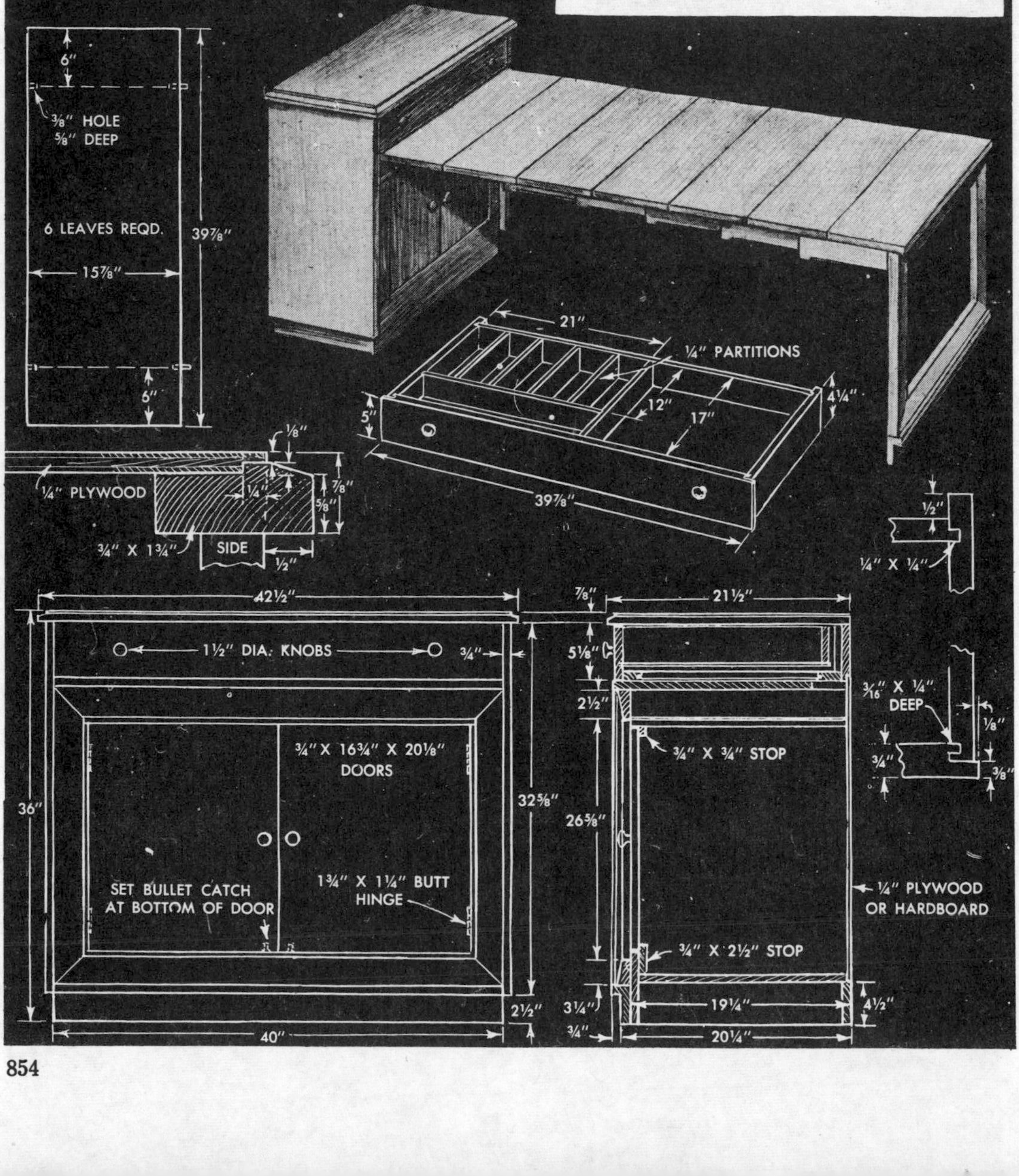
6"
⅜" HOLE
⅝" DEEP
6 LEAVES REQD.
39⅞"
15⅞"
6"
21"
¼" PARTITIONS
4¼"
5"
12"
17"
39⅞"
⅛"
¼" PLYWOOD
¼"
⅞"
⅝"
¾" X 1¾"
SIDE
½"
½"
¼" X ¼"
42½"
⅞"
21½"
1½" DIA. KNOBS
¾"
5⅛"
2½"
³⁄₁₆" X ¼" DEEP
⅛"
¾" X ¾" STOP
¾"
⅜"
¾" X 16¾" X 20⅛" DOORS
36"
32⅝"
26⅝"
SET BULLET CATCH AT BOTTOM OF DOOR
1¾" X 1¼" BUTT HINGE
¼" PLYWOOD OR HARDBOARD
¾" X 2½" STOP
2½"
3¼"
19¼"
4½"
40"
¾"
20¼"

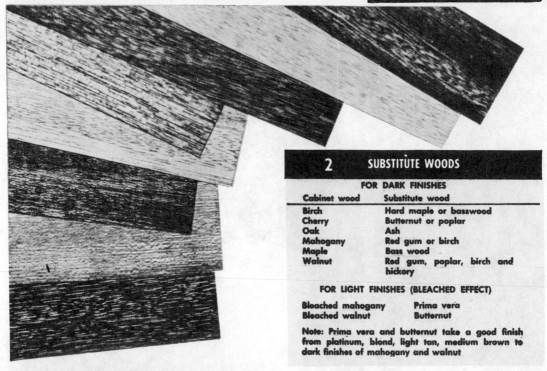

2 SUBSTITUTE WOODS

FOR DARK FINISHES

Cabinet wood	Substitute wood
Birch	Hard maple or basswood
Cherry	Butternut or poplar
Oak	Ash
Mahogany	Red gum or birch
Maple	Bass wood
Walnut	Red gum, poplar, birch and hickory

FOR LIGHT FINISHES (BLEACHED EFFECT)

Bleached mahogany	Prima vera
Bleached walnut	Butternut

Note: Prima vera and butternut take a good finish from platinum, blond, light tan, medium brown to dark finishes of mahogany and walnut

1 CAUSES OF FINISH FAILURES

1—Inferior or defective lumber

2—Excessive moisture in wood

3—Dents, scratches, tool marks, glue spots and stains on work

4—Insufficient or improper sanding of wood before finishing

5—Presence of sanding dust on surfaces when finishing

6—Dust in air settles on surfaces of work while and after finishing

7—Wrong temperature and humidity

8—Inadequate illumination

9—Finishing in direct sunlight

10—Poor grade of finishing materials

11—Old, spoiled finishing materials

12—Incompatibility of materials

13—Wrong type of brush

14—Improperly cleaned brushes

15—Poor brushing technique causing brush marks, skipped areas, runs, sags, and pileup in corners

16—Air bubbles in shellac, sealer, varnish, and lacquer

17—Faulty spray-gun technique

18—Wrong spraying consistency

19—Improper adjustment of spray gun

20—Insufficient drying between coats

21—Improper sanding between coats

22—Wrong rubbing and polishing materials

23—Faulty rubbing and polishing

YOU *CAN* FINISH FURNITURE

Haste trips up most beginners when finishing furniture. Passing over important little steps in surface preparation is the biggest mistake. Take it easy and you'll find that you can finish furniture beautifully the very first time

By E. R. HAAN

ADDING THE BEAUTIFUL finishes which give that store-bought look to home-built furniture is a part of furniture making that throws the average home craftsman for a loop. And yet, it actually requires far less skill than the cabinetry. The cause of most finish failures on the part of the home craftsman is haste. In his eagerness to complete the piece and put it in use, the tendency is to overlook many seemingly unimportant little steps and, consequently, his efforts to produce a fine piece of furniture, finish-wise, result in disappointment. In addition to impatience, other causes of finish failures that plague the beginner are given in Fig. 1.

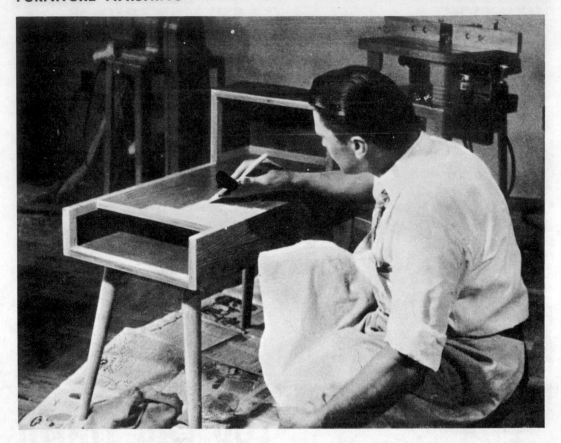

Starting Out Right

A transparent finish emphasizes both the beauty and the defects of wood. Therefore, when building fine furniture to be so finished, select each piece of wood carefully and avoid that which has undesired knots, mineral streaks, sap and heartwood. As it is impossible to obtain lumber without any defects at all, enough should be purchased so that undesired areas can be cut out as waste. For exacting standards in fine cabinet work this may mean a waste of 30 to 40 percent. Where economy must be considered, it is possible to cut costs by using certain substitute woods as listed in Fig. 2, and finish them to resemble the more expensive ones.

Finishing nails should be set below the wood surface and the holes filled with wood putty as in Fig. 3. Sunken screwheads can be concealed with "boat plugs" which show surface grain as in Fig. 4. You can cut these from relatively thin wood by using a "hole punch" of proper size to assure a perfect fit. Such plugs should match the wood grain around the holes. Glue them in place and sand them flush after the glue has dried.

Take care to avoid glue stains as they prevent uniform staining. Remove un- avoidable glue drops with a sharp wood chisel or scraper, then sand the surface smooth. To eliminate shallow dents, moisten them and then apply a warm iron as in Fig. 5. If the dent does not raise enough, make several razor slits with the grain and then repeat the process.

Sanding Prior to Finishing

Much time and effort can be saved by using power sanders, a belt sander, Fig. 6, for heavy cutting, and a reciprocating pad sander, Fig. 7, for fine finishing. The pad sander is better for cutting off fine ends of wood fibers but is not intended for heavy work. Three grades of sandpaper, coarse, medium and fine, as recommended by the machine manufacturers, are used successively to produce a perfectly smooth and scratch-free surface.

When hand-sanding wood, you also use three grades of open-coat aluminum-oxide abrasive paper, Fig. 8, detail A. Use No. 1/0 to remove tool marks and light glue spots, No. 3/0 to level and smooth and No. 6/0 to produce the final smooth finish. For flat surfaces you should hold the sandpaper on a wooden block or other type of holder. The block or holder shown in detail B, has a felt

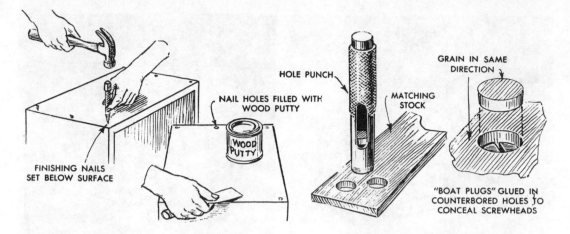

HOLE PUNCH

MATCHING STOCK

GRAIN IN SAME DIRECTION

NAIL HOLES FILLED WITH WOOD PUTTY

WOOD PUTTY

FINISHING NAILS SET BELOW SURFACE

"BOAT PLUGS" GLUED IN COUNTERBORED HOLES TO CONCEAL SCREWHEADS

3   **WAYS TO CONCEAL NAILHEADS**

4   **AND FLATHEAD WOOD SCREWS**

backing. For curved surfaces, hold the sandpaper on a ½-in.-thick felt pad as in detail C. For small-radii molding always use a finger behind the paper to make it conform to the curvature. For sanding many pieces of similar molding you can make a sanding block having the same contour, as in detail D.

Always sand with the wood grain to avoid cross scratches that are hard to remove. Pressure should be light, letting the grit do the work. Slightly bevel, or break, all sharp edges with two or three strokes of No. 6/0 sandpaper, but not more than this as the edge then will become noticeably rounded. A sharp edge causes finishing material to build up on either side of it but prevents good coverage on the edge itself.

Fuzzy grain that remains on some woods after sanding is removed by first applying a glue size (glue, 1 oz. and water, 1 pt.), letting it dry for 24 hours and then sanding. After the bare wood on any furniture job has been completed, dust off all surfaces with a soft brush or use a vacuum cleaner with a small brush attachment.

Room Conditions for Finishing

Many home craftsmen do their finishing under adverse room conditions of temperature, humidity, air circulation, cleanliness and illumination. Temperature should be 70 deg. F. or more. Humidity should not exceed 90 percent as this greatly prolongs drying time and much more dust than normal will settle and spot the finish.

There should be a constant change of air. This equalizes inside and outside humidity and eliminates volatile vapors that may be harmful to breathe and are a fire hazard as well. Too fast a change of air should be avoided as it raises dust. When using a spray gun, a discharge fan and a respirator for the worker are necessary.

Lighting above and on the side of the work as in Fig. 9 (top) should be adequate so that the application of finishing materials can be seen by slight reflection, and thus can be controlled. Finishing and drying should never be done in direct sunlight as this may cause haze and discoloration. The room should be as free as possible of dust. A room that is separate from the workshop is best. Fine finishing never should be attempted outdoors or in an open garage or workshop that is exposed to even a slight wind. This invariably results in a ruined, dust-speckled finish.

Plan on using only the best finishing materials available. Price often is a good criterion. Use fresh materials, avoiding the temptation to economize by using the contents of an opened can over three months old. Old material may never dry,

5   **REMOVING SHALLOW DENTS**

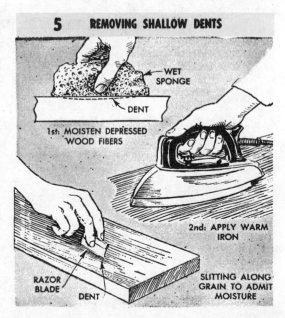

WET SPONGE

DENT

1st: MOISTEN DEPRESSED WOOD FIBERS

2nd: APPLY WARM IRON

RAZOR BLADE

DENT

SLITTING ALONG GRAIN TO ADMIT MOISTURE

6 BELT SANDER FOR HEAVY CUTTING

Skil photo

7 PAD SANDER FOR FINE FINISHES

Miller Falls photo

may contain dust deposited in it by a previously used brush, may be oxidized and covered with a skin, may have undergone chemical changes so that a resulting finish will be cloudy.

One kind of finishing material may have a formulation not compatible with another. For example, the solvent of a sealer or top coat applied on a stain or primer may cause the stain to bleed or prevent it from drying. A lacquer top coat should never be applied over a pigmented oil stain, nor over varnish, although varnish can be applied over lacquer. Some materials serve as both sealer and top coat, and are not compatible with regular varnishes and lacquers.

Tips on Brushes and Spray Guns

Using the right kind and size of brush contributes to better work. A soft, long-bristle brush, 2 to 3 in. wide, is best to apply sealer, varnish and lacquer. An inexpensive soft brush, 2 or 3 in. wide, is adequate for applying stain. A stiff-bristle brush, 3 to 4 in. wide is best for applying filler. Get good quality brushes.

Many finish failures are caused by improper cleaning and storage of brushes. They should be cleaned immediately after using them. Brushes used for stain and filler are cleaned with turpentine, benzine or white gasoline. Those used for varnish are cleaned with turpentine or special solvent used for some varnishes, but never with benzine or white gasoline, which causes the varnish to curdle and form small particles that come off in subsequent jobs. Brushes for shellac are cleaned with wood

8   SANDING BLOCKS AND PADS FOR FLAT AND CONCAVE SURFACES

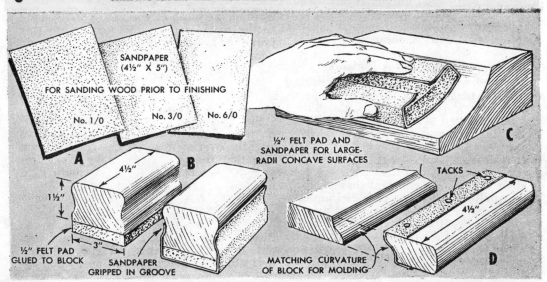

SANDPAPER (4½″ X 5″)

FOR SANDING WOOD PRIOR TO FINISHING

No. 1/0   No. 3/0   No. 6/0

A   B

4½″

1½″

3″

½″ FELT PAD GLUED TO BLOCK

SANDPAPER GRIPPED IN GROOVE

½″ FELT PAD AND SANDPAPER FOR LARGE-RADII CONCAVE SURFACES

C

TACKS

4½″

MATCHING CURVATURE OF BLOCK FOR MOLDING

D

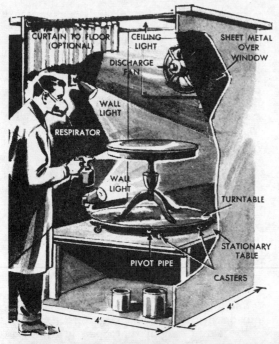

alcohol, and those for lacquer and lacquer sealer are cleaned with lacquer thinner.

To clean a brush properly, submerge it in solvent suitable for material in the brush, working this well into the bristles with your fingers as in Fig. 10. Repeat the process with fresh solvent until the brush is cleaned thoroughly. Shake the brush to throw out dirty solvent each time. Then straighten out the bristles by combing with a wire brush and wrap the brush in aluminum foil for storage as in Fig. 11.

The same solvents are used for cleaning a spray gun, which should be cleaned immediately after use. Clean the cup first, then pour in fresh solvent and spray this through the nozzle. Next, unscrew the nozzle to inspect it and the orifices for cleanliness. If the orifices are clogged, disassemble the gun and submerge the parts in solvent until the orifices are clean. Don't push wire through the orifices.

Any finishing materials should be stirred to mix the ingredients and produce the right consistency. Shellac, sealer, varnish and lacquer are stirred carefully to avoid forming air bubbles which are transferred to the work surface and may cause tiny craters. The brush is dipped into the liquid about one third of its bristle length, and then is drawn over the can rim to remove the excess. In large half-empty cans the brush can be slapped against the inside to do this.

Shellac, varnish and lacquer are "flowed" on with a full brush, first with long and slightly overlapping strokes in the grain direction, then with light cross strokes for uniform spreading, and finally with light finishing strokes with the grain.

Spraying Technique

A spray booth equipped with a fan to discharge the fumes, a turntable and suitable lighting, as shown in Fig. 9, is highly desirable. The average home spray gun op-

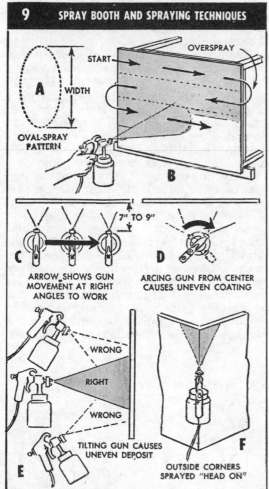

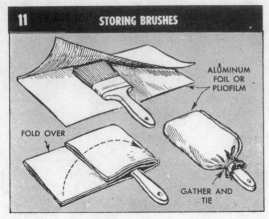

11   STORING BRUSHES

ALUMINUM FOIL OR PLIOFILM

FOLD OVER

GATHER AND TIE

crates on a pressure of about 35 lbs. p.s.i., which permits spraying of liquids having about 20 percent solid material. Spray guns working on 90 to 110 lbs. of pressure can spray from 35 to 45 percent solid material in liquids. Finishing materials are brought to proper spraying viscosity by adding solvent. Then they are strained through a 60-mesh wire screen before being used.

The gun nozzle is adjusted to spray a fan pattern 5 to 6 in. wide, detail A, Fig. 9, when holding the gun from 7 to 9 in. from the surface. For each 10 lbs. of additional pressure, the gun is held 1 in. farther away. Holding the gun too close results in an uneven coating that has ripples and runs. Holding it too far away results in a dry, sandy spray with excessive dusting.

Always start spraying a vertical surface at the top and work downward with successive cross strokes as in detail B. Pull the gun trigger just before the spray hits the work, and release it just after it passes the work. You can spray the two vertical edges before making the horizontal strokes to minimize over-spraying. Always spray full wet coats just short of running.

Keep the spray axis at right angles to the work and at a uniform distance from it as in detail C. Arcing the gun from a central position, detail D, results in a heavier deposit at the center frequently causing runs. Holding the gun downward produces a heavier deposit at the upper fringe of the spray pattern, and holding it upward will make a heavy deposit at the lower fringe, detail E.

In spraying horizontal surfaces, you start at the edge nearest you and proceed to the farthest edge with successive horizontal strokes. Then the spray dust that lands on the uncoated surface will be dissolved by a full spray stroke. Reversing this procedure will cause spray dust to settle on the finished surface. Outside corners are sprayed head-on as in Fig. 9, detail F, with the nozzle set horizontally to produce an even deposit.

AFTER PREPARING the surfaces of a piece of furniture for finishing as described earlier, you are ready to apply the finishing materials. As mentioned before, proceed slowly. At this point, especially, many home craftsmen make the mistake of hurrying. Producing an exceptionally fine finish often requires more time than building the project.

Clear Finishes on Furniture

The procedure for finishing close-grain and open-grain wood, as given in Fig. 15, is the same except that open-grain wood requires filling. Complete drying of each application is of utmost importance, as well as light sanding and scrupulous cleaning between all coatings.

Transparent top coats are applied after stain, toner and filler have been sealed. This prevents the solvent of the top coat from softening the material underneath and allowing it to bleed. Many pigmented stains and toners are self-sealing, but are intended for use under varnish or shellac, not under brushing lacquer, which softens them. Most sealers are similarly affected by brushing lacquer. Therefore, if a lacquer top coat is desired, the procedure to prevent the above trouble consists of "fogging" a lacquer sanding-sealer over the stain, toner or filler with a spray gun. So applied, this sealer dries before it can affect the underlying material. When dry, the sealer coat is followed by lacquer coats sprayed on, not brushed on, as brushing lacquer has a retarded drying time and may dissolve the sealer coat. Lacquer cannot be applied over varnish, but in refinishing work, varnish can be applied over lacquer.

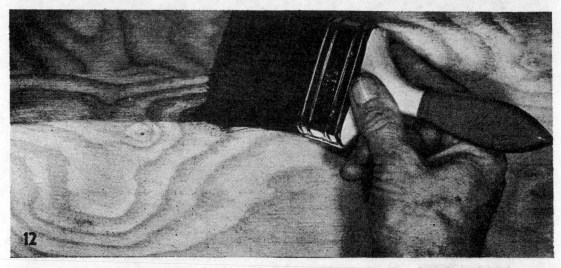

Staining or toning tends to add color beauty to wood and, in some cases, helps accentuate the grain

Stains and Staining

Wood is tinted by staining or toning as in Fig. 12. Getting the right color and shade is first done experimentally on scrap wood of the same kind as the furniture to be finished. Types of stains are given in Fig. 13. A pigmented stain does not have the color clarity of penetrating stain, which contains a dye. Pigment stain usually is applied by brush or cloth and is allowed to stand for 5 to 10 min. before the excess is wiped off with a clean, soft cloth. The time varies with the wood and the shade desired. If the stain gets dry or gummy before wiping, the cloth is dampened with benzine or turpentine. The stain should dry from 3 to 4 hrs. before the next finishing step. Pigment stain is more effective on softwood than on hardwood. On some softwoods, which absorb stain unevenly, it is best to first use a wash coat of ½-lb. cut shellac, which is allowed to dry, and then sand before applying the stain. Penetrating stains are most effective on hardwoods. Penetrating sealer-stains have become highly popular, as they stain and seal in one operation. Varnish stains should not be used on new work where the grain is to be left visible.

Stains having high-color clarity and permanence can be made by dissolving aniline dye in powder form in water, wood alcohol or lacquer thinner as in Fig. 14. These can be used under lacquer. The mixing proportions are powder, 1 oz., to wood alcohol, 1 qt., or the same amount of hot water just below boiling temperature. For lighter or darker shades the amount of the solvent is varied. After preparing this stain it should be passed through a fine strainer. Using alcohol makes a nongrain-raising stain, but if water is used, the resulting stain raises wood grain, which then requires resanding. After application, the stain is wiped to produce a uniform tone. Water stain requires from 12 to 24 hrs. of drying time. The alcohol stain dries very fast and must

Ready-mixed stains are of three general types: pigmented, penetrating and combination sealer-stain

Mix-your-own stain consists of dissolving powdered aniline dye in water or in wood alcohol

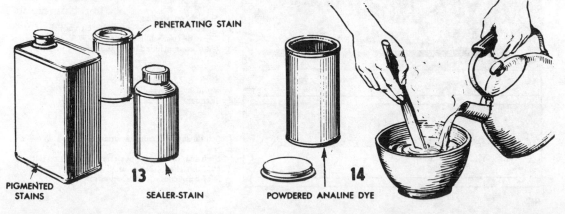

PENETRATING STAIN

PIGMENTED STAINS

13

SEALER-STAIN

POWDERED ANALINE DYE

14

15   10 BASIC STEPS IN FINISHING

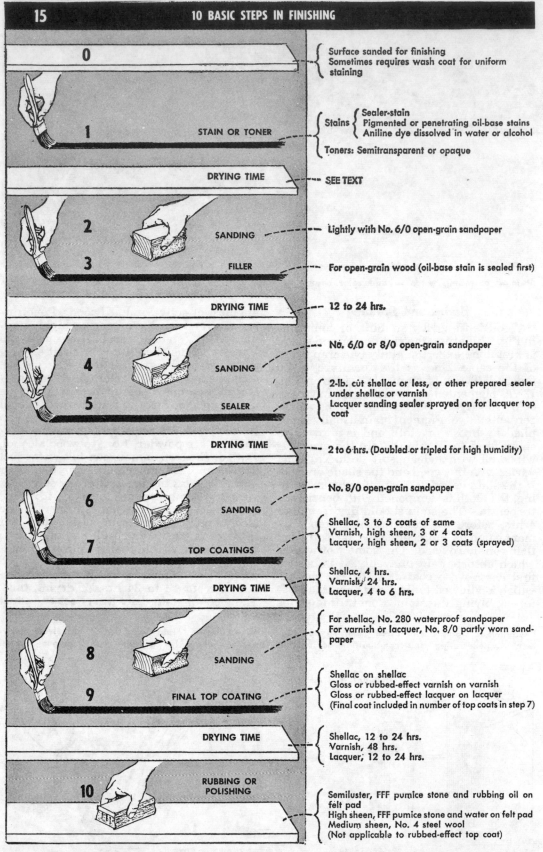

0
Surface sanded for finishing
Sometimes requires wash coat for uniform staining

1 — STAIN OR TONER

Stains { Sealer-stain
Pigmented or penetrating oil-base stains
Aniline dye dissolved in water or alcohol

Toners: Semitransparent or opaque

DRYING TIME — SEE TEXT

2 — SANDING — Lightly with No. 6/0 open-grain sandpaper

3 — FILLER — For open-grain wood (oil-base stain is sealed first)

DRYING TIME — 12 to 24 hrs.

4 — SANDING — No. 6/0 or 8/0 open-grain sandpaper

5 — SEALER
2-lb. cut shellac or less, or other prepared sealer under shellac or varnish
Lacquer sanding sealer sprayed on for lacquer top coat

DRYING TIME — 2 to 6 hrs. (Doubled or tripled for high humidity)

6 — SANDING — No. 8/0 open-grain sandpaper

7 — TOP COATINGS
Shellac, 3 to 5 coats of same
Varnish, high sheen, 3 or 4 coats
Lacquer, high sheen, 2 or 3 coats (sprayed)

DRYING TIME
Shellac, 4 hrs.
Varnish, 24 hrs.
Lacquer, 4 to 6 hrs.

8 — SANDING
For shellac, No. 280 waterproof sandpaper
For varnish or lacquer, No. 8/0 partly worn sandpaper

9 — FINAL TOP COATING
Shellac on shellac
Gloss or rubbed-effect varnish on varnish
Gloss or rubbed-effect lacquer on lacquer
(Final coat included in number of top coats in step 7)

DRYING TIME
Shellac, 12 to 24 hrs.
Varnish, 48 hrs.
Lacquer, 12 to 24 hrs.

10 — RUBBING OR POLISHING
Semiluster, FFF pumice stone and rubbing oil on felt pad
High sheen, FFF pumice stone and water on felt pad
Medium sheen, No. 4 steel wool
(Not applicable to rubbed-effect top coat)

be applied rapidly, preferably by spraying, to assure uniformity. When brushed on large surfaces it should be applied in two half-strength coats with a wide brush, working fast for quick and uniform coverage. A drying time of 2 to 3 hrs. is allowed.

In using any stain, the light-colored mineral streaks in wood are first darkened, using a small brush, after which the over-all surface is stained. Stain will not penetrate glue spots, or many other spots, which should be removed previously. Bleaching new wood generally is not recommended. Instead, it is better to use lighter wood or to use toners for lightening dark wood.

Toning or Glazing

This process is practically the same as staining with pigmented stain. Colored pigments reduced to a thin paint are used to partly or wholly obscure the wood grain. By so changing the appearance of wood, less-expensive kinds often can be used.

To produce bleached or frosted effects the pigment is white, which may be tinted. It is applied over the entire surface as in Fig. 16. When the color starts to dull, the toner is delicately wiped in the direction of grain with a clean, lint-free, soft cloth, folded to suit as in Fig. 17. The amount of wiping largely controls the degree of transparency obtained although the toner itself is thin and semitransparent after it has been applied.

For contrasty grain effects in open-grain woods, such as oak, walnut or mahogany, toning is more opaque, with little or no wiping, and after the coating has dried, the wood grain is filled with a contrasting paste wood filler as in Fig. 18.

Toners may be pigmented sealers applied over a sealer-stain or over ordinary stain. They may consist of colors ground in japan and thinned with turpentine, or they may consist simply of flat enamel or enamel undercoater, 1 part, and turpentine, 2 parts. Toners should dry from 12 to 24 hrs., or according to the manufacturer's recommendations.

Paste Wood Filler

To make the surface of open-grained wood smooth, it is filled with paste wood filler. This is never done directly on bare wood or over an oil-base stain without a wash coat of ½-lb. cut shellac or other sealer. The shellac wash coat consists of 4 or 5-lb. cut shellac, 1 part, dissolved in wood alcohol, 8 parts. Filling can be done directly on sealer-stain after this has dried. The sealer or sealer-stain is sanded with No. 8/0 sandpaper before filler is applied.

The filler is reduced to the consistency of a heavy cream for large pores, and to

Light, semitransparent toner being brushed on. Lower part of photo shows the untreated surface

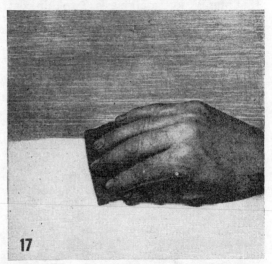

Above, toner partly wiped off, giving frosty effect.

Below, wiping off filler applied over dark toner

19

Lacquer is best sprayed on. Work should be mounted on turntable in a spray booth, or taken outdoors

that of milk for small pores. Two thin coats applied 12 hrs. apart are better than a single thick coat. A solvent may be recommended on the can for reducing the filler, or equal parts of benzine and turpentine can be used. A variety of colors can be obtained by adding stain or pigment to the filler, pigment being reduced with benzine before it is added.

Filler is brushed well into the grain, covering an area not greater than can be wiped before the filler turns flat. The excess is wiped off first across the grain with burlap, then with the grain, using a soft cloth. This is done carefully to avoid pulling the filler out of the pores. If excess filler is not all removed, the subsequent finish will appear blotchy. Rags used for wiping off filler are disposed of immediately as they are subject to spontaneous combustion. A stiff stencil brush is used to clean filler from moldings, carvings and scrollwork. Dried filler is picked off with a sharpened dowel. When dry, the filled surfaces are sanded with No. 8/0 sandpaper.

Pad sander fitted with felt shoe helps reduce the work of polishing, as well as the work of sanding

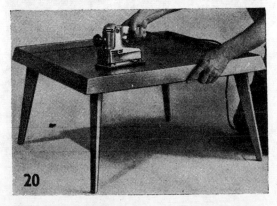

20

Sealing

Where sealer-stain was used and no filler over it, the separate step of sealing is eliminated. Ordinary stain is sealed before applying filler. Filler, when dry, also is sealed. Sealers should not be applied thickly, as they are brittle and tend to check.

Shellac is the most-common sealer for use under varnish. It should be a 2-lb. cut or less. A lacquer sanding sealer is used under a lacquer top coat sprayed on. Some synthetic sealers also serve as top coats. Most sealers dry in 2 to 6 hrs., but this time is doubled or tripled when humidity is high, especially for shellac. A sealer should be so dry that it can be sanded with No. 8/0 sandpaper to a powder without clogging the sandpaper. Sealers can be applied with a soft, long-bristle brush, or sprayed. Lacquer sealers are sprayed—not brushed—over any undercoat that may bleed.

Shellac Top Coat

Although a shellac top coat is damaged easily by water and alcohol, such damage is simply repaired by recoating with shellac. A wax coat over shellac will retard the action of water and alcohol. White shellac is used on lightwood and on walnut. Orange shellac may be used on mahogany and other dark woods, but tends to darken them further. Shellac tends to discolor in a few months after having been exposed to air. It should not be applied heavier than a 2-lb. cut, and only wood alcohol is used to thin it. A good top coat of shellac is built up by three to five applications, each being allowed to dry fully and then sanded. Drying time for shellac top coats is given in Fig. 15. For sanding shellac, No. 280 wet-or-dry paper is best, applying a little light machine oil to the surface to minimize heating from friction.

Varnish and Lacquer Top Coats

A substantial top coat consists of three or four applications of varnish, or two or three applications of lacquer. The lacquer coats are sprayed on, Fig. 19. All coats should have a hard, high-sheen surface, but the final coat may be one that gives a rubbed-effect or stain finish. The stain finish should not be used for undercoats as it then will produce a cloudy appearance.

Most varnishes are thinned with turpentine, but the so-called plastic finishes require special thinners. Varnish should not be shaken or stirred before application as this produces air bubbles which are transferred to the work. Varnish is brushed on in a full-flowing coat. See Fig. 15 for drying time. Lacquer is clearer than varnish. When thinning lacquer for spray-gun application the best grade of thinner is used. Lacquers are applied in full wet coats and can be sanded and recoated in 4 to 6 hrs. but the final coat should dry from 12 to 24 hrs. before it is rubbed.

Sanding Between Coats

Light sanding with partly worn No. 8/0 sandpaper between coats is done to cut the glaze and to make the next coat adhere better. It also removes dust specks and high spots. Care is taken to avoid cutting through the coats, espcially at corners and sharp edges. Heavy runs should not be sanded until a 48-hr. period has elapsed. Care is taken to avoid heating which results in gumming and peeling. After surfaces are sanded, the dust is brushed off and the surfaces wiped with a tack rag to remove all traces of dust before applying the next coat. A tack rag is a lint-free rag dampened slightly with thinned varnish, and used when nearly dry.

Rubbing and Polishing

Proper rubbing of thoroughly dry varnished or lacquered surfaces produces a smooth, satin finish. Rubbed-effect or satin-finish varnish or lacquer should never be rubbed as they do not have sufficient hardness for this. Rubbing always is done with the grain of the wood, using light pressure. A pad sander can be used for this purpose as in Fig. 20.

Where a real fine finish is not required No. 4/0 steel wool may be used. A higher sheen is obtained by lubricating the work with soapy water. A dull satin finish is produced by rubbing with FFF pumice stone and rubbing oil, using a ½-in. felt pad about 2½ by 4 in. in size. No other oil than rubbing oil should be used. The pad is first dipped in the oil, then in the pumice stone, which is repeated as necessary, keeping enough oil on the pad to prevent rubbing dry. All traces of oil and pumice are wiped off after rubbing. A highly polished finish is produced by rubbing with FFF pumice stone and water, using the same procedure of wetting the pad. After cleaning off the work, a rubbing with rottenstone and water on the following day will bring out a high luster. ★ ★ ★

Valuable Advice From Master Craftsman on Refinishing Antiques

A master craftsman, wise in the ways of refinishing antiques to the smoothness of old ivory and with a gleaming, rich luster, gave me the following tips: First, clean the work with a good paint and varnish remover, using a cheap brush to apply a generous coat over a small area. Let the remover stand about 15 min. and, without wiping it off, apply a second coat. Then mix a gallon of warm water with a cup of household ammonia and use the mixture with a stiff-bristled brush to scour the treated surface. Dip a rough cloth (an old towel is excellent) into the ammonia water and wipe the area. Rinse at once with clear water, removing all traces of ammonia and the work should be good and clean. Remember to clean only a small area at a time, for if varnish remover is applied over too large an area, it will harden into a cement-like finish. Should that happen, apply more remover—several coats, 15 min. apart—until you can wipe the surface clean. Before further refinishing is done, make any necessary repairs to the work. Then sand with 1/0 or 2/0 garnet or sandpaper until very smooth. Wipe clean and apply the first coat of shellac, using a 4-lb. cut. Thin a pint of shellac with a pint of denatured alcohol. Use orange shellac on dark woods, such as mahogany, cherry and walnut, and white shellac on the lighter woods. Using a pure bristle brush, apply two coats of shellac with the grain of the wood, allowing 4 or 5 hrs. between coats. Between succeeding coats, allow 24 to 48 hrs. drying time. Sand after each coat using 6/0 or 7/0 garnet paper. Never apply shellac in damp or humid weather, and if the shellac gums up on the sandpaper, allow more drying time. When you have built up the desired number of coats, mix 3 heaping tablespoonfuls of fine pumice with paraffin oil to attain a creamy mixture. Then dip a pad of 000 steel wool in the mixture and rub the work briskly with the grain. When finished, wipe the surface with a soft cloth. Repeat this process twice.—Ray Wilkie, Lexington, Ky.

HAND-RUBBED FINISH

On home-shop furniture projects the final touch of the craftsman is best expressed in a hand-rubbed finish

THAT GLASS-SMOOTH satiny finish you see on high-grade furniture is still done by skillful hand-rubbing with powdered abrasives. What happens to the surface of the finish during the rubbing process is shown graphically in Fig. 1. Rubbing the dry finish removes brush marks, orange peel (the wavy effect caused by spraying lacquers without the proper retarders), dust specks and bubbles. All are common defects and are almost impossible to avoid in some degree unless the finish can be applied under ideal conditions of dust-free air and rigid temperature control. The first rubbing removes defects and levels the finish, giving it a dull, flat appearance. Then the surface is brought to varying degrees of sheen, or gloss, with a flour-fine abrasive and a final polishing. In current practice the finish is left dull flat on antiques. For period furniture a semigloss is preferred but on modern designs the finish usually is rubbed to a high satin polish.

Although rubbing may be done with a cloth pad, a thick felt pad is best. Felt has just enough "give" to follow slight irregularities without danger of cutting through the finish. Powdered pumice, FFF grade or finer, is commonly used for the first rubbing. Pour the powder into a tumbler of water as in Fig. 2 and allow it to settle before pouring off the water. Mix the sediment to a creamy paste. Some finishers

BEFORE RUBBING

AFTER RUBBING

1

Pour abrasive powder into a glass tumbler about two thirds full of water and allow to settle. Then pour off most of the water and mix to a creamy paste

Brush the paste onto the surface to be rubbed, applying it in a thin film of uniform thickness. Be sure that the brush used is clean and free from grit

2

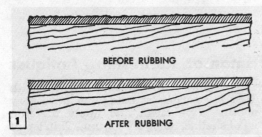

3

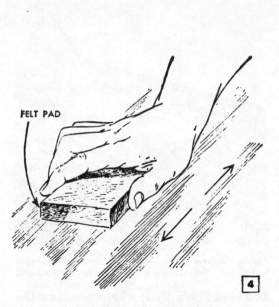

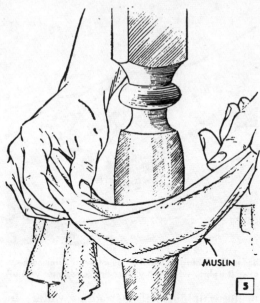

Use a felt rubbing pad for polishing flat surfaces with the grain and make sure that the pad is clean

Turnings can be polished with a clean cloth charged with abrasive cream. Use only light polishing pressure

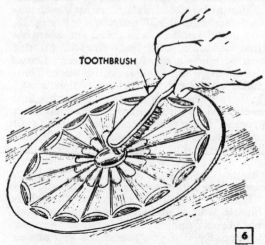

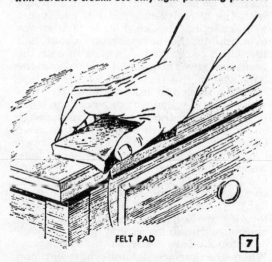

Above, paint small carvings with abrasive cream and polish with a toothbrush. Below, some finishers apply wax with a cloth pad to get a uniform coating

Above, be careful not to cut through finish when sanding or rubbing corners and edges. Below, some finishers prefer to apply paste wax with a steel-wool pad

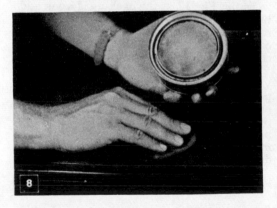

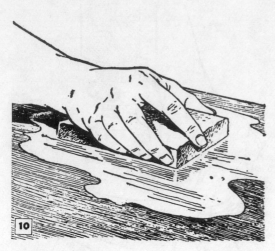

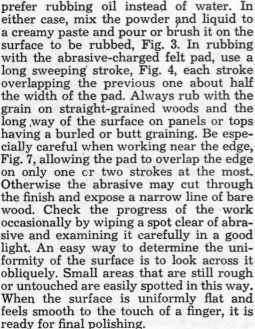

Before polishing certain types of work, finishers go over it lightly with 8/0 wet-or-dry sandpaper and oil

Expert finishers often polish varnished work simply by rubbing the surface with the palm of the hand

prefer rubbing oil instead of water. In either case, mix the powder and liquid to a creamy paste and pour or brush it on the surface to be rubbed, Fig. 3. In rubbing with the abrasive-charged felt pad, use a long sweeping stroke, Fig. 4, each stroke overlapping the previous one about half the width of the pad. Always rub with the grain on straight-grained woods and the long way of the surface on panels or tops having a burled or butt graining. Be especially careful when working near the edge, Fig. 7, allowing the pad to overlap the edge on only one or two strokes at the most. Otherwise the abrasive may cut through the finish and expose a narrow line of bare wood. Check the progress of the work occasionally by wiping a spot clear of abrasive and examining it carefully in a good light. An easy way to determine the uniformity of the surface is to look across it obliquely. Small areas that are still rough or untouched are easily spotted in this way. When the surface is uniformly flat and feels smooth to the touch of a finger, it is ready for final polishing.

Turned legs, pressed or carved moldings and both overlay and relief carvings require a different treatment. Turnings are rubbed by means of an abrasive-charged muslin cloth as in Fig. 5, special care being taken not to rub the finish off the high places. Small carvings are rubbed with an old toothbrush after painting the surface with the abrasive cream. On large carvings a worn scrubbing brush is often used to advantage. In finishing carvings be careful to brush as much as possible lengthwise of the high places, not across them. This often will require brushing in several directions. As a rule, carvings and the short-radius portions of turnings are left in a dull gloss finish. When a lathe turning is the project, rubbing can be done with the work turning at slow speed, Fig 15.

In polishing a finer abrasive is used. Also, it should be noted that if nothing but water is added to the 3F pumice slush, Fig. 13, continued rubbing will grind the abrasive finer and finer. A thorough rub with pumice will produce a medium-low sheen. Leave the spent rubbing slush on the work. Then make a final rub with clean cotton waste.

For a polished finish, let the work stand overnight and then continue the rubbing process, using rottenstone and rubbing oil or water. Rottenstone does not actually cut like pumice but it will bring up a polish quickly if the work has been pumice-rubbed absolutely level. After rubbing, clean thoroughly with a clean damp rag.

Lacquer presents a harder surface than varnish and is often rubbed with wet-or-dry abrasive papers which cut faster than pumice. Even if you prefer the soft action of pumice, a quick cut-down with 8/0 paper lubricated with water or oil, Fig. 10, will greatly lessen the labor of pumice rubbing. The paper should be soaked a few minutes in water, Fig. 12, as the backing is weak and brittle when dry. A satisfactory satin finish, can be obtained with 8/0 paper alone, but can be followed by rottenstone or rubbing compound for higher gloss if desired.

Rubbing compounds are available in a variety of types and grits for coarse or fine polishing. In all types of rubbing, they are preferred by many finishers to the older pumice and rottenstone abrasives. Compounds are supplied in paste form and may be used with or without a lubricant, depending on type.

Within the scope of rubbing technique, French polishing is worth considering.

Wet-or-dry abrasive paper should be soaked in water for flexibility and strength. Right, in the final stages of pumice rubbing, add water to the spent slush to reduce cutting action

Don't try this with homemade mixtures of shellac and alcohol—buy a good ready-made product and you will be surprised how easily and quickly you can give any varnish or lacquer surface a high gloss. First, give the finish a good rub with 8/0 paper and water. Dry thoroughly. Pour a little of the polish on a soft cloth or gauze pad, and apply to the work with a circular motion, Fig. 14. Add more polish as needed. Make a final wipe with long sweeping strokes with the grain.

Frenching with a ready-made polish is an easy and fast way to build a high polish. Left, turned projects can be rubbed or polished while revolving in the lathe

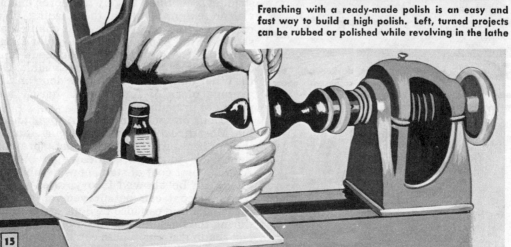

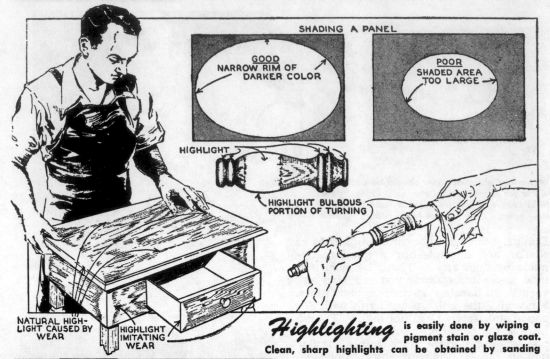

SHADING A PANEL

GOOD
NARROW RIM OF
DARKER COLOR

POOR
SHADED AREA
TOO LARGE

HIGHLIGHT

HIGHLIGHT BULBOUS
PORTION OF TURNING

NATURAL HIGH-
LIGHT CAUSED BY
WEAR

HIGHLIGHT
IMITATING
WEAR

Highlighting is easily done by wiping a pigment stain or glaze coat. Clean, sharp highlights can be obtained by sanding

Shading certain areas darker with stain or a different color with enamel is easily done with the spray gun, using a small pattern for good atomization to produce even blending

ANTIQUING

SHADING plays an important part in the finishing of period furniture, and also has a considerable role in the decoration of other projects in both wood and metal. Briefly, the technique is simply a matter of lightening or darkening certain areas of the work to contrast with the general tone of the piece. Related terms include highlighting, glazing, antiquing, smutting, etc.

Spray shading: The spray gun is an excellent tool for shaded effects, and is capable of either sharp or soft shading. Sharp shading is confined largely to colored enamels, an example being the shading of a cream-colored chair with blue enamel, as shown in the photo at left. The color separation is strong and sharply defined—it is a kind of shading that is plainly visible. On the other hand, soft shading, as done on the average piece of furniture, is hardly apparent at first glance.

Various methods are used in spray shading. Most direct is to shade the work during the application of the stain coat, spraying lightly on some parts, heavy on others. Again, a first coat of stain, considerably diluted, can be' allowed to dry, after which a second coat can be sprayed for shaded areas. Shading can also be done at any time during the finishing schedule by using special shading stains. These can be purchased ready-mixed or made by mixing powder stain with thin shellac or lacquer. Soft

Glazing is the term for a shading medium or technique. In the example above, the ground coat is blue, left photo. The white glaze is brushed on, center, and then wiped to expose the highlights, as shown in right photo

spray shading should be done with a small spray pattern and with the gun held 10 to 20 in. from the work.

Highlighting: If you don't have a spray gun—or perhaps even if you do—you can do shaded work by the reverse technique of highlighting. This is easily done with pigment oil stain, penetrating oil stain, and to some extent is practical with almost any type of stain. Cleaner wiping for highlights can be obtained if done on a second coat of wiping stain applied over a sealer. That is, you stain first for a uniform body color, not too dark. Then apply a sealer coat. Over the sealer coat brush on a second coat of pigment wiping stain. Clean this off rather thoroughly with a rag to leave the stain only on areas which are to appear darker.

Highlighting can also be done mechanically on the first stain coat after it is dry by using fine sandpaper or steel wool, as shown in the photo. This is sometimes useful to obtain a few very sharp highlights. It has the fault that if overdone, patching by restaining is not always easy.

Glazing: Glazing is the term which most nearly describes the whole art of using a wiped, translucent shading medium. You can glaze a piece of work and then wipe it for highlights. You can glaze the work with the idea of antiquing it. Or you can use a glaze coat for a textured ground or to imitate wood grain. The glaze itself can be any wiping stain, any thin paint, etc., but is specifically a product called glazing liquid. This can be purchased ready made or can be made with varnish, 4 parts, boiled linseed oil, 2 parts, and turpentine, 1 part. Pigment colors in oil or japan are added as needed to obtain desired colors. The glaze coat is applied over a foundation coat of sealer or colored enamel. It is sprayed or brushed over the whole area and is immediately wiped with a cloth or blended out with a dry brush. It can also be applied with a cloth and wiped with the same cloth, a kind of rubbing-on process.

A soft-brown glaze on an off-white enamel ground (bone-white finish) is effective. The same on a cream ground gives a pleasing soft, shaded effect. For a clear finish, the glaze coat should be somewhat darker than the wood or the stained color of the wood. For colored enamel finishes, any of hundreds of color combinations can be used. An example is shown in the photos.

For most work, the glaze should be wiped rather thoroughly. Graining effects can be obtained by wiping the glaze coat with a dry brush, whisk broom, combs and other gadgets. You can use your finger for tricky texture effects and designs. If a glaze coat becomes too tacky for clean working, it can be wiped with a cloth moistened with naphtha.

General technique: Regardless of how you do this shading, highlighting or antiquing, the work should not be overdone. On clear finishes especially, any shading or highlighting should be soft. A combination of methods is sometimes useful. For example, it is nearly impossible to spray-shade carvings, but it is very easy to apply pigment stain or glaze and then expose highlights by wiping. On the other hand, the spray gun is excellent for shading panels and table tops. Turnings are best treated by wiping since a simple run-over with a rag from end to end will automatically highlight the bulbous portions.

ROTTENSTONE

LINSEED OIL

BOILED LINSEED OIL

SPAR VARNISH

PASTE FILLER

TURPENTINE

ALKANET ROOT

OIL FINISHING

②

MULE-HIDE LEATHER FACING

BUFFING BLOCK

BUFFING STICK

① MATERIALS AND TOOLS NEEDED

After sanding, the wood is moistened with water, using either a sponge or cloth pad ③

Then the surface is steamed by playing the flame of a blowtorch over the dampened wood ④

This raises the grain which is removed by sanding lightly with very fine sandpaper ⑤

MANY articles made of wood, particularly of walnut, cherry and mahogany, can be given a beautiful soft finish with linseed oil. Unlike most finishes, the oil finish is in the wood, not on it, making the surface proof against ordinary wear and scratching and the wood itself highly moisture-resistant.

Materials needed: Few materials are needed, and only two tools—a buffing stick and a buffing block, as shown in Fig. 1. The stick is used somewhat like a file to buff off legs, spindles and other rounded surfaces, while the block is used on table tops and other flat surfaces. Both tools are covered with leather, the time-honored material being mule hide, but other leathers, canvas or cloth are all acceptable rubbers. The No. 1 material is boiled linseed oil. Then, depending on the job and working schedule, you may need some raw linseed oil, turpentine, rottenstone, spar varnish, dark paste filler (walnut), and a handful of alkanet root. The latter makes a staining red oil when steeped in linseed oil, producing a reddish tinge which enhances the appearance of most brownish woods. Any dark red oil stain in powder form can be used.

Surface preparation: One of the key features in oil finishing is that the work must be dead smooth. Final sanding paper should be 5/0 aluminum oxide or garnet. After the wood is perfectly smooth, wipe it with a damp cloth or sponge, Fig. 3, and dry quickly. Some experts use a blowtorch for drying, Fig. 4, but equally good results can be obtained with an electric heater. After the wood is dry, you will find it covered with whiskers. Cut these off with new, sharp sandpaper applied very lightly, Fig. 5. Some workers like 2/0 steel wool for this job because it slices off the very fine fuzz which sandpaper tends merely to flatten.

Oiling: A number of different procedures are used in applying the oil. Simplest but also the most work is straight coats of boiled linseed oil. Each coat is applied by hand or with a cloth or brush. It is immediately rubbed into the wood with the heel of

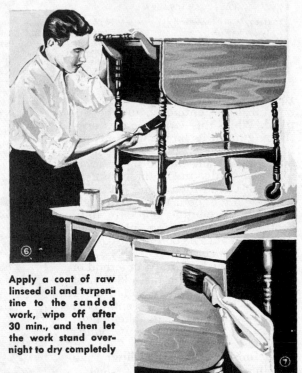

Apply a coat of raw linseed oil and turpentine to the sanded work, wipe off after 30 min., and then let the work stand overnight to dry completely

the hand. More oil can be added until it seems as if the wood has reached its absorption limit. The rubbing continues until the surface oil disappears—don't leave a skin of oil on the surface. The gunsmith's rule is to rub once a day for a week, once a week for a month, once a month for a year and once a year for life. Additional sanding with 8/0 paper can be done at any time as needed.

For furniture work on open-grain wood, the work should be filled with paste wood filler. This can be done on bare wood, or, a coat of raw linseed oil can first be applied as a staining medium, Fig. 6. Filler kills some of the excessive suction of bare wood, allowing the oil coats to build faster with less labor.

A third method starts off with a coat of raw linseed oil, 3 parts, mixed with turpentine, 1 part, Fig. 6. Let this stand 30 min., wipe off clean and let stand overnight. Next, apply paste wood filler, well-rubbed into the end grain. Tow this off in the usual manner and allow 24 hrs. dry. Then you swing into the "once a day for a week" with boiled linseed oil. Before the fourth rub, sand with 8/0 garnet. Before the seventh rub, use 3/0 steel wool. For the eighth coat, add japan drier half-and-half to linseed oil. Let this coat stand until it is tacky and then rub off with burlap or other coarse material, Fig. 9. Now, inspect the pores of the wood. If not filled nearly level, apply a thin mix of paste wood filler.

Final rubbing: The work has now reached the final-rubbing stage. Take your buff stick and rub the leather surface several times over a lump of rottenstone, Fig. 12. Use the buff stick just like you would a file; use the buffing block for flat surfaces. This step of the procedure removes any gummy oil deposit on the surface of the work. The leather will become slick and shiny from the oil it picks up, and should be scraped clean with a knife, Fig. 13. More rottenstone is then applied. A second result of rottenstone rubbing is that fine particles of the stone will embed in the wood, building the pores up perfectly flush. Just one rottenstone rub is enough, but it should be thorough.

Next, seal the surface against further absorption of oil with a coat or two of paste filler well rubbed into the wood end grain

After 12 hrs., apply from three to six coats of boiled oil 24 hrs. apart, rubbing each coat into the wood with the bare hands

Follow the oil treatment with a coat of boiled oil and drier and let dry until tacky; then rub the oil off across the wood grain

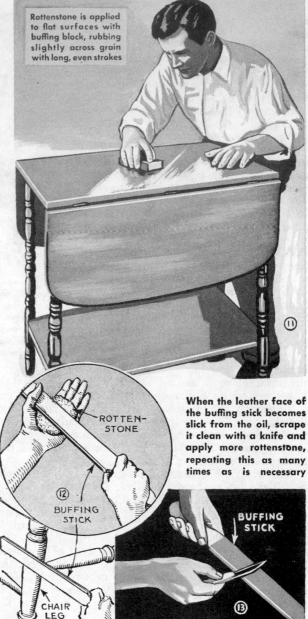

⑩ POLISH FORMULA

Heavy boiled linseed oil	16 oz.
Turpentine	2 oz.
Japan drier	1½ oz.
Venice turpentine	4 teaspoonfuls
Carnauba wax	400 grains

Rottenstone is applied to flat surfaces with buffing block, rubbing slightly across grain with long, even strokes

⑪

ROTTEN-STONE

⑫ BUFFING STICK

CHAIR LEG

When the leather face of the buffing stick becomes slick from the oil, scrape it clean with a knife and apply more rottenstone, repeating this as many times as is necessary

BUFFING STICK

⑬

Polishing: After the rottenstone rub, additional coats of oil mixed with one-third turpentine should be applied. While this is as good as anything, gunsmiths have numerous pet formulas, such as given in Fig. 10. To make this, melt the carnauba wax with the Venice turpentine in a double boiler. Add the oil and drier and let simmer for about 10 min. Then add the gum turpentine and stir until cool. Either this or the simpler oil-turp mix makes a good furniture polish for any surface.

French polish: A fourth method of oil finishing calls for the addition of spar varnish, 1 part, to boiled oil, 4 parts, making what is essentially a thin French polish. This takes about 48 hrs. between coats, but builds much faster than plain oil.

Oil finish for pine paneling: Pine paneling is attractive with a simplified oil finish. Mix gum turpentine, 1 part, with boiled linseed oil, 2 parts, and brush on like paint. The first coat will soak right in. After drying, apply a second coat. This will give a slight sheen to the work, which can be renewed as needed with additional coats. A single coat of the oil-turpentine mixture is often used as a stain under shellac or varnish. This is effective on aromatic red cedar and walnut as well as pine. The oil finish provides a perfectly satisfactory foundation for later coats of enamel or varnish—simply wipe with a rag moistened with turpentine or naphtha to remove any gummy residue, and then go ahead with the new finish.

Linseed oil: The oil used for the hand-rubbed oil finish should be pure, boiled linseed oil. Do not use substitute products. Linseed oil is crushed from flaxseed. The basic product is raw linseed oil, which is thin, dark and slow-drying. Allowed to season several years in the sun, raw linseed oil becomes clearer, heavier-bodied and tacky, making what is known as "stand oil." A short cut to stand oil is kettle-boiled oil, which is thickened by the direct application of heat. Although these heavy oils were popular at one time, they are poor finishing materials, tending to produce a gummy surface film rather than impregna-

tion deep into the pores of the wood.

In modern methods, pure linseed oil is reinforced by the addition of polymerized or heat-treated linseed oil, plus driers. This product has all the toughness of the raw oil film, plus faster drying. This kind should be used wherever linseed oil is indicated; the cheaper sort can be used where drying time is not important.

The hand-rubbed oil finish is a labor of love. If you want a quicker finish with about the same features, you can do the job with penetrating floor sealer. Don't forget that one coat of paste filler is worth 10 coats of oil for building up the surface.

EIGHT OCCASIONAL PIECES YOU CAN MAKE

Includes drop-leaf table for combination living-dining room and sectional wall ensemble with versatile units

DESIGNED as companion pieces to harmonize with dining and living-room furniture of almost any style, these smart occasional pieces can be used to augment other pieces you already have or used by themselves in any particular arrangement you desire. The drop-leaf table pictured above is designed especially for a dining alcove where limited space does not permit room for even a small dinette set. Such is the case in the latest trend toward eliminating a separate dining room in favor of a combination living-dining room. This table is also ideal for the one-room or one-and-a-half-room-apartment dwellers. This piece adequately fills the requirement for a table that takes little space against the wall when not in use, and yet has big-table capacity when needed. To seat four persons comfortably, the leaves of the table are raised to a horizontal position and the whole top is rotated 90 deg. on a center pivot. In this position, the base of the table supports the drop leaves as

1 TABLE OPEN

2 TABLE FULLY EXTENDED

shown in Fig. 1. Retractable brackets in each end of the table pull out to support the leaves when the table is fully extended. A lazy-tong mechanism, taking the place of the usual extension slide, extends to permit insertion of two extra leaves, Fig. 2, providing a top surface 40 x 74 in. When the table is fully extended, you can accommodate six to eight dinner guests. You can either make your own dining chairs for the table or purchase suitable unfinished ones, to which you can apply a finish to match the table. In selecting the type of dining chairs you want, it is suggested that one which is not too bulky be chosen to stay in keeping with the compact table. Actual construction of the table, detailed in Figs. 12, 13 and 14, will be explained step by step later in the article.

The pieces of the functional wall ensemble pictured above are coordinated in size to fit together in a number of separate sectional arrangements in addition to the complete grouping shown. The arrangement pictured above is ideal for a rectangular-shaped room. The window unit can be shifted so that it is positioned correctly in front of the window. Here are other arrangements. For the first example, the secretary, which is pictured in use at the bottom of the opposite page, may be combined with an open-end bookcase at each side. Likewise, the three-shelf unit, with doors at the bottom, may be grouped in the same way. An attractive corner grouping is had by flanking the corner bookcase with end bookcases. Still another arrangement is to place the window unit between two end bookcases. These are but a few of the attractive arrangements that are possible with these sectional pieces. If desired, any one of the three basic units, namely, the secretary, three-drawer chest and two-door chest, may be used individually.

The secretary features a pull-out writing shelf which looks like a drawer when closed. This piece, in the closed position, is shown second from the left. The "drawer" front is hinged with special fixtures and lets down to become part of the writing surface, as illustrated at the right on the facing page. The secretary, like the other pieces, is made primarily from plywood, with solid stock being used for the drawers, base and edging. The edging is used here to give a

hopper-front effect and at the same time to conceal the laminations of the plywood. Figs. 3 and 4 detail the construction of the secretary. In comparing its construction with that of the other pieces you will notice that much of the construction is duplicated. The bases are all the same, as are the drawers and, in most cases, even the manner in which the plywood panels are fitted. The exception is noted in the window, corner and end units which are designed to be flanked by other pieces. Here, the plywood is placed on the inside instead of the outside of the framework. Plywood, ¼ in. thick, is used to cover the sides and back of the secretary, while a heavier stock of ¾-in. plywood is used for the top.

Make the base assembly first. The members are mitered at all four corners, the rear member having a rabbet cut in the top edge to take the plywood back. A small, ⅛-in. cove is run along the top edges of the other pieces, which can be done either before or after gluing and nailing the base together. The hopper edging which frames the front of the cabinet is shaped according to the sectional details included with the

cutaway drawing, Fig. 4. The center and bottom shelves can be of plywood, or glued up from solid stock. These should be cut 31½ in. long and the front edge of the bottom shelf rabbeted for the hopper edging. Then the bottom shelf is glued and nailed

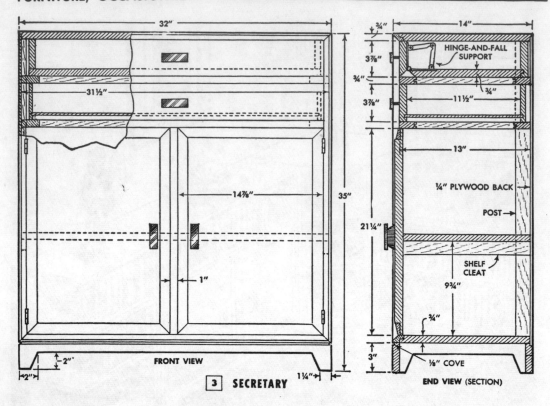

32"

31½"

14⅞"

1"

35"

2"

2"

1¼"

FRONT VIEW

3 SECRETARY

¾"

14"

3⅞"

HINGE-AND-FALL SUPPORT

¾"

¾"

3⅞"

11½"

13"

¼" PLYWOOD BACK

POST

21¼"

SHELF CLEAT

9¾"

¾"

3"

⅛" COVE

END VIEW (SECTION)

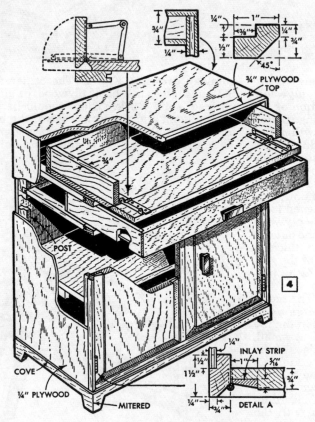

¾"

¼"

¼"

½"

¼"

1"

⅜"

¼"

¾"

45"

¾" PLYWOOD TOP

¾"

POST

4

COVE

¼" PLYWOOD

MITERED

¼"

INLAY STRIP

1"

3/16

¾"

1½"

¼"

¾"

DETAIL A

to the base assembly. The ¾-in. top, including the edging, should have the same over-all measurements as the base. This is rabbeted on all four edges. Note at the ends that the rabbets are cut ¼ in. deep and to the thickness of the top ply of the wood. The top is supported at the rear corners by posts and at the front by the hopper edging. Frames for the drawer and writing shelf are typical open frames, being assembled from ¾ x 1¾-in. stock. Inner edges of the front and rear members are grooved to take tenons formed on the ends of the side members. The frames are fitted into notches cut in the rear posts and supported at the front by nailing into them through the edging rabbet. The ¼-in. side panels will probably overlap the edge of the plywood back and are cut to fit accurately in the rabbets of the top and in the edging strips. The writing shelf is made similarly to a drawer except that the front is hinged. Note in the sectional detail, Fig. 4, that the bottom edge of the front piece is beveled to match a similar cut made on the front edge of the shelf. A stop should be fitted in the underside of the top to prevent the shelf from being pulled all the way out, and a bullet friction catch installed to hold the drop front closed. Construction of the drawer is apparent from the drawing. Plywood is best for the two doors, but solid stock can be used. In producing the raised-panel effect in plywood, an inlay strip is used to conceal the plies as indicated in detail A, Fig. 4. The door and drawer handles pictured are made up special from ¼-in. brass. Fig. 11 shows how these are soldered together T-shaped and then drilled and tapped for attaching with machine screws. The edges are rounded slightly with a fine file and then the brass is buffed to a high polish. A thin coat of clear lacquer will keep the handles bright.

The three-drawer chest is

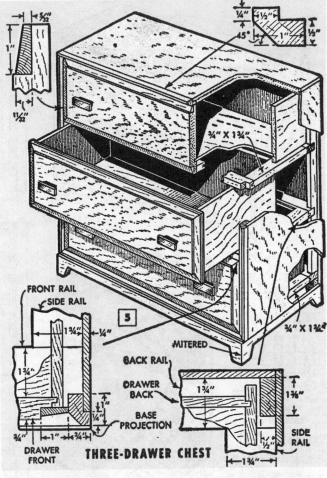

THREE-DRAWER CHEST

FRONT RAIL
SIDE RAIL
MITERED
BACK RAIL
DRAWER BACK
BASE PROJECTION
SIDE RAIL
DRAWER FRONT

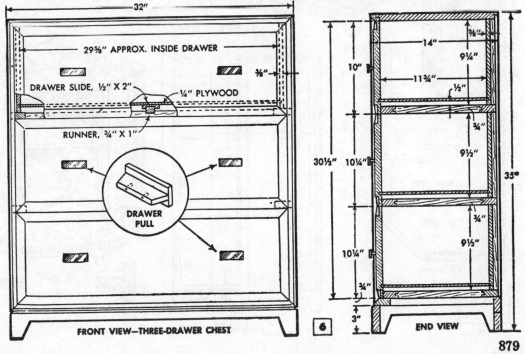

FRONT VIEW—THREE-DRAWER CHEST

29⅝" APPROX. INSIDE DRAWER
DRAWER SLIDE, ½" X 2"
¼" PLYWOOD
RUNNER, ¾" X 1"
DRAWER PULL
32"

END VIEW

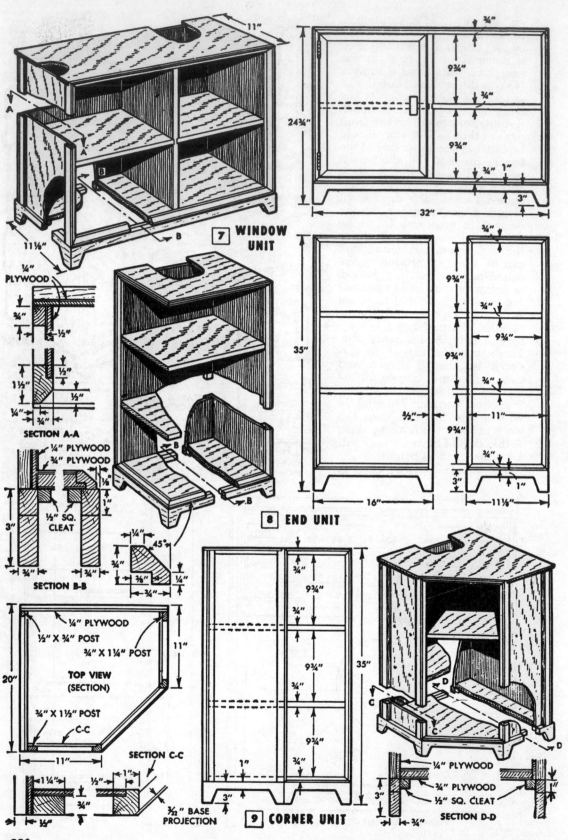

11"

A

A

B

11⅛"

¼"
PLYWOOD

¾"

½"

½"

1½"

½"

¼"

¾"

SECTION A-A

¼" PLYWOOD
¾" PLYWOOD

½" SQ.
CLEAT

3"

¾"   ¾"

SECTION B-B

45°

¾"

⅜"   ¼"

¾"

B

B

7 WINDOW UNIT

¾"

9¾"

24¾"

9¾"

¾" 1"

3"

32"

35"

½"

16"

9¾"

¾"

9¾"

9¾"

¾"

¾"

9¾"

11"

¾"

3"

1"

11⅛"

8 END UNIT

¼" PLYWOOD
½" X ¾" POST
¾" X 1¼" POST

11"

20"

**TOP VIEW
(SECTION)**

¾" X 1½" POST

C-C

11"

SECTION C-C

1¼"   1"

½"

¾"

½"

3/32" BASE
PROJECTION

¾"

9¾"

¾"

9¾"

¾"

9¾"

¾"

1"

3"

9 CORNER UNIT

D

C

C

D

35"

G

¼" PLYWOOD
¾" PLYWOOD
½" SQ. CLEAT

3"

1"

¾"

SECTION D-D

880

basically of the same construction. The cutaway drawing in Fig. 5 and the front and side views in Fig. 6 give the necessary details. Typical chest construction is employed with frames supporting each drawer. Hopper edging is applied as explained before and the drawer fronts are inlaid around the edges. The front view, Fig. 6, details the drawer runners. The strip nailed to the frame engages a wooden channel which is glued and bradded to the bottom of the drawer. This same type of runner is used for the drawer of the secretary. The lower details, Fig. 5, show plan views of the drawer at the front and rear corners.

Window, end and corner units, Figs. 7, 8 and 9, differ basically in construction in that the plywood side panels are placed on the inside of the cabinets instead of the outside. Whether this should be done on the side of the corner unit depends upon the grouping arrangement. If placed next to the window unit as pictured on page 877,

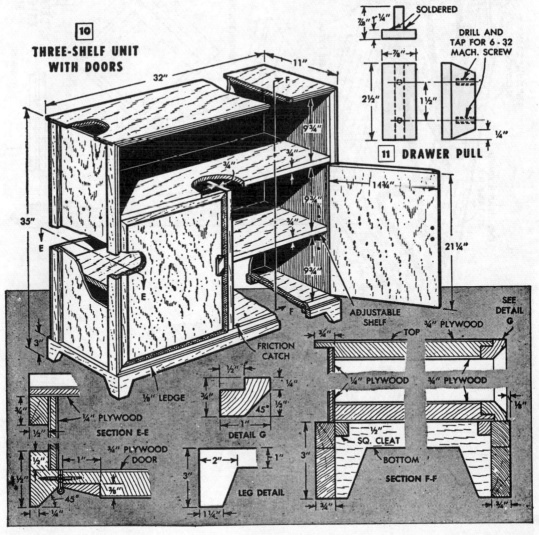

10 THREE-SHELF UNIT WITH DOORS

11 DRAWER PULL

SOLDERED
DRILL AND TAP FOR 6-32 MACH. SCREW

ADJUSTABLE SHELF

FRICTION CATCH

SEE DETAIL G

¾" PLYWOOD TOP

¼" PLYWOOD   ¾" PLYWOOD

½" SQ. CLEAT
BOTTOM
SECTION F-F

⅛" LEDGE
¼" PLYWOOD
SECTION E-E

¾" PLYWOOD DOOR

DETAIL G

LEG DETAIL

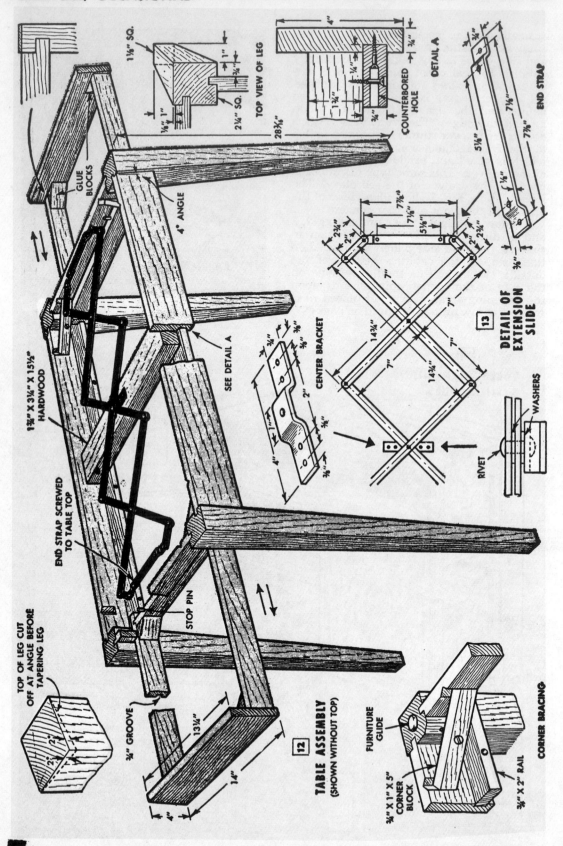

GLUE BLOCKS

1⅛" SQ.

1"
¾"

TOP VIEW OF LEG

⅛" 1"
2¼" SQ.

28½"

4"

¾"

¼"

1¾"

COUNTERBORED HOLE

¾"

DETAIL A

¾"
7⅛"
7⅛"

5⅛"

⅛"

⅜"

END STRAP

4° ANGLE

SEE DETAIL A

1¾" X 3¼" X 15½" HARDWOOD

END STRAP SCREWED TO TABLE TOP

¾"
⅜"
⅜"

2"

CENTER BRACKET

1"

⅜"
⅜"

4"
⅜"

7⅝"
7⅛"
7⅛"
5⅛"
2¼"
2"
2¼"
2"

7"
7"
14¾"
7"
7"
14¾"

13

DETAIL OF EXTENSION SLIDE

WASHERS

RIVET

STOP PIN

TOP OF LEG CUT OFF AT ANGLE BEFORE TAPERING LEG

2" 2"

¾" GROOVE

13¼"

14"

4"

12

TABLE ASSEMBLY
(SHOWN WITHOUT TOP)

FURNITURE GLIDE

¾" X 1" X 5" CORNER BLOCK

¾" X 2" RAIL

CORNER BRACING

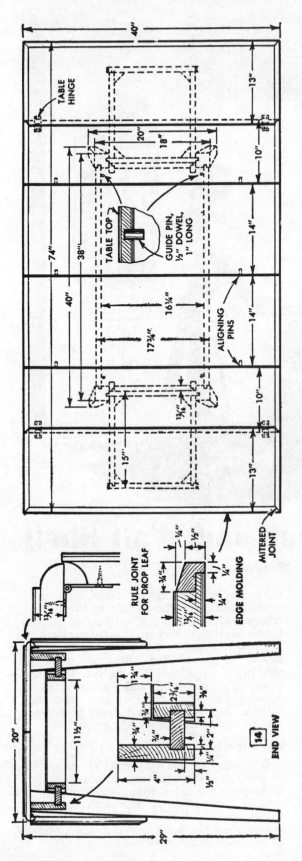

the plywood will have to be applied to the outside. Remember in cutting duplicate parts that the end units will have to be right and left-hand assemblies.

The three-shelf unit, shown fitted with doors in Fig. 10, can be made entirely open, in which case the partition is eliminated and the middle shelf brought out even with the one above it. The sectional details accompanying the cutaway drawing in Fig. 10 show how the ¼-in.-plywood side panels fit in rabbets cut on the inner edge of the hopper edging.

The drop-leaf table, Figs. 12, 13 and 14, has flared, tapered legs which assume the correct slant by making a compound cut at the top and bottom. This is done before tapering the legs in one of two ways: Either set the miter gauge 2 deg. and tilt the saw table 2 deg., or, support the work horizontally on one corner and make the cut with the gauge set at 2 deg. and the table at 90 degs. Only the adjacent inner faces of each leg are tapered, as indicated in the top-view detail, Fig. 12. The leg tapers from a full 2¼-in. square at the top to 1⅛ in. at the bottom. The two side aprons of the table are angle-cut to match the slant of the legs and the ends are rabbeted to fit open mortises cut in the tapered faces of the legs. Note in detail A that the side aprons are grooved along the lower edge to take strips on which the retractable end brackets slide. Half-width aprons are fitted across the ends of the table and then corner blocks are applied in the manner shown in the corner-bracing detail. Notice that a furniture glide is driven into the top of each leg t make the table top pivot easily. The pull-out brackets are made to slide under the end aprons and are corner-blocked for rigidity. A stop pin is provided at each side.

The lazy-tong extension slide is assembled from flat iron and riveted together as indicated in Fig. 13. This is pivoted to a center bracket which in turn is screwed to a hardwood center member installed between the side aprons. Each end of the extension slide is screwed to the underside of the two top leaves of the table. Fig. 14 shows an end view and a plan view of the table top including the two extra leaves. Outer edges of the plywood top are fitted with a mitered edge molding set in a rabbet, and a rule joint is run on the drop leaves for hinging them with regular dropleaf hinges. When cutting the rule joints, be sure to allow sufficient clearance between the male and female members so that the joints will not bind after the finish has been applied to the surfaces. Note in the plan view that steel dowel pins forced in blind holes in the underside of the top align and guide the table top when extending it for inserting extra leaves.

Queen Anne Mirror and Wall Shelf

By C. W. Woodson

EARLY QUEEN ANNE is the period represented by the graceful design of this mirror and companion wall shelf. Mahogany-faced ¼-in. plywood is used throughout for the shelf, and also for the jigsawed panels above and below the mirror. The frame around the mirror glass is made from ornamental picture-frame molding that you buy.

Mirror

Start construction of the mirror by making the frame, which has mitered corners. Before assembling, saw a groove in the upper and lower members to accommodate the plywood panels, as indicated in the lower left-hand detail. Next, make a pattern of the upper and lower panels by enlarging the squared drawings in the detail. Trace the patterns on the plywood and cut them out with a jigsaw. Sand the edges smooth and glue the panels to the mirror frame. Now, set the glass mirror in the frame and glue and nail narrow cleats to the inside edges of the frame to keep the mirror in place. Cleats also are glued to the plywood panels as indicated in the lower left-hand detail and a piece of ³⁄₁₆-in. plywood is glued and nailed over the mirror back as indicated, both to protect and to stiffen the plywood panels.

Wall Shelf

Both sides of the wall shelf are jigsawed at the same time to assure that they are identical. The sides then are mortised to receive tenons cut on the shelf ends and the assembly is glued together. A pattern is made for the back, cut out, then nailed to the back edges of the sides. ★ ★ ★

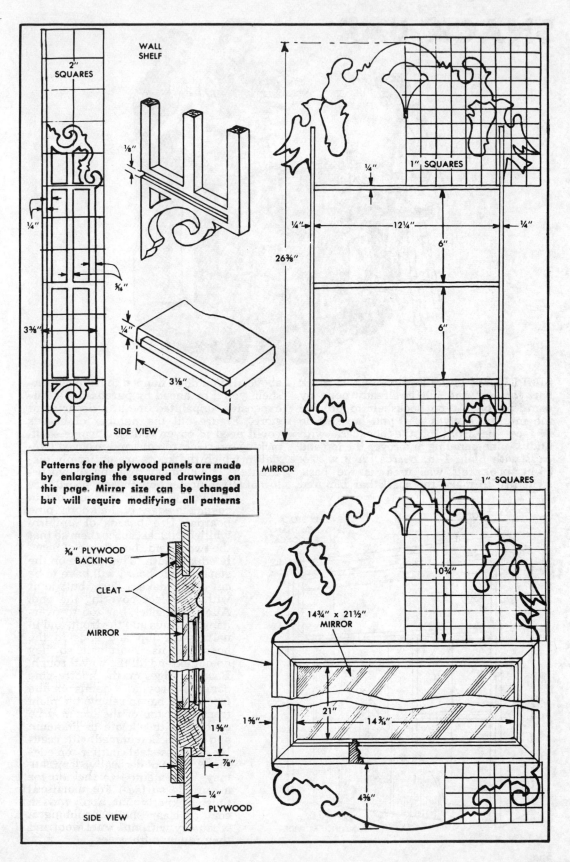

WALL SHELF

2" SQUARES

⅛"

¼"

⁵⁄₁₆"

3⅜"

SIDE VIEW

¼"

3⅛"

1" SQUARES

¼"

26⅜"

¼"

12¼"

¼"

6"

6"

Patterns for the plywood panels are made by enlarging the squared drawings on this page. Mirror size can be changed but will require modifying all patterns

MIRROR

1" SQUARES

10¾"

³⁄₁₆" PLYWOOD BACKING

CLEAT

MIRROR

14¾" x 21½" MIRROR

1⅝"

1⅝"

21"

14³⁄₁₆"

1⅝"

⅞"

¼"

PLYWOOD

4⅜"

SIDE VIEW

SNACK BAR

SIMPLICITY is the keynote of this snack bar, for half the job is already done by using an open-type bookshelf to provide the interior shelves. All you have to do is face the front of the bookcase with knotty-pine paneling and cover the top and ends with plain 1-in. boards. A 9 x 36 x 36-in. bookshelf was used as the basic structure to make the snack bar pictured above. If you don't happen to have a bookshelf, you'll be ahead by purchasing an inexpensive, unpainted one at a department store. Figure out the number of boards you'll need to cover your particular shelf picking out select tongue-and-groove material in which the knots are uniformly distributed. The cutaway drawing shown below at left indicates how the end boards are allowed to project at the front to cover the edges of the knotty-pine boards. Use boards of uniform width or at least space them so that the two outside boards are of nearly equal width. The tongue on the starting face board will have to be cut off to make a flush, butt joint with the piece covering the end. Allow the snack-bar top to overhang the ends and the front, and in nailing the top and ends to the bookshelf, use short nails so they do not extend all the way through. Beveled edges on the knotty-pine paneling provide V-joints on the face of the bar to relieve the plain front. The top of the bar may be covered with oilcloth or linoleum and the edges trimmed with regular stainless-steel counter-top edging. A piece of decorative laminate may be cemented to the top for a durable surface. For a natural finish of knotty pine, apply a wash coat of clear shellac, rubbing it when dry with fine steel wool and then follow with wax.

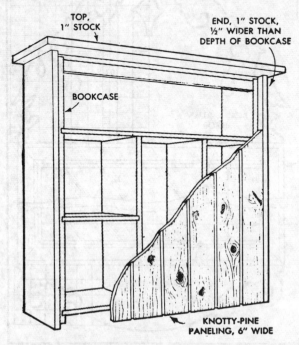

TOP, 1" STOCK

END, 1" STOCK, ½" WIDER THAN DEPTH OF BOOKCASE

BOOKCASE

KNOTTY-PINE PANELING, 6" WIDE

Patio Lounge

By Hi Sibley

LOTS OF LAZY COMFORT is built into this contour patio lounge, and it's a fairly simple thing to make if you have a bandsaw to cut out the curved parts. Staves from nail kegs, which are used to cover the top, add to its body-conforming comfort. Except for the wheels and the member to which they are attached, all parts are cut from ¾-in. material. The side rails are cut from 1 x 10 boards and consist of two separate pieces butted together and held securely by screws in the rear legs. The drawing shows at a glance how the other parts go together. Give it two coats of exterior paint, add a padded cushion and lean back in solid comfort.

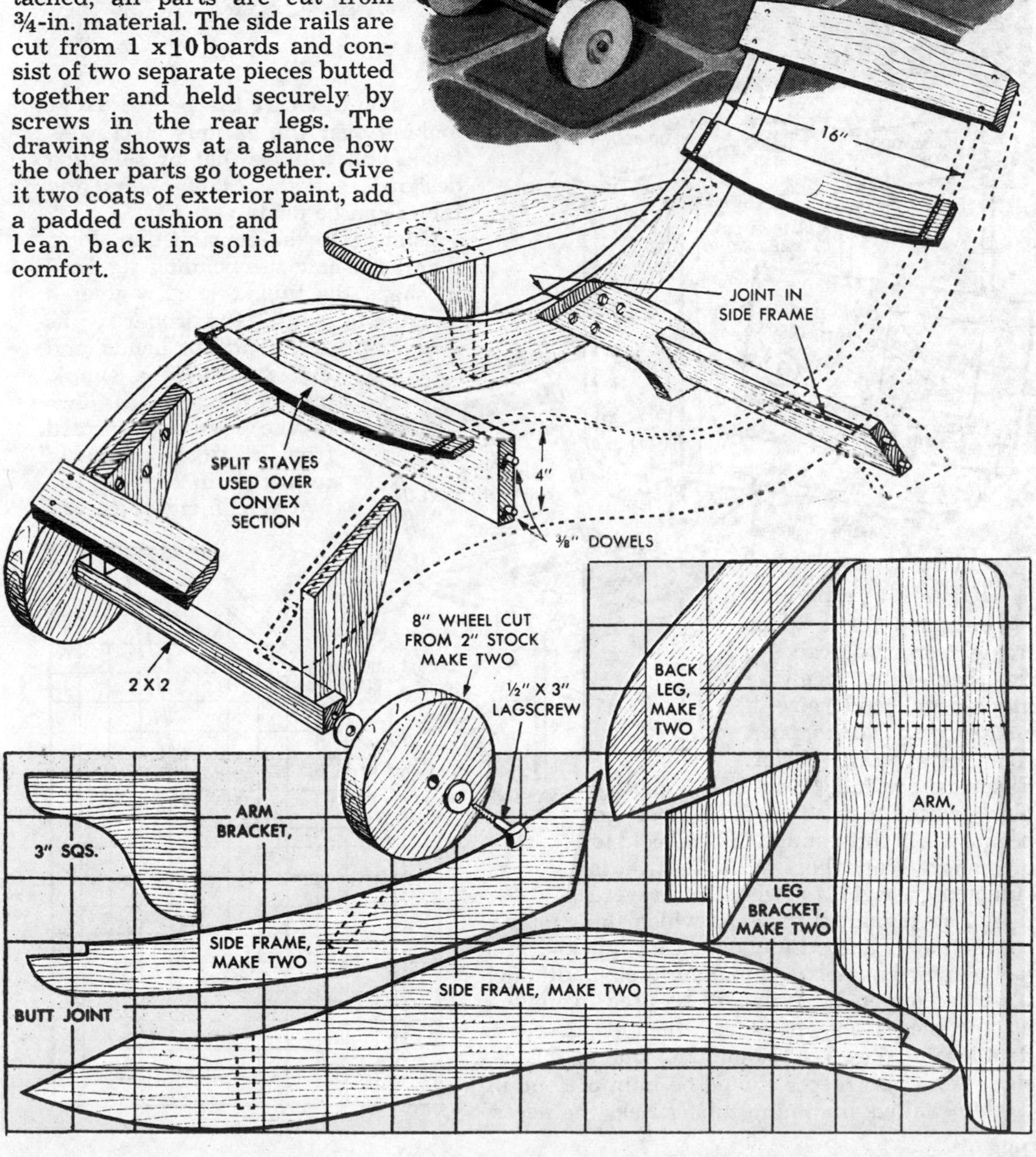

JOINT IN SIDE FRAME

16"

4"

⅜" DOWELS

SPLIT STAVES USED OVER CONVEX SECTION

2 X 2

8" WHEEL CUT FROM 2" STOCK MAKE TWO

½" X 3" LAGSCREW

BACK LEG, MAKE TWO

ARM,

ARM BRACKET,

3" SQS.

LEG BRACKET, MAKE TWO

SIDE FRAME, MAKE TWO

SIDE FRAME, MAKE TWO

BUTT JOINT

Bent-Tube

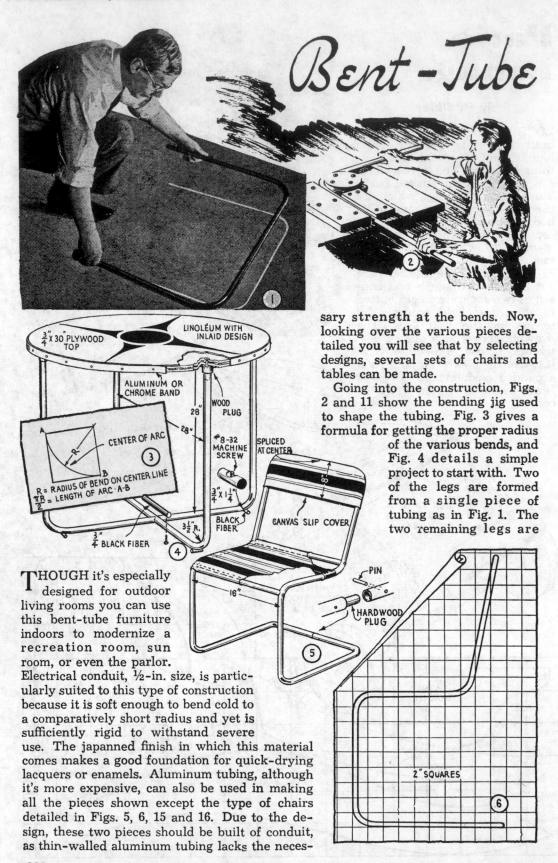

sary strength at the bends. Now, looking over the various pieces detailed you will see that by selecting designs, several sets of chairs and tables can be made.

Going into the construction, Figs. 2 and 11 show the bending jig used to shape the tubing. Fig. 3 gives a formula for getting the proper radius of the various bends, and Fig. 4 details a simple project to start with. Two of the legs are formed from a single piece of tubing as in Fig. 1. The two remaining legs are

THOUGH it's especially designed for outdoor living rooms you can use this bent-tube furniture indoors to modernize a recreation room, sun room, or even the parlor. Electrical conduit, ½-in. size, is particularly suited to this type of construction because it is soft enough to bend cold to a comparatively short radius and yet is sufficiently rigid to withstand severe use. The japanned finish in which this material comes makes a good foundation for quick-drying lacquers or enamels. Aluminum tubing, although it's more expensive, can also be used in making all the pieces shown except the type of chairs detailed in Figs. 5, 6, 15 and 16. Due to the design, these two pieces should be built of conduit, as thin-walled aluminum tubing lacks the neces-

FURNITURE

MADE FROM ELECTRICAL CONDUIT

bent separately and the lower ends are filed concave to fit the first member and form a neat right-angled joint. A short length of ¾-in. round black fiber is fastened over the joint with screws driven through the tubing. This holds the joint and further carries out the modern design. The four feet are of the same material. Hardwood plugs, turned to a tight fit, are driven into the top end of each leg, and screws, which hold the circular plywood top, are driven through the top into these

plugs. Linoleum, of whatever design you choose, is cemented to the top. A chrome or aluminum band around the edge finishes the job.

Now, to build the other two tables, shown in Figs. 7, 8, 9 and 19, you follow the same general procedure in bending the tubing and joining parts together. When you bend thin-walled aluminum tubing, it's best to fill the tube with sand, ramming it hard, and plug the ends as in Figs. 17 and 18. Also, it's a good idea to turn a concave groove in the edge of the bending disk on the jig,

A table just suited to use in the outdoor living room for refreshments, card parties, etc. It's arranged to hold a lawn umbrella which can be anchored with a pin driven into the ground. The inlay design shown in Fig. 4 can be used on this table top, if desired

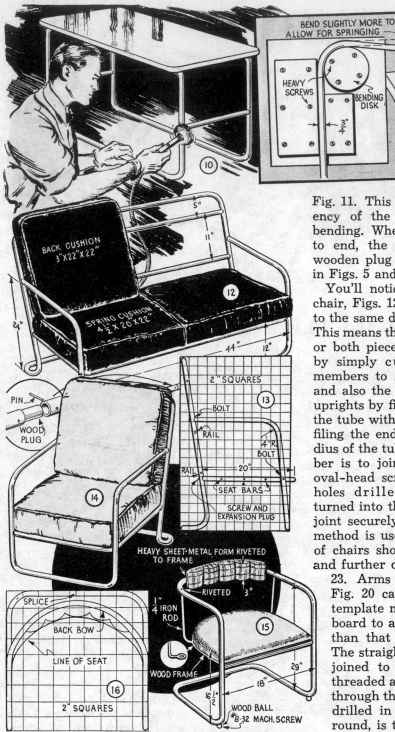

By halving the width, the settee in Fig. 12 becomes the chair shown in Fig. 14, as the end dimensions are the same. Spring-cushioned backs and seats can be made by purchasing the spring assembly ready-made, padding it lightly with cotton and sewing on a covering of cloth or artificial leather. The metal frames can be made of conduit, enameled in color, or polished aluminum tubing

Fig. 11. This will prevent any tendency of the tube to flatten when bending. Where the tubing joins end to end, the joint is made with a wooden plug and two metal pins as in Figs. 5 and 12.

You'll notice that the settee and chair, Figs. 12 and 14, are fashioned to the same dimensions as in Fig. 13. This means that you can build either or both pieces from the same plan, by simply cutting the lengthwise members to suit. Here these parts and also the arms are joined to the uprights by first plugging the end of the tube with a hardwood plug, then filing the end concave to fit the radius of the tube the horizontal member is to join. A chromium-plated oval-head screw inserted through holes drilled in the upright and turned into the wood plug holds the joint securely. Practically the same method is used in joining the parts of chairs shown in Figs. 20 and 22 and further detailed in Figs. 21 and 23. Arms of the chair shown in Fig. 20 can be shaped around a template made by band-sawing a board to a slightly shorter radius than that required on the tube. The straight rails of this chair are joined to the legs with a rod, threaded at both ends and passing through the rail and through holes drilled in the legs. A nut, filed round, is then turned up on each end of the rod. Another way is to simply use the rod as a long rivet, peening over the projecting ends. If you countersink the hole before inserting the rod, the ends can be peened over and the excess filed

FILLING THE TUBE WITH SAND

17

away to produce a neat job. In either case, the ends of the rail are filed concave to fit the tubular legs.

Now about finishing. Conduit can be lacquered or enameled with excellent results. Any quick-drying brush lacquer or enamel will do, the latter perhaps being preferable because it does not set so quickly. First, sand the conduit lightly to remove any loose particles and smooth up rough spots. Then brush on the first coat of enamel or lacquer and allow to dry thoroughly. Before applying a second coat, go over the first lightly with fine sandpaper. Then follow with the finish coat, carefully brushed out to avoid sagging on the rounded surfaces. Where aluminum tubing is used it may be polished highly with a buffing wheel driven by a flexible shaft as in Fig. 10. A coat of clear metal lacquer will help to preserve the high polish.

DRIVING IN A HARDWOOD PLUG

18

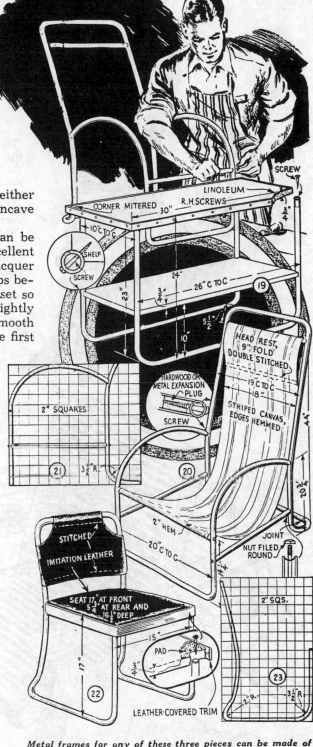

CORNER MITERED   LINOLEUM   R.H. SCREWS   SCREW   30"   ¾"   10" C TO C   SHELF   SCREW   24"   26" C TO C   19   23"   ¾"   5½"   10"

2" SQUARES   21   3½" R

HARDWOOD OR METAL EXPANSION PLUG   SCREW   20

HEAD REST, 9" FOLD DOUBLE STITCHED   19" C TO C   18"   STRIPED CANVAS, EDGES HEMMED   44"   20¼"

2" HEM   20" C TO C   JOINT NUT FILED ROUND

STITCHED IMITATION LEATHER   SEAT 17" AT FRONT 5½" AT REAR AND 16½" DEEP   2" SQS.   23   2" R   3½" R

15"   PAD   17"   ¾"   22   LEATHER-COVERED TRIM

Metal frames for any of these three pieces can be made of either polished aluminum tubing or electrical conduit finished in quick-drying colored lacquer or enamel. By combining these and other designs shown, several sets of attractive porch and garden furniture can be made

LAWN FURNITURE

HERE IS THE "new look" in outdoor furniture, designed by a well-known furniture stylist who has come up with some original and exciting pieces which feature knock-down construction to lick the problem of winter storage. By building these easy-to-make pieces of furniture yourself, the budget for your home grounds need not be unreasonably stretched to include outdoor furnishings. Gay, comfortable and easy to dismantle, this striking lawn furniture incorporates the use of ready-made waterproof cushions. These can be purchased from department stores in sizes to fit the various pieces of the group. The complete back yard ensemble features six pieces, including an Adirondack-type chair, porch chair, serving cart, garden lounge, porch glider and a table-and-bench set. Several of the pieces, such as the porch chair, lounge and glider, also can be used during the winter on an enclosed porch or in a sunroom. Both the lounge and the Adirondack chair have tilting

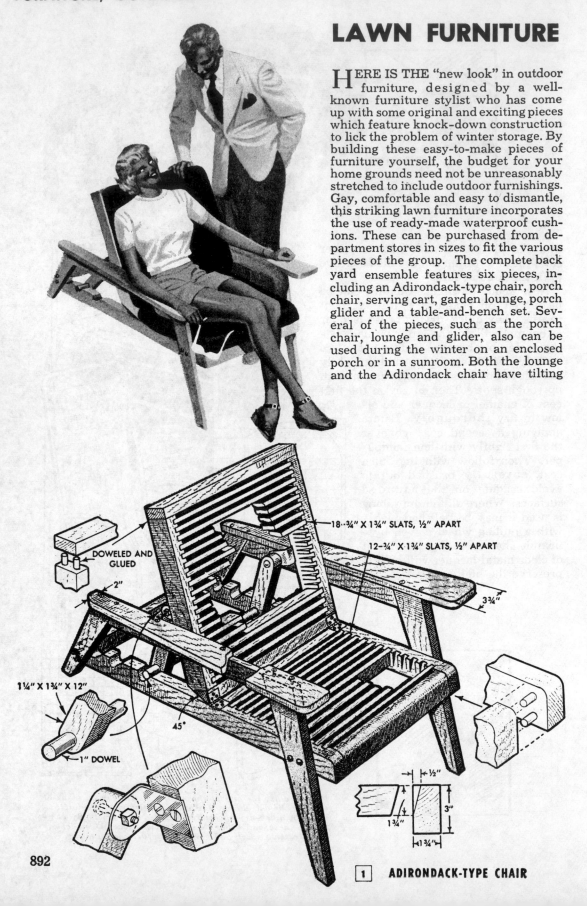

18-¾" X 1¾" SLATS, ½" APART
12-¾" X 1¾" SLATS, ½" APART
3¾"
DOWELED AND GLUED
2"
1¼" X 1¾" X 12"
45°
1" DOWEL
½"
3"
1¾"
1¾"

1 ADIRONDACK-TYPE CHAIR

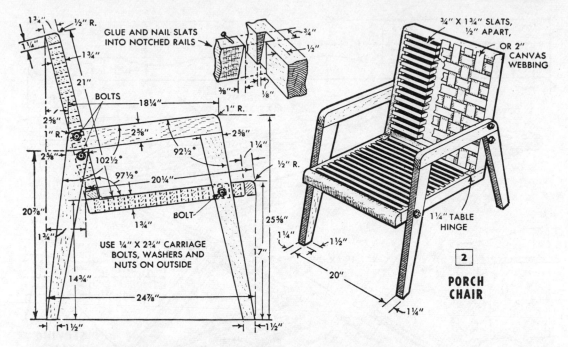

GLUE AND NAIL SLATS INTO NOTCHED RAILS →

BOLTS

USE ¼" X 2¾" CARRIAGE BOLTS, WASHERS AND NUTS ON OUTSIDE

BOLT

¾" X 1¾" SLATS, ½" APART, OR 2" CANVAS WEBBING

1¼" TABLE HINGE

2

PORCH CHAIR

backs that can be adjusted to suit the comfort of the individual. Except in the case of the garden table-and-bench set, a choice of slats or webbing is given in constructing the seats and backs of the furniture. Both types are partially indicated in most of the drawings, and this should not be confused with actual construction details.

While redwood and cypress are two of the most durable woods, especially suitable for outdoor furniture, common lumberyard stock, such as yellow pine or fir, is perfectly satisfactory if the pieces are kept well painted.

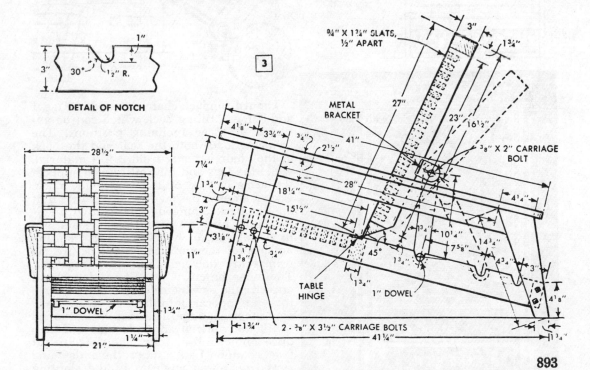

DETAIL OF NOTCH

3

¾" X 1¾" SLATS, ½" APART

METAL BRACKET

⅜" X 2" CARRIAGE BOLT

TABLE HINGE

1" DOWEL

1" DOWEL

2 - ⅜" X 3½" CARRIAGE BOLTS

893

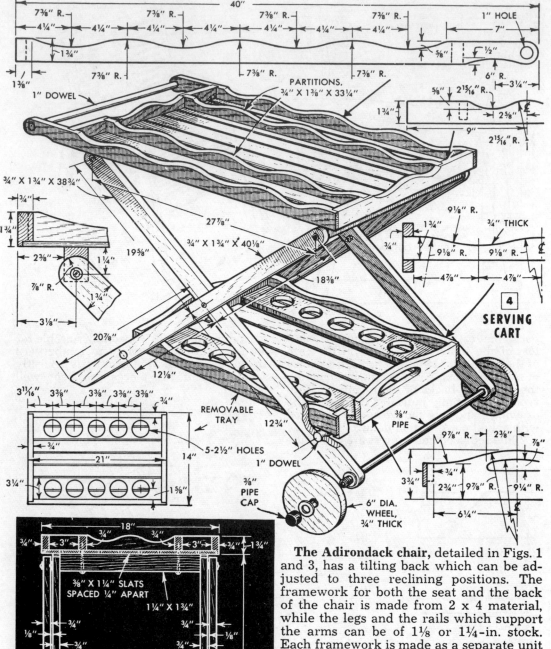

4 SERVING CART

5 END VIEW

The Adirondack chair, detailed in Figs. 1 and 3, has a tilting back which can be adjusted to three reclining positions. The framework for both the seat and the back of the chair is made from 2 x 4 material, while the legs and the rails which support the arms can be of 1⅛ or 1¼-in. stock. Each framework is made as a separate unit and the back is hinged to the seat with 1¼-in. table hinges, set flush. If slats are used instead of webbing, the slanting notches for them must be made before the frames are doweled and glued together. These can be cut with a ¾-in. dado head on a circular saw by utilizing a narrow strip tacked temporarily to the face of the work along the rear edge. The strip is positioned to tilt the work at an angle that will produce a notch 1¾ in. long. The slats are cut from common 1 x 2 lumber, the ends being sawed off at an angle to fit the slanting notches and then nailed in place, flush with

is pivoted to it with sheet-metal brackets in the manner shown in Fig. 1. If webbing is preferred to the slats, use either nylon parachute webbing or common canvas webbing and interlace it as shown. The ready-made cushions will hide the tacks used in fastening webbing to the frames.

The porch chair, Fig. 2, is somewhat similar in construction. The seat and back are hinged together to fold flat for storing, while the legs and arms can be taken off as single units by removing only six nuts and washers. Frames for the seat and back are assembled from 1¼ x 1¾-in. stock, notched if slats are used, before doweling and gluing together.

The serving cart, Figs. 4 and 5, can be wheeled about and features a removable beverage tray which rides on two rungs fitted between the crossed legs. Each pair of legs are duplicates, and registering holes for the pipe axle, dowel rungs and screw fastenings are bored at one time through each set. The upper ends of the legs are pivoted with wood screws to 1¼ x 1¾-in. cleats which support the upper tray.

The garden lounge, Figs. 6 and 7, like the Adirondack chair, has a tilting back which is supported in the same manner except that it is adjustable to four positions. The bed frame of the lounge, including the tilting back, is made of 2 x 4 material, with a second frame of lighter stock being bolted to the underside. This second frame carries the wheel axle and also the notches which engage the tilting back support. The end-view detail shows how the pipe axle is bolted in place with lag screws. The arms of the

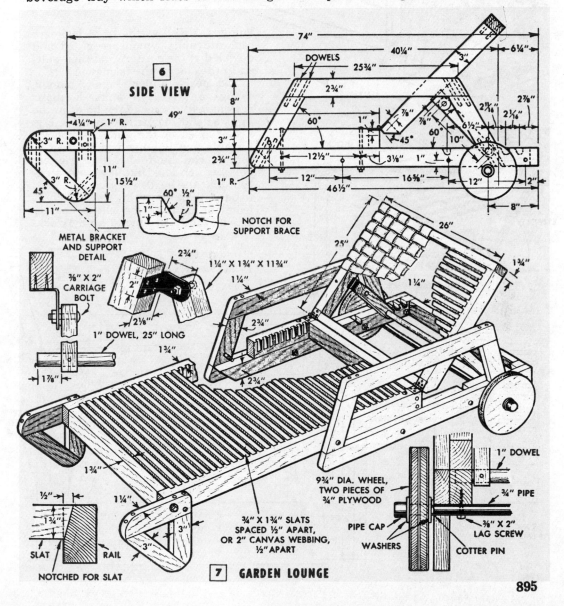

6 SIDE VIEW

NOTCH FOR SUPPORT BRACE

METAL BRACKET AND SUPPORT DETAIL

⅜" X 2" CARRIAGE BOLT

1¼" X 1¾" X 11¾"

1" DOWEL, 25" LONG

¾" X 1¾" SLATS SPACED ½" APART, OR 2" CANVAS WEBBING, ½" APART

9¾" DIA. WHEEL, TWO PIECES OF ¾" PLYWOOD

PIPE CAP

WASHERS

1" DOWEL

¾" PIPE

⅜" X 2" LAG SCREW

COTTER PIN

SLAT   RAIL

NOTCHED FOR SLAT

7 GARDEN LOUNGE

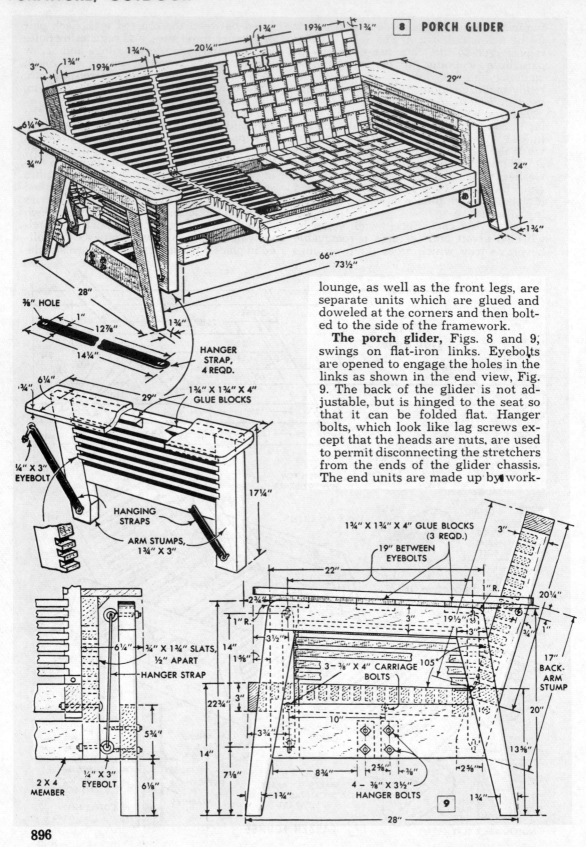

8 PORCH GLIDER

3" 1¾" 19⅜" 1¾" 20¼" 1¾" 19⅜" 1¾"

29"

24"

6¼"

¾"

66"

73½"

28"

⅜" HOLE
1"
12⅞"
14¼"
1¾"

HANGER
STRAP,
4 REQD.

6¼"
¾"
29"

1¾" X 1¾" X 4"
GLUE BLOCKS

¼" X 3"
EYEBOLT

17¼"

HANGING
STRAPS

ARM STUMPS,
1¾" X 3"

lounge, as well as the front legs, are separate units which are glued and doweled at the corners and then bolted to the side of the framework.

The porch glider, Figs. 8 and 9, swings on flat-iron links. Eyebolts are opened to engage the holes in the links as shown in the end view, Fig. 9. The back of the glider is not adjustable, but is hinged to the seat so that it can be folded flat. Hanger bolts, which look like lag screws except that the heads are nuts, are used to permit disconnecting the stretchers from the ends of the glider chassis. The end units are made up by work-

6¼" ¾" X 1¾" SLATS,
½" APART
HANGER STRAP

2 X 4
MEMBER

¼" X 3"
EYEBOLT

3
5¾"
6⅛"
14"

1¾" X 1¾" X 4" GLUE BLOCKS
(3 REQD.)

19" BETWEEN
EYEBOLTS

22"

1" R.

2¾"

1" R.

3½"

1⅝"

14"

22¾" 3"

3¾"

10"

8¾"

7⅛"

1¾"

3 - ⅜" X 4" CARRIAGE
BOLTS

105°

4 - ⅜" X 3½"
HANGER BOLTS

2⅝" ⅜"

2⅝"

3"

19½"

1"

3"

3"

20¼"

1"

¾"

17"
BACK-
ARM
STUMP

20"

13⅝"

1¾"

28"

9

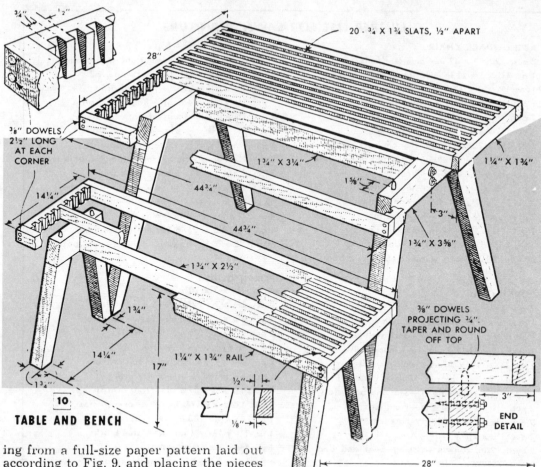

20 - ¾ X 1¾ SLATS, ½" APART

28"

¾" DOWELS 2½" LONG AT EACH CORNER

14¼"

1¾" X 3¼"

1⅝"

44¾"

44¾"

1¾" X 2½"

1¾"

1¼" X 1¾" RAIL

14¼"

17"

1¾"

½"

⅛"

1¼" X 1¾"

3"

1¾" X 3⅝"

⅜" DOWELS PROJECTING ¾". TAPER AND ROUND OFF TOP

END DETAIL

3"

10

TABLE AND BENCH

ing from a full-size paper pattern laid out according to Fig. 9, and placing the pieces right over the pattern to obtain the correct slant for the legs and top arm rails.

The picnic table-and-bench set, Fig. 10, also can be taken completely apart for storing. The tops of both the table and benches lift off, being held in place merely by stub pins which engage registering holes. Hanger bolts in the ends of the center stretchers permit the U-shaped legs to be removed in a jiffy. Except for size, the construction of the three pieces is exactly alike. As the slats are spaced ½ in. apart, it is best to paint them before they are nailed in place. Note that here the tapering notches are cut the full width of the end rails. This can be done with a small dado head by gluing a strip of beveled siding temporarily to the inside face of the work to bring the line of cut parallel with the saw table. The siding strip is glued with paper between it and the work so that it can be pried off easily when all the notches have been cut. However, to simplify the job, the notches can be cut straight through and the 1 x 2 slats glued in place and nailed from the outside face. The legs are cut from 2 x 4 material and glued and doweled to the apron pieces. Screws can be used instead of dowels at the corners of the bench tops.

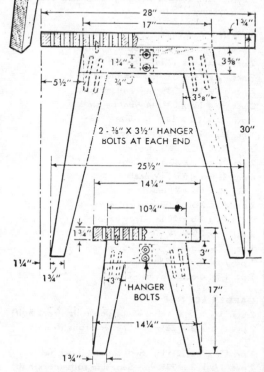

28"

17"

1¾"

1¾"

3⅝"

5½"

¾"

3⅝"

30"

2 - ⅜" X 3½" HANGER BOLTS AT EACH END

25½"

14¼"

10¾"

1¾"

3"

1¾"

1¼"

1¾"

3"

HANGER BOLTS

17"

14¼"

1¾"

END VIEWS OF TABLE AND BENCH

LUMBER LIST FOR LAWN FURNITURE

ADIRONDACK CHAIR

2 pcs. 1¾ x 3 x 42 in.—Side seat rails
1 pc. 1¾ x 3 x 21 in.—Front seat rail
1 pc. 1¾ x 3 x 17½ in.—Center seat rail
1 pc. 1¼ x 3 x 17½ in.—Back seat rail
2 pcs. 1¾ x 3 x 27 in.—Side back rails
1 pc. 1¾ x 3 x 21 in.—Top back rail
1 pc. 1¾ x 2¼ x 17½ in.—Bottom back rail
30 pcs. ¾ x 1¾ x 18½ in.—Seat and back slats
2 pcs. 1¼ x 3¾ x 22 in.—Front legs
2 pcs. 1¼ x 3¾ x 14⅝ in.—Back legs
2 pcs. 1¼ x 2½ x 29⅞ in.—Arm aprons
2 pcs. ¾ x 3¾ x 41 in.—Tops of arms
2 pcs. 1¼ x 1¾ x 12 in.—Back stays
1 pc. 1-in. dia. x 20 in. long—Dowel rung
33 yds. 2-in. canvas webbing—Seat and back covering

PORCH CHAIR

2 pcs. 1¼ x 1¾ x 20¼ in.—Side seat rails
1 pc. 1¼ x 1¾ x 20 in.—Front seat rail
1 pc. 1¼ x 1¾ x 17½ in.—Back seat rail
2 pcs. 1¼ x 1¾ x 21 in.—Side back rails
1 pc. 1¼ x 1¾ x 20 in.—Top back rail
1 pc. 1¼ x 1¾ x 17½ in.—Bottom back rail
27 pcs. ¾ x 1¾ x 18½ in.—Seat and back slats
2 pcs. 1¼ x 2⅝ x 23½ in.—Front legs
2 pcs. 1¼ x 2⅝ x 21¾ in.—Back legs
2 pcs. 1¼ x 2⅝ x 19 in.—Arms
20 yds. 2-in. canvas webbing—Seat and back covering

SERVING CART

2 pcs. ¾ x 1¾ x 40 in.—Top side rails
2 pcs. ¾ x 1¾ x 17 in.—Top end rails
2 pcs. ¾ x 1⅜ x 33¼ in.—Partitions
7 pcs. ⅜ x 1¾ x 33¾ in.—Bottom slats
2 pcs. ⅜ x 1⅝ x 33¾ in.—Bottom slats
1 pc. 1¼ x 1¾ x 14½ in.—Brace
1 pc. 1¼ x 1¾ x 16½ in.—Brace
2 pcs. ¾ x 1¾ x 38¾ in.—Legs
2 pcs. ¾ x 1¾ x 40⅛ in.—Legs
4 pcs. ¾ x 6 x 6 in.—Wheels
2 pcs. ¾ x 1¾ x 21 in.—Tray sides
2 pcs. ¾ x 3¾ x 13½ in.—Tray ends
7 pcs. ⅜ x 1¾ x 20 in.—Tray bottom
2 pcs. ½ x 3¼ x 19½ in.—Glass holders
1 pc. 1-in. dia. x 17½ in.—Dowel
1 pc. 1-in. dia. x 17 in.—Dowel
1 pc. 1-in. dia. x 17¾ in.—Dowel

GARDEN LOUNGE

2 pcs. 1¾ x 3 x 49 in.—Seat side rails (front half)
2 pcs. 1¾ x 3 x 22½ in.—Seat end rails (front half)
1 pc. 1¼ x 3 x 22½ in.—Seat end rail (back half)
2 pcs. 1¾ x 3 x 23¼ in.—Seat side rails (back half)
1 pc. 1¾ x 3 x 26 in.—Top rail for back
1 pc. 1¾ x 2½ x 22½ in.—Bottom rail for back
2 pcs. 1¾ x 2¾ x 44¾ in.—Back side rails
2 pcs. 1¼ x 2¾ x 29 in.—Tops of arms
2 pcs. 1¼ x 2¾ x 46⅜ in.—Bottoms of arms
2 pcs. 1¼ x 2¾ x 14¼ in.—Front arm stumps
2 pcs. 1¼ x 2¾ x 11⅛ in.—Back arm stumps
2 pcs. 1¼ x 1¾ x 11¾ in.—Back supports
2 pcs. 1¼ x 3 x 15½ in.—Front leg horizontals
2 pcs. 1¼ x 3 x 8 in.—Front leg uprights
2 pcs. 1¼ x 3 x 17½ in.—Front leg diagonals
53 pcs. ¾ x 1¾ x 23½ in.—Seat and back slats
4 pcs. ¾ x 9¾ x 9¾ in.—Wheels
1 pc. 1-in. dia. x 25 in. long—Dowel rung
60 yds. 2-in. canvas webbing—Seat and back covering

PORCH GLIDER

4 pcs. 1¾ x 3 x 20⅗ in.—Legs
2 pcs. 1¾ x 3 x 22¾ in.—Top leg rails
2 pcs. 1¾ x 5¾ x 22 in.—Lower leg rails
2 pcs. 2 x 4 x 73½ in.—Leg stretchers
2 pcs. ¾ x 6¼ x 29 in.—Arms
2 pcs. 1¾ x 2½ x 20¾ in.—Top arm rails
2 pcs. 1¾ x 3 x 18 in.—Lower arm rails
2 pcs. 1¾ x 3 x 17¼ in.—Front arm stumps
2 pcs. 1¾ x 3 x 17¾ in.—Rear arm stumps
1 pc. ¾ x 1¾ x 108 in.—Arm slats
1 pc. 1¾ x 1¾ x 4 in.—Arm glue blocks
1 pc. 1¾ x 3 x 66 in.—Front seat rail
1 pc. 1¾ x 3 x 62½ in.—Rear seat rail
2 pcs. 1¾ x 3 x 23 in.—Side seat rails
2 pcs. 1¾ x 3 x 19½ in.—Center seat rails
1 pc. 1¾ x 3 x 66 in.—Top rail for back
1 pc. 1¾ x 3 x 62½ in.—Lower rail for back
2 pcs. 1¾ x 3 x 22⅝ in.—Side rails for back
2 pcs. 1¾ x 3 x 16¾ in.—Center rails for back
56 pcs. ¾ x 1¾ x 20⅜ in.—Side back and seat slats
28 pcs. ¾ x 1¾ x 21¼ in.—Center back and seat slats
105 yds. 2-in. canvas webbing—Seat and back covering

TABLE-AND-BENCH SET (table)

2 pcs. 1¼ x 1¾ x 44¾ in.—Top side rails
2 pcs. 1¼ x 1¾ x 25½ in.—Top end rails
20 pcs. ¾ x 1¾ x 43¼ in.—Slats
4 pcs. 1¾ x 3⅝ x 25⅜ in.—Legs
2 pcs. 1¾ x 3⅝ x 18-1/16 in.—Leg rails
1 pc. 1¾ x 3¼ x 35¼ in.—Brace

(Material per bench)

2 pcs. 1¼ x 1¾ x 44¾ in.—Top side rails
2 pcs. 1¼ x 1¾ x 11¾ in.—Top end rails
9 pcs. ¾ x 1¾ x 43¼ in.—Slats
4 pcs. 1¾ x 3 x 11¾ in.—Legs
2 pcs. 1¾ x 3 x 11½ in.—Leg rails
1 pc. 1¾ x 2½ x 35¾ in.—Brace

...Suitcase Picnic Bench

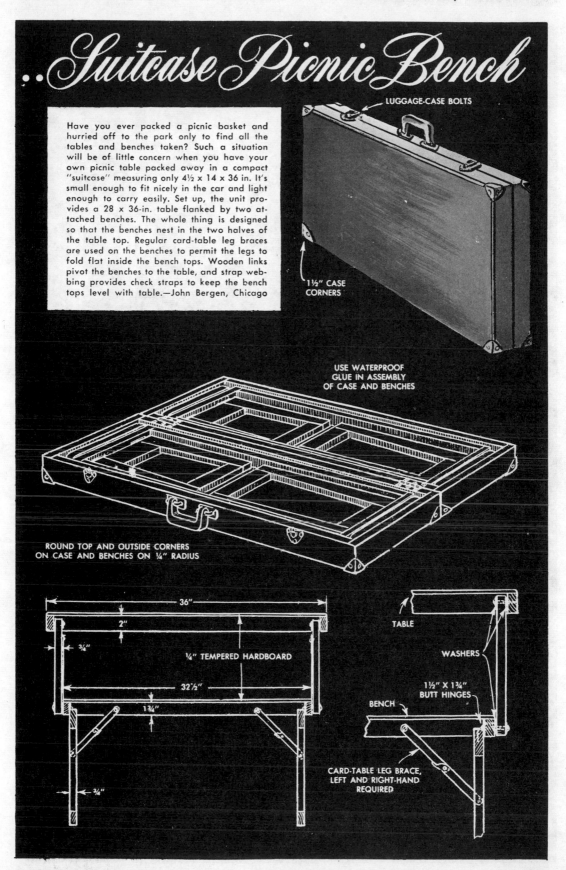

Have you ever packed a picnic basket and hurried off to the park only to find all the tables and benches taken? Such a situation will be of little concern when you have your own picnic table packed away in a compact "suitcase" measuring only 4½ x 14 x 36 in. It's small enough to fit nicely in the car and light enough to carry easily. Set up, the unit provides a 28 x 36-in. table flanked by two attached benches. The whole thing is designed so that the benches nest in the two halves of the table top. Regular card-table leg braces are used on the benches to permit the legs to fold flat inside the bench tops. Wooden links pivot the benches to the table, and strap webbing provides check straps to keep the bench tops level with table.—John Bergen, Chicago

LUGGAGE-CASE BOLTS

1½" CASE CORNERS

USE WATERPROOF GLUE IN ASSEMBLY OF CASE AND BENCHES

ROUND TOP AND OUTSIDE CORNERS ON CASE AND BENCHES ON ¼" RADIUS

36"

2"

¾"

¼" TEMPERED HARDBOARD

32½"

1¾"

¾"

TABLE

WASHERS

1½" X 1¾" BUTT HINGES

BENCH

CARD-TABLE LEG BRACE, LEFT AND RIGHT-HAND REQUIRED

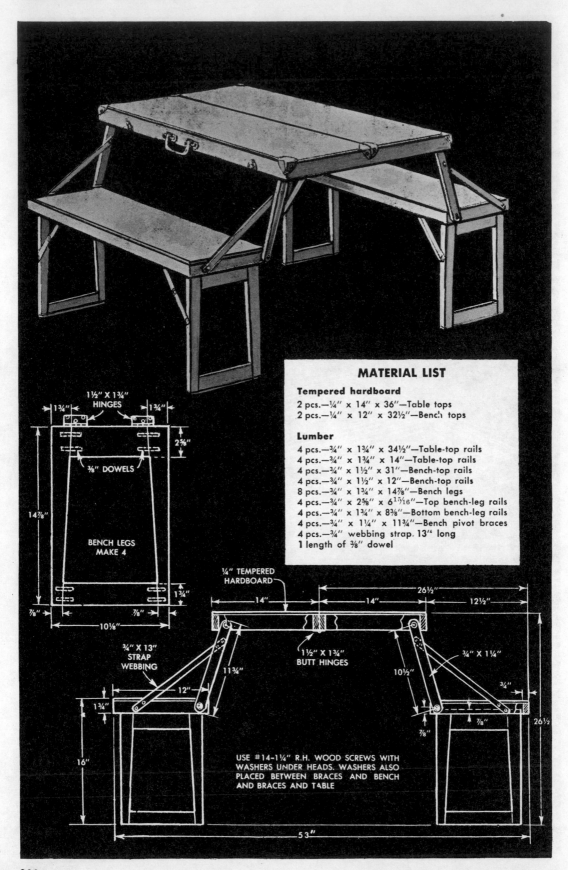

MATERIAL LIST

Tempered hardboard

2 pcs.—¼" x 14" x 36"—Table tops
2 pcs.—¼" x 12" x 32½"—Bench tops

Lumber

4 pcs.—¾" x 1¾" x 34½"—Table-top rails
4 pcs.—¾" x 1¾" x 14"—Table-top rails
4 pcs.—¾" x 1½" x 31"—Bench-top rails
4 pcs.—¾" x 1½" x 12"—Bench-top rails
8 pcs.—¾" x 1¾" x 14⅞"—Bench legs
4 pcs.—¾" x 2⅝" x 6¹⁵⁄₁₆"—Top bench-leg rails
4 pcs.—¾" x 1¾" x 8⅜"—Bottom bench-leg rails
4 pcs.—¾" x 1¼" x 11¾"—Bench pivot braces
4 pcs.—¾" webbing strap. 13" long
1 length of ⅜" dowel

1½" x 1¾" HINGES
1¾"   1¾"
2⅝"
⅜" DOWELS
14⅞"
BENCH LEGS MAKE 4
1¾"
⅞"   ⅞"
10⅛"

¼" TEMPERED HARDBOARD
14"   14"   26½"   12½"
1½" x 1¾" BUTT HINGES
¾" X 13" STRAP WEBBING
11¾"
12"
10½"
¾" X 1¼"
¾"
1¾"
⅞"   ⅞"
26½"
16"

USE #14-1¼" R.H. WOOD SCREWS WITH WASHERS UNDER HEADS. WASHERS ALSO PLACED BETWEEN BRACES AND BENCH AND BRACES AND TABLE

53"

COURT LAYOUTS

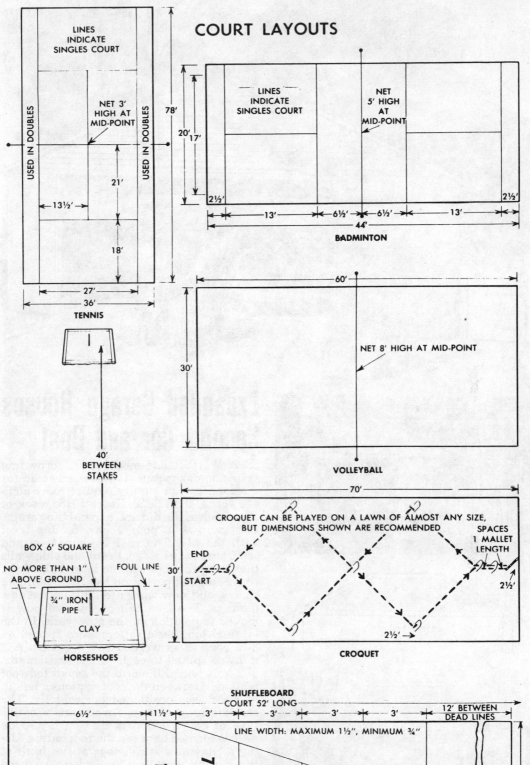

LINES INDICATE SINGLES COURT

NET 3' HIGH AT MID-POINT

USED IN DOUBLES

USED IN DOUBLES

78'

21'

18'

13½'

27'

36'

TENNIS

LINES INDICATE SINGLES COURT

NET 5' HIGH AT MID-POINT

20'
17'

2½'

13'

6½'

6½'

13'

44'

2½'

BADMINTON

60'

NET 8' HIGH AT MID-POINT

30'

VOLLEYBALL

40' BETWEEN STAKES

BOX 6' SQUARE

NO MORE THAN 1" ABOVE GROUND

FOUL LINE

¾" IRON PIPE

CLAY

HORSESHOES

70'

CROQUET CAN BE PLAYED ON A LAWN OF ALMOST ANY SIZE, BUT DIMENSIONS SHOWN ARE RECOMMENDED

SPACES 1 MALLET LENGTH

END

START

30'

2½'

2½'

2½'

CROQUET

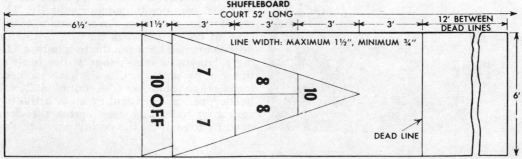

SHUFFLEBOARD
COURT 52' LONG

6½'

1½'

3'

3'

3'

3'

12' BETWEEN DEAD LINES

LINE WIDTH: MAXIMUM 1½", MINIMUM ¾"

10 OFF

7

8

8

7

10

6'

DEAD LINE

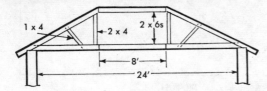

1 x 4 2 x 4 2 x 6s

8'

24'

Expanded Garage Houses Second Car and Boat

IF A WIDER late-model car is crowding your one-car garage; if you need room for a second car, or simply require more storage space, then do as Everett Hedgcock of East Peoria, Ill., did and expand the garage. First step is to pour a new footing level with the old. The roof is shored up and separated at the ridge. Front and side walls then are pulled down, the loose half of the roof being supported on the back wall and shores, and new walls are built on the new footings. The free half of the roof now is moved to position on the new walls. In the original job, 2 x 4 rafters were spaced on 2-ft. centers as were the roof beams. A 2 x 6 was spiked to each rafter, and lengths of 2 x 4s joined them to the separated roof sections. Between the roof sections a length of 2 x 6 was positioned horizontally. The result is a sort of truss. An advantage of this type of construction is that an 8-ft.-wide deck is formed between the roof halves. Using a "haymow type" door at the front of the garage permits this deck to be used for storage of a boat. A doubled 2 x 8 header, set on edge and even with the top course of blocks, is used across the door opening to support the end truss.

GARAGE ENLARGING

NEW CARS and old garages just don't go together. Whether the rear bumper extends an inch or a foot beyond the wall line, the problem is essentially the same—how to gain the extra space needed to close the doors. In some cases, the doors will close but the short length of the building leaves no room for walking around the car to the side door. Easing into such a restricted space without knocking out the rear wall of the building is an added inconvenience, especially when the car is used every day.

There are several ways of stretching an old garage so that new car will fit in it with room to spare. The method used will depend on the construction of the building, the type of doors used, and the amount of room needed. If, for example, the doors swing outward and it happens that the car bumper extends only 3 or 4 in., building out the door jambs, as in Fig. 1, will give the required space. To do this, the doors are removed and two 2 x 4s are spiked or bolted to the sides and across the top of the doorframe directly over the trim boards, as shown in the detail. This arrangement gives the maximum space. Provide a wide sheet-metal drip cap across the top to prevent leakage. Then paint all the new woodwork and rehang the doors. It may be necessary or desirable to build out the ramp

to close an open space under the doors. When an overhead door has been installed or where the doors are of the folding type that rolls on an overhead track along the inside of one wall, about the same amount of space can be gained at the rear wall of the building by using the methods shown in Figs. 2 and 4. Where still more room is required, the lean-to structure detailed in Fig. 3 is the most practical solution. This is built high enough to clear the car hood. Use of waterproof plywood sheathing and flooring simplifies and speeds up this job.

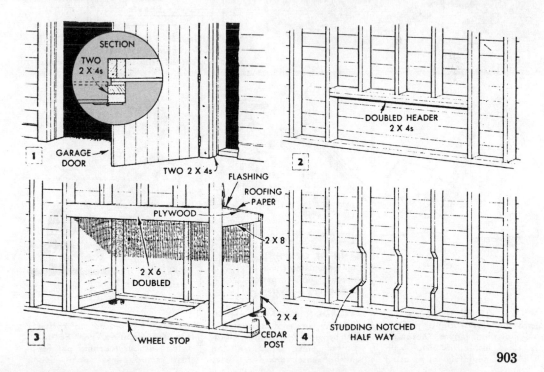

HANGING PLANTER is coconut half-shell with bottle cap over drain hole drilled in bottom

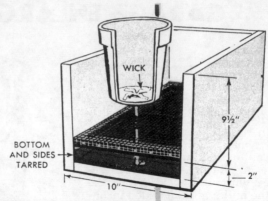

SELF-WATERING PLANTER made by nailing hardware cloth to cleats inside box and tarring

bottom. Wick nailed to bottom and inserted in pot carries water to plants by capillary actión

Gardening

SUB-IRRIGATED PLANTER is assembled with marine glue and screws. Inner surfaces are coated with tar to seal the joints

WATER PISTOL is handy for spraying insecticide on undersides of plant leaves. Thoroughly rinse inside of pistol with water immediately after using

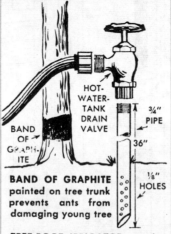

BAND OF GRAPHITE painted on tree trunk prevents ants from damaging young tree

TREE-ROOT IRRIGATOR permits watering of root system for fast growth. It is made of galvanized steel pipe, coupling and hot-water tank drain valve

FLOWERPOT placed on coffee can for painting, can be rotated without touching pot for fast smudge-free paint job

PARCEL-SIZE RURAL MAILBOX mounted on post in garden provides convenient storage for frequently used garden tools

Hints

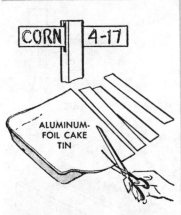

PERMANENT PLANT MARKERS can be made by cutting strips from aluminum pan of type used for frozen foods. Plant names and dates planted are lettered on with ball-point pen

LENGTHS OF GARDEN HOSE strung on heavy cord make soft kneeling pad for garden use. Lengths are held in place by tying loops around end pieces

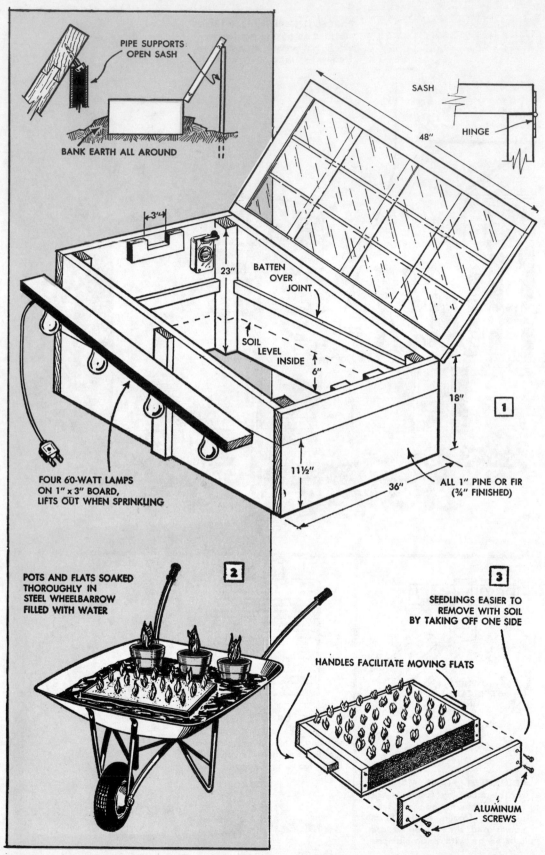

PIPE SUPPORTS OPEN SASH

BANK EARTH ALL AROUND

SASH

HINGE

48"

3"

23"

BATTEN OVER JOINT

SOIL LEVEL INSIDE

6"

18"

11½"

1

FOUR 60-WATT LAMPS ON 1" x 3" BOARD, LIFTS OUT WHEN SPRINKLING

36"

ALL 1" PINE OR FIR (¾" FINISHED)

2

POTS AND FLATS SOAKED THOROUGHLY IN STEEL WHEELBARROW FILLED WITH WATER

3

SEEDLINGS EASIER TO REMOVE WITH SOIL BY TAKING OFF ONE SIDE

HANDLES FACILITATE MOVING FLATS

ALUMINUM SCREWS

MORE GARDEN HINTS

By Hi Sibley

SPRING IS THE TIME not only for planning a garden, but for getting a head start with seedlings so your "crops" are ready for the table weeks ahead of time. It also is time to consider how to keep birds away from the newly planted seedlings, and how to support plants, such as tomatoes, when they are full of heavy, ripe fruit.

For growing young plants from seed, a cold frame, Fig. 1, is the answer if you have enough room. A stock window sash, available at most lumber dealers, is hinged to a box built of creosoted lumber. An underground cable brings house current to a weathertight receptacle which furnishes electricity to a "lift out" board that holds four 60-watt lamps to provide heat on chilly nights and sunless days. The weather-tight receptacle is closed when plants in the frame are sprinkled.

If you have no room for a cold frame, wooden flats, Fig. 3, and clay pots can be located in a basement or utility room for starting seedlings. It is best to give the seedlings a good soaking once a week, rather than a daily sprinkling. This is true especially in homes with forced-air heat where low humidity will cause fast evaporation. A metal wheelbarrow filled with water will permit giving flats and pots a thorough soaking, Fig. 2. Whether you make your own flats or buy them, fix one side of each unit so that it can be removed as indicated in Fig. 3. Each seedling, with its necessary ball of soil, then can be removed readily. After setting out each tomato plant, drive three laths, strung with heavy cord, Fig. 4, around each one for support when the plant is mature. Pole beans require a fence of cord and laths, Fig. 5. For all plants, tin-can lids strung as indicated in the lower detail in Fig. 5 will help keep away hungry birds. Every whisper of wind will blow the lids together noisily and spin them so the sun will glitter on their shiny surfaces.

★ ★ ★

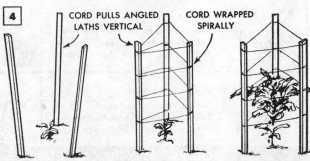

CORD PULLS ANGLED LATHS VERTICAL   CORD WRAPPED SPIRALLY

Supports shown above for tomato plants require only a few laths and some heavy cord. The same materials are used for a "fence" on which pole beans can grow. Lids saved from food tins are strung in pairs to frighten away hungry birds

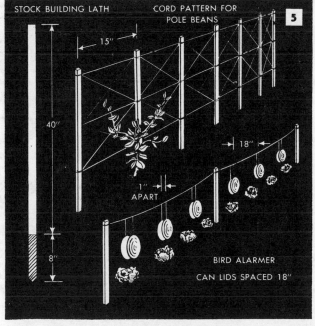

STOCK BUILDING LATH   CORD PATTERN FOR POLE BEANS   5

15"

40"

18"

1" APART

8"

BIRD ALARMER

CAN LIDS SPACED 18"

TOOLS FOR YOUR YARD AND GARDEN

GARDEN TOOLS YOU SHOULD OWN

Power Mowers
Rotary or reel, both save work. Reel shears, makes smooth lawn; rotary cuts weeds, tough grass

Wide Trowel
Helpful for taking up and planting larger bulbs, potted plants. Proper handle is very important

Round-Point Shovel
Helpful for digging in hard or clay soils. Blade should be made of tough and tempered steel

Hand Cultivator
Lightweight, about 18 inches long, for close work in weeding and tilling soil around plants

Spading Fork
Sharp tines penetrate soil easily; more efficient than spade except in soils that are sandy

Weed Knife
Also called dandelion knife. Blade slides under plant crown to remove weeds or wild grass

Rakes
Garden rakes spread fertilizer, soil. Lawn rakes need flexible teeth that won't harm roots

Hose
Larger diameter moves water faster. Some plastic hose sensitive to sunrays, temperature

Narrow Trowel
Makes rows for seeds, small holes for small plants; can be used as weeder in flower beds

Sprinklers
Consider water pressure, land contour, soil type. New lawns, some flowers require fine spray

EQUIPMENT YOU CAN RENT OR SHARE

Lawn Roller
Helps you maintain a smooth lawn, levels frost upheavals, improves germination, rooting

Wheelbarrow
For heavy duty hauling jobs around yard. Usually has more capacity than a garden cart

Aerator
Permits moisture, air, nutrients to penetrate soil freely by making soil porous and loose

Lawn Spreader
Distributes commercial fertilizer, grass seed or top dressing on lawn quickly and accurately

Power Tiller
Prepares soil for lawn seeding or gardening. Pulverizes old plants and soil into fine mulch

Pressure Sprayer
Holds several gallons of spray to control weeds, insects and plant diseases in your yard

Lawn Sweeper
Removes sticks, stones before mowing, stands grass shoots up for even cut, gathers clippings

Hedge Trimmer
Cuts woody growth, controls shape and size of shrubs. Also trims grass missed by mower

Garden Cart
Moves small loads of soil, sand or fertilizer. Dip front down and scoop leaves into hopper

Pruners
Cut back stems of tender flowers as well as tree branches. Long pole type is for tree tops

SUB-SURFACE IRRIGATION FOR FLOWER BED

By Lee G. Braunstein

FOR A TIMESAVING method of watering a flower bed without puddling the surface soil, excavate the bed to the required depth and bury lengths of eaves trough and fittings in the inverted position in it as illustrated. A depth of 1 ft. is about right for perennials; 6 to 8 in. for annuals. The irrigator units also serve to aerate the soil, and make an easy job of applying plant food. The latter is simply poured into the open rain pipe extending aboveground at the head of each row and carried directly to the plant roots by flushing the pipe with a garden hose.

When preparing a flower bed for this type of irrigation, excavate it 1 in. deeper than required if the soil is heavy. Then spread a 1-in. layer of sand on the bottom before assembling the eaves trough and fittings in the bed, as indicated in the drawing below. The strip of screening on which each irrigator unit is placed prevents the earth from filling the trough. Do not omit it. The rain-pipe length on each unit should extend from the drop-outlet section to 1 in. above grade level of a completed bed. Irrigator units may be assembled from galvanized or aluminum parts, but do not mix metals in the same installation. To do so would create an electrolytic situation, resulting in rapid destruction of one of the metals.

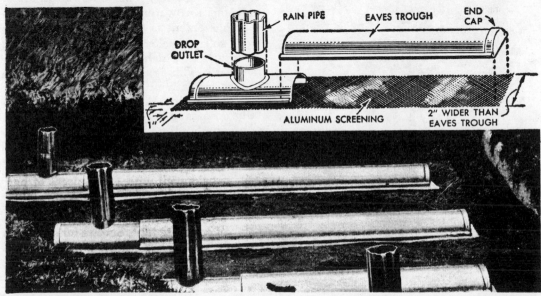

Better WATERING

By ROBERT STAHLER

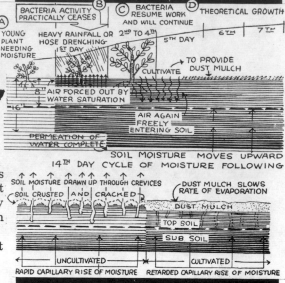

BACTERIA ACTIVITY PRACTICALLY CEASES — BACTERIA RESUME WORK AND WILL CONTINUE — THEORETICAL GROWTH

Ⓐ YOUNG PLANT NEEDING MOISTURE — HEAVY RAINFALL OR HOSE DRENCHING 1ST DAY — Ⓒ 2ND TO 4TH — 5TH DAY — 6TH — 7TH

CULTIVATE — TO PROVIDE DUST MULCH

8" AIR FORCED OUT BY WATER SATURATION — 16" — AIR AGAIN FREELY ENTERING SOIL

PERMEATION OF WATER COMPLETE — SOIL MOISTURE MOVES UPWARD — 14TH DAY CYCLE OF MOISTURE FOLLOWING

SOIL MOISTURE DRAWN UP THROUGH CREVICES — DUST MULCH SLOWS RATE OF EVAPORATION — SOIL CRUSTED AND CRACKED — DUST MULCH — TOP SOIL — SUB SOIL

UNCULTIVATED — CULTIVATED — RAPID CAPILLARY RISE OF MOISTURE — RETARDED CAPILLARY RISE OF MOISTURE

Most gardeners agree that generous flooding several times a week or a light sprinkling almost every evening is very harmful to sturdy growth of many common plants and grasses.

Now for some of the reasons why: First look over Fig. 1, which charts a cycle of theoretical growth from one heavy hosing or rainfall to another, with added details on capillary rise and consumption of moisture. Growing on the outer reaches of the smaller feeding roots of the plant are myriads of tubular, microscopically fine root hairs, Fig. 3. These root hairs take up moisture by a process which agronomists call osmosis. Applied to plant growth, this is the absorption through a thin membrane of a lighter liquid into a heavier one. Thus is moisture, the lighter liquid, drawn through the thin walls of the root hairs by the sugary sap (the heavier liquid) which they contain. A few hours after a drenching rain, try squeezing a handful of wet soil. Not a drop of water will come forth, because the water now surrounds the soil particles in microscopically thin films, and the humus (decayed vegetable and animal matter) is now minute reservoirs which will release their stored moisture to the plants as needed. Feeding roots receive moisture from distances several feet away from the tip ends. This is due to capillary movement of water and to osmosis. Capillary movement is the movement of water from soil particles to other particles and on to others which have lost part of their moisture. This is the reason plants thrive in a comparatively dry soil.

In the section B, Fig. 1, the soil air, vitally necessary to the roots and as a means of escape for the foul gases formed by decaying vegetation, is forced out of the soil by rainfall or hosing, but is soon entering again and bacteria resume activity. As the top soil gradually loses moisture, the roots grow longer and curve downward for moisture now coming up to them by capillary movement, which brings with it plant food washed into low levels by winter and spring rains. In the last section, Fig. 1, notice the abrupt upsweep of theoretical growth. This is due not wholly to the re-

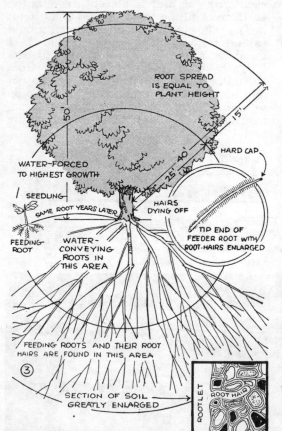

ROOT SPREAD IS EQUAL TO PLANT HEIGHT

50' — 15' — 25' — 40' — HARD CAP

WATER-FORCED TO HIGHEST GROWTH

SEEDLING — SAME ROOT YEARS LATER

HAIRS DYING OFF

FEEDING ROOT — WATER-CONVEYING ROOTS IN THIS AREA

TIP END OF FEEDER ROOT WITH ROOT-HAIRS ENLARGED

FEEDING ROOTS AND THEIR ROOT HAIRS ARE FOUND IN THIS AREA

③

SECTION OF SOIL GREATLY ENLARGED

ROOTLET — ROOT HAIR

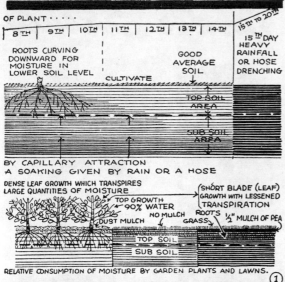

OF PLANT · · · ·

8TH	9TH	10TH	11TH	12TH	13TH	14TH	15TH TO 20TH

ROOTS CURVING DOWNWARD FOR MOISTURE IN LOWER SOIL LEVEL

15TH DAY HEAVY RAINFALL OR HOSE DRENCHING

GOOD AVERAGE SOIL

CULTIVATE

TOP SOIL AREA

SUB SOIL AREA

BY CAPILLARY ATTRACTION
A SOAKING GIVEN BY RAIN OR A HOSE

DENSE LEAF GROWTH WHICH TRANSPIRES LARGE QUANTITIES OF MOISTURE

TOP GROWTH 90% WATER

DUST MULCH — NO MULCH

SHORT BLADE (LEAF) GROWTH WITH LESSENED TRANSPIRATION

ROOTS GRASS — ½" MULCH OF PEAT

TOP SOIL

SUB SOIL

RELATIVE CONSUMPTION OF MOISTURE BY GARDEN PLANTS AND LAWNS. ①

So, contrasting the two cycles, the following method of watering appears to be best: A heavy soaking (2 to 3 in. of water applied to the garden or lawn) at 10-day to 3-week intervals governed by temperature, texture of soil, and water-holding ability. Then cultivate immediately when top soil is sufficiently dry, with one or more cultivations before the next soaking. In time, density of growth makes impossible further cultivation. So, after the final one, some gardeners apply a 1-in. mulch of peat. This mulch applied to freshly cultivated soil will act as a cushion, preventing hard rains from packing the soil, and permitting air to pass in, and foul gases to escape. Naturally, the mulch will obviate the need of frequent waterings and also lessen the danger of foliage diseases.

There are also certain plants which have special, seasonal water requirements. For example, you should keep peonies well watered throughout August for this is the season that new eyes are formed. Immediately after flowering, the foliage of early spring bulbs such as tulips, hyacinths, etc., continue to grow, and store within the bulb next season's foliage and bloom.

Many evergreens have no true dormant season, and are likely to be in active growth in fall and early winter. Thus they may winter-kill if these seasons are dry. Fig. 4 shows how to water tall-growing ornamentals such as shrubs and evergreens. As there are few feeding roots inside the spread of the foliage, Fig. 3, the area outside should be watered as shown in Fig. 4. In all cases, ground soaking is the best method, for it directs the water where needed without waste and reduces chances of foliage diseases.

freshing benefits of the applied moisture, but is the result of bacteria—those working in the dryer soil levels above the roots where they have been making available plant food, which was washed into the immediate vicinity of the roots and rapidly taken up by them. Occurring in uncounted numbers in each tablespoonful of rich garden soil, these bacteria, which are single-cell micro-organisms, break down complex compounds into simple elements and render them as food available to plant life. Were it not for their work, the soil would become lifeless and unproductive.

Now suppose you were to keep your garden and lawn top soil soaked during this theoretical 14-day cycle. As a result the soil would be without air, to the detriment of aerobic (air-loving) bacteria and much of the root system of the plants would perish, while the sparse remainder would function too close to the soil surface. The soil would become sour, full of poisonous gases, and the plant foliage would take on a sickly, yellowish-green color.

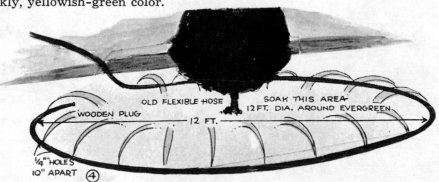

OLD FLEXIBLE HOSE

WOODEN PLUG

SOAK THIS AREA 12 FT. DIA. AROUND EVERGREEN

12 FT.

¼" HOLES 10" APART ④

"Overcoats" for Tender Shrubs

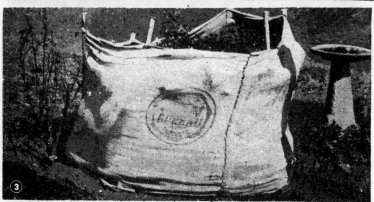

Pole fence on the windward side protects the taller-growing shrubs from severely cold winds

Pieces of corrugated cardboard cut from packing boxes and nailed to stakes make a good windbreak

For low-growing shrubs a combination windbreak and sunshade can be made from burlap and stakes

Sunshades made by tying long grass or cornstalks in bundles and supporting them with a frame

Shrubs

Most high and low-growing shrubs exposed to winter winds and reflected sunlight need additional protection

MANY valuable shrubs, plants and small ornamental trees require some protection from cold winds and drifting snows if they are to survive the winter without damage. Species which are hardy in protected locations during average winters will often winterkill when fully exposed to cold winds for long periods. Others suffer from freezing and thawing of the bark when exposed alternately to bright sunlight in daytime and the cold of long winter nights. Some plants, particularly evergreens, which are located close to white walls that reflect the sunlight on the foliage while the roots are still frozen in the ground, often suffer from "winter-burn," which dries and withers foliage and twigs.

Single shrubs may be protected by driving stakes around the plant and covering these with burlap as in Fig. 3. The purpose of the burlap "fence" is not to keep out the cold, but to keep the temperature more nearly uniform. Tender shrubs, such as English boxwood, need this protection in the colder climates. Sheets of cardboard cut from large packing cartons and arranged about the plants as in Fig. 2 make a good windbreak or a sunshade when necessary. Other materials suitable for making windbreaks are coarse straw, tall grass and dry cornstalks. Small trees may be wrapped with a thick covering of tough grass, Fig. 6, or a long windbreak may be made by using posts and supporting strips to hold the material in place as in Fig. 4.

Low ornamental trees can be wrapped with burlap and the top pruned back to such an extent that it also can be covered with a protecting layer of the same material, Fig. 5. Heavy paper may be used for this purpose, but it must be tied securely in place. When wrapping shrubs, be careful not to break the tender twigs or stems.

Rustic pole fences, Fig. 1, snow fences or latticed frameworks make good two or three-sided windbreaks. Where a low shrub planting covers considerable area, an open board fence along the windward side will offer some protection and also will help to drift protective snow over the planting. Often a pole fence, such as that in Fig. 1, along one side of a hedge or other planting will be sufficient protection. A thin coating of dry straw spread uniformly and held down with light woven wire or poultry netting makes a good covering for hedges or other low growth which require protection from wind and cold. In some locations a sunshade is more important than a covering or even a windbreak. This is especially true on the south side of a white wall or on any southern slope or exposure where heat from the midday sun raises the temperature above freezing for several hours during the day. Evergreens of most varieties never become entirely dormant; some growth takes place the year 'round. After a dry fall water evergreens before the ground freezes. If soil around the roots freezes "dry" the plant is very apt to suffer.

Spring bulbs should be taken from the ground in fall and potted for forcing. Pot them about the second or third week in October and store in cold frames so they remain dormant until removed in January

In January the potted spring bulbs are removed from the cold frames and taken indoors or into a hothouse to artificially induce them to start their spring growth. Bulbs treated this way will bloom in March

Winter Insurance for Your Garden

 Given a little assistance, your flowers will winter well, bloom early.

Dead leaves and grass clippings can be made into valuable mulch by treating them with commercial compost-producing preparations

ABOUT THE MIDDLE OF OCTOBER is the time to dig up and pot spring bulbs if you want to force them for early blooming. Store the potted plants in cold frames until January, then move them indoors or into a hothouse. They will bloom in March. Annual plants should be dug up before the first frost, potted and taken indoors. Replant them outside in spring. To assure vigorous peony bushes, prune the stalks down to within a few inches of the ground in fall. Cover the root area with several inches of mulch, such as peat moss, composted material or a blanket of straw 2 or 3 in. thick.

Annuals that would be destroyed by winter weather should be taken out of the ground before the first frost and placed in pots. The plants will grow all winter indoors and then can be replanted outdoors

Peony bushes have fresh growth every spring and the old stalks must be cut down to provide room for the new growth. Prune the old stalks down to within a few inches of the ground as shown in the photograph

Requiring especially good care if they are to last through the winter are rosebushes. To protect these plants, pile soil around the roots and about half-way up the main stem of the plant. Rosebushes are not pruned in the fall, but in the early spring

To make sure that the dirt piled around the rose-bush does not thaw, once it has frozen, straw or hay is piled over the dirt to insulate it. This is done after the ground has frozen thoroughly. Straw also is piled around the rosebush to protect it

 Trees and shrubs, although hardier than flowers, also require protection.

Freezing does not hurt most plants, rather it protects them. Alternate thawing and freezing is what does the damage, breaking the roots and sometimes heaving the plants above ground level. Insulation by mulching, therefore, is required. Pile soil about 8 in. high around a rosebush, then completely surround the bush with straw. Some trees, such as figs, are unusually sensitive and should be wrapped completely with waterproof paper, as well as having their roots protected with a heavy layer of mulch. Soft trees, such as rose trees, should be wrapped in straw or hay of the type that has long strands, which provides a "blanket" around the tree. Older trees are hardy enough to go through a winter with no assistance, but young trees, because their roots are close to the surface, can be killed by freezing. For this reason, the roots should be insulated with mulch.

Fig trees and some dwarf fruit trees are extremely sensitive to weather extremes and must be wrapped completely in waterproof paper and the roots well mulched

Soft trees, such as rose trees, should be wrapped completely in straw or hay that has long strands, permitting it to be tied around the tree like a blanket. The straw protects the tree against winter weather and early buds against the spring frosts

Roots of young trees should be protected against the damage that can be caused by alternate thawing and freezing, which may break them or heave them out of the ground. Insulate around the root area with a layer of mulch after the ground has frozen

Winterizing treatment for a lawn begins late in the fall with the application of fertilizer and lime, distributed evenly over the lawn with a spreader

Next operation after fertilizer and lime are spread on lawn is to aerate it with one of a number of devices to assure that air and food reach grass roots

After the entire lawn has been aerated thoroughly, spread a top-dressing, such as peat humus, over it

About a month after applying the top-dressing, sweep the lawn to remove debris. Mechanical sweeper pictured makes this job a simple one

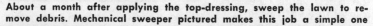

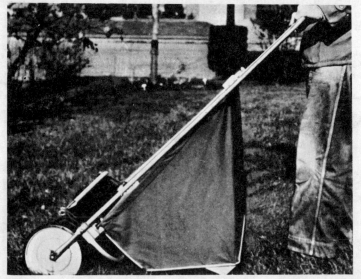

"Scalp treatment" for lawn readies it for winter.

Preparation of your lawn in the fall will have much to do with its health the following spring. The first step in winterizing a lawn is to spread fertilizer and lime, making sure the materials are evenly distributed. A spreader designed for this purpose will give the best results. After the fertilizer has been spread, aerate the lawn with a spiked disk, plate or roller to assure that both air and food reach the grass roots. After aerating the lawn, apply a top-dressing; peat humus is excellent. A month after the top-dressing has been applied, sweep the lawn thoroughly to remove any debris. Mechanical sweepers, mounted on wheels and fitted with rotating brushes make this job a simple one, but an ordinary straw broom will do just as well, although requiring more time. The lawn now is ready for winter. To further guarantee a healthy lawn, there is a precaution to take during the winter. If possible, avoid piling snow very high on a lawn when cleaning walks and drives. The weight of banked snow seems to encourage "snow mold," which often causes large areas of grass to turn brown and die. ★ ★ ★

PLANT PROTECTORS

TO PROTECT newly germinated sweet corn from predatory birds, and to prevent frost damage to seedlings, cover them with fabricated plastic protectors as illustrated. Made in 6-ft. lengths, the lightweight units are easy to store and use since they nest when stacked and in use are simply placed on the ground over the row of plants. Each unit consists of two 6-ft. lengths of 1 x 1-in. wood strips drilled to take U-shaped frames formed from clothes-hanger wire. The stringers are spaced 5 in. apart, the wire frames about 6 in. Next, plastic-coated fabric or wire mesh, such as is used for covering a storm door, porch enclosure, or window openings, is stretched over the frames and tacked to the stringers. In a warm climate, where protection from only predatory birds is needed, window screening may be used instead.

Strips of aluminum foil do a good job of keeping birds away from ripening raspberries when hung on a line stretched over the bushes between stakes as shown at the right. Strips 1½ x 9 in. are cut from heavyweight aluminum foil and are threaded on a length of heavy cord. Spaced about 1 ft. apart, the strips are kept apart by tying knots in the cord on both sides of them. They should be crimped so that the wind will make them flutter and sparkle in the sun.—Hi Sibley, Nuevo, Calif.

"Picture Frame" Gate

By Hi Sibley

THIS DECORATIVE "picture frame" gate will make any yard more attractive. It is practical as well as beautiful. Children and pets are kept inside the yard, wandering stray dogs are kept out. Crimson roses climbing the trellis around the gate give it added beauty.

Four 78-in. lengths of 2 x 3 stock are used as corner posts for the gate, the lower ends being set in concrete. These lower ends are creosoted or treated with wood preservative before being centered in holes dug to the shape indicated. When concrete is poured into these holes, it is "keyed" into the ground when it hardens, assuring that the posts will not loosen easily. To further assure solid anchoring of the posts, drive a number of nails into the lower ends as indicated, so the posts are "locked" into the concrete. The top arches of the trellis frame, and of the gate halves, are sawed in three segments, then screwed together as indicated. The lower ends of the trellis arches, and the corner posts, are half-lapped. To keep out smaller animals, the lower section of each gate half is latticed horizontally with lengths of flat steel, that also offer protection against damage by toddlers' wheeled vehicles.

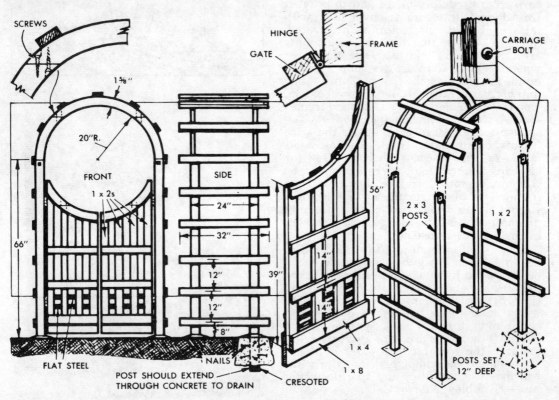

1

"Sasheen" Ribbon photo

Gift wrapping as the experts do it is neat and conservative, and often symbolizes the occasion or the hobby, vocation or personality of the recipient

SECRETS OF ATTRACTIVE PACKAGES

I T'S THE GIFT that counts, of course, but it's the wrapping that makes the first impression and sets the stage for lively anticipation. Two important factors to keep in mind when gift wrapping are neatness and simplicity of design. It is better to be "awfully simple than simply awful." Notice in the examples given that the

Creasing the paper at the edges squares the wrapping

2

designer depends on the paper for coloring and not on ribbon decoration. Also notice that mostly metallic papers are used, their plain colors being highlighted by simple decorations of ribbon bows or practical, useful objects peculiar to the occasion, or to the personality, hobby or vocation of the recipient.

Figs. 3, 12, 14 and 15 are good examples of wrappings designed for the occasion. In Fig. 3, Dad's birthday gift is wrapped with paper in a conservative color. A little ribbon decoration and lettering done with cigarettes completes the package. For a bridal shower or wedding-anniversary gift of silverware, three pieces of silverware stitched to the wrapping and augmented with a ribbon bow definitely key the gift package to the occasion.

What could be more appropriate for a baby-shower gift than a stork decoration as in Fig. 12? The stork is shaped from a

Above, silverware gift personalized by using three pieces as decoration. DAD spelled with cigarettes

Small gift package gains stature when wrapped as above and tied with artificial flowers. Package at right wrapped with velour paper. Shirt cuffs and collar are simulated with the same paper. Tie is ribbon with silver cord for clasp. Stitching is imitated with glitter glued on, and cuff links are small tree ornaments. Below, metallic-paper wrapping decorated with dime-store glass flowers produces a colorful package of unusually neat appearance

large safety pin. Bits of stiff ribbon through the eye of the pin simulate wings; a round toothpick takes care of the beak from which is hung the paper diaper carrying a tiny doll or the name card.

A wrapping symbolic of his hobby or vocation will tickle the vanity of any man. Such a wrapping is not intended to give an inkling as to what's inside nor represent the gift itself. Examples given in Figs. 1, 6, 8 and 10 should start you off. The "candy cane" saw decoration pictured in Fig. 1 is ideal for the handyman. It is a keyhole saw wrapped in red paper and then wound spirally with narrow white ribbon. A ribbon poinsettia adds the floral effect.

Tree decoration at right formed with Hawaiian lei glued on and ornamented with small tree ornaments and silver cord with star at top. Below, artificial fishing fly symbolizes recipient's hobby. Hook should be shielded

7

8

A corsage of live or artificial flowers is an ideal decoration on a gift preceding a social engagement. The corsage can be removed and worn

10

9

For a gift to a man who has a home workshop, try the wrapping below. The decoration is a circular-saw blade. "Sasheen" ribbon forms bow, which is wound to simulate wheel spokes

"Sasheen" Ribbon photo

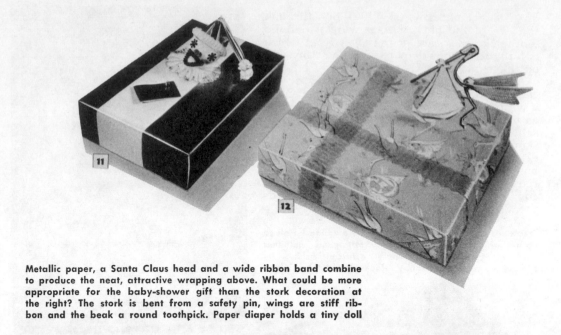

Metallic paper, a Santa Claus head and a wide ribbon band combine to produce the neat, attractive wrapping above. What could be more appropriate for the baby-shower gift than the stork decoration at the right? The stork is bent from a safety pin, wings are stiff ribbon and the beak a round toothpick. Paper diaper holds a tiny doll

Aleen's Floral Supply photo

Packages above show what can be done with colorful paper and simple decorations. Left-end package is decorated with Puffed Wheat and ribbon, while the one at the right end is done with Styrofoam and artificial leaves. Wrappings below are ideal for Christmas packages

Aleen's Floral Supply photo

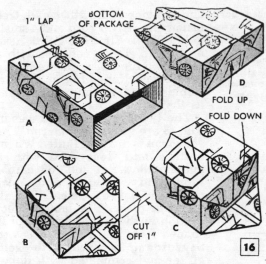

16

Steps in wrapping packages to get neat square ends

17

Amount to cut off varies with different packages

For the sport-shirt fancier, try the wrapping shown in Fig. 6, which also gives the key to the shirt inside. The package is wrapped in velour crepe paper or similar material, after which collars and cuffs are simulated with the same material and glued in place. Stitching is imitated with glitter glued on, and cuff links are tiny ornament balls glued in place. The tie is ribbon with gold cord for the clasp.

The standard, but welcome, necktie gift shown in Fig. 8 becomes more personalized when decorated with a practical symbol of the receiver's hobby—in this case a colorful fishing fly. Point of the hook should be shielded with several wrappings of cellulose tape.

Fig. 10 is a wrapping for the "Big Wheel" with a power saw in his home shop. Done in a wheel motif complete with ribbon spokes, the decoration on this package is a circular-saw blade. Cellulose tape is

folded over the saw teeth to prevent possible injury.

Your "precious things come in small packages" type of gift that always seems so inconspicuous in size will increase in stature if wrapped as in Figs. 4 and 18. Paper or other artificial flowers are used as ties at the ends. Other ties suitable to the occasion may be used.

For a gift preceding a social engagement the package in Fig. 9 depicts a dual-purpose decoration. The package is wrapped in metallic paper and decorated with a corsage of live or artificial flowers, which are removed and worn by the recipient.

When wrapping Christmas gifts it is hard to beat the simplicity and good taste of the wrappings shown in Figs. 7, 11, 14 and 15, and the right and left-hand packages of Fig. 13. The white tree, Fig. 7, is shaped with a Hawaiian lei glued in place

This method of wrapping makes small package larger

Using folded strip of wrapping paper as name card

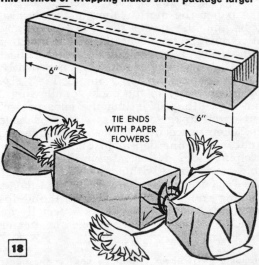

18

19

923

Word NOEL spelled out on base-metal trays. Metal is available at most hobby shops. Letters are outlined with glue, then sprinkled with glitter. Ribbon streamers complete this unusual wrapping

Aleen's Floral Supply photo

and ornamented with small tree ornaments, silver cord and a small gold star. In Fig. 11, a Santa head and white ribbon contrast with a blue metallic paper to produce a neat effect. Notice in Fig. 19 how a folded strip of the paper serves as the name card.

The two Christmas packages of Fig. 13 are very easy to wrap. The snowman is made of Puffed Wheat kernels and decorated with a marshmallow hat and red cinnamon-candy buttons. Arms, ear muffs and hat top are chenille, all glued in place. The lantern decoration in the right-hand detail is shaped from half-round pieces of Styrofoam, sprayed with gold glitter and completed with dime-store leaves and ribbon. Candle flame is a piece of red chenille.

Notice in the two center wrappings of Fig. 13 how simple ribbon decorations relieve the lines of striped paper.

Fig. 14 shows what can be done with gold metallic paper, Styrofoam eggs, gold cord, sequins and evergreen sprigs. The eggs are shaped to resemble tree ornaments, colored and then decorated with pearl-headed pins and sequins.

Green metallic paper, artificial snow and small pine cones are combined to produce the wrapping in Fig. 15. The green-fern effect is achieved by using a flattened fern as a stencil and spraying the snow over it.

The word NOEL is spelled out on the package in Fig. 20 on base metal, obtainable from hobby shops. The metal is formed into trays. Each letter is first drawn on a tray with glue, then sprinkled with glitter and the surplus shaken off, allowing a little to adhere to the wrapping paper. Trays and ribbon are glued to the wrapping.

When designing a gift wrapping remember the plainer the paper the more elaborate the decoration may be, and the busier the design the more conservative must be the decoration. But no matter how well the design is worked out, the whole effect will be lost if the package is not wrapped neatly.

Fig. 16 shows one method of wrapping. First, size the wrapping carefully to the package, allowing 1 in. overlap in width, and letting the ends project an amount equal to the thickness of the package plus ¼ in. Then proceed as indicated by steps A, B, C, D, cutting off one flap as in Fig. 17.

The wrapping method illustrated in Fig. 21 shows how to fold a wrapping without cutting the ends, but requires accuracy to produce a neat package.

After folding and securing one end of the wrapping, creasing the edges as in Fig. 2, especially on metallic papers, squares the package for neater appearance. ★ ★ ★

Steps in wrapping gift without cutting the ends of the paper

RIBBON BOWS

YOU PROBABLY HAVE been delighted, at one time or another, to receive a gift-wrapped package that was made especially attractive by having one or more ribbon bows on it. Quite likely you wished that you, too, could tie such bows, but hesitated to try because they seemed so intricate. As with many things that seem complicated, the bows actually are fairly easy to make. They do require time and patience, and not all the first few attempts will be completely satisfactory, but you soon will find yourself proficient enough to be able to place fancy bows on all the packages you gift wrap.

In Fig. 1 is shown the step-by-step method of making a "magic" bow. First, a length of ribbon is formed into a fairly large loop. Second, the loop is flattened in such a manner that the loose end of the ribbon is even with the end of the flattened loop. The third step requires the flattened loop to be folded in half and a diagonal cut made across each corner at the fold. A narrow ribbon or cord then is tied around the resulting V-notches when the ribbon is unfolded, as shown in the fourth step. The ribbon is refolded, and the open loops are pulled through each other for the fifth step. The pulled-through loops then are shaped with your hands and positioned to result in the flower-like bow shown in the sixth step in Fig. 1.

The French bow in Fig. 2 is formed by "piling" a number of loops one on top of the other, then tying the loops at the center with the loose ends of the ribbon. The resulting pattern of loops is pulled out to form the bow as shown in the right-hand detail. The elongated bow, shown below in Fig. 2 is started in the same manner as the French bow, but some of the loops of the bow are cut so there are a number of loose ends. The dahlia bow, lower, right-hand detail, Fig. 2 also is formed in the same way as the French bow. Then all the loops are cut diagonally at their centers to provide a leaflike appearance.

The tailored bow at the top of Fig. 3 is formed much like the French bow, with loops being piled one on the other, but each succeeding loop is made slightly shorter than the preceding one. The free ends of the ribbon are spread out as shown and the bow tied at the center with a small

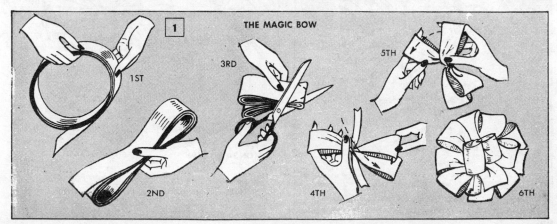

1   THE MAGIC BOW

1ST

2ND

3RD

4TH

5TH

6TH

TAILORED BOW

CARNATION BOW

DAISY BOW

TWO-IN-ONE BOW

INFORMAL BOW

ribbon, or with a cord. The latter is available with strands of silver, gold and other colors woven into it, so it adds to the attractiveness of the bow. The carnation bow in Fig. 3 is started like the magic bow in **Fig. 1.** After the loops are pulled through each other they are grasped in the hand and cut with the scissors to simulate the petals of a carnation. For the daisy bow, fairly wide ribbon is used. The bow is started by piling a number of loops, which then are tied at the center. The loops are pulled through each other and the finished bow is held at the center by a thumbtack or a small hatpin. The latter is best when attaching the bow to a package. As shown in the detail, the two-in-one bow is simply a flattened roll of ribbon that then is folded off-center and cut across the corners to form V-notches, as for the magic bow. Being off-center, the notches, when tied, cause the bow to have one end longer than the other. The loops of this bow also can be pulled apart for a different effect. Tying the informal bow starts by looping the ribbon around your thumb. Loops then are formed as shown. The bow can be left loose and fastened to a package with cellulose tape, or the ends of the ribbon can be pulled through the loop formed on the thumb, and the bow tied firmly.

After you have tied a number of the bows shown here, you might design some of your own. Using two different colors of ribbon for one bow is one method of modifying the designs shown. Bows of the same type tied with narrow ribbon will appear to be different when tied with wide ribbon. Using both wide and narrow ribbon, as well as two colors also makes for different appearance.

The bows presented here were reproduced from an instruction sheet issued by Minnesota Mining and Mfg. Co. ★ ★ ★

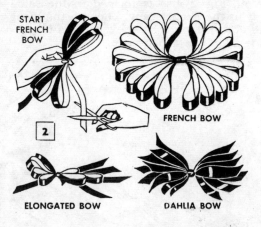

START FRENCH BOW

FRENCH BOW

ELONGATED BOW

DAHLIA BOW

Easier Way To Install
GLASS-BLOCK "WINDOWS"

HOMEOWNERS planning to install small decorative glass-block panels in an exterior wall will be happy to know that the manufacturers of structural glass block have developed a simplified method of installation which eliminates the need of expansion strips and wall ties. Instead, an asphalt emulsion is used, and an expansion space is allowed above the top row of blocks as in the upper detail. The opening must be framed in the same way as for a double-hung window, with adequate lintel support at the head, and it should be not more than 5 ft. wide or 7 ft. high, including a maximum of 25 sq. ft. The first step is to brush a heavy coat of asphalt emulsion onto the wooden frame, applying it in a strip about 3½ in. wide across the sill, lower detail, and up the jambs, center detail. The blocks are laid up in ¼-in.-thick mortar joints consisting of portland cement, 1 part, hydrated lime (high-calcium type), 1 part, and graded plastering sand, 4 to 6 parts. Trowel the joints neatly and, when finished, scrub the panel to remove all excess mortar. Scrape out any loose mortar from the expansion space at the head and finally run a line of calking completely around the opening.

Apply a heavy coating of asphalt emulsion to the sills and jambs. The coating should be at least 3½ in. wide

Above, lay the blocks in mortar joints troweled to a uniform thickness of ¼ in. Below, run a line of calking compound all around the completed panel

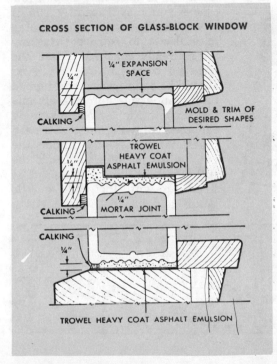

CROSS SECTION OF GLASS-BLOCK WINDOW

¼" EXPANSION SPACE

¼"

CALKING

MOLD & TRIM OF DESIRED SHAPES

TROWEL HEAVY COAT ASPHALT EMULSION

¼"

CALKING

¼" MORTAR JOINT

CALKING

¼"

TROWEL HEAVY COAT ASPHALT EMULSION

DRILLING AND

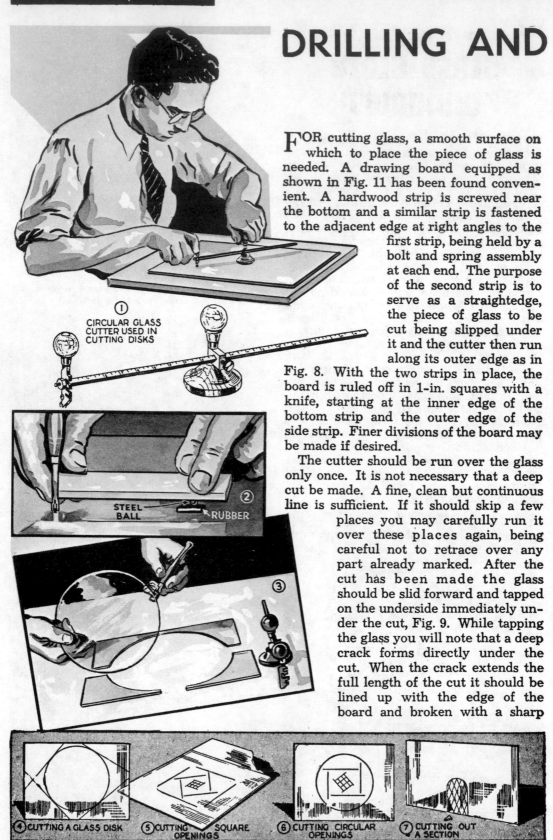

① CIRCULAR GLASS CUTTER USED IN CUTTING DISKS

② STEEL BALL — RUBBER

③

④ CUTTING A GLASS DISK
⑤ CUTTING SQUARE OPENINGS
⑥ CUTTING CIRCULAR OPENINGS
⑦ CUTTING OUT A SECTION

FOR cutting glass, a smooth surface on which to place the piece of glass is needed. A drawing board equipped as shown in Fig. 11 has been found convenient. A hardwood strip is screwed near the bottom and a similar strip is fastened to the adjacent edge at right angles to the first strip, being held by a bolt and spring assembly at each end. The purpose of the second strip is to serve as a straightedge, the piece of glass to be cut being slipped under it and the cutter then run along its outer edge as in Fig. 8. With the two strips in place, the board is ruled off in 1-in. squares with a knife, starting at the inner edge of the bottom strip and the outer edge of the side strip. Finer divisions of the board may be made if desired.

The cutter should be run over the glass only once. It is not necessary that a deep cut be made. A fine, clean but continuous line is sufficient. If it should skip a few places you may carefully run it over these places again, being careful not to retrace over any part already marked. After the cut has been made the glass should be slid forward and tapped on the underside immediately under the cut, Fig. 9. While tapping the glass you will note that a deep crack forms directly under the cut. When the crack extends the full length of the cut it should be lined up with the edge of the board and broken with a sharp

CUTTING GLASS

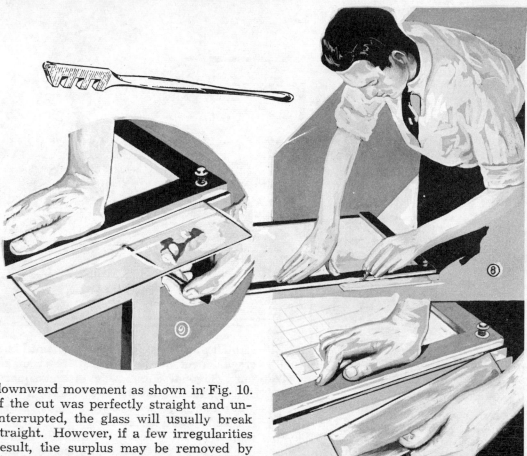

⑧

⑨

⑩

⑪ DETAILS OF GLASS-CUTTING BOARD

3/8" x 1 1/2" STRIPS

DRAWING BOARD

SOLDERED WASHERS

COIL SPRING

1/8

downward movement as shown in Fig. 10. If the cut was perfectly straight and uninterrupted, the glass will usually break straight. However, if a few irregularities result, the surplus may be removed by simply breaking it off with the notches or teeth of the cutter. With a little practice the teeth may be used to great advantage in shaping glass. With them you can remove very small pieces without cracking the piece.

After some experience in straight glass cutting you will get the feel of the cutter and become used to the characteristics of glass. You will then be able to tackle successfully the cutting of round and irregularly shaped pieces. Round pieces of glass are cut with a circle cutter shown in Fig. 1. This cutter is mounted on a rotating arm which pivots in the center of a heavy base. When a cutter of this type is not available, a makeshift arrangement which will do the job can be improvised from a regular cutter, a short square stick, a steel ball and a small piece of rubber or tape as in Fig. 2. The cutter is held to the end of the stick by means of a tack, one of the notches being slipped under the tack head. Mark the desired radius of the cut on the stick, measuring from the cutter wheel to a point where the stick is placed on the ball. With a hammer sink the ball some distance into the wood and then lay the stick and ball on the piece of rubber, which will prevent the ball from slipping out of position. After the glass is cut it is turned over and tapped under the cut until a crack forms all the way around. Next, straight cuts are made in the glass as in Fig. 4, and the corners are

929

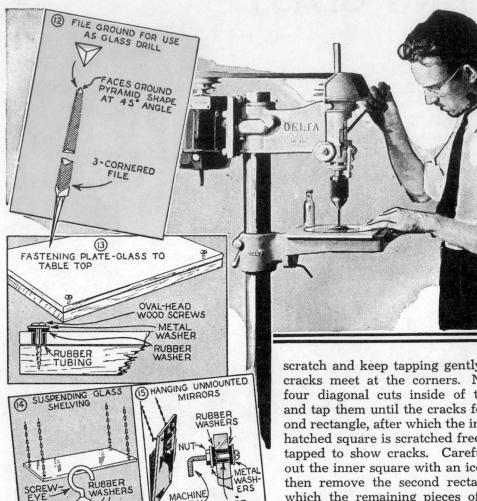

12 FILE GROUND FOR USE AS GLASS DRILL

FACES GROUND PYRAMID SHAPE AT 45° ANGLE

3-CORNERED FILE

13 FASTENING PLATE-GLASS TO TABLE TOP

OVAL-HEAD WOOD SCREWS
METAL WASHER
RUBBER WASHER
RUBBER TUBING

14 SUSPENDING GLASS SHELVING

SCREW-EYE
RUBBER WASHERS
METAL WASHERS

15 HANGING UNMOUNTED MIRRORS

RUBBER WASHERS
NUT
METAL WASHERS
MACHINE SCREW
RUBBER TUBING

broken away exactly as in straight cutting, leaving the disk as in Fig. 3. Ovals and irregular shapes are cut out by scratching around a pattern made from ¼-in. plywood. In making irregular cuts, as much surplus glass as possible should be removed by straight cutting after the design has been scratched into the glass and a complete crack produced by tapping.

The cutting of rectangular and circular openings in glass is more difficult and requires more patience than straight cutting. It is important that only very small pieces of glass be removed at a time. Cutting rectangular openings, Fig. 5, is done as follows: First scratch the edges of the opening to be made, not marking all the way to the corners. Then tap the glass to start a crack at the center of each

scratch and keep tapping gently until the cracks meet at the corners. Next make four diagonal cuts inside of the square and tap them until the cracks form a second rectangle, after which the inner cross-hatched square is scratched free hand and tapped to show cracks. Carefully knock out the inner square with an ice pick, and then remove the second rectangle, after which the remaining pieces of glass are broken away to complete the rectangular opening desired. The edges of the opening may be made smooth by light stroking with a coarse file, after which an emery stone is used for finishing. The procedure for cutting circular openings, Fig. 6, is practically the same except that a circular cut is made first. Cutting out a section of glass as in Fig. 7 is done by first scratching the arc and the straight lines, after which the inside part of the section is scratched diagonally. Cracks are then produced by tapping and the small pieces are broken out one by one.

Holes may be drilled in glass with a drill made by grinding the blunt end of a triangular file to a pyramid shape as shown in Fig. 12. The location of the hole to be drilled should be surrounded with a dam of putty. The dam is filled with turpentine to lubricate the drill, which may be rotated either in a drillpress or with an ordinary bit brace, using only a slight pressure. When the drill starts to break through, the glass should be turned over and the hole completed from the other side, very carefully, of course, to prevent breakage. If a piece of clean white paper is placed under the glass while drilling, it will be spotted by the turpentine as soon as the tip of the drill breaks through, thus warning you of the necessity of turning over the glass. Like other operations with glass, a perfectly smooth wood surface should be used as a support.

Figs. 13, 14 and 15 show methods of mounting glass. If resilient rubber mountings are not used, expansion and contraction of the glass with changes in temperature will cause breakage. These methods of mounting also make the glass less likely to break under shock and vibration.

Glass may be ground smooth on a grindstone or fine emery wheel if the work is done slowly so as to avoid chipping and heating. In all operations on glass, it is important that the glass be kept from getting hot as it will break when unevenly heated. Coarse files may be used for smoothing up rough edges, if light pressure is used in quick sweeping strokes. This treatment is the most rapid method of producing a smooth edge; however, a wet grindstone is the best tool for producing a fine finish. Ground glass may be produced by rubbing the surface of glass with water and coarse emery powder on a rag or piece of leather.

Electrically Heated Wire Will Cut Glass Tubing

With a cutter like the one diagrammed at the right, which consists of a loop of electrically heated Nichrome wire fitted to a plierlike holder of hardwood or plastic, you can cut a number of lengths of glass tubing quickly. The resistance wire is taken from an electric iron, coil heater or a similar appliance. Power is supplied by a 6-volt storage battery or a toy transformer of 10-ampere capacity. In use, the loop is slipped

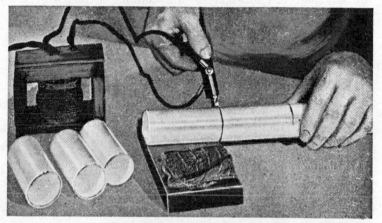

over the tubing and pressed firmly against the glass at the point at which it is desired to make the cut, then current is applied for 4 or 5 seconds, after which the tube is touched to a wet cloth, causing it to break because of the sudden change in temperature. When using this device always remember, however, prolonged contact with the hot wire will cause the glass to melt, rendering it useless.

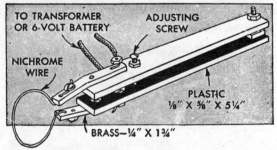

TO TRANSFORMER OR 6-VOLT BATTERY — NICHROME WIRE — ADJUSTING SCREW — PLASTIC ⅛" X ⅝" X 5¼" — BRASS—¼" X 1¾"

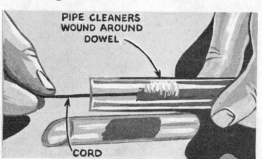

PIPE CLEANERS WOUND AROUND DOWEL — CORD

Easy Method of Cleaning Tubes

Cleaning the inside of a long glass tube is not difficult if the following method is adopted: Select a short piece of dowel that will fit inside the tubing loosely, and drill it lengthwise so that a long cord can be attached. Wind the dowel with one or two pipe cleaners, and then pull it through the tube by means of the cord.

MOLDED CONTOURS
STREAMLINE YOUR PROJECTS

In boat, trailer and sidewalk-car construction contour work pleases the eye and adds strength to the structure. Here's a simple method of contouring with glass fiber, resin and metal lath

By Harold Humphrey

USING GLASS-FIBER CLOTH, ordinary metal lath and resin plastics you can build up almost any desired contour and combine it with flat structural materials such as plywood, hardboard and sheet metals. Usually the finished job owes its professional appearance to the three-dimensional corners, the trailer body illustrated being a typical example. In any type of body construction you'll need to plan in advance the location of the contour work and make the necessary allowances in framing the project. It's regular practice to frame the job, apply the covering of plywood, hardboard or sheet metal and leave the corners open for later application of the contouring.

In this step the procedure is quite simple and you have a choice of several methods of application. The first, used where the nature of the assembly and type of materials will permit, is to apply metal lath to

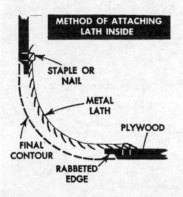

METHOD OF ATTACHING LATH INSIDE

STAPLE OR NAIL — METAL LATH — PLYWOOD — FINAL CONTOUR — RABBETED EDGE

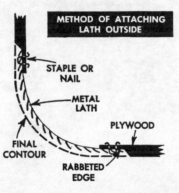

METHOD OF ATTACHING LATH OUTSIDE

STAPLE OR NAIL — METAL LATH — PLYWOOD — FINAL CONTOUR — RABBETED EDGE

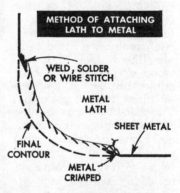

METHOD OF ATTACHING LATH TO METAL

WELD, SOLDER OR WIRE STITCH — METAL LATH — SHEET METAL — FINAL CONTOUR — METAL CRIMPED

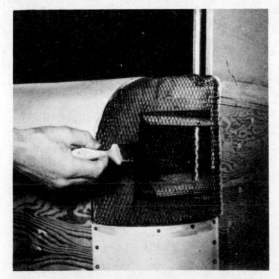

After forming metal lath to desired contour and nailing or stapling in place, next step is to apply brush coat of resin plastic over lath to uniform thickness

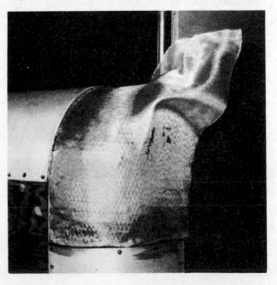

Before plastic brush coat hardens, apply glass-fiber fabric and smooth out in all directions to remove any wrinkles. Trim away any excess with scissors

the inside of the curve as in the left-hand detail below. Note that the metal lath is stapled or nailed to the inside face of the flat material. Also that the edges of the covering material are rabbeted to take the plastic. The method forms a tight, waterproof joint that won't shake loose. The center detail shows the metal lath nailed or stapled in a wide rabbet on the outside of the covering material. This method permits applying the metal lath and plastic from the outside of the body. The third method shows how metal lath is attached to a sheet-metal covering. Here a plastic of the metal-bonding type must be used.

The photos below, left to right, show the step-by-step procedure in building up a typical contoured corner. The metal lath,

Apply a final brush coat over glass-fiber fabric taking special care to brush on plastic mix to a uniform thickness. Work plastic right up to edges all around

Final step in building up contour is applying trowel coat of resin plastic. This is mixed to consistency of light grease so that it is easily worked with trowel

Spread glass-fiber fabric on a flat surface, the garage floor will do, mark size and cut with scissors

available from any building materials dealer, can be cut easily with tinsnips and can be shaped to three dimensional curves by hand. When attaching and shaping the lath keep in mind that it will be covered with at least ⅛ in. of plastic when the job is finished to the final contour. Check the contours carefully before finally nailing or stapling the formed lath in place.

Polyester resins of the type that will bond readily to wood or hardboard, also glass-fiber fabrics are readily available in kit form for covering boat hulls. Or, the resin can be bought by the quart or gallon and the fabric by the yard. The resin comes as a syrup-like liquid and requires the addition of a liquid hardener. For application to the metal lath the mixture must be thickened to a grease-like consistency by the addition of a small amount of powdered asbestos. When mixing resin plastic and hardener follow the instructions.

As the next step brush the mixed material onto the metal lath and before it dries apply the glass fabric and stretch to remove all wrinkles. Trim off the excess at the edges of the opening with scissors. Now coat the fabric with the same plastic mix-

ture, brushing from the center outward to the edges. Allow to harden.

Finally, finish with the trowel coat, which is mixed to a somewhat heavier consistency and laid on with a trowel or wide putty knife. Apply as uniformly as possible, building the material slightly higher than the final contour, then while wet add a second layer of glass fabric. Work out wrinkles and pull the coarse-meshed fabric into the soft trowel coat until it is below the surface. Now smooth the job by hand, taking care to work the surface to a true curvature. Wipe excess material off your hands occasionally with a cloth moistened with acetone. Don't permit the resin to dry on the hands. When applying metal-bonding plastic wear rubber gloves. Trim away any excess glass cloth with scissors and allow the job to dry about 24 hr.

After drying, the trowel coat is worked down to final contour and the curves feathered, or faired, neatly into the flat surface of the covering. This is done with a rasp and sandpaper, working with an eye to true contours and a smooth surface. Any imperfections will show up under the paint or enamel. ★ ★ ★

GLUING

Hardboard Gluing Tip

You will get a better bond when joining other parts to the hard, smooth face of hardboard if it is roughened before applying the glue. This can be done easily with a special serrated surfacer made from a wooden block and a few corrugated fasteners. The fasteners are inserted in a shallow saw kerf cut in one edge of the block. To insure a tight fit, the fasteners are bent slightly so as to apply tension against the sides of the kerf.—Bill Toman

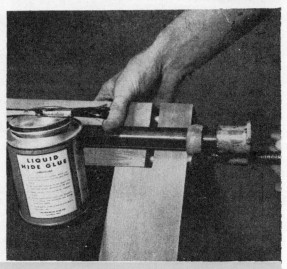

In this doweled joint, end grain is joined to flat grain. End grain should have two coats of glue before joining. Dowel locators assure perfect alignment

A bar clamp is used to draw the joint tight after application of the glue. Care should be taken to assure a perfect fit between all meeting surfaces

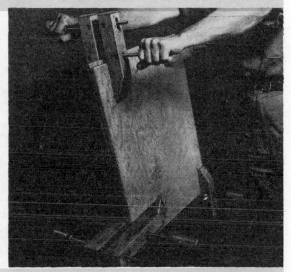

A tub filled with water makes a good "clamp" for flat work such as veneering a small surface. Place a piece of plywood under the tub to distribute pressure

Laminating and veneering can be carried out with hand screws, using four or eight screws, depending on size of work. Adjust hand screws for uniform pressure

GLUE KNOW-HOW has been simplified by the ready-to-mix and ready-to-apply cold adhesives which eliminate heating and the temperature problem at the time of application. Liquid hide glues have supplanted the older hide glues that were supplied in the flake form and required heating for a period of time to reduce them to a usable consistency. Although the older glues were highly effective in durability and holding power, they are not so suitable for use in small manufacturing plants and home shops due to the special equipment required for preparation and application. Both the liquid hide glues and the newer resin glues, the latter having the appearance and consistency of thick cream, are especially useful in home-shop joinery. Both these glues, also the

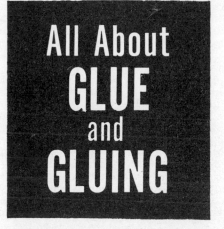

All About GLUE and GLUING

Laminating hardboard to wood is easy with the setup pictured. C-clamps should be equally spaced to distribute pressure uniformly. Wipe away excess glue

Edge clamps are large C-clamps with a sliding fixture that permits applying pressure in two directions. They are especially useful for gluing strips to edges

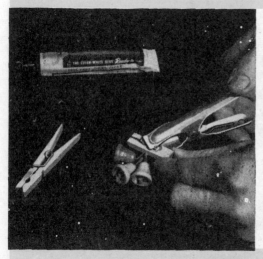

Spring clamps and clothespins of the spring type are used for joining small parts, border inlay and assembly of models. Spring clamps come in several sizes

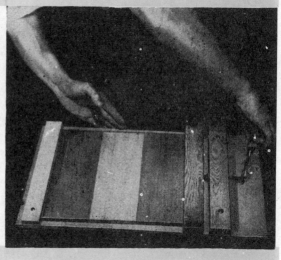

Improvised clamps for edge-gluing can substitute for bar clamps. The simple unit pictured is very effective. Bolt forces the movable jaw against the edge of work

ready-to-mix type supplied in the powder form, require only the simplest clamping equipment. All are water-resistant in the sense that holding power is affected little, if any, by ordinary dampness. When a completely waterproof glue is required, the craftsman uses a resorcinol glue supplied in a two-part container, one part of which contains a dry powder, the other a catalyst in liquid form. When the powder and liquid are mixed in accordance with instructions they form a waterproof glue of great holding power. When gluing woods which contain natural oils such as rosewood, teak, lemon and yew wood, the craftsman uses a casein glue, which comes as a powder and is mixed with water to form a fairly heavy liquid.

Edge-gluing and joint-gluing of frames and cabinet parts require not only the use of the correct glue, but a careful trial fitting of the parts to insure full contact over the whole area of the meeting surfaces. When edge-gluing a number of strips to form a wide panel, the edges of the strips must be jointed true, either by machine or by hand-planing. Craftsmen make a trial assembly of cabinet frames before applying glue to the joints. This will assure a perfect fit of the parts when they are glued and clamped. When gluing cabinet-frame members where end grain is joined to flat grain, it is important to apply two coats of glue to the end grain. Allow the first coat to become tacky, then apply a second coat and join. When joining flat grain, as in edge-to-edge work, the important thing is to apply the glue in a uniform coating. This can be done

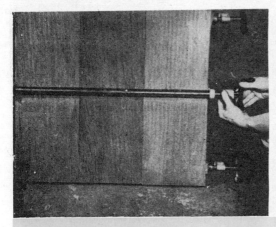

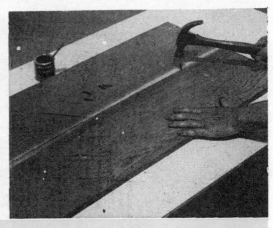

Bar clamps, or carpenter's clamps, are best for edge-gluing a number of strips to form a wide panel or top. Note spacing and alternate position of center clamp

On work where exposed metal is not objectionable, corrugated fasteners are suitable "clamps" for edge-gluing. Usually they are driven into both sides of joint

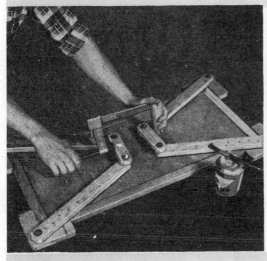

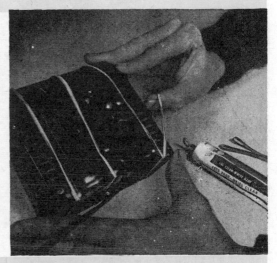

A self-adjusting miter clamp is handy in the home shop. You can make one like this in a few minutes. Note how two members are drawn tight with C-clamp

Ordinary rubber bands of various sizes are just the thing where it is necessary to apply a light, uniform pressure when gluing or cementing small parts

For certain clamping operations requiring light pressure, cellulose tape is useful. Simply spread glue on joining faces, locate parts and wrap with tape

Craftsmen often improvise bar clamps when building or repairing chairs. This simple, two-part clamp is especially effective for this type of parts assembly

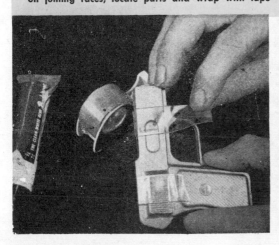

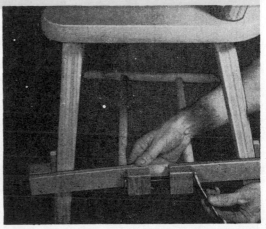

For repairing a single chair, twisted cords can be used to apply pressure until glue sets. Cord clamp is quickly improvised from a length of clothesline

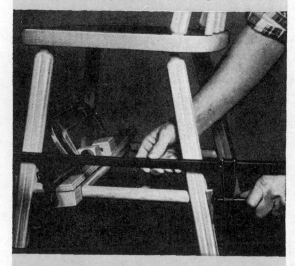

In some cases, chair assembly can be speeded up by applying pressure in two directions simultaneously. Here three bar clamps will be placed at right angles

When the amount of work to be done justifies its purchase, the band clamp is best for chair work. Here the lower assembly is clamped in one operation

with a thin wooden paddle, a brush, or best of all, a glue applicator of the roller type. This applicator operates in a manner similar to a wheel-type paint striper.

Beginning with the two right-hand photos on page **935**, various methods of clamping are pictured. Correct application of the clamps and the amount of pressure applied are the two most important points about clamping. Bar clamps, C-clamps and wooden hand screws, or adjustable clamps, are the most commonly used in the small shop. Bar clamps, or carpenter's clamps, are used chiefly in edge-gluing several strips of stock, also in cabinet-frame assembly. It is important that bar clamps be located square with the work so that pressure is exerted uniformly. Also, when more than two bar clamps must be used, locate the center clamp, or clamps as the case may be, equidistant from those near the ends of the work. The upper left-hand photo on page **937** is a good example of correct bar-clamping. Note that the center clamp is placed with the bar across the opposite face of the work. This position of the third clamp helps to equalize the pressure and also prevents any tendency of the work to buckle. If the work has been cut to the finish size before clamping it will be necessary to protect the edges at the point where the metal clamp jaws engage. This is done by placing small pine blocks between the edge of the stock and the jaws, or by cementing pieces of leather to the face of the jaws. You also can improvise a good substitute for bar clamps, the clamp in the lower right-hand photo on page **936** being a good example.

C-clamps and edge clamps, upper left and upper right-hand photos on page **936**, are used when it is necessary to apply pressure near the edges of the work, as in gluing on an edging strip, or in veneering. Edging clamps, upper right-hand photo, page **936**, are provided with a sliding bracket, or jaw, which makes it possible to apply equal pressure in two directions. Another clamp which belongs in this classification is the simple spring clamp shown in the lower left-hand photo, page **936**. This clamp works in a manner similar to pliers, the spring acting to close the pivoted jaws. Spring-type clothespins also can be used in the same manner.

Improvised miter clamps, rubber bands, cellulose tape, corrugated fasteners, "chevron type" fasteners, all these can be made to serve as clamps in certain gluing operations. In building or repairing chairs, the band clamp, lower photo at the left, is universally useful. It consists of a length of canvas or other tough fabric attached to a special fixture having a snubbing device which permits adjustment of the fabric band to any required length. ★ ★ ★

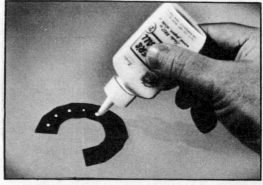

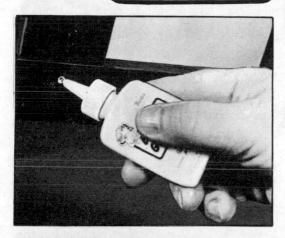

1. An easy way of attaching a letter or other insignia to a sweater is to spread white plastic glue on the back of the insignia and press it onto the garment with a warm electric iron. Either cloth or felt insignia may be attached in this manner

2. Loose crossrail of a chair can be reglued without having to pull members of the joint apart. First drill a small hole in the leg to take the tip of a plastic glue-bottle spout as shown. With the spout held firmly in the hole, squeeze the bottle to force glue into the joint, wiggling the members to get an even distribution of glue. Wipe off excess glue and fill the hole with plastic wood tinted to match

3. When gluing ungummed labels and decorations cut from thin paper, dampen them with a sponge immediately before applying the glue to assure a neat job. The moisture-expanded paper contracts as it dries, leaving a smooth, wrinkle-free appearance

4. Here is an easy way of relieving glue pressure in a dowel joint without having to cut a groove or flat surface on one side of the dowel. Wrap a length of lightweight thread around the dowel to be glued, apply glue and insert it as shown. Excess glue can flow through the spaces made by the thread which then becomes saturated and flattened. This method does not reduce contact surfaces as when a dowel is grooved or flattened, resulting in a stronger joint

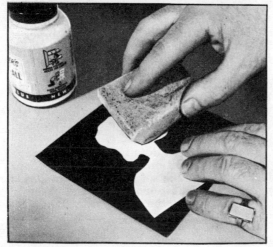

Designed by John Bergen

BUILD YOUR OWN GREENHOUSE

FOR THE PROPAGATION and healthy growth of plants and the production of seedlings for spring planting, there's nothing quite as effective and satisfying as a greenhouse. A separate structure, or true greenhouse, is preferable as it more nearly serves the twofold purpose of propagation and display of plants. However, a lean-to built against the house or garage, or over a basement window, offers safe growing conditions for many common seedlings, cuttings and also for the display of plants not hardened to sudden temperature changes. The one disadvantage of the lean-to type is that it is not always possible to locate it to take full advantage of light and heat from the sun.

True Greenhouse

A separate structure like that pictured above is the choice of experienced gardeners. It offers a much better opportunity for proper management of the house during the growth period of most plants and a better utilization of available sunlight during the season. Note from the following pages that ordinary storm sashes form the glass roof and that both ends of the structure are glazed. The sashes are shown hinged at the top. If desired they also can be hinged at the lower ends. If this is done, each sash should be fitted with a storm-sash bracket so that it can be locked in the open position. The size of the structure detailed permits use of two 3'-0" x 6'-0" storm sashes on each side of the gable. When selecting these be sure there are no pronounced ripples in the glass panes. Ripples in the glass may tend to concentrate the sun's rays and damage plants.

In the sectional detail of the house, page 942, the foundations are shown without footings. In stable soils this construction is permissible. But in loose loam and in sandy or gravelly soils the foundation should be on a footing about 6 x 12 in. in sectional

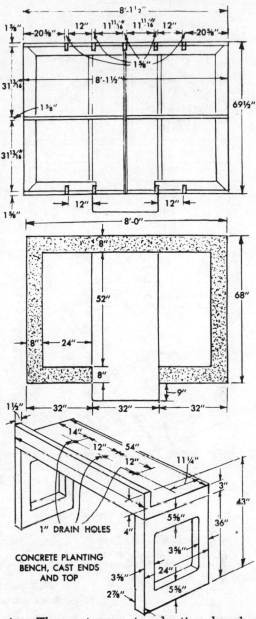

Above, separate structure, or true greenhouse, is most suitable for all-around use of experienced gardener. Center, lean-to greenhouse includes a potting shed

CONCRETE PLANTING BENCH, CAST ENDS AND TOP

1" DRAIN HOLES

Window greenhouse serves as starter for transplants

size. The cast-concrete planting benches detailed above and on the opposite page can be omitted and planting benches constructed of cypress substituted. These can be constructed inexpensively and in considerably less time. If you do cast the benches of concrete be sure to reinforce the top either with reinforcing rods or wire mesh.

The walls can be laid up of cinder block, concrete block, or natural stone. Fill the voids in the top course of blocks with cement mortar and rubble (small stones or coarse gravel) and insert anchor bolts before the mixture hardens. The bolts provide a means of attaching the 2 x 6 plates securely to the wall. When laying the blocks be sure to bed each one in sufficient mortar

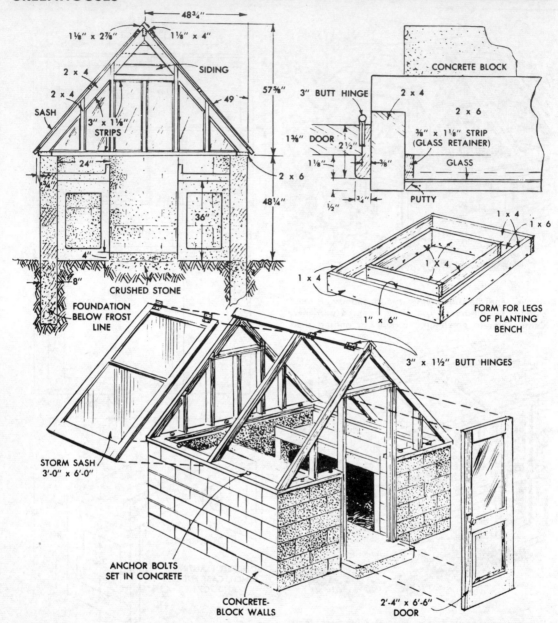

48¾"

1⅛" x 2⅞"   1⅛" x 4"

2 x 4   SIDING

2 x 4

SASH

3" x 1⅛" STRIPS

24"

36"

4"

8"

CRUSHED STONE

FOUNDATION BELOW FROST LINE

57⅝"

49

2 x 6

48¼"

CONCRETE BLOCK

3" BUTT HINGE   2 x 4

2 x 6

1⅜" DOOR   3⅜" x 1⅛" STRIP (GLASS RETAINER)

2½"   GLASS

1⅛"

3⅜"

½"   ¾"   PUTTY

1 x 4   1 x 6

1 X 4

1 x 4

1" x 6"

FORM FOR LEGS OF PLANTING BENCH

STORM SASH 3'-0" x 6'-0"

3" x 1½" BUTT HINGES

ANCHOR BOLTS SET IN CONCRETE

CONCRETE-BLOCK WALLS

2'-4" x 6'-6" DOOR

to assure watertight joints of maximum strength. Keep each course of blocks level and the corners plumb.

Cut all wooden parts of the structure to finished size, trial-fit each one, then prime with a suitable primer, making sure that the priming coat covers all surfaces, especially the end grain. Give the priming coat time to dry thoroughly, then bed the 2 x 6 plates in mortar, allow the mortar to set partially and tighten the nuts on the anchor bolts. Note that the plates are notched to take the 2 x 4 uprights that form the side jambs of the doorframe. The top jamb is end-lapped onto the upright side jambs. The sectional detail through the doorjamb shows the door hinged to swing in. This assembly can, or course, be re-

versed and the door hinged to swing out, if desired. To avoid cutting triangular pieces of glass to fit over the header in the rear gable and over the top jamb above the door, these areas are covered with siding as indicated.

Lean-to Greenhouse and Potting Shed

This unit is designed to be built against the house or garage where space is available for a southern exposure. It should not be built under a wide cornice. Sills of the structure are bolted to a concrete foundation poured to a depth well below the normal frost line. Studs, plates and rafters complete the framing ready for siding and roof boards. The concrete floor, poured over a tamped gravel fill, is an optional

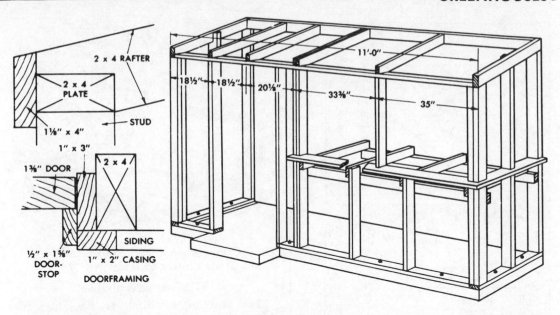

2 x 4 RAFTER

2 x 4
PLATE

STUD

1⅛" x 4"

1" x 3"

1⅜" DOOR

2 x 4

½" x 1⅝"
DOOR-
STOP

1" x 2" CASING

SIDING

DOORFRAMING

11'-0"

18½" 18½" 20½" 33⅜" 35"

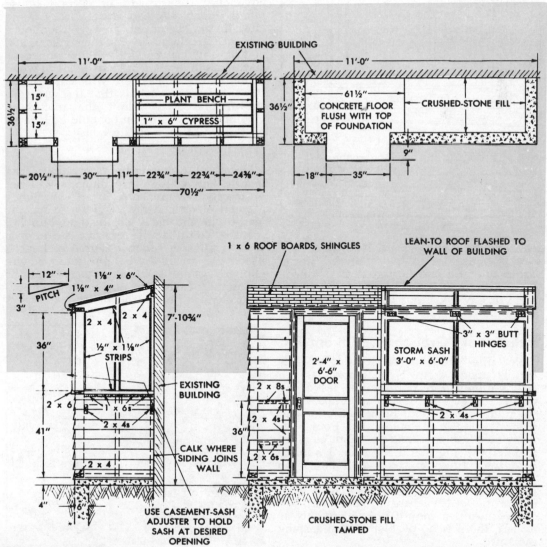

EXISTING BUILDING

11'-0"   11'-0"

36½"

15"

15"

PLANT BENCH

1" x 6" CYPRESS

36½"

61½"

CONCRETE FLOOR
FLUSH WITH TOP
OF FOUNDATION

CRUSHED-STONE FILL

20½" 30" 11" 22¾" 22¾" 24⅜"

70½"

18" 35"

9"

1 x 6 ROOF BOARDS, SHINGLES

LEAN-TO ROOF FLASHED TO
WALL OF BUILDING

12"

PITCH

3"

1⅛" x 6"

1⅛" x 4"

2 x 4   2 x 4

7'-10¾"

36"

½" x 1⅛"
STRIPS

EXISTING
BUILDING

2 x 6

1 x 6s

2 x 4s

41"

2 x 4

4"

CALK WHERE
SIDING JOINS
WALL

USE CASEMENT-SASH
ADJUSTER TO HOLD
SASH AT DESIRED
OPENING

2'-4" x
6'-6"
DOOR

2 x 8s

2 x 4s

36"

2 x 6s

3" x 3" BUTT
HINGES

STORM SASH
3'-0" x 6'-0"

2 x 4s

CRUSHED-STONE FILL
TAMPED

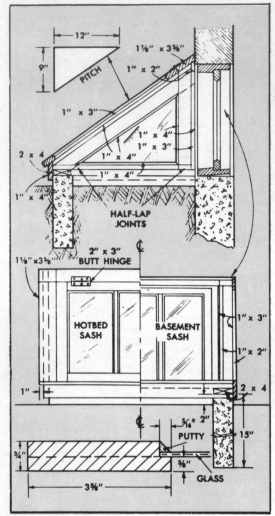

pose. Cypress wood is the most durable because of its ability to resist rot.

Window Greenhouse

For starting seedlings in flats and for advancing the growth of certain house plants which are to be reset out of doors later in the season, a window greenhouse is ideal. The details giving the construction of this unit are not fully dimensioned as certain changes may have to be made when fitting it to the basement window. Note in the construction details that the ends are shown glazed to admit the maximum amount of light. The unit should be located on the south side of the house.

Heating

Unless used during the four seasons, the lean-to and window greenhouses will not ordinarily require heat. In an emergency a small electric heater will serve for the lean-to in the early spring and late fall months. To utilize the separate greenhouse to the fullest a reliable source of heat is necessary. In all except the more severe climates a small greenhouse usually can be adequately heated by means of lead-covered electric heating elements. ★ ★ ★

feature. The greenhouse half of the structure is housed with two standard storm sashes and the end is glazed as detailed. The potting bench and plant bench can be made in any way that best suits the pur-

Individual "Greenhouse" From Jug

Portable "greenhouses" for single plants can be made from 1-gal. glass jugs. To remove only the bottom yet leave the curved lower edge for extra support, use the following method: Remove the cap and place the jug in a shallow pan. Pour boiling water into the pan to a depth of ¼ in. and let the jug stand for 2 or 3 min. to heat the bottom of the jug. Remove the jug and immediately place it in another pan which contains ice water. The bottom of the jug will fracture and drop out. Because the open mouth of the jug acts as a vent, there is no problem of condensing moisture.

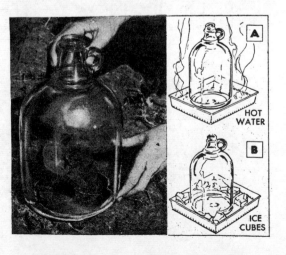

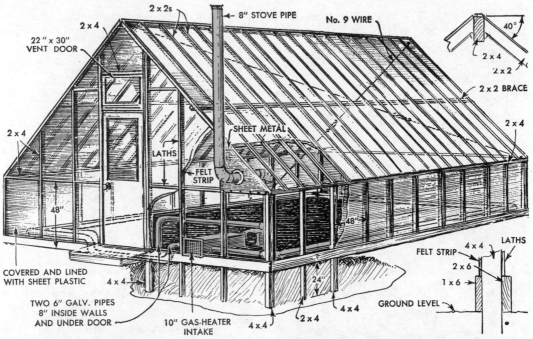

22" x 30" VENT DOOR · 2 x 4 · 2 x 2s · 8" STOVE PIPE · No. 9 WIRE · 40° · 2 x 4 · 2 x 2 · 2 x 2 BRACE · 2 x 4 · 2 x 4 · LATHS · SHEET METAL · FELT STRIP · 48" · 48" · FELT STRIP · 4 x 4 · LATHS · 2 x 6 · 1 x 6 · COVERED AND LINED WITH SHEET PLASTIC · 4 x 4 · TWO 6" GALV. PIPES 8" INSIDE WALLS AND UNDER DOOR · 10" GAS-HEATER INTAKE · 4 x 4 · 2 x 4 · 24" · 4 x 4 · GROUND LEVEL

Plastic Cuts Greenhouse Costs

By H. H. Slawson

LOWER ORIGINAL construction costs plus moderate maintenance expenses, for greenhouses used by either commercial or home flower growers, are promised by innovations in a structure designed and built by horticulturists at the South Dakota Agricultural College. Polyethylene-plastic film is used in place of the glass used in conventional greenhouses. Cost of the plastic for the 18 x 40-ft. structure built at the college was 45 dollars. Material for a home-size unit would be correspondingly less costly. To construct the walls 4 x 4s were sunk in the ground every 8 ft., with 2 x 4s centered between each pair. The corner posts are 4 x 4s. Across the top of these vertical members, which project 4 ft. above the ground and extend 2 ft. into the ground, are nailed 2 x 4s. At ground level, outside the walls, are nailed 2 x 6s, while a 1 x 6 is nailed to the inside of the wall opposite each exterior member. All wood contacting the ground is treated with wood preservative. The roof of the building consists of 2 x 2 rafters fitted against a 2 x 4 ridgepole. A 2 x 2 longitudinal is positioned at right angles to the rafters on each side of the roof, and lengths of 9-ga. wire are fitted through screw eyes and tightened by turnbuckles to form an X-brace on each side of the

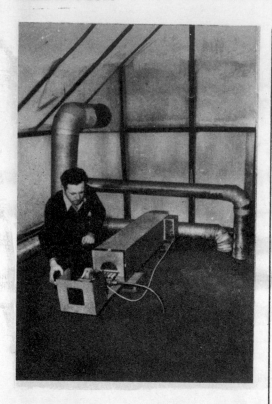

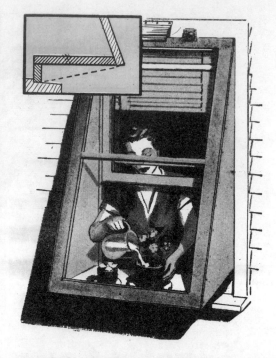

roof as indicated. Rough spots and slivers are removed or sanded before applying the sheet plastic, to minimize the chance of tearing it. The outside layer of polyethylene plastic is 3 mils (.003 in.) thick, stapled in place with laths nailed over it as added reinforcements. The inside layer of plastic is .0015 in. thick, strips of 2-in.-wide roofing felt being used rather than laths. Heat for the greenhouse is supplied by an LP gas heater, the heat being forced through metal ducts positioned 8 in. inside the walls, with the bottom duct 4 in. above the floor. The ducts run underground inside the door. A commercial version of the greenhouse has a concrete floor, with the furnace in an enclosure outside the greenhouse to conserve floor space. A home greenhouse also could have a concrete floor, with a small oil space heater to maintain temperature. The plastic deteriorates during the summer and must be replaced annually, but the college figures that, for a commercial establishment, its replacement cost is less than the cost of replacing broken glass. Also, with the continual improvement in plastics, it is quite possible that a material will be developed that will last much longer. Replacement of the plastic is made in fall, when the weather is fair. The 50-in.-wide material is lapped 3 in., for a tight, strong joint that keeps heat and humidity inside. ★ ★ ★

Small Window Greenhouse Utilizes Storm Sash

A window greenhouse which utilizes the present storm sash can be built in a couple of hours and at a nominal cost. First, the storm sash should be hung on hook-and-eye hangers at the top. The bottom of the sash is extended and a platform of 1-in. stock is fitted between it and the window sill as shown. Hooks hold the platform against the sill to prevent entry from the outside. Two triangular-shaped pieces of ¾-in. exterior plywood form the sides of the greenhouse. Glue and wood screws are used throughout the assembly. Weather stripping is nailed to the window frame so it covers the opening between the top of the storm sash and the frame.

Birdbath is miniature greenhouse with potted plant growing inside a plastic column 12 in. in dia. Frame is aluminum

HAND GRINDER

Speeds up to 25,000 r.p.m. make this tiny power tool a real shop workhorse

WITH THE accessories available, a hand grinder can be made to do just about anything within the capacity of the motor. It can be mounted in fixtures and used as a shaper, router, vertical-spindle sander, drill press, carver, speed lathe and circular saw. Used freehand with grinding wheels of various shapes, rotary files and felt wheels, it can do any work that calls for abrading, cutting or polishing on small workpieces.

The extremely high speed of the motor and direct drive to the cutting and abrading tools results in exceptionally smooth, accurate work on both wood and metal. Free-hand sanding and rotary filing are operations that require very high speeds for acceptable accuracy and easy control of the tool. Drilling tiny holes in model parts of wood or metal calls for sustained high speeds to prevent heating and drill breakage. That's why experienced model-makers, laboratory technicians and hobbyists make wide use of hand grinders and the many accessories available. The simple **saw table detailed on the following page** converts your hand grinder into an efficient circular saw for ripping and crosscutting tiny model parts.—Edwin M. Love.

Used with rotary-file accessories of various shapes, a hand grinder in a fixture makes high-speed shaper

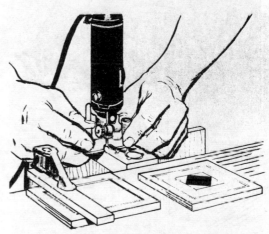

Above, used with veining bits, a hand grinder can't be beat as a router. Below, it's a spindle sander

Precision drilling is assured with this midget drill press. Handles hair-sized bits without breakage

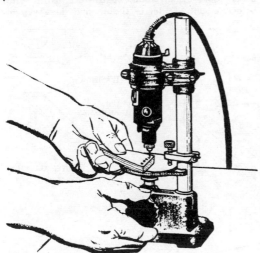

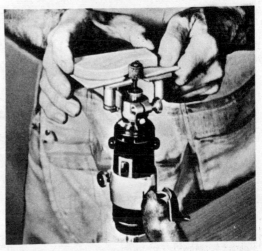

947

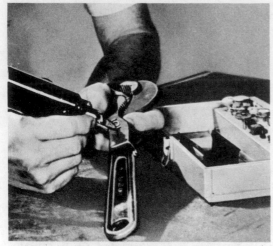

Using various sizes and types of abrasive wheels you can etch your name on tools, do light die sinking, grind small edge tools, work designs on metal or glass

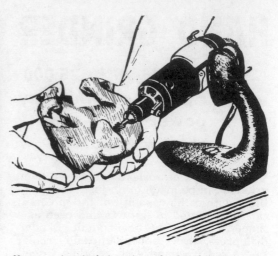

Here carving is being done freehand with grinder held in a fixture. Similar work also can be done with grinder held freehand and workpiece clamped to bench

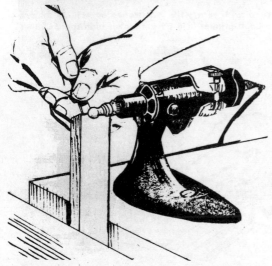

Modelmakers often have use for a midget speed lathe on which pencil-sized turnings can be made. Here's such a lathe in operation with improvised tool rest

Tiny circular saw blade is accessory for hand grinder. Make table of plywood, solid stock as in detail below, mount grinder in fixture and there you are

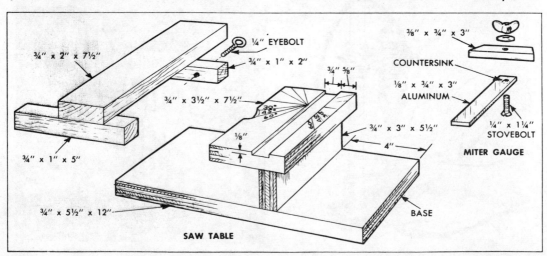

¾" x 2" x 7½"

¼" EYEBOLT

¾" x 1" x 2"

¾" x 3½" x 7½"

¾" x 5/8"

⅜" x ¾" x 3"

COUNTERSINK

⅛" x ¾" x 3"

ALUMINUM

¼" x 1¼"

STOVEBOLT

MITER GAUGE

30°
45°
60°

1/8"

¾" x 3" x 5½"

4"

¾" x 1" x 5"

¾" x 5½" x 12"

BASE

SAW TABLE

GUN CLEANING

BRASS BRUSH

ROLL JAG TIP

DOUBLE-SLOTTED TIP

JAG WITH POINT

PLAIN JAG TIP

SINGLE-SLOT-TED TIP

② WHEN GUNS MUST BE CLEANED FROM MUZZLE, USE A CAP TO PROTECT BARREL

WOOD OR BRASS NOZZLE CAP

③ FRONT SIGHT BARREL

DOUBLE SLOTTED TIP ④

BARREL

PATCH

PLAIN JAG TIP ⑤

HOW VARIOUS TYPES OF PATCH TIPS ARE USED

ROLL JAG TIP

PATCH ⑥

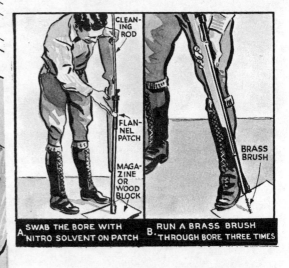

CLEANING ROD

FLANNEL PATCH

MAGAZINE OR WOOD BLOCK

BRASS BRUSH

A. SWAB THE BORE WITH NITRO SOLVENT ON PATCH

B. RUN A BRASS BRUSH THROUGH BORE THREE TIMES

INCREASED accuracy, smoother shooting and longer gun life will reward the shooter who spends a little time in keeping his guns in first-class condition. Given a new gun to start with, a few minutes' cleaning time will keep it in perfect condition whereas the neglected gun becomes increasingly difficult to clean satisfactorily.

Cleaning a rifle or shotgun involves five simple operations, as shown by the photos A to E inclusive. The bore is first swabbed with a flannel patch well saturated with nitro solvent. Cleaning should be done from the breech of the barrel if possible, and the muzzle of the gun should rest on a clean magazine or a block of wood. The patch should be run up and down the bore several times to saturate the powder residue thoroughly with the solvent oil. Any brand of powder solvent available at a hardware store will do. Operation No. 2 calls for a brass brush. Running this up and down the bore will remove the sticky powder fouling partially loosened by the action of the solvent. The brush should be pushed out of the barrel on each down stroke. Reversing the direction of the brush inside the bore does nothing but ruin the brush. Next repeat the first operation. The object of the fourth operation is to dry the barrel thoroughly. Start by wiping the rod clean. You will need four to six clean patches. Run the first patch down, up, down and out at the muzzle end. Run the rest of the patches through the bore once only, discarding each at the muzzle end. The final patch should

FIVE SIMPLE OPERATIONS PUT THE GUN IN PERFECT CONDITION

C. REPEAT SWABBING WITH NITRO SOLVENT   D. DRY THE BORE WITH FOUR TO SIX CLEAN PATCHES   E. OIL WITH GUN OIL ON PATCH

HOMEMADE GUN VISES FACILITATE CLEANING OPERATIONS

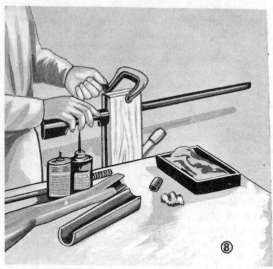

show perfectly clean and dry. If it shows dirt, the preceding operations must be repeated. The final operation is oiling. This is done with a clean patch. Use any good gun oil. This will protect the gun for a period of four to eight weeks. If the gun is to be stored for a longer period than this, use gun grease instead of the lighter oil.

As previously mentioned, cleaning should be done from the breech. Cleaning the gun

from the muzzle permits the rod to rub at this vital point, causing wear which may influence the accuracy of the weapon. Some guns cannot be cleaned from the breech. In this case it is advisable to use a wooden or brass muzzle cap, Figs. 2 and 3, to protect the muzzle. If you use a plain jag tip for cleaning, the chamber should be fitted with a cartridge case plugged with wood. This will prevent the patch from working loose as it sometimes does when pushed into the larger diameter of the chamber.

Fig. 1 shows the five types of cleaning tips commonly used. The single slotted tip is the simplest. It has the advantage of holding onto the patch under all conditions, but has two disadvantages in that the patch sometimes jams when reversed inside the bore, and, the cleaning action is often one-sided, permitting the bare sides of the tip to rub the bore. The plain jag tip gives a uniform cleaning action, and reverses perfectly inside the barrel. The patch sticks to the tip as long as it is inside the barrel, but any chance movement beyond the muzzle or chamber will cause

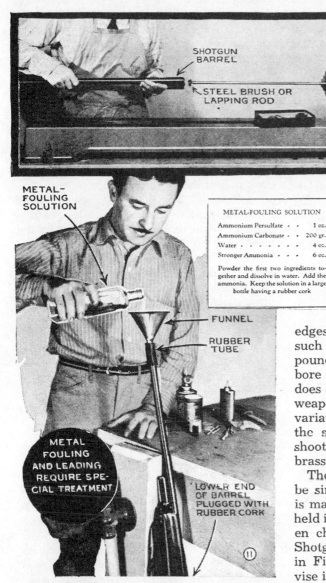

SHOTGUN BARREL

STEEL BRUSH OR LAPPING ROD

⑨

TO FIT BORE OF SHOTGUN
WOOD LAPPING ROD
WOOD ROD FOR STEEL WOOL
ADJUSTING SCREW
ABRASIVE PAPER GLUED IN PLACE
WOOD ROD FOR USE WITH ABRASIVE PAPER ⑩

METAL-FOULING SOLUTION

METAL-FOULING SOLUTION	
Ammonium Persulfate	1 oz.
Ammonium Carbonate	200 gr.
Water	4 oz.
Stronger Ammonia	6 oz.

Powder the first two ingredients together and dissolve in water. Add the ammonia. Keep the solution in a large bottle having a rubber cork

FUNNEL

RUBBER TUBE

METAL FOULING AND LEADING REQUIRE SPECIAL TREATMENT

LOWER END OF BARREL PLUGGED WITH RUBBER CORK

⑪

rotate inside the bore, following the rotation of the rifling. Without this rotation, the patch will drag at right angles across the lands and will quickly destroy the sharp edges of the rifling. The patch should be of such a size as to require three or four pounds pressure to force it through the bore of the rifle. A shotgun cleaning rod does not require a swivel joint, as this weapon has a smooth bore. Other than this variation, the cleaning technique is exactly the same, with the exception that most shooters prefer a wire-gauze cleaner or a brass worm instead of a brass brush.

The cleaning operation as described can be simplified greatly if some type of vise is made to hold the gun. Rifles are easily held in a simple jig consisting of two wooden chocks nailed to a baseboard, Fig. 7. Shotguns can be clamped in the jig shown in Fig. 8. Clamping in a standard wood vise is also satisfactory, but care should be exercised in exerting too much clamping pressure.

Other than powder fouling, the shooter must sometimes give consideration to metal fouling. This is a deposit of metal left by the bullet in the bore. If you shoot lead bullets, the fouling is more specifically designated as "leading." It is obvious that a perfectly smooth, polished bore will pick up very little metal fouling, whereas the roughened, neglected bore will always foul to a greater extent. Metal fouling in itself does no particular harm to the bore, but it may trap powder residue beneath it, leading to corrosion of the bore. Metal fouling can be detected by a careful examination of the bore, in which the fouling will show as long streaks, flaky deposits or even ac-

it to come loose. The same applies to the jag tip with point. The point is an advantage in centering the patch previous to insertion in the bore. The double-slotted tip is a first-rate cleaner, with a uniform action. The roll jag permits rolled or wrapped patches, and is preferred by many shooters on this account. The patch is wrapped around the jag as shown in Fig. 6, and can be made tight or loose as desired. Fig. 5 shows how the plain jag is used, the patch simply being centered on the tip, while Fig. 4 shows the obvious way of using either the single or double-slotted tip.

The cleaning rod itself can be brass or steel and should be of a proper diameter to fit the bore of the rifle. It must be fitted with a swivel joint so that the patch will

tual lumps of metal sticking to the lands and grooves. The fouling is easily removed, if attended to promptly, by using the metal-fouling solution specified in Fig. 11. The liquid is kept in a tightly corked bottle at all times except when actually using the solution, since it loses strength quickly when exposed to air. This can be applied with a cloth patch in the usual manner if the deposit is light. For a more thorough action, the solution is poured into the bore of the gun after first plugging the chamber with a rubber cork. When first poured in, the solution will be as colorless as water but will asume a deep blue color as it begins to dissolve the metallic deposit. The action is complete in about 15 min. Care should be taken in using the metal-fouling solution as it will remove bluing or the finish on the stock. After the solution has been removed from the barrel, the regular cleaning procedure should follow immediately.

Leading can be removed with the metal-fouling solution. Many shooters, however, prefer mercury. A few ounces of this are placed in the barrel. A finger over the muzzle will hold it inside, and a few tips up and down will cause the mercury to amalgamate with the lead deposit. The solution can be used many times. Mercurial ointment is a satisfactory remedy for leading as is also common vinegar or a dilute solution of glacial acetic acid.

Metal fouling in shotgun barrels or any condition of rusting or pitting can be removed usually by mechanical methods as the smoooth bore permits almost any type of polishing. The cleaning operation is most conveniently done in a lathe, mounting the polishing barrel or abrasive in the lathe and holding the gun barrel in the hands, as shown in Fig. 9. Steel brushes and polishing heads for this purpose can be purchased, or the shooter can make his own, as in Fig. 10, to be used with paste abrasive, steel wool or abrasive paper.

GUN RACK

This Gun Rack Hangs in a Corner Where It Takes Little Space

Different from the usual gun rack in that it can be hung in a corner above the floor to make cleaning under it easy, this rack consists of a standard carrying a shelf at the bottom for the gun stocks and a notched holder at the top to receive the barrels. The shelf is cut on a 14-in. radius and is screwed and glued to the lower end of the standard. Metal braces add further support to the shelf. The notched holder at the top is screwed to the standard, which is chamfered at the edges. A ring at the top for hanging the rack engages a hook in the wall. If desired, small holes can be drilled in the notched holder to take cleaning rods.

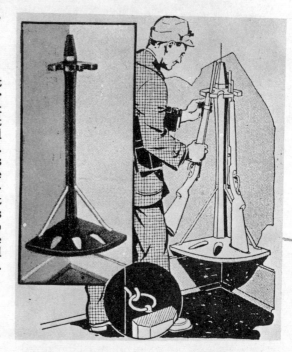

Tote Case for Your Guns

HERE IS AN IDEAL CASE for transporting shotguns and rifles on hunting trips where you are going to use more than one gun. It furnishes protection against marring and breakage, and at the same time is easy to carry. Because of its flat shape, it packs easily into a car or station wagon and at home, between trips, it pro-vides a dry and dustproof storage cabinet.

The construction is simple, as no diffi-cult-to-make joints are used. The over-all dimensions will be determined by the sizes of the guns to be carried in it. The top and bottom pieces are ¼-in. plywood and the sides are of 1 x 4-in. stock. Drill holes for 1-in. screws ⅜ in. from the edges of the

After box is assembled, top and bottom are separated by making a saw cut all around, shown above left

Above center, the 1 x 4 crosspieces are fitted in place. Next, at the right, gun positions are marked

Lower left, cutouts are made on a jigsaw. Center, attaching screws must not be driven through cutout

Lower right, the crosspieces are lined with strips of rubber held in place with broad-headed tacks

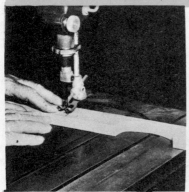

plywood pieces, 6 in. apart on the sides and 5 in. apart on the ends, with a screw at each corner. To assemble the case, a box is made first by joining the 1 x 4 sides to the plywood top and bottom. Coat the edges of the 1 x 4s with glue, put them in position and drive the screws. Next, join the corners with finishing nails driven through the long sides. Space these nails carefully so they won't interfere with the saw cut to be made later.

Now the box is cut all around to form the top and bottom of the case. The cut should be off-center, 2¾ in. from one side and 2 in. from the other. The crosspieces in the top and bottom are made by splitting 1 x 4s in the same proportion as the box was split, the smaller ones being fitted into the top and the larger ones into the bottom. These are laid in place 6 in. from each end and the guns are positioned on them. With a pencil, indicate the cutouts that will be necessary in the bottom crosspiece to take the stocks and barrels. Cut on a jigsaw, making each cut slightly larger than the marking to allow for padding to be added later. Fasten the crosspieces in place with glue and screws, then pad them with ¾-in. strips of rubber cut from an inner tube. Join the top and bottom together with two or three butt hinges or a length of piano hinge. Finally, attach a handle and two suitcase latches to the front side. ★ ★ ★

Clean gutters thoroughly after leaves have fallen, as they cause stoppages. After leaves and debris are removed, flush gutters with a hose and then check for leaks and drainage pitch

GUTTER REPAIR AND MAINTENANCE

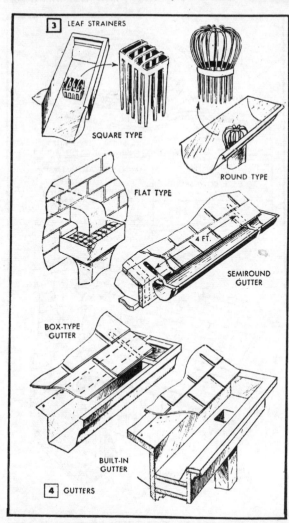

IT'S EASY to put off inspecting and cleaning the gutters and downspouts on your home from year to year until they finally deteriorate to a point where they are beyond repair and must be completely replaced. Yet, it is possible to lengthen the serviceable life of these important fittings from five to ten years by thoroughly cleaning them and making minor repairs on a yearly schedule that any homeowner can carry out himself. Leaky, damaged and partially clogged gutters not only give unsatisfactory service, but they also can be the indirect cause of other, more serious, troubles, such as water getting into the attic or seeping into brick walls, causing unsightly efflorescent stains, Fig. 5, and a gradual deterioration of the brickwork near the cornices. For these reasons, regular servicing of the gutters is a sure way of reducing home-upkeep costs.

Keep gutters clean: Immediately after the leaves come down in the fall is the time to get busy and clean out gutters and downspouts to avoid stoppage resulting from accumulations of leaves and dirt. Even if leaf guards or strainers have been installed at the downspout openings, an accumulation of wet leaves will prevent proper drainage and may cause water to overflow and seep into the walls of the house. Rotting leaves combine with cinders and soot to form an acid that hastens rusting of the sheet-metal gutters. For these reasons, it is essential to remove the leaves, and other debris, as soon as possible after they col-

Photo 5 shows efflorescent stains on brick wall subjected to water seepage from roof or gutter. Loosen tight stoppages in downspout by using sink-drain auger, then flush with a hose

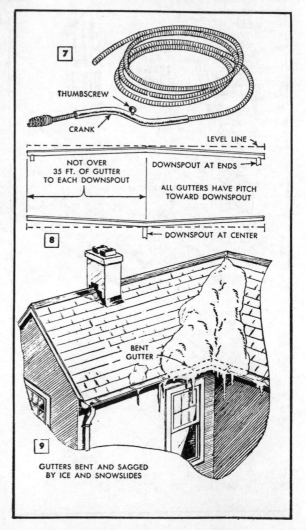

lect, Fig. 1, and then flush the gutters with a hose, Fig. 2. While flushing, inspect both gutters and downspouts for leaks and repair them immediately.

Clearing stopped downspout: If the gutters are not fitted with leaf strainers, Fig. 3, leaves may accumulate in the leaders, Fig. 16, and completely close the passage. In cold weather, water may collect and freeze in clogged elbows and downspouts. Although these parts are corrugated for the purpose of preventing damage from freezing, a large amount of water freezing solidly behind a leaf dam may expand the metal sufficiently to force open the rolled joint. An auger of the type used for clearing obstructions in sink drains, Figs. 6 and 7, can be used to loosen tightly packed leaves in either the leader or downspout. After the mass has been loosened, insert the hose in the leader with the water turned on at full pressure. Sometimes full pressure from the hose alone will do the trick. Where the downspout connects directly to the storm sewer, r..asses of wet leaves and dirt may collect at the bend below grade. To clear this, remove the downspout and insert a drain auger at the joint where the lower end of the downspout enters the bell tile above grade. Then flush with a hose.

Down pitch of gutters: To drain properly pitch gutters down slightly toward the drop outlet at the end as in Fig. 8. Especially long runs may be fitted with a drop outlet at both ends, or one in the center as shown. Each downspout will handle about 30 to 35 ft. of gutter

THUMBSCREW

CRANK

LEVEL LINE

NOT OVER 35 FT. OF GUTTER TO EACH DOWNSPOUT

DOWNSPOUT AT ENDS

ALL GUTTERS HAVE PITCH TOWARD DOWNSPOUT

DOWNSPOUT AT CENTER

BENT GUTTER

GUTTERS BENT AND SAGGED BY ICE AND SNOWSLIDES

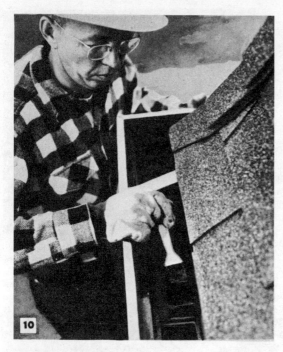

Sheet-metal gutters of all types should be protected with asphalt-base corrosion preventives. After gutters are thoroughly cleaned, material is applied with brush

have been loosened, it will be necessary to renail or replace them, as the gutter will sag permanently without their support.

Rust prevention: Gutters and downspouts of nonrusting metals, such as copper and aluminum, have been widely used in both new and old construction, but the semi-round and box types of galvanized sheet metal are perhaps the most common. When the galvanized coating is impaired, rust attacks the bare metal and eventually eats through, causing leaks. Sometimes soldered joints pull loose, either because of stresses caused by expansion of freezing water, or because of an inadequately soldered joint. For the same reasons, slip-joint connectors sometimes open and, generally, they should be replaced. Effective rust protection for the inside surfaces of gutters and downspouts is attained by applying a heavy coating of elastic roofing cement, smokestack paint or the asphalt-base compounds used on the underside of autos as a corrosion preventive. Any of these materials will adhere tightly to clean metal and, after drying, they are sufficiently flexible to expand and contract with the metal, thus providing an unbroken protective film. This film, in most cases, also resists acids which form when wet leaves and soot are combined. Asphalt-base coatings should be used only on the inside of the gutter, as they tend to bleed through oil paints applied to the outside of the gutters. The coating is simply brushed onto the bare, clean metal, Fig. 10, after rust and loose dirt have been removed. Small breaks in the metal generally can be stopped with ordinary roofing cement, but large breaks will require a fabric retainer. First, coat the surrounding surface with cement, as in Fig. 11, and then press a piece of muslin or light canvas against the wet surface, Fig. 12. Finally, another coat of cement is applied over the fabric as in Fig. 13. To coat the inside of a downspout, alter an old paintbrush by cutting off the handle and

length. On some types of homes a noticeable pitch of the gutters detracts from architectural lines and in this case the gutters are installed horizontal, or level. This also is true of attached wooden gutters which usually are installed in this manner. Gutters installed level must not be permitted to sag, as otherwise some water will be left standing to evaporate after each summer shower. This accelerates rusting and provides an ideal breeding spot for mosquitoes. If metal gutters become bent or sagged in places, the cause is usually ice or snowslides from a high, steep roof, Fig. 9. As a rule, the gutter is quite easily straightened if none of the hangers has been pulled loose. In case some hangers

Small breaks in the metal can be closed by a fabric patch. First, apply compound with a brush as in Fig. 11, then press the canvas patch in place as in Fig. 12. Apply final coat over the fabric, including edges

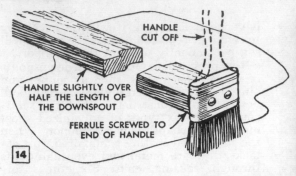

HANDLE CUT OFF

HANDLE SLIGHTLY OVER HALF THE LENGTH OF THE DOWNSPOUT

FERRULE SCREWED TO END OF HANDLE

14

15

Applying protective compounds to the inside surfaces of downspouts pays off by greatly increasing the useful life of these parts. Material is applied to the inside surfaces with an improvised brush

screwing the ferrule to one end of a long strip of wood which serves as a handle, Figs. 14 and 15.

Replacing gutters: Gutter and downspout units and accessories of the semiround type are detailed in Figs. 16 and 17. Box-type gutters, Fig. 4, also are used extensively and the fittings and method of attachment vary considerably. Ordinarily gutters come in 8 to 12-ft. lengths, with 10-ft. lengths being perhaps the most commonly furnished. Corner fittings and drop outlets are separate units. Leaders connect gutters to downspouts in most types of installations. When ordering the materials and parts for a major replacement job be sure to include a sufficient number of hangers, Fig. 16, to permit a 4-ft. spacing throughout the length of the gutters. Order 1-in. nails for fastening the hangers and obtain all the slip-joint connectors required. Order leaf strainers for each drop outlet, and also get the proper type of downspout hangers, or bands. If only one or two sections of the gutter require replacement, measure the old ones and renew with the same type and size. When hanging new gutters, don't forget to make sure that the pitch is the same as that of the one being replaced.

Installing gutter hangers: New hangers should be nailed to the roof boards and not over the shingles, as exposed nails are likely to rust away in time and cause a leak. Removing shingles to expose the roof boards

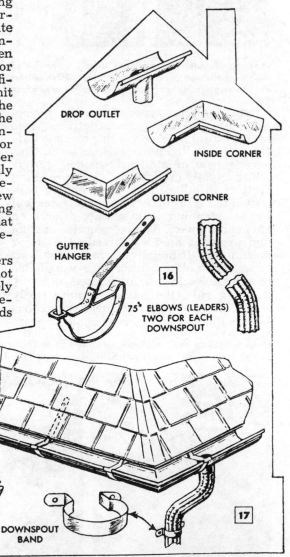

DROP OUTLET

INSIDE CORNER

OUTSIDE CORNER

GUTTER HANGER

16

75° ELBOWS (LEADERS) TWO FOR EACH DOWNSPOUT

END CAP

SLIP-JOINT CONNECTOR

DOWNSPOUT BAND

17

18

When applying new gutter hangers on old roofs, shingles should be lifted so that hanger can be nailed directly to the roof boards. On asphalt-shingle roofs, the individual shingles are easily removed for this job

19

LIFT UP SHINGLES OF THIRD COURSE AND REMOVE NAILS IN SECOND COURSE

20 BLOCK

PRY NAILS UP ¼" AND EXTRACT WITH HAMMER BEARING ON BLOCK

LOWER STRIP OF FIRST COURSE ALSO LOOSENED

21

UPPER STRIP OF FIRST COURSE REMOVED

GRIND A V-NOTCH

10" FILE

22 TOOL FOR CUTTING SHINGLE NAILS

must be done with care to avoid damage. First, remove the nails from two or more individual shingles of the second row, or course. The nailheads are exposed by simply lifting up the butt ends of the third course as in Fig. 19. Pry up the nailheads with a wide-bladed screwdriver as in Fig. 20. To prevent damage to the shingle, place a strip of ⅛-in. metal or a short block of hardwood under the screwdriver blade as shown. Remember that the nails holding the second course of shingles usually go through the upper ends of shingles in the first course. Finally, removal of the nails holding the first course of shingles, which usually is of double thickness, permits you to pull the shingles out as in Fig. 21, exposing the roof boards. In some types of construction, especially on wide cornices, there will be a layer of roll roofing under the first course. It is not necessary, of course, to remove this, as the hangers can be nailed over it, provided all nail holes are sealed with roofing cement before re-laying the shingles. After prying off the old hangers and nailing on the new ones as in Fig. 18, drive the nail part way down, and then coat the area around the nail with roofing cement so that when the nail is driven down fully, the cement will form a watertight seal around the nailhead. Now, replace the double course of shingles, making sure that they are located in the same position as they were originally. Drive the new nails slightly to one side or the other of the old holes and, before driving them clear down, apply roofing cement around the heads to form a seal. Be sure all old nail holes are filled with cement. Finally, the loosened shingles of the second course are nailed down again to finish the job. The procedure is repeated at each new hanger position. In a general way the same thing applies to wooden shingles. However, these are more rigid than asphalt shingles and require a few variations in procedure. It is necessary to cut the nails holding each shingle with a special tool improvised from an old file, Fig. 22. The V-notch at one end is ground to a beveled edge and in use the tool is forced under the shingle until the V-shaped cutting edge contacts the nail. A few light taps on the outer end of the tool generally cuts the nail cleanly. When replacing a wooden shingle, the two lower nails are started at approximately the same position as the original nails. Fill the old nail holes with roofing cement. Pry up the shingles of the next course above, slip a piece of sheet metal over the nailheads and press the upper shingle down to force the nails home. Don't tap the shingle with a hammer as you may break it.

When hangers must be attached to metal

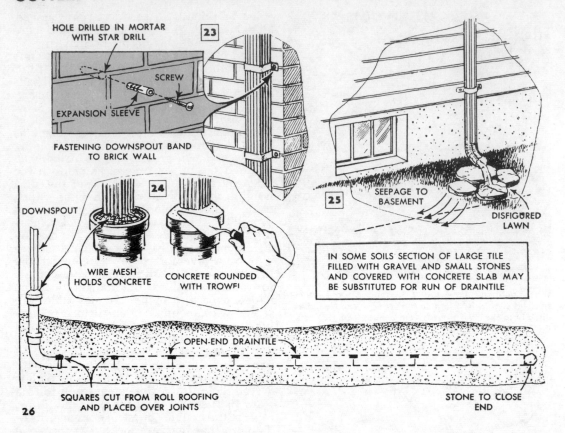

HOLE DRILLED IN MORTAR WITH STAR DRILL

23

SCREW

EXPANSION SLEEVE

FASTENING DOWNSPOUT BAND TO BRICK WALL

DOWNSPOUT

24

WIRE MESH HOLDS CONCRETE

CONCRETE ROUNDED WITH TROWEL

25

SEEPAGE TO BASEMENT

DISFIGURED LAWN

IN SOME SOILS SECTION OF LARGE TILE FILLED WITH GRAVEL AND SMALL STONES AND COVERED WITH CONCRETE SLAB MAY BE SUBSTITUTED FOR RUN OF DRAINTILE

OPEN-END DRAINTILE

SQUARES CUT FROM ROLL ROOFING AND PLACED OVER JOINTS

STONE TO CLOSE END

26

roofing, it's a common practice to solder them in place. Before soldering, the metal must be thoroughly cleaned, fluxed and preheated with a blowtorch. Downspout bands are simply nailed to wooden trim surfaces. However, when fastening the bands to brick, it is necessary to use masonry nails or screws. Screws are driven into expansion sleeves which are placed in holes drilled in the masonry with a star drill as in Fig. 23.

Cementing downspout into draintile: When downspouts are connected to draintile leading to the storm sewers, the opening where the downspout enters the tile should be sealed with cement mortar supported by wire mesh pressed into the bell end of the tile. Usually the bell end is only a few inches above grade and if the opening is not closed tightly, small stones, dirt and trash may clog the tile. To seal the joint, first cut and bend a disk of ½-in. wire mesh to fit into the open end of the tile. Bend up the edges of the wire disk so that it will wedge tightly in place. Then cut a round opening in the disk so that you can insert the lower end of the downspout. After the latter is in place, mix a heavy cement mortar and trowel it into the opening, building it up at the top to form a sloping surface that will shed water, Fig. 24.

Installing splashers and draintile: When water from the downspout is discharged at ground level, some provision must be made for spreading the flow of water, as otherwise the force of the stream of water will wash away sod and soil. Also, if drainage from the foundation is poor, water may seep into the basement. Where there is ample drainage away from the foundation, a few flat stones placed below the end of the downspout may suffice as a splasher, Fig. 25. However, unless the arrangement is only temporary, it is better to install concrete splashers of sufficient size to direct the water away from the building in a spreading flow. In some soils, a run of open-end draintile installed below grade as in Fig. 26, will serve as a dispersal unit. Sometimes, builders install a long run of tile in this manner and place a section of large draintile (24 to 36 in. in diameter) at the lower end of the run. The large draintile section is placed on end with the bell end up and filled with coarse gravel and small stones to form a dry well. The top of the tile is closed with a cast-concrete cover. Sometimes a tile elbow is cast integral with the cover and the lower end of the draintile is led into the elbow. In gravelly or sandy soils, this installation works quite satisfactorily.

Fun for Your Halloween Party

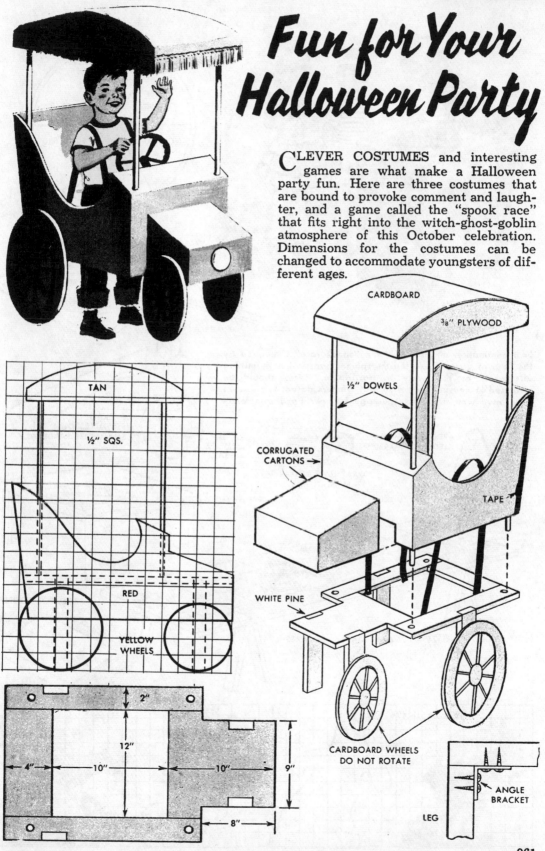

CLEVER COSTUMES and interesting games are what make a Halloween party fun. Here are three costumes that are bound to provoke comment and laughter, and a game called the "spook race" that fits right into the witch-ghost-goblin atmosphere of this October celebration. Dimensions for the costumes can be changed to accommodate youngsters of different ages.

TAN

½" SQS.

RED

YELLOW WHEELS

CARDBOARD

⅜" PLYWOOD

½" DOWELS

CORRUGATED CARTONS →

TAPE

WHITE PINE

CARDBOARD WHEELS DO NOT ROTATE

ANGLE BRACKET

LEG

2"

12"

4"   10"   10"

9"

8"

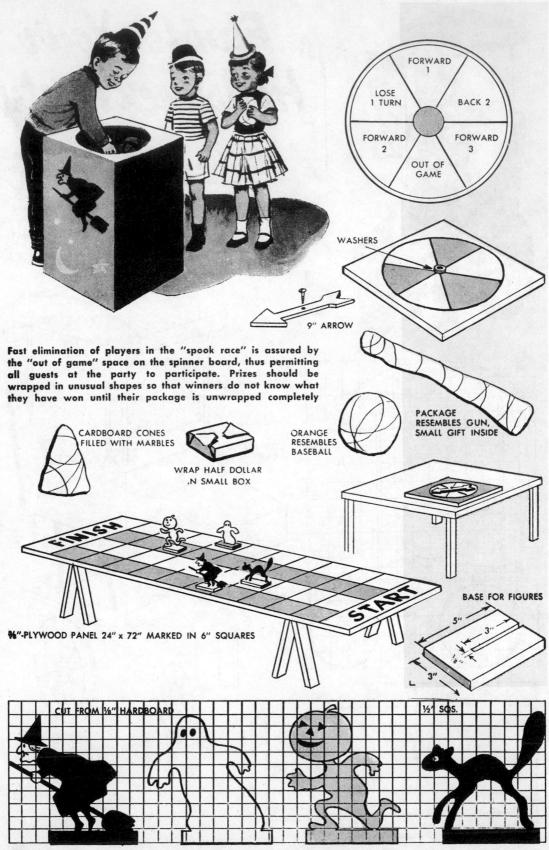

FORWARD 1

LOSE 1 TURN

BACK 2

FORWARD 2

FORWARD 3

OUT OF GAME

WASHERS

9" ARROW

Fast elimination of players in the "spook race" is assured by the "out of game" space on the spinner board, thus permitting all guests at the party to participate. Prizes should be wrapped in unusual shapes so that winners do not know what they have won until their package is unwrapped completely

PACKAGE RESEMBLES GUN, SMALL GIFT INSIDE

CARDBOARD CONES FILLED WITH MARBLES

WRAP HALF DOLLAR .N SMALL BOX

ORANGE RESEMBLES BASEBALL

FINISH

START

⅜"-PLYWOOD PANEL 24" x 72" MARKED IN 6" SQUARES

BASE FOR FIGURES

5"

3"

⅛"

3"

CUT FROM ⅛" HARDBOARD

½" SQS.

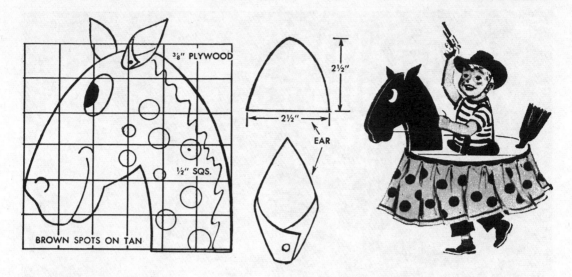

³⁄₈" PLYWOOD

2½"

2½"

EAR

½" SQS.

BROWN SPOTS ON TAN

Horses and the wild West have appeal for all youngsters. After the Halloween party this sturdy bronco probably will see service as a cow pony on the backyard ranch. Ears for the horse are cut and folded from leather or plastic; the tail is a whisk broom

12"

12"

³⁄₈"

Mask from costume shop is worn by "bird in gilded cage." If the bird can't eat the jelly-bean "bird seeds," the other guests at the party can and will enjoy them

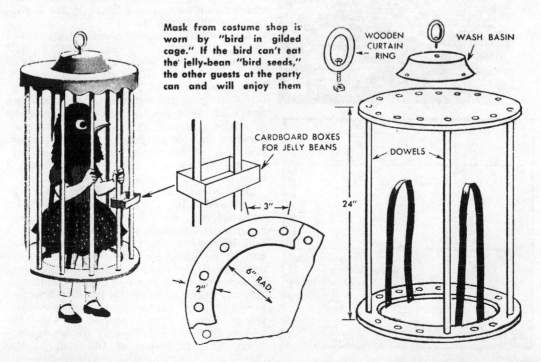

WOODEN CURTAIN RING

WASH BASIN

CARDBOARD BOXES FOR JELLY BEANS

3"

2"

6" RAD.

DOWELS

24"

BIMETALLIC MACHINIST'S HAMMER

By Joseph M. Giambalvo

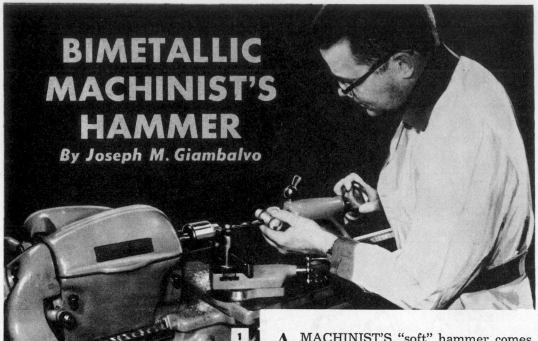

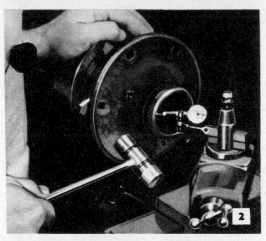

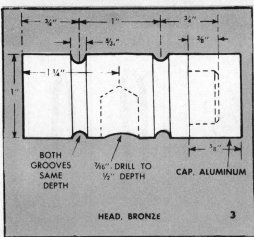

BOTH GROOVES SAME DEPTH

7/16". DRILL TO 1/2" DEPTH

CAP. ALUMINUM

HEAD, BRONZE 3

A MACHINIST'S "soft" hammer comes in handy when setting up a job in the lathe, milling machine or drill press. With the chuck, vise or strap clamps eased onto the work it usually takes only a light tap or two with the hammer to bring an indicator to the correct reading, Fig. 2, or position semifinished work for the final cut. The soft hammer also is used in assembly of finished parts where it is necessary to strike positive blows without the rebound of the rubber or rawhide mallet, and without denting or marring finished metal surfaces or sharp edges.

A bimetallic hammer, such as that shown in Fig. 6, is especially useful both in set-up and assembly work. The polls (ends of the head) are of different metals, one of bronze and one of aluminum. This combination greatly extends the hammer's range of usefulness where it is necessary to strike nonmarring blows. The hammer serves a twofold purpose in the school shop. It's an excellent project for advanced machine-shop courses and when finished it becomes a useful tool.

As dimensioned in Fig. 3, the head will weigh about 10 oz. when finished. This is a good average weight for precise and easy handling. Although the details in Figs. 7 and 10 show a press fit of the aluminum cap, or poll, and an easy fit of the handle in the head, you have a choice of procedures in carrying out these two steps. Some machinists prefer to have the handle threaded into the head rather than slip-fitted and soldered as in Figs. 7 and 10. In this procedure the head is drilled through, counterbored and tapped, and the end of the

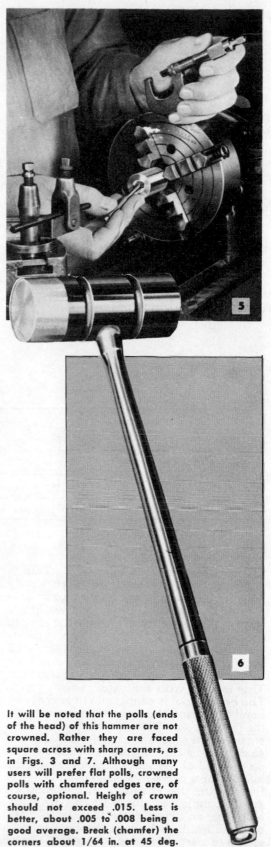

handle is shouldered, clearance-grooved and threaded. This type of assembly is quite satisfactory if you form more nearly a full-depth thread, say about 80 to 90 percent. This will assure that the handle seats solidly when turned into the head. The shoulder on the handle should be undercut slightly and must fit the counterbore snugly, otherwise the head may tend to loosen with use.

Much the same procedure can be followed when fitting the aluminum cap to the head. Although these procedures are not detailed, they can be carried out with only slight changes in the dimensions given in Figs. 3, 7 and 10.

Fig. 3 details the hammer head assembled, that is, with the cap fitted in place. The head is turned from bronze to 1 in. in diameter and is grooved and drilled for the handle, Fig. 1. The hole for the handle, also the center lines of the grooves, are located as in Fig. 8. Note that when the head is assembled with the cap in place the hole

It will be noted that the polls (ends of the head) of this hammer are not crowned. Rather they are faced square across with sharp corners, as in Figs. 3 and 7. Although many users will prefer flat polls, crowned polls with chamfered edges are, of course, optional. Height of crown should not exceed .015. Less is better, about .005 to .008 being a good average. Break (chamfer) the corners about 1/64 in. at 45 deg.

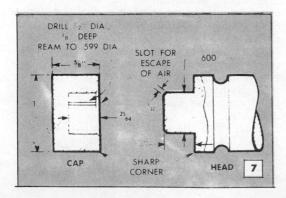

DRILL $\frac{1}{2}$ DIA.
$\frac{1}{8}$ DEEP
REAM TO .599 DIA.
SLOT FOR ESCAPE OF AIR
600
$\frac{5}{8}''$
1
$\frac{25}{64}$
32
CAP
SHARP CORNER
HEAD

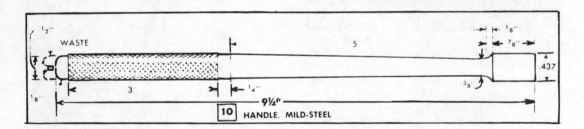

10 HANDLE, MILD-STEEL

taking the handle is off-center. This is done purposely in order to more nearly balance the head. Important steps in machining the head and cap for a press fit are shown in Figs. 4, 5 and 7. After the bore in the cap has been checked for correct diameter (ream if you have a correct-size stub reamer) cut a shallow slot to permit air to escape as the parts are pressed together. This is done with the work at rest, Fig. 4. The boring tool is simply run in and out by hand-operating the lathe carriage, moving the tool about .002 at each stroke. The corner of the bore is chamfered 1/32 in. at 45 deg. and a corresponding chamfer is run on the end of the tenon shouldered on the head. For a press fit some machinists prefer to run the chamfers at a somewhat greater angle, say about 60 deg. If available use an arbor press to assemble the cap and head. Otherwise do the job in an accurate vise, shimming the parts if necessary to assure correct alignment. After this step is completed, chuck the head and take a final light finishing cut all over, or polish with an abrasive.

The handle, Figs. 9 and 10, is a simple lathe job. Start with a 10-in. length of cold-rolled stock and rough the taper and the fillet at the small end of the taper. Run 3 in. of fine knurl on the big end of the handle. Finish by filing and polishing with abrasive. Before turning the small end of the handle to the final dimension, .437, be sure to check the diameter of the hole in the head. In making this check remember that the handle is sweat-soldered into the head and this calls for an allowance of .002 or so.

Then clean the parts thoroughly, tin the joining surfaces and press together. Heat with a flame until the solder flows. Remove any excess solder from the joint while it is still soft. ★ ★ ★

Although many hand tools are supplementary or entirely unnecessary in a shop fully equipped with power tools, some hand tools such as hammers, clamps, rules, wrenches, pliers and vises are indispensable. As an example, if you have a drill press with accessories, you may not need a hand brace and bits. If you already have a jointer and a surfacer, as pictured on the following pages, you can get along without hand planes. If you have a portable circular saw, you may do without a hand saw.

But one should keep in mind that a fairly complete kit of the common hand tools is useful, almost indispensable, in making

IDENTIFICATION and SELECTION

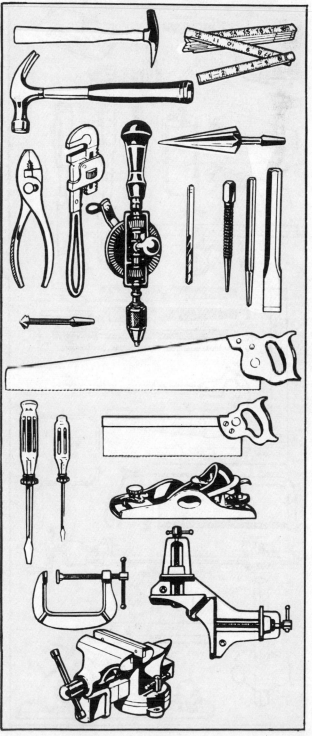

Home Repair Toolkit

CURVED-CLAW HAMMER 13-oz. head

SCREWDRIVERS (2" and 4")

6" SLIP-JOINT PLIERS

6-ft. TAPE RULE or **FOLDING RULE**

PUTTY KNIFE with either regular or wide blade

9" ADJUSTABLE WRENCH

10" PIPE WRENCH

HAND DRILL with assorted bits

MARKING GAUGE

CROSSCUT SAW (8 to 10 teeth to the inch)

SOLDERING IRON (100-W. or larger)

10" TRY SQUARE (or combination square)

HACKSAW (for 10" to 12" blade)

¼" and ½" WOOD CHISELS

FOUR 8" FILES WITH HANDLES (one 3-cornered file, one mill file, one each round and half-round)

VISE WITH 2½" JAWS (or woodworking vise with rapid-acting screw)

1/16" NAIL SET

KEYHOLE SAW

CENTER PUNCH

AUGER-BIT BRACE (ratchet type)

AUGER BITS (¼" to ½" by 16ths)

7" BLOCK PLANE

8" SMOOTH PLANE

COMBINATION OILSTONE

C-CLAMPS (two each of 2", 3" and 6" sizes)

LEVEL

KNIFE (with replaceable blades)

SANDING BLOCK (and assorted grades of sandpaper)

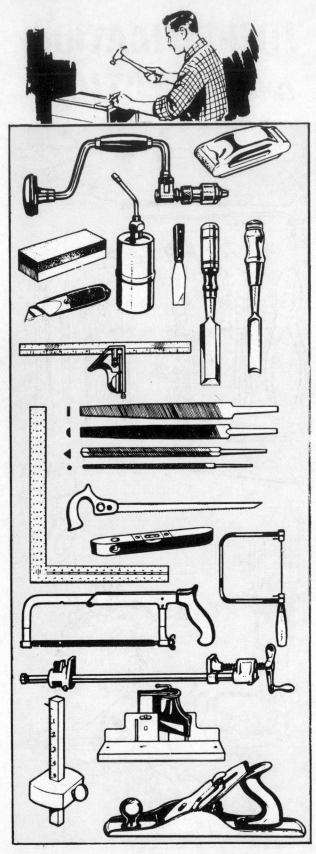

those simple home repairs. So, the best thing to do is buy hand tools as you need them unless, of course, you already have a fairly complete kit.

Although a list of hand tools rarely meets all individual requirements, it can serve as a guide from which you can select those you do need. The two lists on these pages are offered as suggestions to help you in making a selection. In some cases you have a choice between tools which have similar applications. One example is the steel (carpenter's) square and the combination square. In most home shops the combination square will serve the purpose. Not all tools listed below are illustrated.

Add These as Needed

MAGNETIC TACK HAMMER

8″ SCREWDRIVER

COPING SAW

SET OF OPEN-END WRENCHES (6/16″ to 7/8″)

8″ OR 10″ ADJUSTABLE END WRENCH

26″ RIPPING SAW

16″ BACK SAW (for miter box)

MITER BOX

12-oz. BALL PEEN HAMMER

ADDITIONAL AUGER BITS (½″ to 1″ by 16ths)

EXPANSIVE BIT (⅝″ to 1¾″)

TWIST DRILLS (number sizes 1 to 60, fractional sizes 1/16″ to ¼″ or larger)

SOLDERING TORCH (for flame soldering)

ADDITIONAL WOOD CHISELS (¾″ and 1″, or larger)

BAR CLAMPS (two 24″, two or more 36″ or longer)

MITER CLAMPS

SIDE-CUTTING PLIERS

LONG-NOSE PLIERS

11″ JACK PLANE

18″ FORE PLANE

¼″ AND ½″ INSIDE OR OUTSIDE GOUGES (or both)

ASSORTED SIZES OF FILES (as needed)

FILE-CLEANING BRUSH

PIN PUNCHES (set of four in graduated sizes)

TAPERED REAMERS (two sizes, ⅛″ to ½″ and ¼″ to ⅞″, to fit auger brace)

¼″ AND ½″ COLD CHISELS

ROSEHEAD COUNTERSINK FOR SCREW-HEADS (to fit auger-bit brace)

BENCH BRUSH

Many tools such as chisels, punches and auger bits are available in sets. Usually these are more useful and more economical to buy.

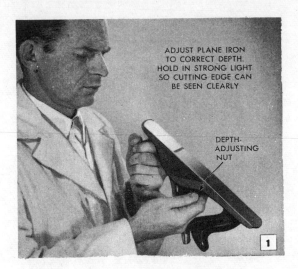

ADJUST PLANE IRON TO CORRECT DEPTH. HOLD IN STRONG LIGHT SO CUTTING EDGE CAN BE SEEN CLEARLY

DEPTH-ADJUSTING NUT

ACCURATE WORK
with a hand plane
By C. W. Woodson

The right plane, correctly sharpened, set and handled, will lift ribbon-thin shavings from hard or soft wood, produce a true, flat surface

WHEN SURFACING STOCK, HOLD PLANE AT ANGLE TO GIVE SHEAR CUT

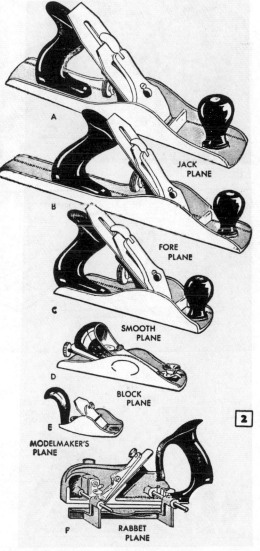

A
JACK PLANE

B
FORE PLANE

C
SMOOTH PLANE

D
BLOCK PLANE

E
MODELMAKER'S PLANE

F
RABBET PLANE

A—JACK PLANE IS USED TO TRUE EDGES OF ROUGH BOARD AND TO PREPARE SURFACE OF BOARD FOR SMOOTH PLANE OR FORE PLANE

B—FORE PLANE IS USED FOR GENERAL WORK ON BOTH EDGE AND SURFACE OF BOARD

C—SMOOTH PLANE IS COMMONLY USED WHEN NECESSARY TO REDUCE THICKNESS OF BOARD TO ROUGH DIMENSIONS

D—BLOCK PLANE IS GENERALLY USED FOR PLANING END GRAIN AND FOR TRUING SMALL PARTS

E—MODELMAKER'S PLANE HAS ROUND BOTTOM, IS USED IN MAKING SHIP-MODEL HULLS

F—RABBET PLANE, AS NAME IMPLIES, IS USED IN MAKING RABBETS OF VARIOUS WIDTHS AND DEPTHS WHEN ASSEMBLING CABINETWORK

SKILL WITH A HAND PLANE enables a craftsman in wood to produce a surface on the face or edge of the stock so very smooth and true that it does not require sanding to finish. Excepting those made for specialized purposes, typical hand planes are pictured in Fig. 2, A to F inclusive. Of these the first four, A to D inclusive, are perhaps the most commonly used. The notes above outline the uses to which each plane is adapted.

Carpenters' toolkits usually contain only the jack plane and block plane, while that of the craftsman or repairman may contain

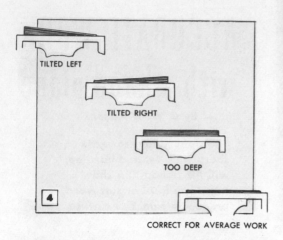

TILTED LEFT

TILTED RIGHT

TOO DEEP

4

CORRECT FOR AVERAGE WORK

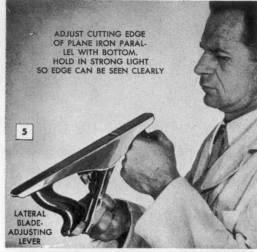

ADJUST CUTTING EDGE OF PLANE IRON PARALLEL WITH BOTTOM. HOLD IN STRONG LIGHT SO EDGE CAN BE SEEN CLEARLY

5

LATERAL BLADE-ADJUSTING LEVER

AT START OF CUT APPLY PRESSURE WITH LEFT HAND

6

WHEN NEARING END OF CUT APPLY PRESSURE WITH RIGHT HAND

7

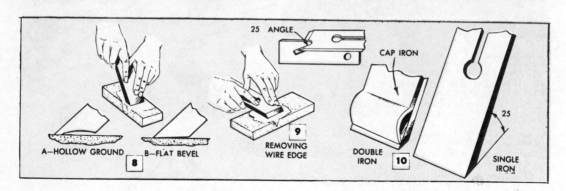

25 ANGLE

CAP IRON

25

A—HOLLOW GROUND   B—FLAT BEVEL

8

9

REMOVING WIRE EDGE

DOUBLE IRON   **10**   SINGLE IRON

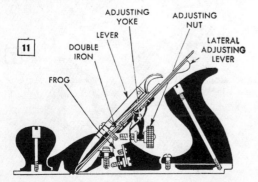

11

ADJUSTING YOKE

ADJUSTING NUT

LEVER

DOUBLE IRON

LATERAL ADJUSTING LEVER

FROG

all those pictured except the modelmaker's plane, which is more or less a specialized tool used by modelmakers and violin-makers for working curved surfaces to a template. In addition to those pictured, carpenters and finishers sometimes select the jointer plane in place of the fore plane, B. The jointer plane is the same general construction as the fore plane except that the frame is longer.

The trick of planing a board smooth and edging it true begins with a sharp plane blade, or iron, as it is called. If you sharpen the iron by hand, you will get a flat bevel,

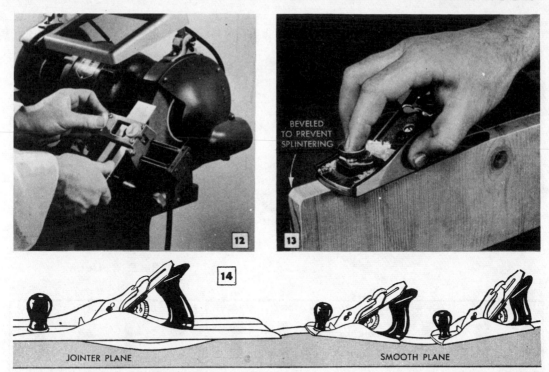

JOINTER PLANE   SMOOTH PLANE

BEVELED TO PREVENT SPLINTERING

B in Fig. 8. The method produces a wire edge which is removed by inverting the iron on the oilstone and giving it a few light, circular strokes. If the blade is sharpened with a grinder attachment as in Fig. 12, the curvature of the wheel will produce a hollow-ground bevel, A in Fig. 8. This is then shortened somewhat by stroking on the oilstone to produce a second flat bevel. The procedure results in a keen edge that will stand up well due to a greater thickness of metal to back up the cutting edge. Ordinarily the bevel is ground to 25 deg., Fig. 10, but some users reduce the bevel to 22½, or even 20 deg., when it is necessary to produce an exceptionally keen edge. A bevel gauge, Fig. 9, is handy to determine the exact bevel, especially when hand sharpening. When sharpening, it's a common practice to form a very narrow bevel (about 1/32 in.) at the corners of the cutting edge. This assures that the plane will not leave a mark, or shoulder, at the edge of the cut when planing a surface. When sharpening the plane iron on a grinder, use extreme care not to heat the edge to the point where the metal changes color. Dip the edge frequently in water or use a vitreous grinding wheel which does not overheat the metal and draw the temper.

Modern hand planes with iron frames usually are fitted with a double iron, Fig. 10. This consists of the single iron, or cutting iron, and the cap iron which serves as a chip breaker. The two are assembled with a special screw and are locked in position on the frog with the lever as in Fig. 11. For average work the cap iron is set with its lower edge about 1/16 in. above the cutting edge of the single iron, but some users prefer to set the cap iron to less space, especially when planing wood that is cross grained.

The next step is setting the cutting edge of the iron parallel with the bottom, or sole, of the plane and to the correct depth for the type of work to be done. Figs. 1, 4 and 5 show the procedure. The details in Fig. 4 are, of course, greatly exaggerated for purposes of illustration. The blade is tilted right or left with the lateral adjusting lever, Fig. 5, and is raised or lowered with the depth-adjusting nut, Figs. 1 and 11.

When surfacing stock, hold the plane at an angle to give a shear cut as in Fig. 3. When edging, or jointing, stock apply pressure with the left hand at the start of the cut, Fig. 6, and with the right hand when nearing the finish of the cut, Fig. 7. This procedure assures a true edge. The block plane, having a single iron set at a low angle, is especially suited to smoothing end grain, Fig. 13. Bevel the corner of the stock to prevent splintering. It's important to select the right plane for the job. To joint the edge of rough-sawed stock, use a fore plane, or better, a jointer plane rather than a smooth plane. The reason is shown in the exaggerated view in Fig. 14. The smooth plane will follow irregularities, but the jointer plane, having a long frame, will cut down the high spots and produce a true edge. ★ ★ ★

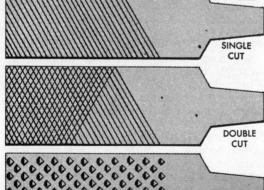

1

HANDLE
FERRULE
TANG
HEEL
LENGTH

BETTER

By E. R. Haan

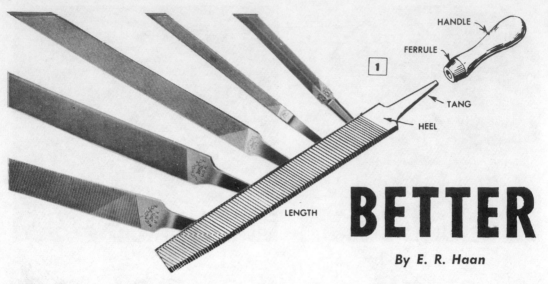

MILL	PILLAR	SQUARE	TAPER	CANTSAW	KNIFE	CROSSCUT	ROUND	HALF ROUND	PIT	CROSSING
QUADRANGULAR			TRIANGULAR				CURVED			

2

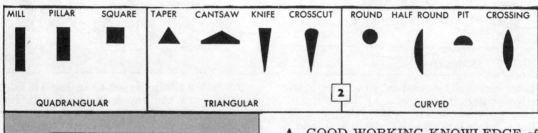

TAPERED

BLUNT

3

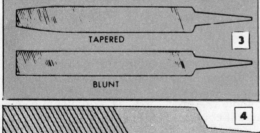

4

SINGLE CUT

DOUBLE CUT

RASP CUT

CURVED TOOTH

A GOOD WORKING KNOWLEDGE of files and filing will pay you substantial workshop dividends in the form of better home projects and devices completed with less effort at lower cost. No homeowner's toolkit is complete without one or more of several types of files.

For occasional all-around use you can get a household utility file, which is a flat, 8-in. file having a fine cut on one side, a coarser cut on the other and a safe edge. A handle is cast at one end instead of a tang. Other files varying in size and shape and coarseness can be acquired from time to time as needed. Most files in common use vary from 4 to 10 in. in length. These lengths refer to body length as shown in Fig. 1, excluding the tang.

A File for Every Purpose

The various types of files are classified according to the shape of the body and type and cut of the teeth. An important consideration when selecting a file for a job is the kind of material to be filed. In respect to the shape, or cross section of the body, files are rectangular, square, triangular, round and half round. There are several variations of these shapes, most of which are referred to by words developed by trade usage, which indicate purpose and shape of a file as shown in Fig. 2. Concerning their lengthwise design files may be

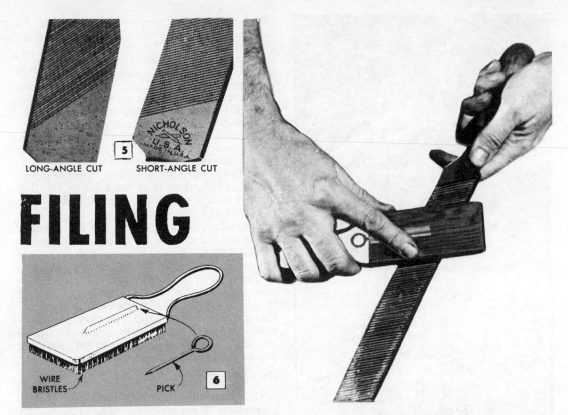

LONG-ANGLE CUT   SHORT-ANGLE CUT

5

FILING

WIRE BRISTLES   PICK   **6**

tapered toward the tip or they may be blunt as shown in Fig. 3.

Kinds of Teeth

File teeth may be single cut, double cut, rasp type or curved as shown in Fig. 4. Usually, single-cut files are used for finishing under light pressure. Double-cut files remove metal faster but require more pressure. The angle of the cut on a file varies as shown in Fig. 5. This may be a "long-angle cut," or a "short-angle cut." The checker-board arrangement of teeth on a rasp-cut file is designed for extremely rough work on wood, leather and some soft metals. Files having curved teeth are single cut and are used mostly for soft metals. File teeth generally classify into sizes that vary in degree of coarseness, such as the following: dead smooth, smooth, second cut, bastard, coarse and rough. Each of these varies in proportion to the size of a file. Thus, a 10-in. second-cut file will be coarser than a 6-in. second-cut file. Most files have a smooth, second or bastard cut.

For superfine finishing work, Swiss-pattern files, also referred to as diemakers' files, are made within closer tolerances than the conventional American-pattern files. Both have similar cross sections but differ in shape. Swiss-pattern files usually have longer tapers and smaller points. Also, they are available in finer cuts ranging from No. 00, the coarsest, to No. 6, the finest.

Cutting Action of Files

The sharp, hardened teeth of files are pointed toward the tip and cut only on forward strokes, which produce chips or filings. A sharp file will cut with very little downward pressure, although this will vary somewhat with the depth of bite and the material being worked. With a sharp file, practically no pressure is required for finishing work. Excessive pressure dulls the teeth. Insufficient pressure, which allows the teeth to slide over the work without cutting it, also tends to dull the teeth. Sliding also may be caused by clogged teeth.

Keep Files Clean

Files cease to cut properly and tend to scratch the work when the gullets between the teeth fill with chips or filings. When the latter condition exists, remove filings with a wire brush or file card as shown in Figs. 6 and 7. To remove filings that are compacted tightly in the gullets forming "pins," use a soft-iron pick shown in Fig. 6. To minimize formation of "pins," rub chalk on the file. This is especially good for fine finishing. For rough filing, the file should be "chalked" and then brushed clean.

Support and Height of Work

Work should be supported rigidly when any appreciable filing is done, and particularly when accurate filing is required. For

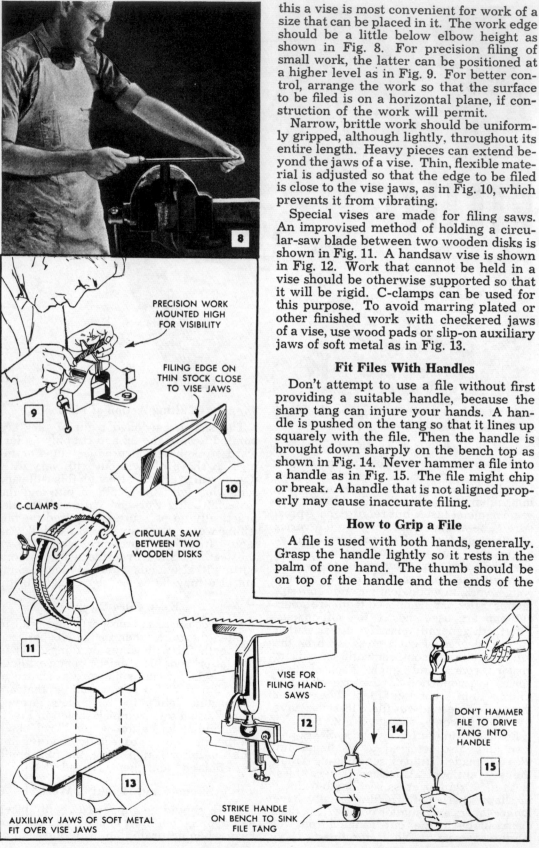

this a vise is most convenient for work of a size that can be placed in it. The work edge should be a little below elbow height as shown in Fig. 8. For precision filing of small work, the latter can be positioned at a higher level as in Fig. 9. For better control, arrange the work so that the surface to be filed is on a horizontal plane, if construction of the work will permit.

Narrow, brittle work should be uniformly gripped, although lightly, throughout its entire length. Heavy pieces can extend beyond the jaws of a vise. Thin, flexible material is adjusted so that the edge to be filed is close to the vise jaws, as in Fig. 10, which prevents it from vibrating.

Special vises are made for filing saws. An improvised method of holding a circular-saw blade between two wooden disks is shown in Fig. 11. A handsaw vise is shown in Fig. 12. Work that cannot be held in a vise should be otherwise supported so that it will be rigid. C-clamps can be used for this purpose. To avoid marring plated or other finished work with checkered jaws of a vise, use wood pads or slip-on auxiliary jaws of soft metal as in Fig. 13.

Fit Files With Handles

Don't attempt to use a file without first providing a suitable handle, because the sharp tang can injure your hands. A handle is pushed on the tang so that it lines up squarely with the file. Then the handle is brought down sharply on the bench top as shown in Fig. 14. Never hammer a file into a handle as in Fig. 15. The file might chip or break. A handle that is not aligned properly may cause inaccurate filing.

How to Grip a File

A file is used with both hands, generally. Grasp the handle lightly so it rests in the palm of one hand. The thumb should be on top of the handle and the ends of the

PRECISION WORK MOUNTED HIGH FOR VISIBILITY

FILING EDGE ON THIN STOCK CLOSE TO VISE JAWS

C-CLAMPS

CIRCULAR SAW BETWEEN TWO WOODEN DISKS

VISE FOR FILING HAND-SAWS

DON'T HAMMER FILE TO DRIVE TANG INTO HANDLE

AUXILIARY JAWS OF SOFT METAL FIT OVER VISE JAWS

STRIKE HANDLE ON BENCH TO SINK FILE TANG

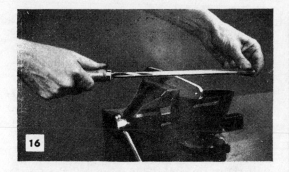

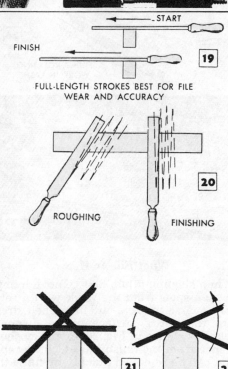

fingers should point toward your face. With the thumb and fingers of the other hand take a light hold on the tip as shown in Fig. 16, or rest them on it as in Fig. 17. A tight, clumsy grip, as in Fig. 18, can make accurate filing almost impossible. Start the forward stroke at the top of the file. It should be a full-length stroke, ending at the heel as in Fig. 19. At the beginning of a stroke on flat work the downward pressure on the tip should be a trifle more than that on the heel. At the center of a stroke the pressure should be equalized and at the end of a stroke it should be slightly greater at the heel. Short strokes wear down the teeth on only a portion of a file and shorten its useful life.

The two most common errors committed by beginners are: Rocking a file on straight work and dragging it over the work on backstrokes. Even when the rocking movement is barely perceptible, the work surface becomes rounded as shown in Fig. 22. It is necessary to rock the file on round work, however. Then the handle is held high when the tip contacts the work. Bring the handle down as the stroke is continued. When filing hard metals, raise the file on the backstroke to clear the work. This is not necessary on soft metals where file contact with the work is an advantage, since it helps to dislodge filings.

START

FINISH

19

FULL-LENGTH STROKES BEST FOR FILE WEAR AND ACCURACY

ROUGHING   FINISHING

20

21 FOR FAST ROUGHING, BEVEL SIDES OF WORK, THEN DRESS TOP

22 ROUNDED SURFACE ON WORK DUE TO ROCKING FILE

HALF-ROUND FILE   CROSSING FILE

23 FILING CONCAVE SURFACES

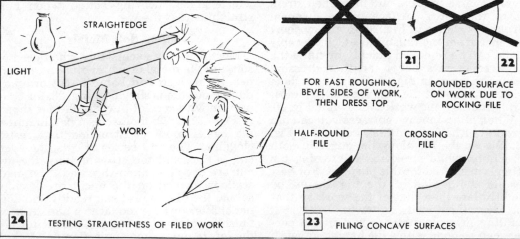

LIGHT   STRAIGHTEDGE   WORK

24 TESTING STRAIGHTNESS OF FILED WORK

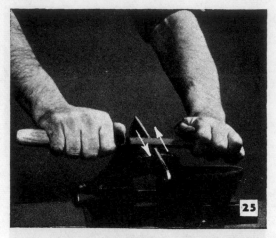

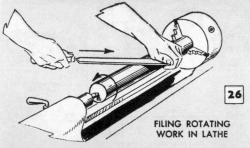

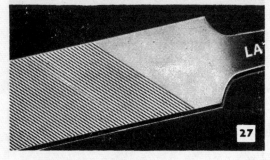

FILING ROTATING
WORK IN LATHE

What File to Use

When starting a job, first remove humps and high spots from the work with a relatively coarse, double-cut file. Then dress down the entire surface, using diagonal strokes as shown in Fig. 20, to a very short distance from the finish line. Considerable metal can be removed quickly by filing the work edges at a bevel and then dressing down the top as in Fig. 21. Finishing is done with a single-cut file, using strokes almost straight across the work as shown in Fig. 20.

When filing concave surfaces you can use a round or half-round file as shown in Fig. 23. Sweep the file along the curve in both directions while stroking. A crossing file often is preferred for this purpose. For best results the radius of the file should be slightly less than that of the work so that the file will cut at its center.

Filing grooves, notches and inside corners can be done with a file having a "safe," or uncut, edge. With the latter, each adjoining edge of the work can be dressed down to the finish line separately. An attempt to file down two adjoining surfaces of a corner at once often results in excessive filing on one surface.

Instead of guessing at the amount of metal to be removed by filing, scribe the work so that the depth of cutting can be governed accordingly. When a filing job nears completion, hold a straightedge or square on the surface. Humps and hollows will show up plainly if you hold the work between your line of vision and a source of light as shown in Fig. 24. Then, the surface can be trued by means of drawfiling.

Drawfiling differs from crossfiling in that both ends of the file are grasped as shown in Fig. 25, and pushed and pulled over the work with a lengthwise stroke. Drawfiling eliminates irregularities and scratches of crossfiling, and results in a straight, smooth surface if done properly. When a considerable amount of stock must be removed you can use a flat, double-cut or bastard file first. Then finish with a mill file. Files with a long-angle cut are best for this purpose since they are least likely to leave marks. However, the same effect can be obtained with a file having a short-angle cut if it is held so that the cut is at a 45-deg. angle to the work edges.

Filing Rotating Work

When filing round stock rotating in a drill press, or in a lathe as in Fig. 26, keep the file moving forward as the work rotates toward you. Also, move it toward one side during the forward stroke. This minimizes grooving and helps to discharge filings. Never hold a file stationary against the work. Work mounted in a drill press should be supported with a "dead center" or a bearing at its lower end to take side strain. The best file to use on rotating work is a long-angle-cut lathe file shown in Fig. 27, which gives shearing action when held straight across the work.

Filing Soft Metals

Most files clog excessively when used on soft, ductile metals such as aluminum, copper, brass, lead and babbitt. An ordinary double-cut file is shown in Fig. 28, for comparison with special-purpose files as shown in Figs. 29 to 32, inclusive. The aluminum file has a tooth construction that resists clogging. The first series of cuts, the overcut, is fine, and the crossing cuts, the upcut, are deep and open-throated. The small scallops formed on the upcut break chips so that the file cleans itself readily and does not chatter or take too large a bite. A good finish is obtained by moving the file toward the left to get a shearing action on strokes.

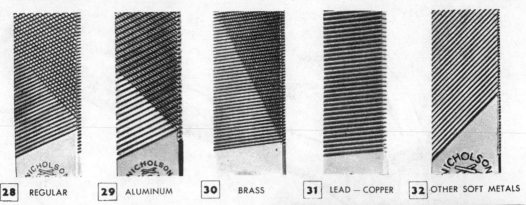

| **28** REGULAR | **29** ALUMINUM | **30** BRASS | **31** LEAD — COPPER | **32** OTHER SOFT METALS |

Fig. 30 shows a file for brass. Note the long-angle overcut and the short-angle upcut. This file has sharp, sturdy, nonclogging teeth that minimize grooving and do not tend to run the file off the work. A file for cutting exceptionally soft metals, such as lead, babbitt and pure copper is shown in Fig. 31. The single, short-angle cut removes metal rapidly under light pressure, and with even less pressure produces a smooth finish.

A shear-tooth file, shown in Fig. 32, combines fast cutting action with good finish on many other types of soft metals, alloys, plastics, hard rubber and wood. On a forward stroke this file is pushed slightly toward the right to prevent running toward the left.

The tough, dense composition of stainless steel dulls ordinary files rapidly. Therefore, files having unusually high wearing qualities are used on this type of metal. They require only light pressure with slow, even strokes to remove metal quickly and to produce a smooth finish.

The teeth of ordinary files are not tough enough to withstand hard, rough surfaces and sharp edges of iron and steel castings, since only a few teeth contact the work at one time. For such work foundry files are used. The teeth on these files are more rugged and have massive backing to support the cutting edges, but they cut more slowly than regular files.

Another special type of file is used for die castings, which also tend to damage and clog teeth of ordinary files. A small, pointed file having a safe edge is used for sharpening augers as shown in Fig. 33. Other small, flat files are made especially for cleaning ignition points and similar small work.

File Care

A file should never be thrown on a bench, since this might chip or break it. Store files in notched crosspieces or place them vertically in a wall rack of the kind shown in Fig. 34. Rust destroys the sharp edges of

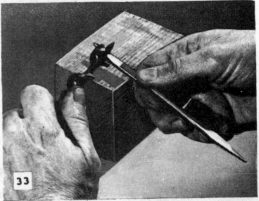

33

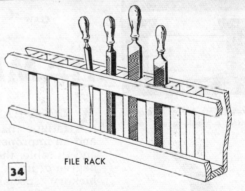

34 FILE RACK

the teeth. Where humid conditions prevail, files not in use should be wrapped in moistureproof material. Excessive oil and grease accumulating on files can be absorbed by chalk. After rubbing chalk on a file it should be brushed clean with a file card. ★ ★ ★

Candle wax will aid in preventing file teeth from clogging when working brass, aluminum or other soft metals. Clean the file thoroughly with a file card, then rub a candle stub over the full area of the teeth. After the job is done, the file can be warmed slightly to aid in brushing away the remaining wax. Use only enough heat to loosen the wax; excess heat will destroy the file temper.

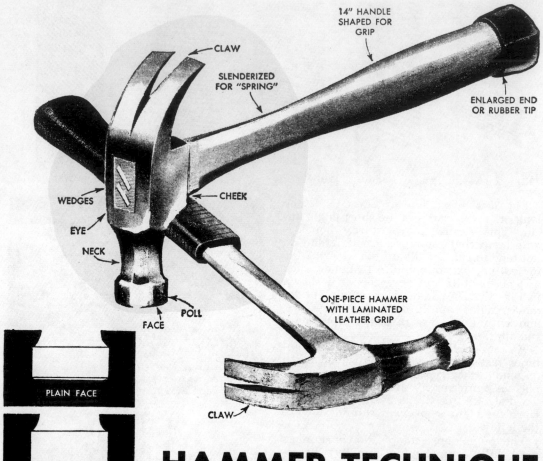

14" HANDLE SHAPED FOR GRIP

CLAW

SLENDERIZED FOR "SPRING"

ENLARGED END OR RUBBER TIP

WEDGES

EYE

NECK

CHEEK

POLL

FACE

ONE-PIECE HAMMER WITH LAMINATED LEATHER GRIP

CLAW

PLAIN FACE

BELL FACE

Carpenters prefer hammer with a bell-faced poll

CURVED CLAW

STRAIGHT CLAW

HAMMER TECHNIQUE

A GOOD HAMMER makes fewer "mistakes" and causes less fatigue than a poorly made one having a cast-iron head and an improperly shaped handle. A quality hammer is tough and durable, the head is heat-treated to give it just the right degree of hardness and the handle is made of straight-grained hickory especially selected and shaped to give the tool correct balance. The face of the poll is polished smooth and the edges are ground to a uniform bevel to prevent chipping. The angle at the neck of the poll gives the head sufficient toe-in to make the tool hang correctly. The claws are ground to "nipper" ends for getting into narrow spaces between nailheads and the surface of the work. A tapered slot between the claws has the right bevel to grip not only the head but also the body of a nail firmly. Handles are shaped to give a certain amount of spring to ease shock and minimize strain on the arm muscles of the user. Handles are flared at the butt ends and in some cases are fitted with rubber tips to afford an easy, nontiring grip. Some hammers have handles of steel, forged integral with the head and fitted with laminated leather disks to form a comfortable, shock-absorbing grip.

Sizes and types of claw hammers: Claw hammers come in various weights, 5, 7, 13, 16 and 20-oz. heads being more or less standard. Some manufacturers also indicate hammer sizes by numbers. These range from 1 to 4, No. 1 being the largest and No. 4 being the smallest. A No. 1½ hammer with a 16-oz. head usually is selected as the size being best for all-around use.

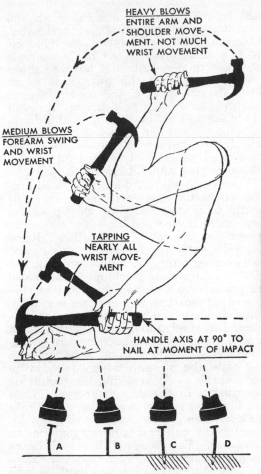

HEAVY BLOWS
ENTIRE ARM AND SHOULDER MOVEMENT. NOT MUCH WRIST MOVEMENT

MEDIUM BLOWS
FOREARM SWING AND WRIST MOVEMENT

TAPPING
NEARLY ALL WRIST MOVEMENT

HANDLE AXIS AT 90° TO NAIL AT MOMENT OF IMPACT

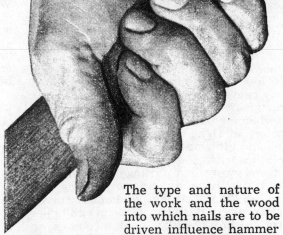

A   B   C   D

If misdirected hammer blow bends nail as in detail A, it usually is possible to correct fault by striking a second blow at an equal opposite angle, detail B. When nail is deflected by oblique grain as at C, strike it with hammer head angled in the opposite direction, detail D

The type and nature of the work and the wood into which nails are to be driven influence hammer size selected for a given job. Hardwoods require a greater driving force and a heavy hammer may be needed to save time and conserve the energy of the user.

Although the face of the poll is always crowned there are variations in the degree of the crown, or convexity. Finishers working on interior trim like a hammer with a pronounced crown, or bell face, on the poll, as this enables them to drive a nail flush or slightly below the surface of the wood without denting it. However, such a hammer requires skillful handling and for ordinary work users generally select a hammer having less crown. Ordinary claw hammers are regularly supplied with two styles of claws. On the first, or common claw hammer, the claws have a pronounced

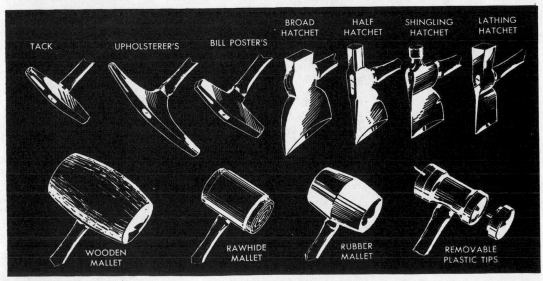

TACK   UPHOLSTERER'S   BILL POSTER'S   BROAD HATCHET   HALF HATCHET   SHINGLING HATCHET   LATHING HATCHET

WOODEN MALLET   RAWHIDE MALLET   RUBBER MALLET   REMOVABLE PLASTIC TIPS curve making them especially suited to pulling nails. On the other style the claws are very nearly straight and are heavier which adapts them for prying and for ripping off siding or roofing boards.

Using a claw hammer: Grip the hammer near the end of the handle. This hold gives the maximum leverage, power and drive. When fine work requires the ultimate in control you'll see experienced users extend the thumb along the handle, especially when handling a light hammer on fine work where the blow that isn't pin-pointed may cause irreparable damage. The trick in starting a nail is to use light taps with the hammer, holding the handle approximately at right angles to the axis of the nail and utilizing the wrist as a pivot. Master this trick and you won't injure your fingers, even when starting nails in difficult positions. After starting, or setting, the nail use the full stroke. When heavy blows are required, the wrist, forearm and upper arm are brought into simultaneous use to deliver the full driving power of the hammer. The movement is timed in such a way that at the moment of impact the hammer handle is in a position approximately at right angles to the axis of the nail, just as in the procedure of starting a nail. As the head of the nail nears the work surface the force of the blows should be lessened as otherwise the nailhead may be sunk below the surface far enough to break the wood fibers. It is particularly important to avoid this when installing wooden siding.

Should a nail bend slightly due to its striking a knot or oblique grain, it usually is possible to correct the condition simply by striking the head of the nail at a slight angle or slightly off center in a direction opposite to that of the bend. In hardwood,

nails frequently start to bend when the point strikes wood grain of greater density. Often the nail can be driven home by striking it a sharp blow at an angle, causing the point to penetrate the adverse grain without increasing the degree of bend. When the character of the work makes it necessary to drive a nail directly through a knot, always drill a pilot hole of a diameter slightly smaller than the body of the nail. In fine work with hardwoods, finishers make a practice of drilling pilot holes before driving and setting finishing nails.

When pulling a nail where the head projects above the surface of the work sufficiently to permit wedging the tip of the claw under it, proceed by stages as undue pressure may break off the nailhead. Raise the nail slightly, then release the claws and take another bite. When pulling a nail, the initial stroke should be stopped just before the poll of the hammer contacts the surface of the work, as the leverage is greatly reduced when the poll becomes the fulcrum. Lift the hammer and insert a block or wedge before applying pressure in the second stage. When using a hammer to pull nails, the pressure always should be moderate to avoid breaking the handle or loosening it in the socket, or eye. When you find yourself in a position with only one hand free you can start a nail easily by gripping the nail and hammer together in one hand. The head of the nail bears against the side of the hammer at the midpoint and a forceful push or a light tap will set the nail so that it will stay in position.

Care of hammer: For the safety of yourself and others who may be near by, never use a hammer with a loose head. Take time to put in new wedges or install a new handle. When the tool is not in use keep

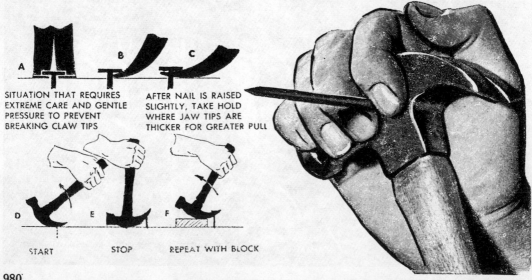

SITUATION THAT REQUIRES EXTREME CARE AND GENTLE PRESSURE TO PREVENT BREAKING CLAW TIPS

AFTER NAIL IS RAISED SLIGHTLY, TAKE HOLD WHERE JAW TIPS ARE THICKER FOR GREATER PULL

START   STOP   REPEAT WITH BLOCK

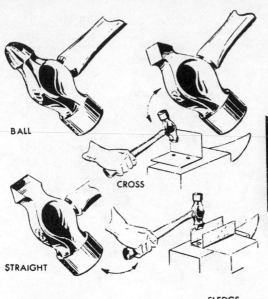

BALL

CROSS

STRAIGHT

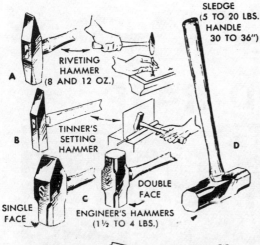

A — RIVETING HAMMER (8 AND 12 OZ.)

B — TINNER'S SETTING HAMMER

SINGLE FACE

C — ENGINEER'S HAMMERS (1½ TO 4 LBS.)

DOUBLE FACE

SLEDGE (5 TO 20 LBS. HANDLE 30 TO 36")

D

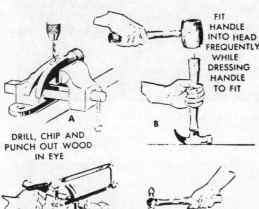

A — DRILL, CHIP AND PUNCH OUT WOOD IN EYE

B — FIT HANDLE INTO HEAD FREQUENTLY WHILE DRESSING HANDLE TO FIT

C — CUT OFF PROJECTING END

D — DRIVE IN TWO WEDGES TO EXPAND HANDLE IN HEAD. THEN FILE FLUSH

RENEWING HAMMER HANDLE

the head oiled to prevent rusting. Wipe off the oil before using.

Tack hammers: Use a 5-oz. regular tack hammer, a 7-oz. upholsterer's hammer or an 8-oz. bill-poster's hammer for driving tacks. Hammers having one poll magnetized for holding the tack while starting are preferred by most users. The magnetized poll is used only for starting the tack.

Hatchets: Ordinary hatchets used by lathers and roofers have a polled head with a cross-checked face for driving small nails. The narrow cutting blade is adapted to trimming wooden lath and shingles. The various types are shown on page 234.

Mallets and soft-faced hammers: Wooden mallets are generally used to drive wood chisels. Soft-faced hammers made from various materials such as rawhide, rubber and plastic are adapted to striking finished or polished surfaces of metal without marring or denting the work. Some types of soft hammers have interchangeable tips of various materials.

Mechanic's hammers: Three types of ball-peen hammers are illustrated, also several types of heavier hammers adapted to bending and riveting of sheet metal, driving cold chisels and similar jobs. Note that the peening hammers shown in the upper left-hand detail have both round polls (ball peen) and wedge-shaped polls (cross and straight peen) which adapt them to peening rivets as well as metal surfaces. Several special types, including engineer's hammers and small sledges are shown in the center details A to D inclusive.

Replacing hammer handles: Details at the lower left, A to D inclusive, show four essential steps in replacing a hammer handle. These steps apply to all types of hammers with only minor variations. When replacing the handle, never burn the old wood out of the eye as the heat may draw the temper of the head. ★ ★ ★

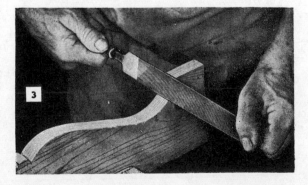

USE A WOOD RASP

for finishing scroll cuts, squaring tenons, half laps, rounding and beveling corners, squaring holes and shaping work to contour

By Edwin M. Love

RASPS AND CURVED RIFFLERS are cutting tools having a number of teeth arranged in a staggered pattern on the flat and curved faces. Rasps and rifflers differ somewhat from files in that the teeth are cut individually while those of the common file are continuous, usually arranged at an angle with the blade to give a shear cut. In Fig. 1, sections A, B and E are common rasp shapes. The others are common file shapes which are useful in smoothing and shaping wood when the larger and coarser sizes are used. The combination file, or rasp-file as it is sometimes called, pictured second from the right in Fig. 1, comes in half-round cross section. The teeth on one half of the blade are rasp-cut, that is, they are individual and are formed in a staggered pattern. Those on the other half of the blade are file-cut, each forming a continuous cutting edge across the width of the blade.

In addition to common rasps and rifflers there are several variations which are coming into wide use by craftsmen who must

Above, tenons and half laps cut slightly oversize are easily reduced to required dimensions with a cabinetmaker's rasp. Below, a rasp makes short work of removing the saw marks from the edges of scrolls

No other hand tool quite equals a rasp for finishing contoured shapes of models in wood and plastic

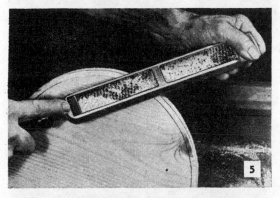

This new tool is handled like a rasp, cuts very fast and smooth in woods, plastic, nonferrous metals

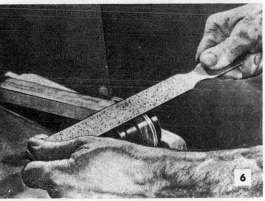

Above, tungsten-carbide grains are cutting edges of this new tool. Below, perforations in metal form cutting edges of this tool. Cuts in any direction

shape and smooth wood by hand methods. Figs. 5 and 11 picture two of these in use. Each unit consists of a handled frame and a perforated steel strip, or blade, which is replaceable. The perforations form multiple cutters, each of which is an individual beveled blade. The tool in Fig. 5 is used as a rasp. A companion unit utilizes the same blade, but is fitted with handles so that it can be used as a plane. The tool pictured in Fig. 11 can be used either as a rasp or plane by changing the position of the handle. Another variation which can be used either as a rasp or file is pictured in Fig. 6. It is simply a file-shaped piece of flat steel having tungsten-carbide grits fused to both flat faces, fine on one side, coarse on the other. Fig. 7 pictures another hand tool for smoothing wood which has the novel feature of being able to cut in all directions with equal facility. It consists of a perforated steel sheet mounted on a special holder which permits its use in much the same manner as a sandpaper block. Still another rasplike tool is shown in Fig. 13. The body of the unit is a toothed steel helix having a drill point. It will cut in any direction and can substitute for a round rasp, a drill, and a compass saw. Although the variations described are not conventional rasps, they can serve similar uses.

Figs. 2 to 13 inclusive, picture typical work with rasps, rifflers and the newly developed units that can fill in as rasps. The rifflers, Fig. 9, are toothed in a manner similar to rasps. Common sectional shapes are shown in Fig. 9, details A to E inclusive. Note that rifflers are curved, which permits them to be used on both convex and concave surfaces, Figs. 10 and 12.

Rasps are handled, or stroked, like files as they are designed to cut on the forward stroke. When smoothing a flat surface, relax pressure slightly near the end of the cutting stroke. This is especially important when using a rasp with both hands, as otherwise the surface may be rounded slightly. A shearing stroke will prevent chatter marks when it is necessary to work end grain in hardwoods.

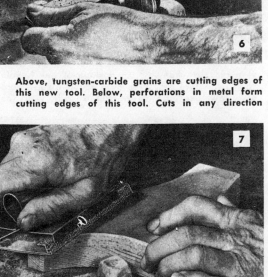

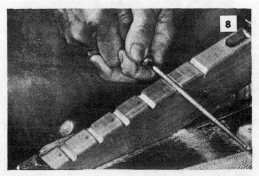

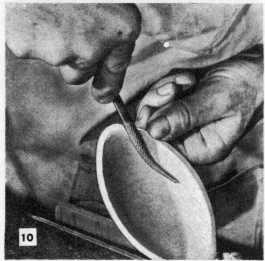

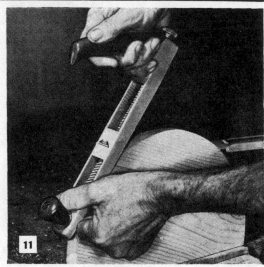

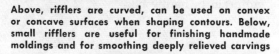

Above, rifflers are curved, can be used on convex or concave surfaces when shaping contours. Below, small rifflers are useful for finishing handmade moldings and for smoothing deeply relieved carvings

Above, this tool can be used either as a plane or as a rasp by changing the position of one handle. Below, this tool can serve as a round rasp, a compass saw and also as a drill. It cuts very fast

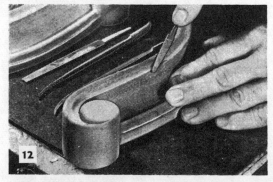

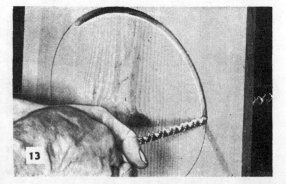

SCREWDRIVING CRAFTSMANSHIP

NEARLY ALL TYPES of craftwork in wood, in which parts must be assembled into a unit, call for the use of wood screws in some part of the construction. It's important to select the right screw and driver for the job to be done. Wood screws most commonly used are those of the regular type having a single slot, Figs. 6 and 18. The two most commonly used drivers are known as the wing and cabinet types, Fig. 10. All other types are simply variations of the basic types.

Figs. 1, 2 and 3 show the importance of selecting a driver having a bit of the correct width and thickness. In Fig. 1, detail A shows the proper width. In detail B, Fig. 2, the correct thickness is shown, and Fig. 3, detail C shows what happens to the screw slot if the blade is too narrow, or is tilted, or has damaged corners. Also, the upper details in Fig. 3 show how the surface of the work can be damaged if the screw is seated with a blade that is too wide. If the blade is too thin or too narrow for the job, you may twist it as in the upper detail, Fig. 2.

Wing-type drivers are preferred for driving flathead screws that seat flush with the surface. Cabinet-type drivers are used when driving screws into counterbored holes, and often when driving round and ovalhead screws, Fig. 7. Spiral ratchet drivers, Fig. 4, speed up the job of driving a great number of screws, as in boatbuilding. Much the same is true of the driver bit designed for use with a brace, detail A, Fig. 5. When space is limited, a ratchet driver of the type shown in detail B, Fig. 5, is used. The cabinet driver also is made in a very small size, detail D, Fig. 5.

1   **A** CORRECT SIZE

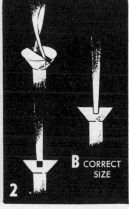

2   **B** CORRECT SIZE

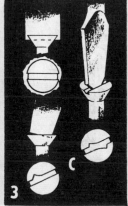

3   **C**

SPIRAL RATCHET DRIVER

4   90°

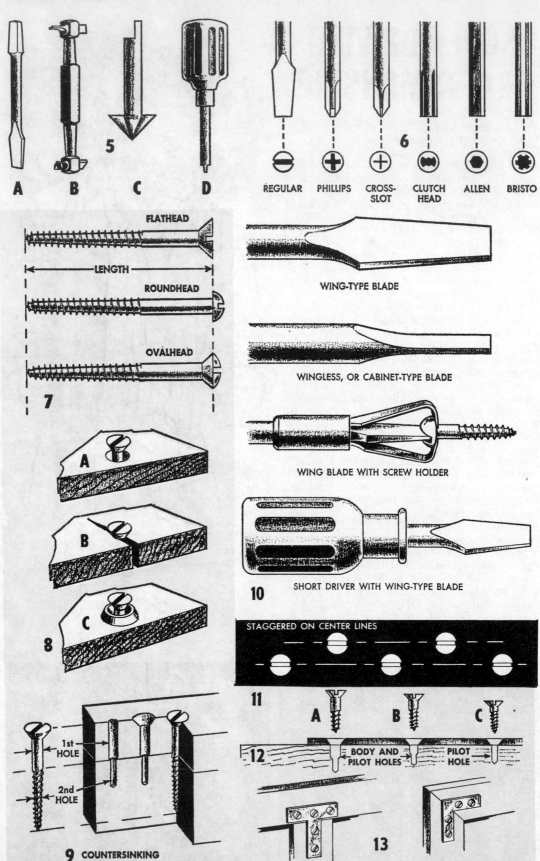

A   B   5   C   D

6   REGULAR   PHILLIPS   CROSS-SLOT   CLUTCH HEAD   ALLEN   BRISTO

FLATHEAD

LENGTH

ROUNDHEAD

OVALHEAD

7

WING-TYPE BLADE

WINGLESS, OR CABINET-TYPE BLADE

WING BLADE WITH SCREW HOLDER

A

B

C

8

10   SHORT DRIVER WITH WING-TYPE BLADE

STAGGERED ON CENTER LINES

11   A   B   C

12   BODY AND PILOT HOLES   PILOT HOLE

1st HOLE

2nd HOLE

9   COUNTERSINKING

13

Flathead screws should be countersunk, detail A, Fig. 8, or run down on finishing washers, detail C. Driving a flathead screw without countersinking may result in splitting, detail B. Countersinking can be done with a rose countersink, Fig. 5, detail C, or with a combined countersink and drill, Figs. 14 and 15. The rose countersink is available in two types, one for use in spiral-ratchet drivers and some types of push drills, having a notched shank, Fig. 5. The other type has a squared shank for use in a bit brace. The combination unit drills the body hole and pilot hole and runs the countersink in one operation, Figs. 9, 14 and 15. By adjusting a stop on some types, the tool also will run down a counterbore for a wooden plug, Fig. 15. It is designed to be driven by a ¼-in. portable drill. Each unit is marked with the number and length of the screw for which it is intended.

Good work calls for a screw of the proper type and length. In Fig. 16, details A, B and C, the screw in detail C is the correct length and is properly countersunk. In Fig. 17, details A, B and C, the longer screw, detail B, would normally be used for maximum strength in softwood. For hardwood the screw in detail C would be about right for average work. For fastening metal to wood, Figs. 12 and 13, screws A and B in Fig. 12 will give the greatest holding power and resistance to shearing strains if the body and pilot holes are drilled to the correct size. When the work requires that screws be driven in line near the edge of the stock on a spacing of 1 in. or less, it's best to stagger the line as in Fig. 11 to avoid any possibility of splitting the stock.

Fig. 18 shows representative sizes of wood screws which are numbered from 1 to 18 inclusive. The table gives the body diameter in inches and indicates the twist-drill size, also the auger bit number. ★ ★ ★

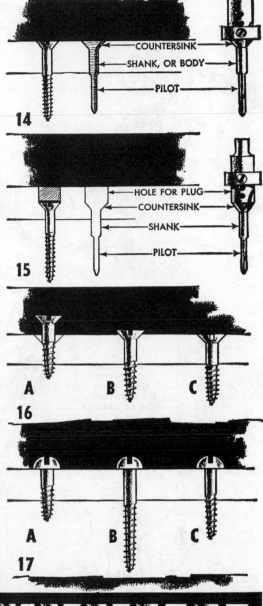

NUMBER OF SCREW	1	2	3	4	5	6	7	8	9	10	12	14	16	18
BODY DIAMETER	5/64-	3/32-	3/32+	7/64+	1/8	9/64-	5/32-	11/64-	11/64+	3/16+	7/32-	15/64+	17/64+	19/64-
TWIST-DRILL SIZE 1 (SEE FIG. 9)	5/64	3/32	7/64	7/64	1/8	9/64	5/32	11/64	3/16	3/16	7/32	1/4	17/64	19/64
AUGER-BIT NUMBER							3	3	3	3	4	4	5	5
TWIST-DRILL SIZE 2 (SEE FIG. 9)		1/16	1/16	5/64	5/64	3/32	7/64	7/64	1/8	1/8	9/64	5/32	3/16	13/64
AUGER-BIT NUMBER												3	3	4

NOTE—SOME FRACTIONAL SIZES GIVEN ARE ONLY APPROX. ALL FRACTIONAL SIZES IN INCHES

CHISEL TIPS

By C. W. Woodson

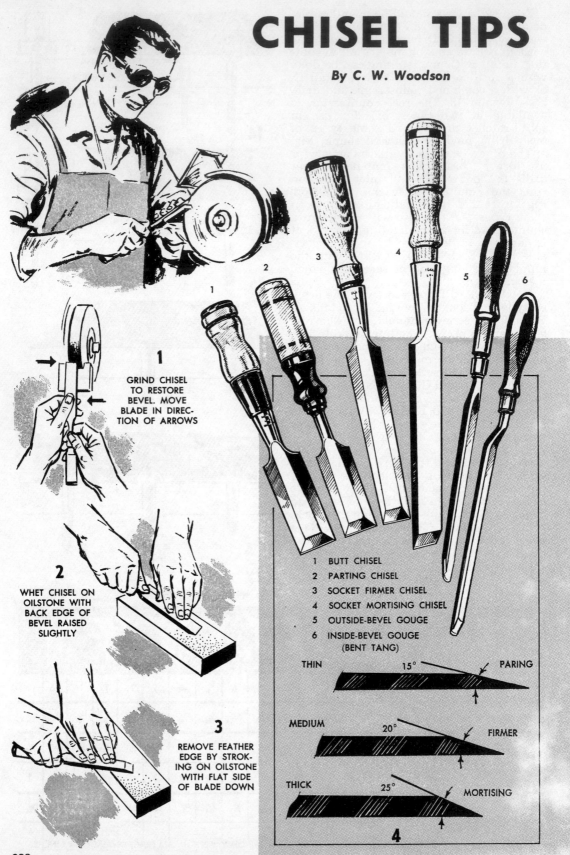

1 GRIND CHISEL TO RESTORE BEVEL. MOVE BLADE IN DIRECTION OF ARROWS

2 WHET CHISEL ON OILSTONE WITH BACK EDGE OF BEVEL RAISED SLIGHTLY

3 REMOVE FEATHER EDGE BY STROKING ON OILSTONE WITH FLAT SIDE OF BLADE DOWN

1 BUTT CHISEL
2 PARTING CHISEL
3 SOCKET FIRMER CHISEL
4 SOCKET MORTISING CHISEL
5 OUTSIDE-BEVEL GOUGE
6 INSIDE-BEVEL GOUGE
    (BENT TANG)

THIN — 15° — PARING

MEDIUM — 20° — FIRMER

THICK — 25° — MORTISING

4

For Craftsmen Who Work With Hand Tools

WHEN REPRODUCING old pieces and also in many types of custom work, skilled craftsmen still use wood chisels and gouges of various types to make cuts found in common cabinet joinery. In order to take full advantage of the versatility of these hand tools one must know the types and uses of chisels and gouges, how to handle them in hand work and how to sharpen each one to attain the keenest cutting edge.

In Fig. 4, illustrations 1 through 6 show types of wood chisels and gouges in common use. Chisel No. 2 also is referred to as a paring chisel; the others are usually referred to by the names given. The gouges, Nos. 5 and 6, Fig. 4, are of the types used for paring cuts. These tools are made in styles other than those shown. Sizes of all the chisel types vary in blade widths and lengths according to work requirements,

Fig. 11. Blade widths of chisels run from ⅛ to 2 in. Note the difference in the edge bevels indicated in the lower details in Fig. 4. The paring chisel has a very long bevel at a 15-degree angle and is intended to be driven entirely by hand on light, accurate work. The firmer chisel edge is formed at a 20-degree bevel and serves as a general-purpose cutting edge to be driven by hand pressure alone and also by mallet blows. The mortising chisel is a sturdy, heavy-duty hand tool with a short beveled edge designed to withstand heavy mallet blows and moderate prying as must be done when making mortises.

Figs. 1, 2 and 3 outline the basic steps in sharpening a chisel. Note also in this connection the details in Figs. 5, 6 and 7. In sharpening on a high-speed grinder use a vitreous wheel and, if available, a sliding tool rest. In whetting the edge on the fine

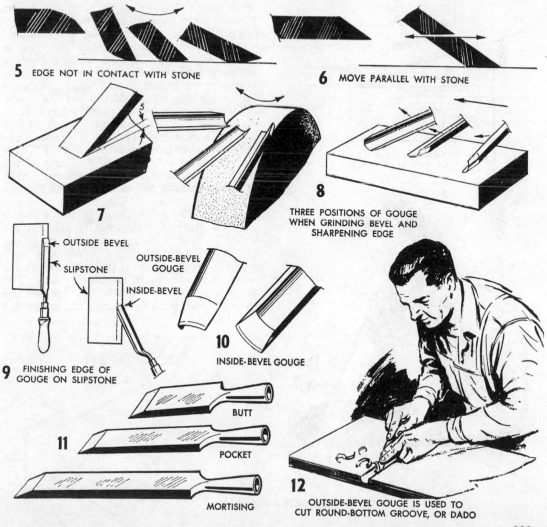

5 EDGE NOT IN CONTACT WITH STONE

6 MOVE PARALLEL WITH STONE

7

8 THREE POSITIONS OF GOUGE WHEN GRINDING BEVEL AND SHARPENING EDGE

OUTSIDE BEVEL

SLIPSTONE

OUTSIDE-BEVEL GOUGE

INSIDE-BEVEL

9 FINISHING EDGE OF GOUGE ON SLIPSTONE

10 INSIDE-BEVEL GOUGE

BUTT

POCKET

11

MORTISING

12 OUTSIDE-BEVEL GOUGE IS USED TO CUT ROUND-BOTTOM GROOVE, OR DADO

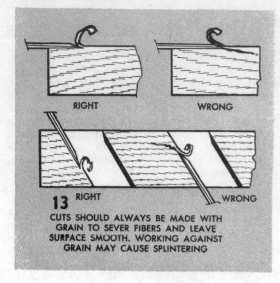

13 RIGHT WRONG

CUTS SHOULD ALWAYS BE MADE WITH GRAIN TO SEVER FIBERS AND LEAVE SURFACE SMOOTH. WORKING AGAINST GRAIN MAY CAUSE SPLINTERING

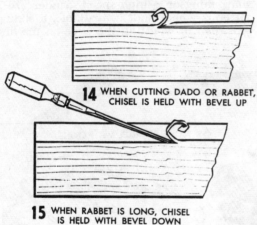

14 WHEN CUTTING DADO OR RABBET, CHISEL IS HELD WITH BEVEL UP

15 WHEN RABBET IS LONG, CHISEL IS HELD WITH BEVEL DOWN

16 LAYING OUT TENON WITH MARKING GAUGE

LAYOUT LINES SCORED DEEPLY

17

side of the oilstone, hold paring and firmer chisels with the back edge of the bevel raised about 5 degrees as in Fig. 7. When whetting a short beveled edge, such as that on the mortising chisel, it's a common practise to hold the bevel flat on the stone as in Fig. 6. Avoid rocking the blade as the whetting strokes are made, as otherwise the effect will be to form several bevels as in Fig. 5. Gouges with inside and outside bevels, Fig. 10, are sharpened and whetted as in Figs. 8 and 9. Inside-bevel gouges cannot, of course, be sharpened on a flat-faced grinding wheel; use only on a round-faced wheel or a taper oilstone. Both types are finished on a slipstone, Fig. 9. As a rule, grinding is needed only when it is necessary to form or reform the bevel or when the cutting edge is nicked.

Although many craftsmen skilled in handling chisels and gouges have developed methods which suit their own requirements, the techniques outlined in Figs. 13 through 26 are in common usage. Several rules apply to nearly all chisel and gouge operations: Always work with the grain. Always score gauge lines deeply when laying out tenons and matching mortises and when making round-bottom grooves or dadoes as in Fig. 12, also when rabbeting with a chisel as in Figs. 14 and 15. Scoring prevents the wood from breaking beyond the gauge line when cutting out the waste.

To get a neat job of rounding a corner, make the light chip-raising cuts A in Fig. 23. Note also the chip-raising, or chipbreaking cuts being made in Fig. 21. These chip-breaker cuts prevent splitting of the stock and make it easier to remove waste. When forming a tenon of any size or type make scorings as in Fig. 16 and shoulder cuts, Fig. 17, first. Then, if the wood is straight grained, you usually can lift the waste in one cut from each side as in detail A, Fig. 26. But if the wood is even slightly cross grained, proceed to lift the waste in stages as in details B and C, Fig. 26. Always work from both edges of the stock. Finish with the paring chisel. ★★★

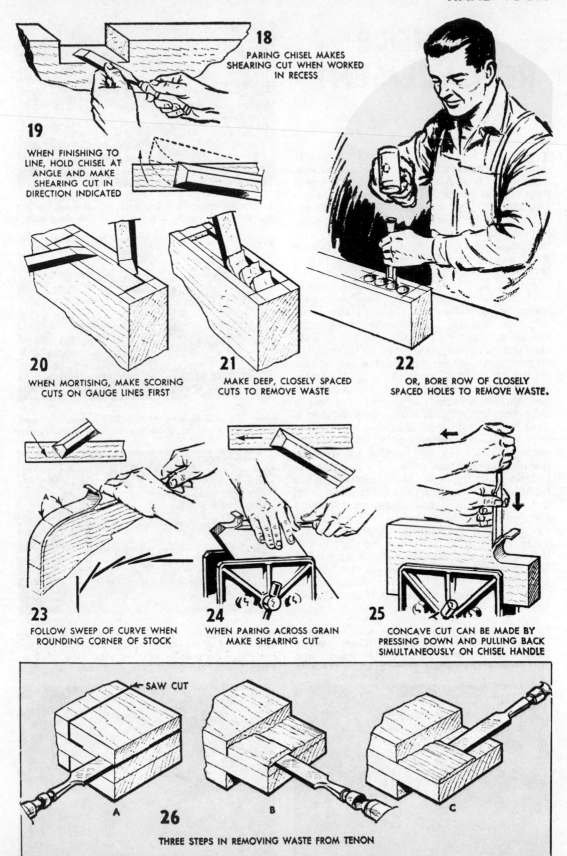

18 PARING CHISEL MAKES SHEARING CUT WHEN WORKED IN RECESS

19 WHEN FINISHING TO LINE, HOLD CHISEL AT ANGLE AND MAKE SHEARING CUT IN DIRECTION INDICATED

20 WHEN MORTISING, MAKE SCORING CUTS ON GAUGE LINES FIRST

21 MAKE DEEP, CLOSELY SPACED CUTS TO REMOVE WASTE

22 OR, BORE ROW OF CLOSELY SPACED HOLES TO REMOVE WASTE.

23 FOLLOW SWEEP OF CURVE WHEN ROUNDING CORNER OF STOCK

24 WHEN PARING ACROSS GRAIN MAKE SHEARING CUT

25 CONCAVE CUT CAN BE MADE BY PRESSING DOWN AND PULLING BACK SIMULTANEOUSLY ON CHISEL HANDLE

SAW CUT

A   B   C

26 THREE STEPS IN REMOVING WASTE FROM TENON

HANDLE REPLACEMENT

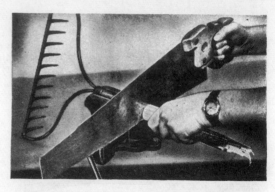

If rake handle cannot be removed after prying out pin, saw off handle as close to ferrule as possible

Do YOU HAVE a favorite old rake out in the garage from which the handle is missing? Or a spading fork with a taped handle that splits a little more each time you use it? If you've been planning to replace these or other garden tools this year but haven't bought the new ones yet, why not pause to look around? See how many good tools you could have just by fitting the old broken ones with new handles.

Fitting tool handles can be done easily with ordinary hand tools. The photos on these pages take you through the basic steps of applying new handles to a rake, spade, spading fork or ax. You will note that the rake tang is pinned to the handle, so care must be taken to drive the handle all the way onto the rake to align the holes in the handle and tang. As shovel handles are made in a variety of shapes, it is best to take the blade with you when buying a new handle for your shovel.

A hammer handle is fitted in much the same way as the ax handle pictured in the photo sequence, except for shaping the handle to fit the eye. Most hammer heads have an eye which tapers both ways from the center of the head. Therefore, cut down the end of the handle so its fits through the eye and projects approximately ½ in. beyond the head. Taper the handle to suit the eye on the handle side of the head. When the head is mounted on the handle, the latter is spread to fit the outer section of the eye by driving a wedge into the wood. End of the handle is cut flush with the head.

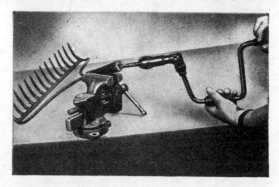

Using metal drill, remove wood to loosen the tang, and with a punch, drive the tang from the ferrule

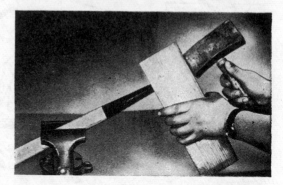

To attach handle, drive tang into hole by tapping on handle. Drill through hole in ferrule until bit strikes tang and drive pin in hole to engage tang. Joining tang and ferrule properly aligns the holes

After shaping new handle to fit ferrule, drive ferrule on end of handle as above. If necessary to enlarge hole in handle to take rake tang, drill as below, using bit about 1/16 in. smaller than tang

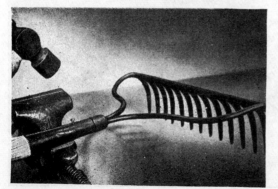

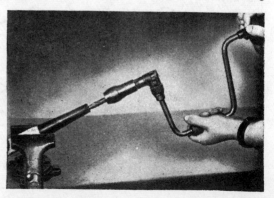

To remove handle from spade, cut off rivet heads with hacksaw or center punch and drill them out

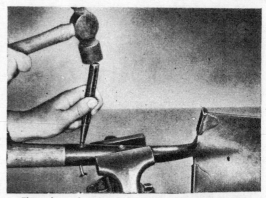

Then clamp ferrule of spade firmly in vise and drive cutoff rivets from handle with a punch

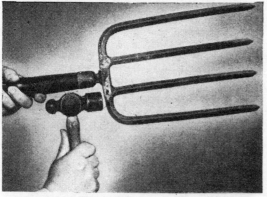

Shape end of the handle with a rasp so it can be driven fully into ferrule for maximum strength

After driving handle in ferrule, drill for rivets. Latter should extend about ⅛ in. before peening

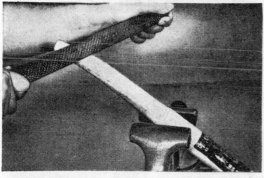

Remove spading fork from handle by tapping close to handle, as above. To replace, insert tang in new handle and tap fork between tines, as below

Above, soak fork handle in hot water for a half hour before fitting. Shovel handles, below, sometimes must be shaped or cut away to fit ferrule

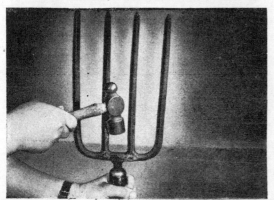

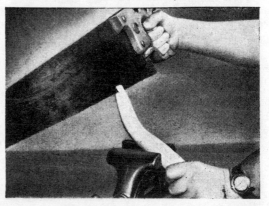

Saw off broken ax handle at head and drill wood in eye with metal bit. Remove wood with a punch

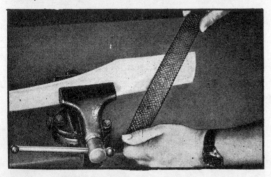

Clamp new handle in vise and rasp to fit eye, checking fit with ax head as shaping proceeds

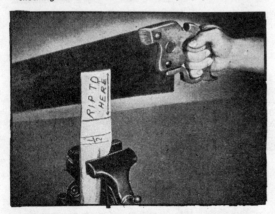

Slot handle for softwood wedge, above. Check fit, below, with ax on edge. End of handle and blade edge ⅔ from front should touch bench top

HANDLE WEDGE

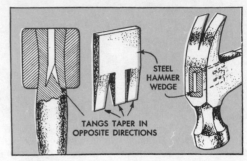

STEEL HAMMER WEDGE

TANGS TAPER IN OPPOSITE DIRECTIONS

If you have trouble keeping a steel wedge from working out of the end of a tool handle, use a wedge like the one shown, which can be made from a flat piece of metal. Slot it in two places to provide three equal parts or tangs. Then bevel or taper the two end tangs on one side only and the center tang on the opposite side. When the wedge is driven into the end of a handle, the tangs will bend slightly in opposite directions and thus secure the wedge firmly in place.

HANDLES

Having the ferrules of a wood chisel become loose is annoying. The trouble can be corrected by peening or notching the inner edges of the ferrules with a cold chisel, as indicated. Tiny prongs or barbs formed by this procedure become embedded in the wood when the handles are forced into place and hold them securely.

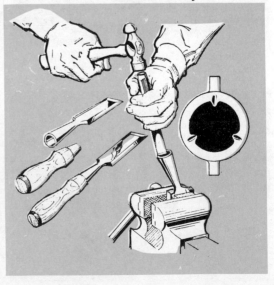

HOW TO WORK WITH
HARDBOARD

HARDBOARD may not be new to you. You, perhaps, have already used it for drawer bottoms, bypassing cabinet doors, as an underlayment for a tile floor or to surface the top of your workbench.

In the material itself, there are a dozen advantages to be considered in using this manmade product. The do-it-yourselfer who works with it for the first time will find its hard, smooth surface ideal for painting. The material is all good since there are no knots or other surface imperfections to bother with. Being without grain, it has equal surface strength in all directions which means it cannot check to spoil the finish, nor split or crack like wood. It offers good and permanent resistance to moisture and can be formed into bends and curves. Best of all, it can be worked almost as easily as wood with hand and power tools, although its hard surface dulls cutting edges more quickly. It can be surface-nailed, screwed, glued and clamped like wood.

Hardboard comes ⅛, 3/16 and ¼ in. thick and in standard or tempered panels. If you want it for outdoor use, or for indoor use where high-humidity conditions prevail, you ask for tempered since it is harder and is treated to withstand moisture. If you want it for indoor use, you ask for standard. Popular sheet size is 4 x 8 ft., although smaller panels of standard size can be had.

WHAT IS HARDBOARD?

Basically, hardboard is reconstructed wood. It is manufactured by separating wood fibers, leaving each surrounded by its natural adhesive agent, and rearranging them in a "felted" or matted form under heat and pressure. The hardboard panel resulting from the process is a dense, grainless board which has great strength, durability and adaptability.

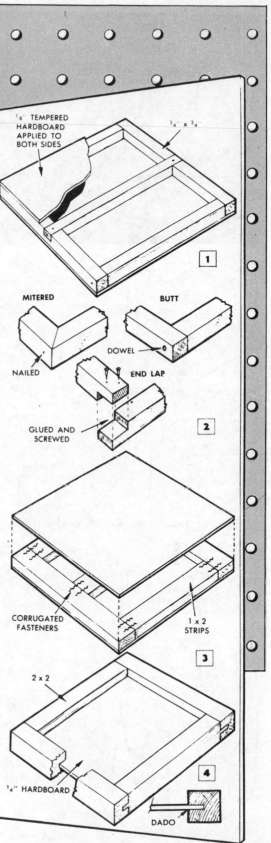

⅛" TEMPERED HARDBOARD APPLIED TO BOTH SIDES

¾ x ¾

1

MITERED

BUTT

NAILED

DOWEL

END LAP

GLUED AND SCREWED

2

CORRUGATED FASTENERS

1 x 2 STRIPS

3

2 x 2

¼" HARDBOARD

DADO

4

To achieve "balanced construction" when making hollow panels, you must remember this: Hardboard of the same thickness must be used on both sides of the panel. If 1/8-in. tempered board is used on one side and 1/4-in. standard on the other, the pull will be unequal and the panel will have a tendency to warp. Likewise, when wood veneer is applied to a hardboard core, veneer of the same thickness must be added to both sides to minimize warping.

Figs. 1, 3, 4 and 9 show four different ways to construct hardboard panels. With the exception of the panel shown in Fig. 4, both hardboard facings are applied to a perimeter framework of wood strips which are cross-braced for additional rigidity when the panel is more than 12 in. wide. One cross brace is sufficient for panels up to 24 in. wide. Wider panels should be cross-braced at 12-in. intervals, or at equal intervals if the width is less than a multiple of 12. If the panel measures 2 x 4 ft., one cross brace, running parallel with the 4-ft. perimeter strips, is sufficient. Crisscross bracing is not necessary. In all panels of balanced construction it is best to provide vent slots so the panel can "breathe." These are shallow saw kerfs made in the perimeter strips on two sides of the panel where they will not be noticed. Fig 2 shows three ways of joining the 3/4-in.-sq. perimeter strips. Cross braces are either half-lapped or butted. Where wider perimeter strips are used, such as 1 x 2s, the strips can be joined with corrugated fasteners as shown in Fig. 3. The hardboard facing may be attached to the wood strips with nails or screws, nails and glue, or glue alone when clamps are available. Nails and screws can be countersunk and covered with wood putty. Glue is preferred to other type fasteners, particularly if the panel is to be machined later for fit.

The lightweight panels, made as shown in Fig. 1 are recommended for swinging and bypassing cabinet doors, for the walls of built-in storage cabinets and as shelves for bookcases and closets. When a more substantial panel is required, heavier perimeter strips are recommended, Fig. 3.

Fig. 4 shows how a panel can be made

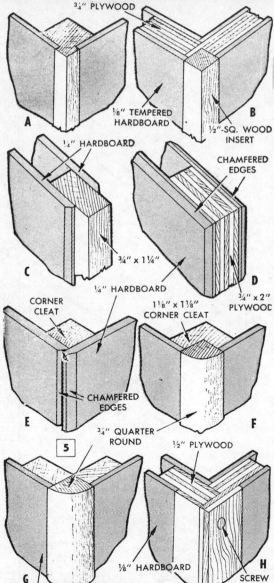

HARDBOARD BOOKCASE

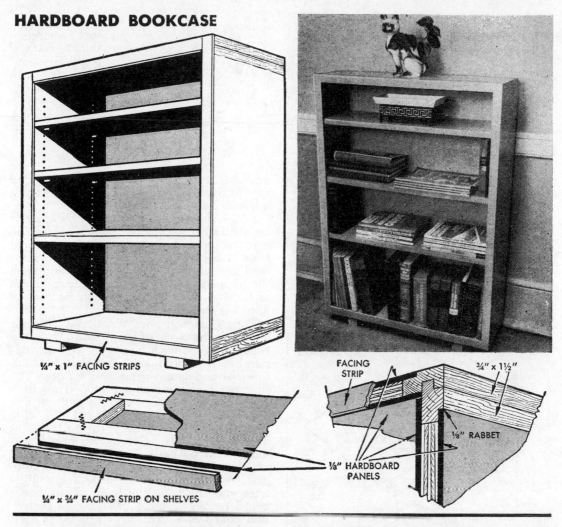

¼" x 1" FACING STRIPS

¼" x ¾" FACING STRIP ON SHELVES

FACING STRIP

¾" x 1½"

½" RABBET

⅛" HARDBOARD PANELS

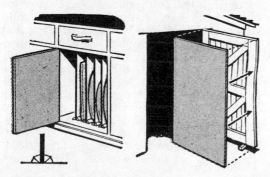

from a single sheet of ¼-in. hardboard. Here the wooden frame members are grooved, or dadoed, to fit over the edges of the hardboard. It is standard practice to cut the insert a scant smaller than the depth of the grooves to provide clearance should the hardboard expand. Cross bracing is not necessary unless the hardboard spans an area of more than 16 in. Cross bracing, when necessary, consists of battens equal in thickness to the lip of the perimeter strips which are applied to both sides of the hardboard, 16 in. apart. The same sunken-panel effect can be achieved in another way which eliminates grooving. This is done by gluing ½ x 1-in. or ¾ x 1-in. wood strips to both sides of the hardboard at the edges.

Fig. 6 shows how laminated-hardboard panels can be built up by bonding together two or three layers of ¼-in. material, using either contact cement or regular glue. Such panels, which are relatively warp-free, are ideal for cabinet doors, both hinged and sliding types, counter tops and bread and meat carving boards. If such doors are to be hinged, a lip can be formed by running a rabbet around the edges and then chamfering the corner as shown in the detail. This can be done either with a bench saw or a jointer. In the case of a two-layer door, the rabbet can be formed by simply cutting the bottom piece ½ in. smaller all around than the top one. If glue is used instead of contact cement, the work should be clamped to assure a good bond. If hardboard is used which is smooth

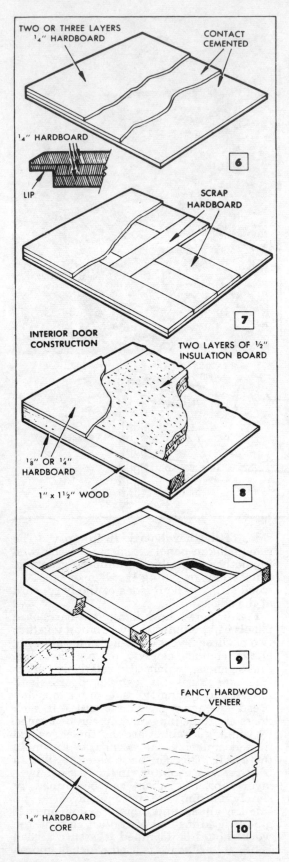

TWO OR THREE LAYERS ¼" HARDBOARD

CONTACT CEMENTED

6

¼" HARDBOARD

LIP

SCRAP HARDBOARD

7

INTERIOR DOOR CONSTRUCTION

TWO LAYERS OF ½" INSULATION BOARD

⅛" OR ¼" HARDBOARD

1" x 1½" WOOD

8

9

FANCY HARDWOOD VENEER

¼" HARDBOARD CORE

10

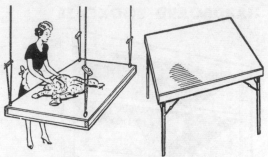

on one side only, the rough, "screened" side should first be sanded somewhat to assure a better bond.

Fig. 7 shows how hardboard scraps can be utilized in laminated panels. Here the core, or center layer, is made up piecemeal from random-size scraps which are assembled and glued to one face piece and then the opposite facing is added. Scrap pieces of hardwood of uniform thickness can be used for the core.

Fig. 8 shows how flush-type interior doors can be made of hardboard. Here the center is filled with layers of ½-in. insulation board to produce a door that has both thermal and sound-deadening values. The side perimeter strips are ripped about 2 in. wide from 1-in. stock, the bottom one 3 in. wide. A cross brace at least 4 in. wide to accept a lock is located in the frame at doorknob height. Corrugated-metal fasteners can be used at the corners of the wooden frame but the cross brace should just be glued. Spots of glue are applied here and there on the back of the hardboard panels to bond them to the insulation-board core. This type of door is most easily assembled by gluing the frame to one sheet of hardboard, installing the sections of insulation board and finally attaching the second hardboard panel.

Hardboard also may be used as the core of fine-wood panels, Fig. 10. For example, when a press is available, mahogany veneer can be applied to both sides of ¼-in. hardboard. Such panels are sturdier and more warp-free than natural-wood panels of the same thickness.

Fig. 5 shows eight methods of making corner joints. You'll notice here that strips of plywood can be used as well as solid wood. Details C and D show two ways that panels can be assembled where both surfaces are exposed. All of these methods afford protection to the edges which are subject to chipping. Details F and G show how common quarter-round molding can be used to both conceal the hardboard edges and provide a neat rounded corner. Chamfering is another good way to overcome chipping of the exposed edges and at the same time take away the plain square

edge. Details C and E show two examples.

Hardboard leftovers can be put to good use in making drawers. Fig. 11 shows how the sides and backs can be built-up by applying ⅛-in. hardboard to scrap-wood frames and then grooving to receive the hardboard bottom. A solid-wood core is used for the drawer front and faced both sides with hardboard. Figs. 12 and 13 show how facing strips of ⅛ or ¼-in. wood can be used to cap the exposed edges of hollow built-up panels so that when painted they give the appearance of solid-wood construction. Note the corner joint.

Where it is desired to glue shelves or partitions in dadoes in hollow, hardboard panels, cross bracing is installed at the proper points, Fig. 14, so that the grooves can be made to receive them. As a rule, you'll find in joining two panels together at a corner, Fig. 15, that a more accurate job can be done if the edge members are cut first. Trying to do this after the panels are assembled can be an awkward job and lead to an ill-fitting joint. ★ ★ ★

HARDBOARD STORAGE RACK

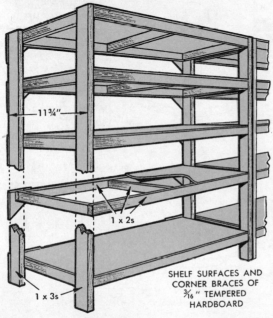

11¾"

1 x 2s

1 x 3s

SHELF SURFACES AND CORNER BRACES OF 3⁄16" TEMPERED HARDBOARD

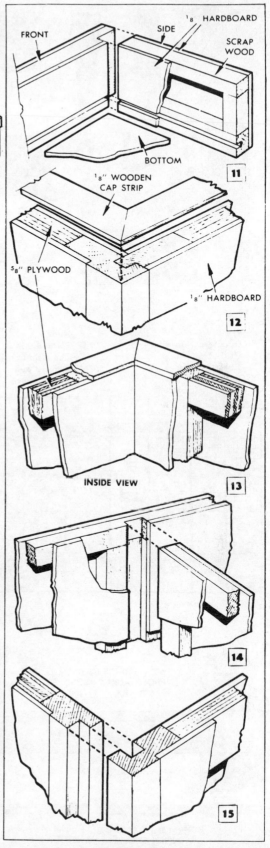

FRONT ⅛ HARDBOARD SIDE SCRAP WOOD

BOTTOM

11

⅛" WOODEN CAP STRIP

⅝" PLYWOOD

⅛" HARDBOARD

12

INSIDE VIEW

13

14

15

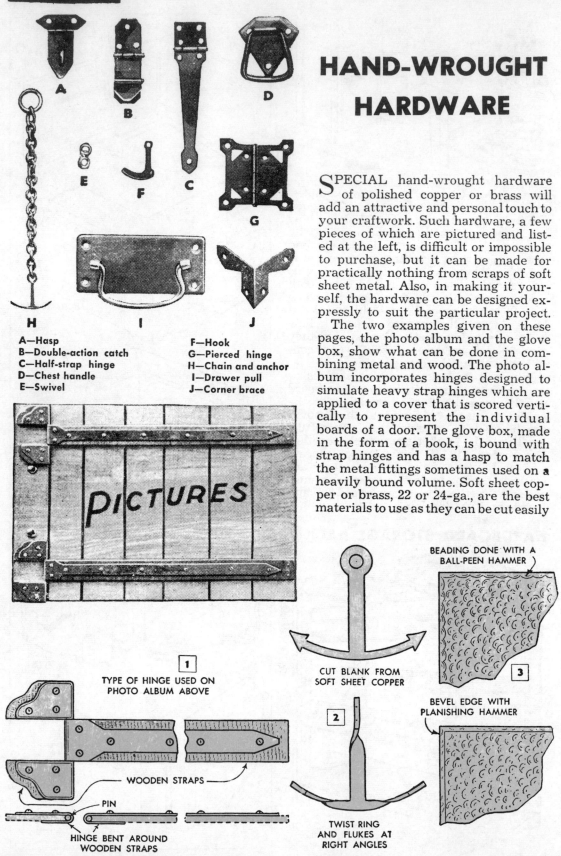

A—Hasp
B—Double-action catch
C—Half-strap hinge
D—Chest handle
E—Swivel
F—Hook
G—Pierced hinge
H—Chain and anchor
I—Drawer pull
J—Corner brace

HAND-WROUGHT HARDWARE

SPECIAL hand-wrought hardware of polished copper or brass will add an attractive and personal touch to your craftwork. Such hardware, a few pieces of which are pictured and listed at the left, is difficult or impossible to purchase, but it can be made for practically nothing from scraps of soft sheet metal. Also, in making it yourself, the hardware can be designed expressly to suit the particular project.

The two examples given on these pages, the photo album and the glove box, show what can be done in combining metal and wood. The photo album incorporates hinges designed to simulate heavy strap hinges which are applied to a cover that is scored vertically to represent the individual boards of a door. The glove box, made in the form of a book, is bound with strap hinges and has a hasp to match the metal fittings sometimes used on a heavily bound volume. Soft sheet copper or brass, 22 or 24-ga., are the best materials to use as they can be cut easily

1 TYPE OF HINGE USED ON PHOTO ALBUM ABOVE

WOODEN STRAPS

PIN

HINGE BENT AROUND WOODEN STRAPS

2 TWIST RING AND FLUKES AT RIGHT ANGLES

CUT BLANK FROM SOFT SHEET COPPER

BEADING DONE WITH A BALL-PEEN HAMMER

3

BEVEL EDGE WITH PLANISHING HAMMER

even with a pair of old scissors. Figs. 1 to 9, inclusive, give suggestions for making several simple pieces of special hardware. Fig. 1 details the strap hinge for the photo album. Note how the barrel of the hinge is formed by bending the ends of the metal around a nail and inserting the ends under the wooden straps. The anchor, Fig. 2, can be used purely as a decorative overlay, or it may be twisted as suggested, then attached to the end of a chain and used on a nautical project. The barrel joints of hinges and hasps, Fig. 6, are formed by cutting tabs on the ends of the parts and crimping them around a nail with pliers. The flat hook shown in Fig. 7 has a finger grip to facilitate engaging it in a flat staple.

Outside corner braces of polished or hammered copper add both strength and ornamentation to fancy wooden boxes, Fig. 3. An attractive finish for these as well as the other metal fittings is produced by hammering the surface lightly with the round nose of a ball-peen hammer. Edges of the metal are beveled by tapping lightly with a planishing hammer, after which the surface is polished with steel wool and coated with clear lacquer.

Figs. 4 and 5 show an easy way of forming the links for a decorative chain. Copper wire is wound around an iron rod of the proper size and then formed into links by sawing lengthwise through the wire winding. The links are assembled into a chain by interlacing them and squeezing the ends together. Such chain is suitable for ship-model fittings or other purposes where it is not subject to strain.

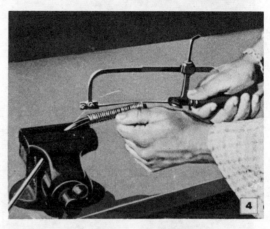

After winding copper wire around rod of proper size, the wire winding is cut lengthwise to form links

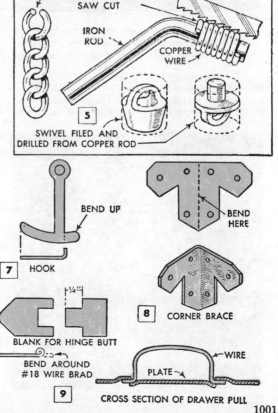

ASSEMBLE RINGS AND BEND TO CLOSE SAW CUT

IRON ROD

COPPER WIRE

SWIVEL FILED AND DRILLED FROM COPPER ROD

5

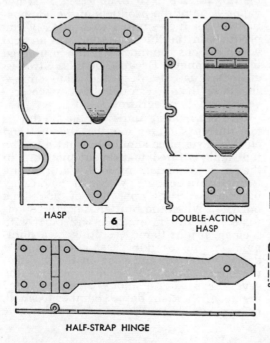

HASP

DOUBLE-ACTION HASP

6

HALF-STRAP HINGE

BEND UP

7 HOOK

¼"

BLANK FOR HINGE BUTT

BEND AROUND #18 WIRE BRAD

9

BEND HERE

8 CORNER BRACE

WIRE

PLATE

CROSS SECTION OF DRAWER PULL

Tuning Up
The Heating System

Before starting the automatic gas-heating plant, see that unit is thoroughly clean and that mechanism has been checked over by a competent serviceman

When the oil-fired heating plant is idle during summer months, fuel and electrical supplies are shut off. Check and lubricate working parts before starting

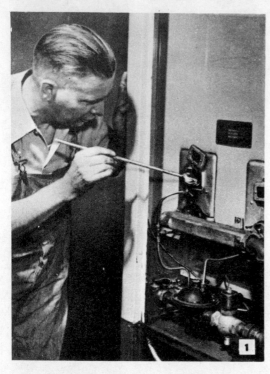

ALL HEATING PLANTS, including modern automatic units, require regular attention to keep them operating efficiently and economically. Minor repair and servicing at the beginning of the season can prevent service interruptions and even breakdowns during the peak heating load of the winter months and also will help to prevent fuel waste and costly repair over longer periods of time.

Gas-fired heating units: Gas-fired systems require very little attention other than annual cleaning and inspection and a periodic check to see that the correct ratio of the air-gas mixture is maintained. Usually expert servicemen from the local utility company will attend to this adjustment for a nominal charge, but keeping a check on certain operating details is up to the individual owner. When starting a gas burner, the pilot light is ignited immediately after the gas has been turned on. (*Caution:* Never allow unburned gas from the pilot to accumulate in the flame chamber before igniting it. If this should happen, shut off the gas to the pilot and open the drafts and inspection door and allow time for the unburned gas to dissipate.) If the pilot burner cannot be reached conveniently with an ordinary match, use a piece of newspaper rolled up tightly to form a lighting torch 8 to 10 in. long, Fig. 1. Water vapor—one of the products of the combustion of gas fuel—unites with other waste products in the flue gases to form an acid which attacks the mortar joints in unlined brick chimneys. Because of this, vitreous-enameled or stainless-steel flue linings should be installed in old chimneys to prevent rapid disintegration.

Oil-fired heating units: When the unit is idle during summer months, the fuel and electrical supplies should be shut off. The fuel tank is filled to prevent moisture in the air from condensing in the tank during temperature changes. Water in the oil may interfere with the operation of older-type burners. When the burner is correctly adjusted, the oil-air mixture will burn with a clean, bright flame resulting in a minimum loss in the flue gases and negligible deposits of coke and soot on the walls of the flame chamber and flue. Among the several causes of a smoky, stratified flame are insufficient air, flame chamber to small, or burner nozzle projecting too far into the

Although a competent serviceman should be called to inspect and make any major adjustments and repairs necessary to ready your heating plant for the coming season, there are a number of minor adjustments and points to check on automatic units that you can do yourself

chamber. Too much air may extinguish the flame entirely or cause objectionable sputtering and roaring while the burner is operating. Inadequate draft control also can cause similar symptoms. All moving parts of the burner requiring lubrication should be carefully checked at the start of the season and inspected at regular intervals thereafter, Fig. 2.

Coal stokers: To avoid recurring trouble with a stoker, it is important to use coal of the recommended grades and lump sizes. High-grade stoker coals contain the minimum of noncombustible materials and are mixed with large and small particles in the proper ratio to quantity. If the coal is too fine, air passage through the retort will be restricted and the combustion process retarded. On the other hand, unduly large lumps may bridge at the bottom of the hopper and either jam the feed screw, causing the shear pin to break or the clutch to disengage, or may block off the supply of fuel to the retort entirely and cause the fire to go out. Other than use of the proper grades of fuel, servicing of the stoker-fired plant is simple. Fly ash and soot are cleaned regularly from the furnace or boiler as in Figs. 5 and 8. Removal of the clinker usually is daily routine. Beyond this, a stoker fire should be disturbed as little as possible.

Hand-firing: In addition to firing by approved hand methods, economical operation of the plant depends on keeping the equipment in serviceable condition. All doors into the furnace either above or below the fire should close tightly. If

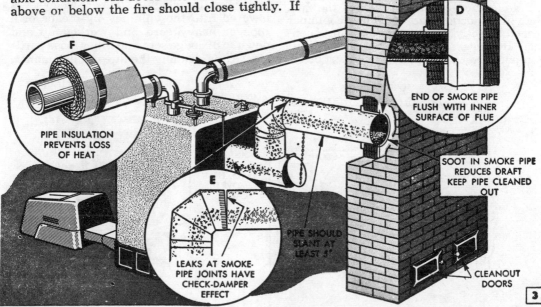

A CALK AROUND FLUE

B TOP OF CHIMNEY 2' ABOVE RIDGE OR 3' ABOVE FLAT ROOF

C MOST CHIMNEYS NEED OCCASIONAL TUCK POINTING

D END OF SMOKE PIPE FLUSH WITH INNER SURFACE OF FLUE

SOOT IN SMOKE PIPE REDUCES DRAFT KEEP PIPE CLEANED OUT

F PIPE INSULATION PREVENTS LOSS OF HEAT

E LEAKS AT SMOKE-PIPE JOINTS HAVE CHECK-DAMPER EFFECT

PIPE SHOULD SLANT AT LEAST 3'

CLEANOUT DOORS

3

necessary, tighten up the hinge pins and file or scrape the meeting surfaces of doors and frames to reduce air leaks to the minimum. An excessive air leak around the cleanout door above the fire will act as a partial check, while leakage through the ashpit door or the draft door will make the fire difficult to control. Clean the furnace periodically throughout the heating season to prevent accumulations of ash and soot which act as insulation on heat-transfer surfaces. Check carefully at the end of the season for cracks in the firebox and for warped or cracked grates, Fig. 6.

Instead of wetting down the ashes in a furnace when removing them in order to check flying dust, one homeowner suggests the following method of doing the job. Shovel the ashes into a shallow container placed directly in front of the ashpit opening. Remove ashes only when the draft damper is completely open, and most of the

dust will be pulled into the ashpit by the draft.

Smoke pipe: During mild weather, the slow rate of ignition of the lower grades of solid fuels produces considerable soot which coats the inside surfaces of the smoke pipe. As long as the pipe is hot, corrosion of the metal progresses at a very slow rate but, when the fire is allowed to go out in the spring, moisture collects in the pipe and combines with the soot coating to form highly corrosive acids. These acids quickly destroy the effectiveness of ordinary galvanized sheet-metal pipe. If a check shows the smoke pipe to be badly corroded, it should be renewed. Although much more expensive, cast-iron or stainless-steel smoke pipe resists corrosion and will last for 10 years or more. In any case, when installing new pipe be sure that the slip joints are tight and fully joined, Fig. 3, E. Use draw bands on all joints and support the pipe with metal bands or wires attached to the basement ceiling. Smoke pipe should clear woodwork by at least 15 inches.

Chimneys: To avoid draft interference, the chimney should have a separate flue for each heating unit. Unused openings into flues should be bricked up or closed with metal flue stops. Smoke-pipe joints at the chimney are closed with mortar to prevent air leakage. The end of the smoke pipe should come flush with the inside of the flue, Fig. 3, D. Top of the chimney should be at least two feet above the ridge of a peaked roof, Fig. 3, B. Remove tree branches or other obstructions to air movement above or near the chimney. Cleaning the flue can be done with a burlap bag filled with rags, straw or sawdust and a couple of bricks for weights. This "sweeper" is lowered into the chimney by means of a rope or heavy cord and worked up and down to dislodge soot and other loose particles. After cleaning the flue in this manner,

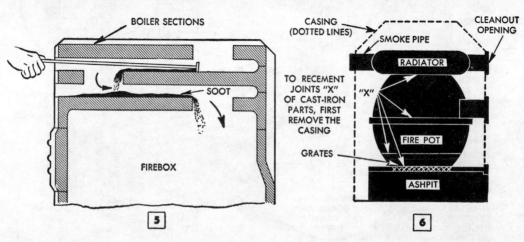

remove the accumulation of soot and other debris through the cleanout door. See that the latter closes tightly. In time, mortar joints disintegrate on the part of the chimney which is exposed. Old chimneys require tuck pointing occasionally to preserve them in serviceable condition, Fig. 3, C. Loose mortar is scraped away and the open joints are soaked with water before pointing with new mortar (1 part cement to 3 parts sharp sand). The joint between the chimney cap and the projecting tile flue, Fig. 3, A, should be made watertight by calking.

Locating thermostat: The best-quality thermostatic-control units are extremely sensitive to changes in temperature and should never be located near an outside door, window, fireplace, radiator or above a lamp, Fig. 9. The best location is on an inside wall where the unit will be shielded from drafts through hallways, stairways or windows. Blow the dust out of the unit occasionally and remove the outer housing and clean the contact points as directed by the manufacturer. See that the hole where the connecting wire comes through the plaster is plugged tightly. An air leak at this point will affect the operation of the unit, possibly causing it to vary as much as 10 deg. from the true inside temperature. If the heating unit is equipped with an airstat or aquastat, these units should be serviced in much the same manner. Check all electrical connections to see that they are clean and tight.

Warm-air heating systems: Unlike the older gravity warm-air systems, the late-model warm-air furnaces have forced-air circulation. Some forced-air systems bring air in from outside, but most all ordinary installations simply recirculate the air in the house as the normal air exchange in the average home is sufficient for good health. As the air is drawn through the cold-air returns, it passes through one or

Corrugated insulation on warm-air ducts stops any heat loss to the basement. Seal joints in the covering with gummed paper or cloth tape applied tightly

Heat-transfer surfaces of hand or stoker-fired boilers must be kept free from soot and fly ash. Use a wire flue brush having a flexible handle like that shown

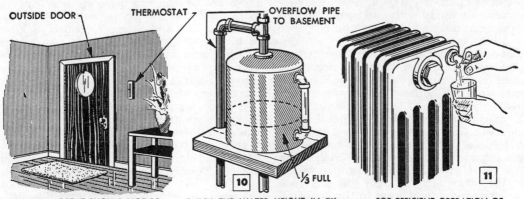

THERMOSTAT SHOULD NOT BE NEAR OUTSIDE DOOR, WINDOW, FIREPLACE, RADIATOR, ETC.

CHECK THE WATER HEIGHT IN EXPANSION TANK OF OPEN HOT-WATER SYSTEM WITH THE ALTITUDE GAUGE

FOR EFFICIENT OPERATION OF A HOT-WATER SYSTEM, AIR IN RADIATORS MUST BE RELEASED

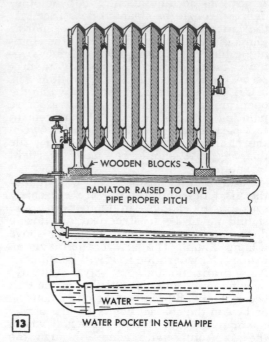

WOODEN BLOCKS

RADIATOR RAISED TO GIVE
PIPE PROPER PITCH

WATER

WATER POCKET IN STEAM PIPE

12 Older-type boilers should be covered with a 1-in. layer of asbestos cement which will reduce loss of heat

13 Use blocks to raise a steam radiator and restore the drainage pitch of pipe lowered by settling of house

more filters. The renewable-type filters are replaced at least once during the average heating season. The replaceable filter should be renewed when light cannot be seen through it, Fig. 4. Joints in cast-iron furnaces, Fig. 6, should be recemented after three to five years of use. It's a simple job to remove the sheet-metal casing and lift off the separate sections down to the ashpit. Clean out all the old cement and brush dirt and loose particles out of the joints before recementing. Be sure to relocate the parts in exactly the same position. A chalk mark across each of the joints makes this easy. Excess cement forced from the joints as the parts are replaced is wiped off and the joint is smoothed with a brush or cloth. To prevent heat loss, cover warm-air ducts with corrugated asbestos paper as in Fig. 7, using gummed paper or cloth tape to seal the joints.

Hot-water systems: Do not flush a hot-water heating unit unless this is necessary in making repairs or when cleaning sediment out of the boiler. "Stale" water contains the minimum of oxygen and lime and will cause less corrosion of metal parts than fresh water. Before starting the season with a hot-water system having an open expansion tank, Fig. 10, check the water level with the altitude gauge to see that the system is full. On the dial-type gauge, the red arrow is set to the required water height and water is added until the black arrow is brought to the same height

as the red arrow. On a closed-type system, the water level is maintained automatically and forced-circulation systems have automatically controlled circulating pumps. Air entrapped in the hot-water system impedes water circulation. Pressure is relieved by bleeding the entire system at the radiator valves as in Fig. 11. Bleeding off the air will lower the water level. Check and add fresh water if necessary. Then bleed the system again after a week or so to remove any air carried into it with the fresh water which was added.

Steam-heating systems: In the newer one-pipe steam system, a single pipe conducts live steam to each radiator and returns condensate to the boiler. When the radiators of the one-pipe system fail to heat, the cause usually is faulty air valves. Lime deposits and corrosion cause sticking of the moving parts, preventing air from escaping and steam from entering the radiator. Sometimes the faulty valves can be repaired but, as a rule, it will pay to replace them. Pounding or hammering in a one-pipe steam system usually is caused by water trapped in the radiators or somewhere in the return pipes. Settling of buildings often lowers a pipe below the correct drainage pitch and water collects in the low end beneath the radiator. Hammering is caused by steam being forced through the water in intermittent spurts. The simplest remedy is to raise the radiator on small wooden blocks as in Fig. 13. Hammering also is caused by water collecting in a steam valve that is only partly opened. Be sure the steam valves are either fully opened or closed at all times. Sediment collects in both hot-water and steam boilers after years of use and is removed by draining and flushing the system with clean water. Never drain the boiler when it is fired. If an emergency repair makes drainage necessary, draw the fire and wait until the system has cooled to room temperature before draining and refilling. Small quantities of water can be added while the system is in operation should it be necessary to replenish the water supply, but the fire should be low and the water added slowly to avoid a sudden temperature change which might crack the boiler castings.

Vapor-vacuum systems: This type of heating plant is practically trouble-free unless air leaks develop. These can occur at the radiator and boiler valves, at the water gauge and the diaphragm joint of the damper regulator and, more rarely, at pipe connections. Operation of the system is controlled by a vacuum valve on each radiator which is actuated by steam pressure. When the pressure drops, the valve closes and prevents air from entering the radiator. Leaks in the vacuum system generally are easy to locate when the boiler is carrying a full head of steam. The method of repair will depend on the location and nature of the leak. Liquid compounds are available which are effective in sealing small leaks in both steam and vacuum-heating systems. Of course, excessive leaks at the water gauge, around valves, at the damper regulator, or in a pipe joint are permanently repaired only by replacement of the defective parts.

Insulating pipes and boilers: Long runs of both hot-water and steam pipes should be insulated to prevent heat loss with a ready-formed insulating covering as in Fig. 3, F. Asbestos cement is applied to the pipe fittings and valves. Late-model boiler units are provided with insulation, but older boilers should be coated with asbestos cement to reduce heat loss to the basement. A 100-lb. bag of this special cement will cover the average boiler of either the square or round type. Mix the cement with water to form a thick paste and trowel it on the boiler to a thickness of about one half inch. Cover this first coating with 1-in. wire mesh, as in Fig. 12, and then apply another ½-in. layer to cover the wire. Smooth the job with a wet sponge and cover with muslin or cheesecloth pressed onto the cement while it is still wet.

Radiators: As a rule, it is not advisable to cover older-type radiators in any way, as coverings tend to retard air circulation. Nor is it advisable to coat old radiators

with bronzing paints, as the metallic pigments in these paints tend to overlap on drying and form a reflecting surface which retards heat transfer.

A minor disadvantage of the single-pipe steam-heating system is that a certain amount of steam condenses and leaves water in the bottom of the radiators. To maintain top heating efficiency, this trapped water must be removed. This is usually done by disconnecting the radiator, tipping it on end over a shallow pan and allowing it to drain. However, there is a much easier method of doing this by simply siphoning the water with a syringe and hose. You'll need about five or six feet of ¼-in. rubber hose and a bulb syringe with check valves, which can be purchased at most drugstores. The hose is connected to the intake side of the bulb and, after removing the air valve at the top of the radiator, the end of the hose is inserted in the opening until it touches the bottom of the radiator sections. Siphoning action is produced by simply squeezing the bulb, remembering to keep the end of the outlet hose below the water level in the radiator.

Identifying heating-system valves: In case a leak develops or some other emergency occurs in a hot-water heating system, it may save considerable expense if any member of the household is able to manipulate the valves to correct or minimize the trouble. Instead of trusting to memory, attach tags, which give clear and complete information, to the various controls. Arrows can be used to indicate the direction of turn to open or close the valves.

Low-Cost Shop Heating System

When it is necessary to have heat in the farm workshop, basement or small garage, you can install an efficient hot-water system by using ordinary pipe fittings and a coal-burning water heater. The heater, preferably one of the larger sizes, can be placed in any convenient location in the building. The radiators, or coils, are assembled from pipe and fittings as pictured. Provide an expansion tank located at some point higher than the highest radiator. All horizontal pipes must be carefully leveled when installed, as otherwise the system may become air-locked.

Charles L. Stratton, Hollis, N.H.

Improved System Sterilizes and Filters Furnace Air

Changes in the filtering system of his forced-air furnace were used by one homeowner to alleviate hay fever and asthma suffered by members of his family. Filters in the furnace were replaced by an electrostatic type manufactured by the Goodyear Tire and Rubber Co. under the trade name Pliotron. The filters consist of matted polyethylene plastic fibers held in an aluminum frame by pieces of hardware cloth. When an air current passes through the filters, an electrostatic charge is generated. Dust particles are attracted by the charge and held in the plastic. The filters are cleaned by rinsing in water, or, if especially dirty, in mild soap and water. Washing does not affect the electrostatic characteristic of the plastic. To further purify the air circulated by the furnace, the homeowner installed a germicidal light in the furnace plenum. Similar to a fluorescent lamp in appearance, and also requiring a starter and ballast, the 30-watt lamp produces ultraviolet rays.

OIL BURNER CHAMBER RELINED WITH "CERAMIC" FELT

DAMAGED CERAMIC linings in oil-burning home furnaces can now be relined with "ceramic felt" at a fraction of the cost involved when the customary firebrick-relining job is made, according to Socony Mobil Laboratories. Reason for the smaller cost is a drastic reduction in installation time; ½ hr. for ceramic felt and about 6 hrs. for removal and replacement of a brick lining. The latter must be installed by a competent repairman, but a felt lining can be installed by the homeowner at a considerable saving.

Originally developed for insulating aviation jet engines, the new material is made of alumina and silica fibers bonded together to form a flexible blanket-like substance. Manufacturers of two of these products now on the market report that as a combustion-chamber lining, it weighs much less than a brick lining, permits the furnace to develop maximum temperature faster and reduces noise.

Ceramic felt may be purchased in mat form, or as a kit that consists of a stainless steel outer liner and enough felt material for most any installation. The outer liner helps to keep the felt in place and provides a rigid backing. Mat thickness of ½ in. and a density of 10 to 12 lb. is recommended. The material may be installed in any damaged brick, precast or steel combustion chamber that has enough strength to serve as a retainer for the new

Socony Mobil Oil Co., Inc.

liner. It should not be used when the bricks in an existing chamber are oil-soaked due to a misfire, in which case a new brick lining is needed.

The usual repair procedure is to first remove the access plate of the furnace and obtain the following measurements: diameter of the chamber, chamber height, distance of blast tube from chamber floor and diameter of blast tube. Then place the mat on a flat surface, outline the liner to be cut from the above dimensions, and cut it to fit as shown in the drawing below left. To find the liner length, multiply the diameter of the chamber by 3.14 and add 6 in. for overlap at the ends. Allow ½-in. clearance around the blast tube, and locate the hole for the latter about 6 in. from one end so that the lap occurs close to the tube. Use a pair of heavy scissors or a knife to cut the felt. Installation of the liner is easy. Simply roll it up as in the illustration above and place it in the chamber so that the end with the hole can be slipped over the blast tube. Then push the liner into position against the old chamber wall as shown below and the furnace is ready to go again. ★ ★ ★

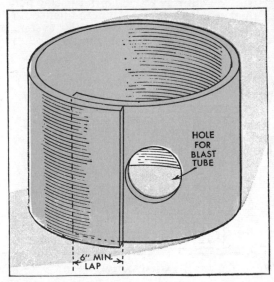

HOLE FOR BLAST TUBE

6" MIN. LAP

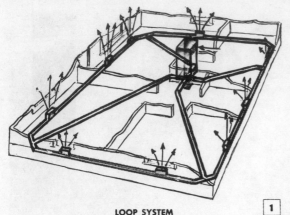

LOOP SYSTEM [1]

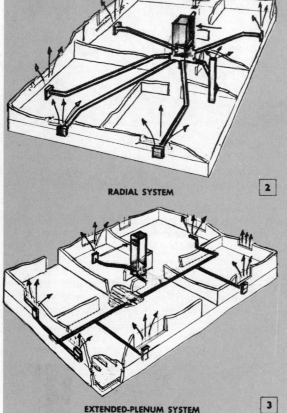

RADIAL SYSTEM [2]

EXTENDED-PLENUM SYSTEM [3]

CRAWL-SPACE-PLENUM SYSTEM [4]

PERIMETER HEATING

These forced-air systems mean warm floors and more comfort for one-story basementless homes built over concrete slabs or crawl spaces

WARM-AIR perimeter heating not only improves living comfort in basementless homes but also has the advantages of simplicity and comparably low cost. Perimeter heating differs from ordinary forced warm-air heating in three ways: (1) Warm-air ducts are installed in or under the floor, keeping it warm and providing radiant heat for the rooms above. (2) Warm-air outlets with diffusing-type registers are located along outside walls at floor level and preferably under windows. This placement of the registers provides a curtain, or blanket, of warm air where it is needed most, thus eliminating the usual temperature differential in rooms. (3) Return air is taken back to the furnace through high grilles in partitions instead of through grilles located at floor level.

Four common arrangements: Perimeter-heating systems are applied in different ways. The loop system, Fig. 1, is used in basementless homes having slab-type floors of concrete. The warm-air ducts, which are embedded in the concrete, extend from the furnace to, and entirely along, the perimeter of the slab. The radial system, Fig. 2, can be used in homes built over either slabs or crawl spaces. This system does not assure an entirely warm border in slab floors, and usually is not used where the floor area exceeds 1000 sq. ft. The radial system is better suited to homes built over crawl

Certain photos and data courtesy of
National Warm Air Heating and Air Conditioning Association

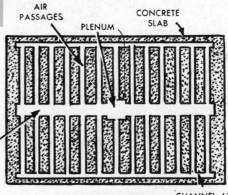

AIR PASSAGES
PLENUM
CONCRETE SLAB
MAIN DISTRIBUTION CHANNEL

LATERAL SYSTEM

CHANNEL AT OUTSIDE WALL FOR REGISTER SUPPLY [5]

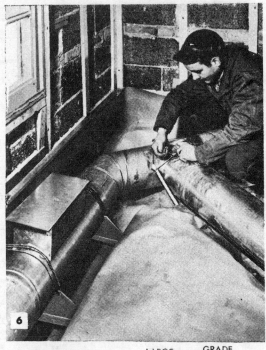

spaces, and in such installations the floor area may be over 1000 sq. ft. In long, narrow homes or where the furnace cannot be located centrally, the extended-plenum system, adaptable for crawl spaces, Fig. 3, has definite advantages in obtaining better heat distribution. The plenum is the chamber in or adjacent to a furnace from which warm air enters the distribution ducts. Fig. 4 shows a crawl-space-plenum system which is adaptable to small homes. It has stub ducts about 6 ft. long extending from the plenum. A fifth system, called the lateral system, Fig. 5, is used for large slab-floored buildings. It must be designed especially for the building to provide uniform space heating and to avoid excessively warm floors.

Dry location essential: Standing water and damp earth under a heated crawl space or a concrete slab are the cause of more unsatisfactory heating installations in basementless homes than any other single factor except possibly inadequate insulation. *Where such conditions cannot be corrected a heating system that introduces heat under or into the floor should not be used.*

You can minimize the collection of surface water under a slab or crawl space simply by installing drainage tile around the footings as in Fig. 7, A. The tile lines should have a slope of ¼ in. per ft. They should connect to a combination sewer or a storm sewer, or to some other point of disposal such as a dry well, Fig. 7, B. The outside of the foundation walls also should be covered with a ½-in. layer of portland-cement plaster. After this has cured, apply a coat of damp-proofing compound or hot tar. Diversion of surface water is particularly necessary on the side of a house facing a rise of ground. In locations where the water table is apt to rise during spring months or after prolonged rainfall, it may be advisable to provide drainage lines under the house as in Fig. 7, C. The tile is covered with a substantial layer of coarse gravel or crushed stone. A moisture barrier over the gravel, Fig. 8, also is required.

Under-slab fill: Never use cinders as fill under a slab floor. Only coarse gravel with the fines removed is suitable. The layer should be at least 4 in. thick and must be

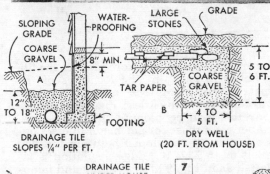

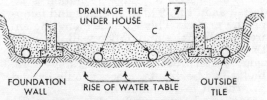

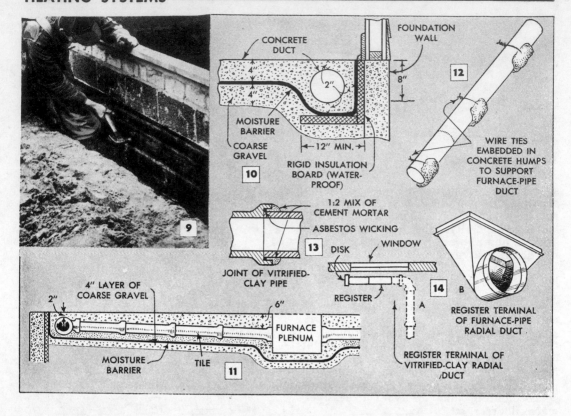

thoroughly tamped. Before placing the fill, trenches are dug at the locations of the ducts so that the gravel layer under them will be of equal thickness, Fig. 10. Trenches near the furnace plenum should be 6 in. deeper than those for perimeter ducts. Connecting ducts are sloped between the two levels as in Fig. 10. Edge insulation is installed as in Fig. 9 after leveling and tamping the gravel. This extends along the entire length of the foundation wall, between it and the slab, Fig. 10. It should be of the rigid, waterproof type, preferably 2 in. thick. The horizontal pieces should extend inward not less than 12 in.

Moisture barrier under slab: Before the slab floor is poured, the gravel fill is covered with a layer of 55-lb. asphalt roll roofing, Figs. 8, 10 and 11, which forms a moisture barrier. The edges are overlapped from 4 to 6 in. and sealed with roofing cement. The barrier should extend up along the foundation walls to the floor surface. Wherever it must be cut to fit around pipes, it should be sealed as in Fig. 19.

Placing ducts in trenches: Trenches should be deep enough to permit a 2-in. layer of concrete to be poured entirely around all the ducts as in Figs. 10 and 11. The concrete covering over ducts at the plenum should be about 6 in. thick, Fig. 11. The reason for this is to obtain uniform heat penetration through the floor—the air entering the ducts at the plenum being

so much hotter than it is at the perimeter.

Installing sheet-metal ducts in slab: Furnace pipe of 28 ga. may be used for ducts. For small homes the 6, 7 or 8-in. sizes are sufficient. The size selected should be used throughout the system. Round ducts are recommended. Perimeter ducts are located so that the center of the registers will be from 7 to 9 in. inside the finished wall line to clear drapes and curtains, Figs. 16, B, and 25, B. Sheet-metal ducts must be held in place securely when the slab is being poured. This can be done by embedding wire in humps of concrete placed under the ducts to hold them at the correct height. Tie the wires around the ducts after the concrete humps have hardened, Fig. 12. Sheet-metal brackets, Fig. 6, often are used to support the pipe. Register fittings of sheet metal can be used at the ends of radial ducts as in Fig. 14, B, or rectangular forms as shown in Fig. 6 can be used.

Vitrified-clay ducts: Vitrified-clay pipe also may be used for ducts, Fig. 15. It is supported by gravel or sand, preferably fine gravel. The joints are calked with asbestos wicking, about one third their depth, then filled with a 1:2 mix of portland-cement mortar, Fig. 13. Both short and long-radius fittings are used for changes of direction. The open ends of pipe at register locations of a radial system are closed with vitrified-clay disks, Fig. 14, A, which are held in place while pouring the slab.

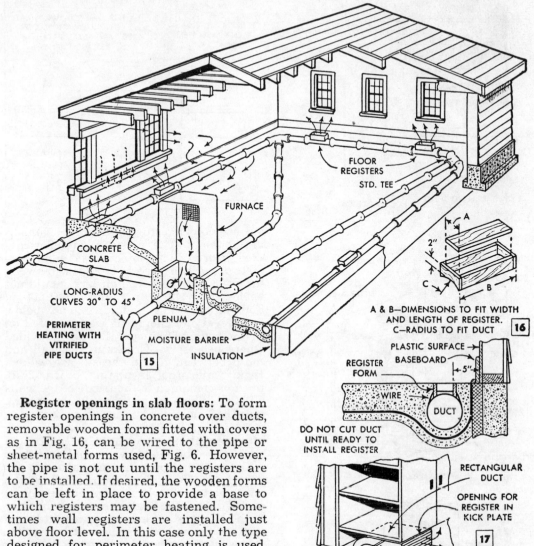

FLOOR
REGISTERS
STD. TEE

FURNACE

CONCRETE
SLAB

LONG-RADIUS
CURVES 30° TO 45°

PERIMETER
HEATING WITH
VITRIFIED
PIPE DUCTS

PLENUM

MOISTURE BARRIER

INSULATION

15

A & B—DIMENSIONS TO FIT WIDTH
AND LENGTH OF REGISTER.
C—RADIUS TO FIT DUCT

2"

A

C

B

16

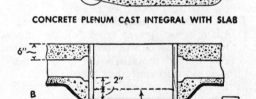

PLASTIC SURFACE
BASEBOARD

REGISTER
FORM

5"

WIRE

DUCT

DO NOT CUT DUCT
UNTIL READY TO
INSTALL REGISTER

RECTANGULAR
DUCT

OPENING FOR
REGISTER IN
KICK PLATE

17

DUCT AND
REGISTER UNDER
KITCHEN CABINET

DIMENSION SAME AS
DISCHARGE OPENING
OF FURNACE

2" CONCRETE FLOOR

SLAB

MOISTURE
BARRIER

6"

DUCT   PLENUM

A

CONCRETE PLENUM CAST INTEGRAL WITH SLAB

6"

2"

B

FLOOR

18

**HUB END OF VITRIFIED-CLAY DUCTS
BUTT AGAINST FORM**

Register openings in slab floors: To form
register openings in concrete over ducts,
removable wooden forms fitted with covers
as in Fig. 16, can be wired to the pipe or
sheet-metal forms used, Fig. 6. However,
the pipe is not cut until the registers are
to be installed. If desired, the wooden forms
can be left in place to provide a base to
which registers may be fastened. Sometimes wall registers are installed just
above floor level. In this case only the type
designed for perimeter heating is used.
Slotted baseboards may be used instead of
registers, an installation particularly adaptable for crawl-space-plenum systems. Fig.
17 shows how a duct and register are placed
under a kitchen cabinet that occupies the
entire wall space. A wall-type register is
used in bathrooms.

Concrete plenum cast with slab: In slab
floors the plenum can be cast integral with
the slab, using an inside form which is
suitably braced. See Figs. 11 and 18, A.
Sheet-metal ducts are allowed to extend
through the form and are cut off flush with
the wall of the plenum after the forms are
removed. Vitrified-clay pipe is butted
against the forms as shown in Fig. 18, B.
The floor, laid after the forms are removed,
should be not less than 2 in. thick, and
should come from 1½ to 2 in. below the
bottom of the ducts. If a metal plenum is
used, it should be entirely enclosed in concrete. The plenum may be provided with

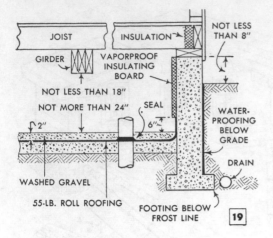

Figure 19

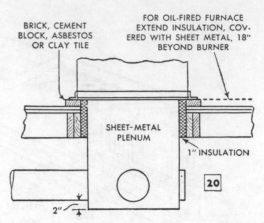

Figure 20

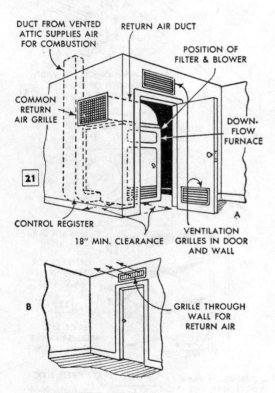

Figure 21

a floor drain over a small dry well as a precaution against the possibility of water collecting in the plenum due to an overflowing bathtub or water closet.

Crawl-space requirements: As shown in Fig. 19, a crawl space used for perimeter heating must be completely sealed against the entrance of moisture, and it also must be insulated and sealed at the walls to prevent infiltration of cold air. High humidity in a crawl space should be prevented as it causes rapid deterioration of the wooden structural parts of a house and also causes rusting of ducts. The earth floor of a crawl space is covered first with a layer of coarse gravel at least 4 in. thick. Over this is laid

a continuous moisture barrier, the same as in slab floors. The moisture barrier is covered with a 2-in. protective layer of concrete or washed gravel. The space between the floor and the house girders should not be less than 18 in. nor more than 24 in. Foundation walls should extend below frost level and should be waterproofed on the outside. Drainage tile are provided where necessary. Cracks in the wall and those between it and the sill are calked. Rigid waterproof insulating board, 2 in. thick, is cemented to the inside of the walls with roofing cement. It should overlap the upturned moisture barrier of the floor.

Escape of air from a crawl space to an attic should be prevented by sealing all stud spaces in outside walls and partitions with insulating batts having vapor-barrier coverings. Vent openings as well as the entrance to a crawl space should be tightly sealed during the heating season. The floor of the house is not insulated, as heat transmission through it is one of the requirements of perimeter heating. Neither are the warm-air ducts insulated. The ducts may be either round or rectangular in shape and are suspended from joists, observing regulations as to clearance from combustible materials. Besides the warm-air outlets to the house, there should be one or more warm-air ducts opening into the crawl space; also a return-air duct, Fig. 22. The crawl space should never be used for storage.

Plenum for crawl spaces: The plenum for a crawl space is a square or rectangular sheet-metal chamber having the same size opening as the discharge opening of the furnace. A round plenum should not be used unless approved by the furnace manufacturer. The framed opening in the floor should be about 1 in. larger than the plenum, Fig. 20, and the space between the two should be packed with fireproof insulation. When connected to a down-flow furnace, both plenum and furnace should be supported on a base of noncombustible

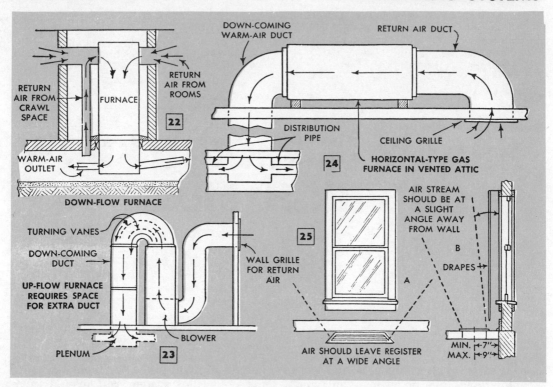

RETURN AIR FROM CRAWL SPACE

FURNACE

RETURN AIR FROM ROOMS

22

WARM-AIR OUTLET

DOWN-FLOW FURNACE

DOWN-COMING WARM-AIR DUCT

RETURN AIR DUCT

DISTRIBUTION PIPE

CEILING GRILLE

24

HORIZONTAL-TYPE GAS FURNACE IN VENTED ATTIC

TURNING VANES

DOWN-COMING DUCT

UP-FLOW FURNACE REQUIRES SPACE FOR EXTRA DUCT

WALL GRILLE FOR RETURN AIR

PLENUM

BLOWER

23

25

AIR STREAM SHOULD BE AT A SLIGHT ANGLE AWAY FROM WALL

B

DRAPES

A

AIR SHOULD LEAVE REGISTER AT A WIDE ANGLE

MIN. 7"
MAX. 9"

material such as brick, cement block, asbestos or clay tile. The joint between plenum and furnace must be tightly sealed with furnace cement or a suitable calking compound. The bottom of the plenum should be at least 1½ to 2 in. below the distribution pipes.

Return-air grilles: One or two return-air grilles in partitions next to the furnace, Fig. 21, A, generally are adequate for small homes. The grille, or grilles, should be of proper size and centrally located where air can flow to them unobstructed. A common return-air grille to the furnace should never be located in a kitchen, bathroom or bedroom. Fig. 21, B, shows how grilles are located over doors that are left closed most of the time. Those placed over bedroom doors should be the type that can be closed manually. When a furnace is installed in a confined space, the return-air grille in the wall of the enclosure should connect to a duct that is sealed to the furnace.

Furnace selection: Practically any automatic oil or gas-burning furnace designed for forced-air heating can be used. Although a down-flow furnace usually is the most adaptable type for perimeter heating, Fig. 22, the conventional up-flow furnace may be used if it is provided with two ducts as in Fig. 23. A horizontal gas-burning furnace can be placed in a vented attic as in Fig. 24.

If the building is so tightly constructed that a sufficient amount of air for combustion is not supplied by natural infiltration,

a duct to provide combustion air can be run up to a vented attic as shown in Fig. 21, A. Clearance between the furnace and the closed door of the enclosure should not be less than 18 in. Similar clearance all around the furnace gives easy access for keeping the space clean and for servicing the furnace. A door providing access should have a grille at its bottom and another grille should be fitted in the partition above the door to provide for normal ventilation of the enclosure.

Automatic temperature controls: Automatic controls are furnished with the furnace. The room thermostat, which operates the burner, should be located at the recommended height on a partition well away from warm air coming from the registers, and also where temperatures are least likely to fluctuate from opening doors or using a fireplace. For perimeter heating, slow, continuous forced-air circulation is preferred, with the burner operating at frequent intervals, the room thermostat being adjusted to a differential of 1½ deg. In down-flow furnaces, failure of the blower to function will cause the filter motor and blower to become overheated. To prevent damage an additional limit-control switch is installed to turn off the burner when such trouble occurs. Registers should be of the type designed to discharge warm air in a fan-shaped spread and away from the walls as in Fig. 25, A and B. Registers should be fitted with adjustable dampers, or valves.

★ ★ ★

WHAT YOU SHOULD KNOW ABOUT HIGH FIDELITY

Everyone is talking about it, and lots of people are actually doing something about it. Yes, within the last few years, high fidelity has been playing an increasingly important role in home entertainment. Why? Because more and more music lovers are beginning to realize that the electronic improvements which have made it possible to reproduce music in the living room with all the splendor and realism of the original presentation are available at prices within the reach of even the most modest budget. In fact, if you can afford any music system, you can afford high fidelity.

Why high fidelity?

If you analyze a basic high-fidelity system you might be surprised to learn that it consists of the same components as an ordinary phonograph. Why, then, should you replace that phonograph with a high-fidelity system? Actually, comparison between the two systems is about as valid as comparing a three-piece band to a complete symphony orchestra. Both, of course, are capable of producing music, but here the similarity ends. While the ordinary phonograph can reproduce the essentials which permit you to recognize and even enjoy a particular selection, it remains for the hi-fi set to capture the "presence," the range and the depth, which actually brings the entire orchestra into your living room. In fact, if you will play your favorite recording on a hi-fi system you may discover tones and even entire passages which were completely lost in the ordinary instrument. It will take but one demonstration to know that if you enjoy music, you need high fidelity.

What is high fidelity?

In short, high fidelity is the reproduction of music as it was originally played. Nothing added, nothing lost, nothing to destroy the illusion that you are sitting "front row, center" in Orchestra Hall. That's a tall order, and even the most expensive system doesn't quite fill the bill. Yet, a system containing well-balanced, moderately priced components can come so close to the real thing that it will take an expert to actually tell the difference.

Now, if you're convinced that you need high fidelity, you may be tempted to rush to your nearest hi-fi distributor and place your order. But wait a minute. Would you purchase a new car without fully investigating its capabilities? Of course not! First you would investigate which automobile gives you the most for your money—which will provide the power, economy, comfort and versatility you require. The same applies to high fidelity. You can invest a considerable amount of money in features which you may never need. On the other

FREQUENCY IN CYCLES PER SECOND

PICCOLO

VIOLIN

VOICE

BASS VIOL

LOWER LIMIT OF HEARING

IMPORTANT HARMONICS OF MUSICAL INSTRUMENTS

UPPER LIMIT OF HEARING

The fundamental frequency ranges of the human voice, bass viol, violin and piccolo are shown in this drawing

hand, you can just as easily invest in a system which does not provide the desired quality and versatility. The selection of a system which will meet your specific requirements, therefore, should be preceded by careful planning. This involves a basic knowledge of high-fidelity considerations. All sound consists of waves with frequencies from about 20 to 20,000 cycles per second. Now, let us take a closer look at the composition of individual sounds such as found in voice and music. Fig. 1 illustrates the fundamental frequency ranges of some typical instruments. These ranges consist of tones from 26 to 4608 c.p.s. Each tone, however, consists not only of the fundamental, but also of a number of overtones, called harmonics. Were it not for these harmonics, a tone of a certain pitch, played on one type of instrument, would sound exactly like the tone produced by any other instrument. The harmonics, which are exact whole-number multiples of the fundamental frequency, determine the quality, or timbre, of a particular sound, Fig. 2.

The number and strength of the harmonics impart the specific characteristic to each individual instrument. For faithful reproduction of music, a system must provide equal amplification for the fundamental, as well as for the harmonic frequencies. Since important harmonics are often as high as three or four times the fundamental frequency, the hi-fi set must have a frequency range from about 20 to 20,000 c.p.s. to adequately reproduce the various sounds of a complete orchestra.

Now, let us consider the response of the human ear. Laboratory tests have proven conclusively that the older we get, the more restricted is the range of frequencies we can actually hear. In fact, many older persons can not hear sounds above 10,000 or 12,000 cycles, even if these are reproduced. Yet, this frequency restriction does not seem to impair the enjoyment that these people obtain from listening to high fidelity. Why is this true? Referring again to Fig. 1, notice that only the harmonics of the highest tones are above the range of hearing. These tones do not often occur within a single musical selection, so that the amount of music actually lost is very small. It is quite possible, therefore, that a music system whose frequency response

These tones are of the same pitch but are produced by different instruments—a piano and cello organ pipe

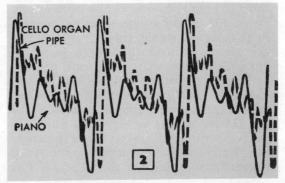

CELLO ORGAN PIPE

PIANO

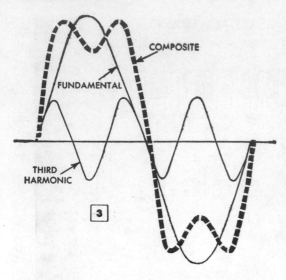

Diagram here shows how introduction of a small third harmonic component changes shape of the sine wave

is constant only to 12,000 or 15,000 cycles may sound as good as one with an extended frequency response, provided that the output of the system is *clean and undistorted* at all frequencies which are reproduced.

This brings us to the subject of distortion. Catalogue descriptions of electronic equipment often refer to two types of distortion —*harmonic distortion* and *intermodulation distortion*. Just what do these terms mean, and why are they objectionable? We have seen that a musical tone consists of a fundamental and harmonic frequencies. While the music system must be able to reproduce all of these, it should not introduce additional harmonics which are not present in the original tone. Unfortunately, electronic components, not being perfect, have a tendency to change the shape of a signal to some extent. Fig. 3 shows what can happen to a sine wave whose shape has been changed slightly. The distorted wave is composed of the fundamental to which a third harmonic frequency has been added. Since this third harmonic was not present in the original signal, the sound output of the system is said to contain harmonic distortion.

Harmonic distortion in itself, while undesirable, is not necessarily unpleasant unless it reaches major proportions. Since the added frequency is harmonically related to the fundamental, it merely tends to change the "character" of the sound, and thereby affects "naturalness" of the response. Far more serious is the ever-present intermodulation distortion.

A music system is seldom, if ever, called upon to handle a single frequency. Rather, it must reproduce the hundreds of frequencies which are provided simultaneously by an orchestra. Unless all of the equipment is perfectly designed, some of these frequencies will interact with each other and produce new frequencies which are not harmonically related. These new frequencies, therefore, present actual discords which can make the resultant output sound very unpleasant. This is intermodulation distortion, and it is more difficult to eliminate than simple harmonic distortion. However, modern hi-fi equipment has reduced even this to such a small percentage that it is generally inaudible.

The foregoing characteristics (frequency response and distortion) must be considered when buying or building any piece of electronic equipment. Additional considerations, such as power output and other forms of distortion and noise will be discussed under the headings of the individual components to which they apply.

How to select your hi-fi system

If you are among the fortunate few to whom money is no object, you will have little difficulty in selecting a hi-fi system. Just walk into any of the better music stores, listen to their selection of commercially assembled units and order the system that sounds best. There is no doubt that many of the commercial systems can provide outstanding performance, but the accompanying price tags are likely to spoil the taste of the less-fortunate music lover who must work with a strictly limited budget. Yet, you can enjoy true high fidelity without having an unlimited bank account. Today, you can choose from dozens of attractively styled, individual components to assemble a relatively low-cost system which meets your specific requirements. A little advance planning, followed by a listening test, will enable you to get the most enjoyment for every dollar spent.

Typical hi-fi demonstration room. Switch panel, right, permits comparison of many component combinations

A basic hi-fi system consists of a record changer, an amplifier and a speaker system. To this can be added, perhaps at a later date, a radio and television tuner and a tape recorder. Each part must be carefully selected because the final quality of reproduction depends not so much on the price of the overall system as it does on a careful balance of components within a given price range.

Components for a complete basic system can be purchased for less than $100 or more than $1000. In spite of this wide price difference, it is comforting to know that even an expert will, under certain conditions, be hard pressed to differentiate between the most expensive system and a well-balanced, moderately priced one. As a start, therefore, you should determine how much of your total budget should be allotted to the individual parts. The chart shown here is designed to help you in setting up your hi-fi budget.

Once you have an idea of how much to spend for each item, you can study a cata-

TOTAL COST OF BASIC SYSTEM	Select Turntable and Cartridge Priced at About	Select Amplifier Priced at About	Select Speaker and Enclosure Priced at About
$150	$35- 50	$45- 60	$40- 70
200	45- 60	60- 75	65- 95
300	60- 80	75-125	95-165
500	90-120	100-220	130-310

logue to determine what units are available in your price range. Catalogues including hi-fi equipment are available free of charge from most radio-parts distributors.

After listing these units on a sheet of paper, you can study their characteristics in order to select those which best meet your needs. Tentative catalogue selection should be followed, wherever possible, by an actual listening test in one of the high-fidelity demonstration studios. These are located in most large cities.

If your town has no facilities for a listening test, you can order the components by mail. If parts are ordered from a reliable distributor, a careful catalogue selection will usually result in complete satisfaction.

Now, a word about radio-parts distributors: Some of them have a customer-satisfaction policy in the form of an unconditional 15-day, money-back guarantee. Others provide 15 or 30-day exchange privileges. All of them should stand behind their products to the point of repairing or replacing any component which does not live up to manufacturers' specifications. Be wary of any distributor who is not willing to give such a guarantee in writing, either in his catalogue or in a letter by a responsible company official.

Now, let's consider the qualifications which the individual components must meet in order to merit high-fidelity status.

The record player

Record players are generally divided into two categories—the manual player and the automatic changer. Manual players are used primarily in broadcast and recording studios where the ultimate in perfection is required. For home use, however, even in some of the most expensive systems, the

THE RECORD CHANGER

automatic changer is usually preferred. Not only is the changer less expensive than a professional-type manual player, but it provides the convenience of playing a whole stack of records without numerous interruptions.

The primary requirement of any good record player is the ability to maintain a constant turntable speed. Any speed variation will show up as a very annoying "wow," "rumble" and "flutter." Catalogue specifications for hi-fi changers fail to provide exact figures on this type of distortion, preferring to stick to such hazy statements as "heavily weighted turntable and four-pole motor reduce speed variations to a minimum." Fortunately, most changers sold for high-fidelity purposes are capable of holding speed variations below the audible level. Make sure, however, that the unit you select has a four-pole motor.

Other desirable features of a good record changer are:

1. Automatic shut-off after the last record is played.

2. Muting switch or network which eliminates noise during the changing cycle.

3. Intermix changing of 10 and 12-in. records of the same speed.

4. Ability to handle any of the more popular hi-fi cartridges without extensive tonearm modifications.

While selecting the changer, give some thought as to how the unit is to be mounted. Separate wooden mounting boards and metal bases are available for most models. If you plan to install the unit in a cabinet you will want the precut mounting board, unless you have the facilities for making the required cutouts yourself. If the changer will stand out in the open, a metal base is needed. This, of course, is an additional expense and must be included in the price of the changer.

The phono pickup

The phono pickup, or cartridge, together with the playback stylus (needle) is the first link in the actual chain of phono reproduction. As such, it has a very difficult job to perform and must be selected with special care.

As you probably know, sound is placed on a record in the form of very narrow grooves which "wiggle" from side to side in step with the frequency of the applied sound. The playback stylus must follow these grooves faithfully, while the cartridge must convert the side-to-side movement of the stylus into equivalent voltage variations.

Until recently, magnetic or variable reductance-type cartridges have been accepted as the finest available for high-fi-

**THE CARTRIDGE
AND STYLUS**

delity reproduction. Today, however, some manufacturers have produced ceramic units which, they claim, have all of the advantages of the magnetic types (low distortion and wide frequency response) without any of its disadvantages (need for pre-amplification and equalization). Since the type of cartridge you select determines to some extent the characteristics of the subsequent amplifier, you must give this unit considerable thought.

As a start, let us look at some of the major recording characteristics. The grooves of a 78 r.p.m. record are considerably wider than those of a 33⅓ or 45 r.p.m. recording. Since the reproducing stylus must ride within these grooves for faithful reproduction, it is obvious that the radius of the stylus tip for the slow-speed record must be smaller than the corresponding dimensions for the reproduction of 78 r.p.m. records. Manufacturers specify a radius of .001 in. (1 mil.) for long-playing and a radius of .003 in. (3 mil.) for standard records. The results of using the wrong stylus are illustrated in Fig. 4.

High-fidelity cartridges are usually available as single-stylus types or triple-play units. The single-stylus cartridge incorporates either a 1-mil. or a 3-mil. unit and is less expensive than the triple-play cartridge which contains two styli for the reproduction of both standard and microgroove records. A lever or knob on the triple-play unit permits instant selection of the correct stylus for the record to be played. If your record collection contains standard as well as long-playing records, the triple-play cartridge is your best buy. If you wish to play either long-playing or standard records exclusively, the single-stylus cartridge will result in considerable savings.

A high-fidelity cartridge should have a flat frequency response from about 30 to 15,000 c.p.s. with less than three percent distortion. Some units will provide far bet-

ter performance but prices increase rapidly as these minimum specifications are exceeded. Furthermore, it is doubtful if the average listener can tell the difference between the reproduction of the finest available cartridge and those providing the minimum hi-fi requirements, except during an A-B comparison test (instantly switching from one unit to the other while a record is being played). If facilities for a listening test are available, by all means make a tentative catalogue selection of several cartridges and try these later, one at a time. But, if you order directly from a catalogue, you will probably be quite happy with the cartridge having the best specifications in a given price range.

The stylus

Reproducing styli are made primarily with three types of tips—osmium, sapphire and diamond. Osmium styli have practically disappeared from the high-fidelity scene

**GOOD STYLUS PICKS UP HIGH FREQUENCIES;
POOR ONE SKIPS THEM AND DAMAGES RECORD**

**A STYLUS WITH THE PROPER TIP RADIUS
RIDES WELL WITHIN THE RECORD GROOVE**

**TOO LARGE A TIP RADIUS CAUSES STYLUS
TO RIDE ON TOP OF GROOVE, RESULTING
IN LOSS OF HIGH-FREQUENCY RESPONSE**

**TOO SMALL A RADIUS PERMITS STYLUS TO
VIBRATE WITHIN GROOVE AND PRODUCE NOISE**

An osmium needle after 12½ hours' use. Sapphire needle after 40 hours. Diamond needle after 700 hours

because they wear out too quickly. The choice, therefore, is between diamond and sapphire. Since the initial cost of the cartridge depends largely on the type of styli it includes, the choice merits considerable attention. A sapphire-tipped stylus, for example, may cost around $2.00 while an identical diamond-tipped unit may cost more than $15. Is the additional cost justified? The answer is yes—if you listen to a lot of records. Fig. 5 shows the relative wear on the three different types of stylus materials. Notice that the sapphire tip begins to show considerable wear after 40 hours of use while the diamond tip is still as good as new after 700 hours. The wearing quality of diamond makes it the logical choice for the avid listener. But, if you do only a moderate amount of listening, the sapphire tip is perfectly suitable. In either case, however, make sure that separate replacement styli are available for whatever cartridge you buy.

Amplifiers

The amplifier is considered the heart of the high-fidelity system. Its function is to increase the strength of the small voltages from the phono cartridge to the point where they can drive a loudspeaker. In spite of its importance, it is here that the proper selection can result in considerable savings.

The characteristics to be considered in choosing your amplifier are—power output, distortion, frequency response, inherent hum and noise and compatibility with the rest of the system. These characteristics are going to require a lot of thought, so let's take each point individually.

Power output and distortion

Of course, the amplifier must have low distortion, but the important thing to remember is that the distortion must be low at the *rated power output of the amplifier*. Almost any amplifier, hi-fi or otherwise, has low distortion at very low volume. It is at relatively high levels that the high-fidelity unit proves its worth, while the ordinary unit fails completely.

When looking through a catalogue of high-fidelity equipment you will no doubt be impressed, if not confused, by the large number of amplifiers listed. There are units in all sizes; some with controls, others without; some with their power supplies built in; others with the power supply mounted on a separate chassis; some with a price tag of less than $50; others costing four and five times that much. When comparing prices with given specifications, it becomes immediately apparent that the cost of an amplifier is proportional to the amount of power it can deliver at relatively low distortion values. In other words, the greater the power output capability of an amplifier, at distortions of two percent or less, the greater its cost. In view of this fact, the question which comes to mind immediately

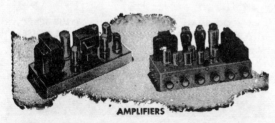

AMPLIFIERS

is, "How much power do I need for high-fidelity music reproduction?" To answer this question several important factors must be considered.

To begin with, let us consider the power provided by a full symphony orchestra. Everyone knows that the *dynamic range* (the difference in power between the loudest and softest passages) of such an orchestra is quite large. But, did you know that the ratio between the loudest and the softest passages can reach proportions as high as 10 million to 1? Of course, in recording, this dynamic range is somewhat compressed. The volume of the loudest passages is reduced to prevent overcutting the record grooves, and the low passages are increased in volume so that they will be louder than the "noise" which is inherent in all records. Yet, many good records have a dynamic range as high as 100,000 to 1. This means that if the volume of the amplifier is turned up so that the softest music is audible, the power at the highest peaks will be 100,000 times as great. A good amplifier must be capable of providing this much power without noticeable distortion.

The amount of actual power, in watts, required to produce such a wide range has been the subject of considerable study. While a discussion of these studies is beyond the scope of this book, the general conclusions indicate that an amplifier driving a reasonably efficient speaker system must provide between 10 and 15 watts of power in order to reproduce the "maximum orchestral level" in a fairly large living room. The average listening level will be considerably less than one watt, with the higher power being required to reproduce the peaks.

Now, if you are living in a small apartment, the reproduction of music at "orchestra level" might very easily upset your neighbors. Furthermore, it is doubtful if you, yourself, would care to listen to high-volume levels. Accordingly, a five-watt amplifier should be more than adequate where the volume must be restrained. In larger homes, particularly when the system is installed in a heavily draped and carpeted room, a 10 to 15-watt amplifier may be required. For multiple-speaker installations, where each speaker must provide maximum orchestral levels, amplifiers with 30 or more watts will be needed. In all cases, distortion at maximum desired output level should be three percent or less.

Frequency response

As in all other high-fidelity components, the frequency response of the amplifier should be flat over the entire audible range. In your catalogue you will find several amplifiers with a flat response from a few cycles to more than 100,000 c.p.s. Such

FREQUENCY RESPONSE

units, however, are relatively expensive and the improvement in actual listening quality is not commensurate with the increase in cost. In general, an amplifier with a flat response from 20 to 20,000 c.p.s. within 3 db (a unit of measure of sound intensity) will provide excellent results.

Hum and noise

Hum and noise, which are ever-present in all electronic equipment, can be particularly troublesome in high-fidelity amplifiers. It is absolutely essential that this be reduced to a level below audibility if maximum enjoyment is to be obtained. Hum may be caused either by insufficient filtering in the power supply or by improper design. Noise is usually produced within the vacuum tubes or resistors in the high-gain amplifier stages. Noise will appear as a soft hiss in the loudspeaker when the volume control is advanced.

HUM AND NOISE

In catalogue specifications the combined hum-and-noise figure is given in "db below rated output." In general, amplifiers with noise figures from about 70 to 90 db below rated power output are satisfactory. The higher the number, the quieter the amplifier.

Controls

In selecting your amplifier, considerable thought should be given to the number and types of controls incorporated in the unit. While it can never be said that an amplifier has an excessive number of controls, it must be remembered that the greater the number of controls, the more expensive the amplifier, and *the more difficult it may be to adjust.*

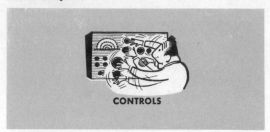

CONTROLS

The controls to be included in the amplifier depend, to a great extent, on the other components in the overall system. For example, if a radio tuner is purchased at the same time, all of the required controls may already be located on the tuner. If similar controls are included also in the amplifier, the duplication of functions will serve only to increase the cost of the system without improving its quality. For systems which will include a tuner, the various controls should be located on this unit rather than on the amplifier, since it will then be possible to have them all handy on a single chassis. In such cases, a basic amplifier without any controls is perfectly adequate. But, if you start with the phono system and add other components later, the amplifier should contain at least a volume, bass, and treble control. The tone controls will permit tone compensation for personal preference and room acoustics. In addition, the amplifier should have several extra input jacks (for components which may be added later) and a front-panel selector switch for the various inputs.

Now, let's consider some of the other controls which may be incorporated in typical hi-fi amplifiers, and briefly discuss their functions. Probably the most important of these is the *record compensator*. For years, high-fidelity records have been made by a number of different recording studios. Unfortunately, most of these have their own specific ideas on how a record should be cut. As a result, there may be considerable variation in the characteristics of records by different companies. In professional recording, it is customary to reduce the amplitude of low frequencies with respect to the "highs." This is done by all companies, but many of them disagree on the specific

frequency at which this reduction should start and on the amount of reduction that should be used. In playback, the low frequencies are "boosted" with respect to the highs, in order to provide an overall flat response. But, a single *bass boost* circuit can not compensate perfectly for the various recording methods; hence, a record compensator. Such a selector inserts various filters into the amplifier, so that records of most major studios can be reproduced in the prescribed manner.

The loudness control. This unit replaces the volume control in some of the more expensive amplifiers. It is well known that the frequency response of the human ear depends to some extent on the loudness of the sound. At low volumes, it is difficult to hear the low bass and high treble frequencies even if these are being reproduced by the amplifier. The loudness control automatically compensates for the deficiencies of the ear by increasing the volume of the "lows" and "highs" with respect to mid-frequencies as the volume control is turned down. Of course, the proper compensation can be obtained manually with the tone controls, so that the loudness control, while convenient, is not absolutely essential.

Variable rolloff and turnover controls. The function of these controls is the same as that of the record compensator, except that they permit individual compensation of bass and treble frequencies. Furthermore, they can be adjusted for any type of record since they are continuously variable. The record compensator provides fixed compensation for only those records for which it was specifically designed. Therefore, it is far easier to use than the individual controls. However, it does not have the versatility of the variable rolloff and turnover controls.

Cutoff filter. The cutoff filter is used primarily when reproducing old, worn, or noisy records. It is designed to limit the high-frequency response of the amplifier so that the response, as well as the noise which is predominant in the high-frequency region, will be reduced. Cutoff filters are often incorporated in record-compensator circuits.

Preamplifiers

It was mentioned earlier that a preamplifier is needed if the record changer incorporates a magnetic phono cartridge. The reason for this is simple. Since the voltage output of these cartridges is too low to drive a basic amplifier to its full-rated power output, a "preamp" is used as a "booster" unit.

Loudspeakers

Perhaps the weakest link in the entire chain of music reproduction is the loudspeaker. It is here that an increase in cost will result in the greatest improvement in reproduction. For this reason, several units

SPEAKERS AND ENCLOSURES

in various price ranges should be selected for auditioning. If you are ordering your system from a catalogue, the following information may help you in making your final selection:

Hi-fi speakers are available in sizes ranging from 8 to 15 in. in diameter. In general, the larger the speaker the more expensive and the more efficient it will be.

The least expensive hi-fi speakers have large, single cones and relatively heavy magnets (in excess of 10 oz.) for good low-frequency response and low distortion. Such speakers are most efficient at low frequencies although their response can extend well into the high-frequency region. These larger speakers are known as "woofers." More expensive units, called *coaxial* speakers, have a large cone for good low-frequency reproduction, plus a small cone or horn for extended high-frequency response. A frequency divider known as the *crossover network* channels the low frequencies to the woofer and the highs to the smaller speaker called a "tweeter." The tweeter is mounted on the same axis as the woofer—hence the name coaxial. Since each speaker must now handle only a limited-frequency range, it can do so with less interaction and distortion.

Instead of a coaxial speaker, a separate woofer and tweeter may be purchased. The primary advantage of such a system is its greater flexibility. You can start your system with a good single-cone speaker and add a separate tweeter and crossover network as additional funds become available.

The most elaborate speakers consist of three separate units: The low-frequency woofer, the mid-range squawker and the high-frequency tweeter. These parts may be assembled on a single frame, as with a triaxial speaker, or they may be obtained separately.

Catalogue specifications do not mean as much with speakers as with other components. It is quite possible for a unit to have a wide frequency response and yet sound worse than one with a limited range. Whenever possible, the final selection should be made by means of a listening-comparison test. When making tentative catalogue selections, plan to listen to several units meeting your requirements. Remember—the larger the speaker, the larger the enclosure, if optimum performance is to be obtained. For small rooms or apartments, 8 or 12-in. speakers are suitable. For large rooms a 12 or 15-in. unit should be selected. *In all cases, the power-handling capability of the speaker must be equal to or exceed the maximum power output of the amplifier.*

The speaker enclosure

While the phono cartridge, the amplifier and loudspeaker represent the "meat" of any high-fidelity system, the speaker enclosure certainly adds the "flavor." Like a well-balanced meal, which would taste flat without seasonings, even the finest hi-fi system sounds lifeless and unnatural unless the speaker is properly baffled.

The enclosure is more than just a housing for the loudspeaker. It actually provides the means for transferring the vibration of the speaker cone to the surrounding air, so that the resultant sound waves are reproduced with maximum efficiency. Particularly effective at the low audio frequencies, a properly designed enclosure makes it possible to hear bass tones which would otherwise be highly distorted, if not altogether lost. Thus, the enclosure becomes a vital part of the hi-fi system; one which must be engineered with the same care as any other component.

Those Little Things Count..

In the Sound of Your Hi-Fi System

By John Gayner

YOU PROBABLY recall the day you first flipped the switch of your spanking-new hi-fi system and listened with delight to the clarity and realism of the music coming from the loudspeaker.

Does it sound as good now? Are the trumpets as saucily brassy and the voices as crisp and clear as they were? Or do the records sound scratchy? Fuzzy? Do they crackle and pop? Does Como seem to "tremolo" when he didn't before, and does your favorite piano piece seem to w-a-a-w-a-a-w-a-a-w?

If your system has lost some of its original brilliance you are no longer getting a good return from your investment. And,

when you uncover and cure certain maladies by the simple means described here, you may find that the original sparkle and clarity have wilted away so gradually that you may not even have noticed the change. The improvement, therefore, will be all the more startling.

Like an automobile, a hi-fi system requires periodic checks and some special care to remain in top-notch condition. Elec-

Worn stylus can cause as much distortion and more damage than a defective electronic component. Periodic stylus inspection with inexpensive microscope, above, lets you know when it's time for a change

BALL-POINT CONTACT INSURES TOP PERFORMANCE, EASILY FOLLOWS RAPID GROOVE VARIATIONS

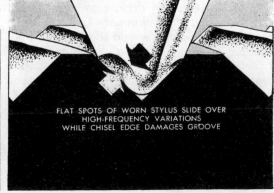

FLAT SPOTS OF WORN STYLUS SLIDE OVER HIGH-FREQUENCY VARIATIONS WHILE CHISEL EDGE DAMAGES GROOVE

Stylus pressure, too much or too little, is detrimental to high fidelity. Most hi-fi record players have accessible pressure adjustment in tone arm, as above. Inexpensive pressure gauge placed on turntable permits accurate adjustment for optimum results

Level that turntable. It may cure those sticking or groove-jumping habits of your pickup arm. Simple bubble levels are available from hi-fi dealers to make this an easy job. You may find that it will also improve stereo balance and overall fildelity

tronic parts age, components change in performancé and, even in the absence of major troubles, after a year or so of use the characteristics of the system may no longer be the same as they were originally. Such gradual deterioration, if it becomes noticeable, can be localized and corrected only by a qualified audio technician.

But there are a number of routine checks that you, yourself, can and should make at regular intervals. They take only a few minutes of your time and require a very small outlay, but they can prolong the life of your equipment and eliminate some rather expensive service calls. Here are some of them:

STYLUS WEAR—The stylus (needle) of your record player does not come to a point. It's rounded so that it contacts both walls of the V-shaped record groove. After some use that rounded tip wears down and develops chisel-like edges. Instead of accurately tracing the delicate patterns of sound impressed into the groove it chops and hacks its way through the wave peaks and valleys.

Result is distortion: Fuzzy, hard-to-listen-to sound, with the high flutes and piccolos going or gone.

And, it murders your records!

To avoid this, check the stylus tip regularly with a microscope. Your audio dealer sells a little, inexpensive pocket unit that lets you inspect without removing the stylus. If it shows signs of wear, don't play another record with it! Replace it!

The styli of most phono cartridges can easily be changed according to directions given in your instructions manual. If you don't have the manual, ask your dealer for it or write directly to the factory. They'll be happy to send you one.

And, even if the cartridge originally came with a sapphire stylus, replace it with a diamond. These cost more, but they last 10 to 20 times as long and represent a worthwhile investment. It's a good idea to inspect a sapphire stylus for wear after every 10-hour period of use—a diamond at 100-hour intervals.

STYLUS PRESSURE—If your phono cartridge bears down too hard it will permanently distort the relatively soft plastic material of the record. If it rides too lightly it will climb the walls of the groove and may even jump out. Either condition causes serious distortion.

Answer: Buy a stylus pressure gauge (cost —about $1-$4) and adjust for the correct tracking pressure called for in the manual. On most record players or changers, such as the Glaser-Steers unit shown here, the adjustment is easily made.

Note this: On some changers, stylus pressure may rise above the recommended maximum as the record stack on the turntable rises. Make sure that it remains within permissible limits from one record to the top of the stack. If it doesn't, don't load the changer with its full complement of records.

TURNTABLE LEVEL—If your record player—changer or manual—rests on an incline, the stylus bears more heavily on one wall of the record groove than on the other. Again, distortion and excess wear

Dirt, dust and grime are archenemies of both records and stylus. Lightweight "atomic jewel" attached to tone arm neutralizes static electrical charge which causes dust to cling to record grooves

Wipe away "crackle, snap, pop" with swish of chemically impregnated cloth before playing any record. Below: plastic cover, available for most record changers, is useful accessory for uncased instruments

are the results. In stereo, balance may be affected. An inexpensive bubble level, made for the job, will show any turntable tilt and permit you to compensate for it by raising one side of the unit. *DUST, DIRT, GRIME*—Those fine, spiraling grooves in your records are as attractive to dirt as a mud puddle is to a 4-year-old. Dirt not only causes annoying crackle and pop, it can also cause serious wear. Every time the stylus crashes into a microscopic "rock" of dirt it imbeds it deeper into the soft vinyl plastic. What should be a zig in the shape of the groove becomes a zag and the sound suffers. It takes its toll of the stylus too, acting like a fine abrasive and prematurely wearing the tip to a dangerous chisel shape.

Removal of "C" washer from changer spindle lets you lift off turntable to expose driving mechanism. Careful cleaning and lubrication may eliminate "wow" and "flutter" which has marred your listening pleasure and save costly service call

One way to help keep dust off the record is to neutralize its static electrical charge. That way the record won't attract and hold the tiny dust particles. You can do it with a silicone anti-static spray, with an impregnated "Jockey" cloth that cleans the record at the same time, or with an "atomic jewel" that attaches to the pickup arm. Another low-cost and useful item is a small brush which attaches to the tone arm and sweeps the record ahead of the stylus.

If your record changer sits out in the open, a plastic cover is a handy item to shield against all forms of dirt. And a little common sense in handling your precious records—such as always replacing them in their original jackets as soon as possible and handling them by their edges to prevent dirt-attracting grease and moisture from getting into the grooves—will greatly increase their useful life.

TURNTABLE WOW—The word "wow" tells the story. That annoying repetitive waver in pitch is caused by an alternate slow-down and speedup of the turntable. If it stems from a defective or badly-

designed unit, a major repair—or even replacement—is called for. But before you resign yourself to such an expense, try the following quick cure: Using carbon tetrachloride, clean the inner rim of the record player's turntable and the rubber idler and drive wheels. Use a bit of elbow grease, if necessary, to rub off any shiny areas on the rubber drive parts and carefully check these for flat spots. Unless they are perfectly round, replace them with parts obtainable from your dealer or from the factory. If the record player uses small drive belts, inspect these for deterioration or cracking. Consult the manual for proper lubrication.

Barring some major defect, these measures will usually correct any speed-variation tendencies.

Though some of the above troubles may seem minor compared with the more spectacular electronic gremlins that sometimes infest hi-fi systems, they are just as often responsible for the loss of quality. The occasional few minutes of time spent, and the almost negligible cost of pampering your records and record player will be well repaid in greater listening enjoyment and longer life for your equipment and record collection.

Practical Amplifier for Low-Cost Hi-Fi

By Daniel F. Mitchell, W9OFB

REMEMBER the bygone days when all you had to do for an evening of musical entertainment was to turn on the phonograph, adjust the volume and settle down in your favorite easy chair? Of course, the music sounded a bit thin—there was practically no bass and very little treble—but then, you didn't have to worry about turntable rumble, and record noise was not particularly troublesome. If you sat close to the speaker, you didn't need to turn up the volume high enough to make the loud orchestral passages sound like the rattling of cutlery, and if the low passages were masked by the inherent hum of the amplifier, at least there was no trouble with uncooperative neighbors whose taste in music didn't happen to coincide with your own. By mentally supplying the missing high and low tones it was almost possible to liken the resulting sound to something you may have heard at Orchestra Hall.

The advent of high fidelity and its ever-increasing acceptance by the music-loving public has changed all this. Today, full-frequency records and high-fidelity FM broadcasts provide excellent sources of high-quality music. Reproducing equipment capable of faithfully translating the recorded or transmitted signals into corresponding sound waves is readily available. But, as the art of high-fidelity reproduction improved, so did the complications. The modern hi-fi amplifier is more like the control console of yesteryear's broadcast studio than a piece of home equipment. There are controls to compensate for certain characteristics, and other controls to compensate for the compensation. All of them, of course, have specific functions and tend to provide the technically informed "perfectionist" with the means for approaching the "unattainable ultimate" in music reproduction. To the more casual music lover, however, they represent a profusion of confusion and they are often left in compromise positions which may not provide perfection but eliminates the need for readjustment with each consecutive selection.

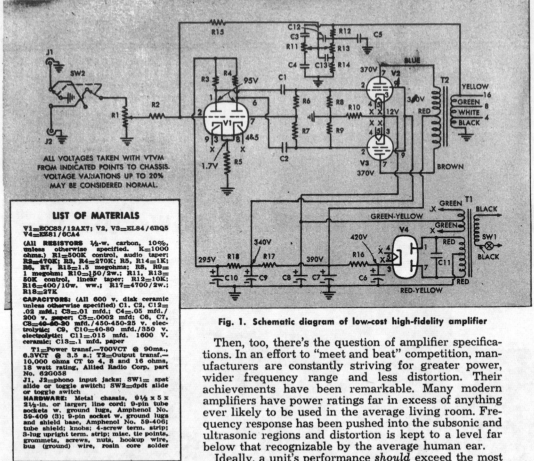

Fig. 1. Schematic diagram of low-cost high-fidelity amplifier

LIST OF MATERIALS

V1=ECC83/12AX7; V2, V3=EL84/6BQ5
V4=EZ81/6CA4

(All RESISTORS ½-w. carbon, 10%,
unless otherwise specified. K=1000
ohms.) R1=500K control, audio taper;
R2=470K; R3, R4=270K; R5, R14=1K;
R6, R7, R15=1.5 megohms; R8, R9=
1 megohm; R10=150/2w.; R11, R13=
50K control, linear taper; R12=10K;
R16=400/10w. ww.; R17=4700/2w.;
R18=27K

CAPACITORS: (All 600 v. disk ceramic
unless otherwise specified) C1, C2, C12=
.02 mfd.; C3=.01 mfd.; C4=.05 mfd./
200 v. paper; C5=.0002 mfd; C6, C7,
C8=40-60-30 mfd./450-450-25 v. electrolytic; C9, C10=40-80 mfd./350 v.
electrolytic; C11=.015 mfd. 1600 V.
ceramic; C13=.1 mfd. paper

T1=Power transf.—700VCT @ 90ma.,
6.3VCT @ 3.5 a.; T2=Output transf.—
10,000 ohms CT to 4, 8 and 16 ohms,
18 watt rating, Allied Radio Corp. part
No. 62G058

J1, J2=phono input jacks; SW1=spst
slide or toggle switch; SW2=dpdt slide
or toggle switch
HARDWARE: Metal chassis, 9½ x 5 x
2½-in. or larger; line cord; 9-pin tube
sockets w. ground lugs, Amphenol No.
59-409 (3); 9-pin socket w. ground lugs
and shield base, Amphenol No. 59-406;
tube shield; knobs; 4-screw term. strip;
3-lug upright term. strip; misc. tie points,
grommets, screws, nuts, hookup wire,
bus (ground) wire, rosin core solder

Then, too, there's the question of amplifier specifications. In an effort to "meet and beat" competition, manufacturers are constantly striving for greater power,
wider frequency range and less distortion. Their
achievements have been remarkable. Many modern
amplifiers have power ratings far in excess of anything
ever likely to be used in the average living room. Frequency response has been pushed into the subsonic and
ultrasonic regions and distortion is kept to a level far
below that recognizable by the average human ear.

Ideally, a unit's performance *should* exceed the most
stringent of practical requirements. Yet, beyond a

Fig. 2. Pictorial wiring diagram. Completed wiring should be checked against schematic diagram, above

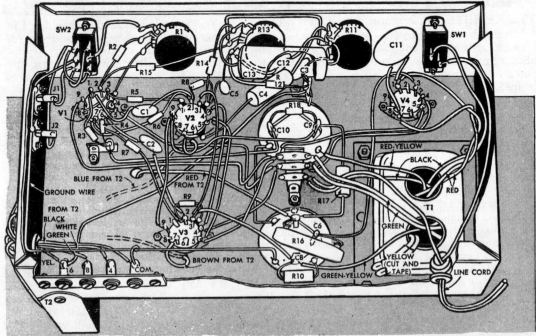

practical limit, every watt of excess power, every fractional percentage of distortion reduction adds more to the cost of the unit than is compensated for by the improvement of music reproduction.

The amplifier shown here is unconventional by present-day standards. Instead of using additional parts and circuits in an effort to obtain theoretical perfection, it was designed with the view, "how much can be omitted without compromising practical listening quality?" The result is a neat little 10-watter which, performancewise, needs offer no apology to its more elaborate and more expensive counterparts.

Built entirely with readily available components, the amplifier is designed for use with a radio tuner and a good-quality crystal or ceramic phono cartridge. (For use with a low-output magnetic cartridge, a separate equalized preamplifier is required.) Two inputs and a front-panel selector switch permit rapid switching from tuner to record player and vice versa.

Compact Design

In the original model all parts were mounted on a small 9½ x 5 x 2½-in. aluminum chassis, punched and drilled as shown in Fig. 3. This compact design presents no construction difficulties and permits the unit to be mounted in a relatively small space. However, due to the high power requirements of the output tubes, the chassis becomes quite warm and adequate ventilation must be provided. Where more space is available, the use of a larger chassis with its greater heat-dissipating properties is recommended.

Wiring the amplifier, as illustrated in Fig. 2, is simple. Following the layout shown will help prevent wiring errors and assure performance similar to that of the original model. Note that the red and blue plate leads of the output transformer, T2, enter the chassis through small holes located near the plate pins of the output-tube sockets. Keeping the major portion of these leads above the chassis reduces the possibility of oscillations caused by undesired feedback from output to input stages.

The electrolytic filter capacitors are mounted above the chassis on insulating Bakelite mounting plates and their ground lugs are connected together and to a ground wire which is grounded to the chassis only at the input jacks. Ground connections for most small parts are made to ground lugs on the saddle-type tube sockets of the stage with which these parts are associated. This wiring procedure eliminates ground loops and reduces amplifier hum to a level below audibility. Component leads should be covered with "spaghetti" wher-

ELECTRICAL SPECIFICATIONS

FREQ. RESPONSE: 1 db from 30 to 25,000 cps

HARMONIC DISTORTION: 1% at 1000 cps at 16 watts

POWER RESPONSE FOR LESS THAN 3%

    HARMONIC DISTORTION:
      16 watts from 100 to 5000 cps
      11 watts from 30 to 10,000 cps

INTERMODULATION DISTORTION: 2% at 5 watts
   (60 and 7000 cps signal at 4:1) 4% at 10 watts
                      5.8% at 15 watts

HUM AND NOISE: 70 db below 10 watts at max. volume
              75 db below 10 watts at min. volume

SENSITIVITY: .6 volts in for 10 watts out

ever such leads might short out to the chassis or to the wire leads of some other part.

After completing the wiring, carefully check each connection to make sure that all are securely soldered. It is also a good idea to check the actual wiring against the schematic diagram of Fig. 1 in order to catch any possible wiring error.

The quality of music available from any hi-fi system is no better than that provided by the poorest component in the assembly. The use of a good quality amplifier, therefore, does not insure high-fidelity results unless the auxiliary units—the pickup and the speaker system—are capable of matching the performance of the amplifier. The relatively low cost of this amplifier will permit a greater outlay for a speaker, record player or phono cartridge where the increased investment will pay far greater dividends in terms of listening enjoyment (particularly in the low and medium-price ranges) than a corresponding expenditure for an amplifier with more spectacular electrical characteristics.

Though rated at 10 watts, this amplifier is actually capable of much greater power output before reaching the point where distortion becomes really serious. The associated loudspeaker should have power handling capacity of at least 20 watts.

Fig. 3. Chassis layout. Dimensions are approximate and may be changed to fit individual requirements

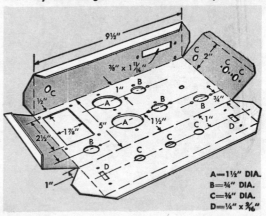

A—1½" DIA.
B—¾" DIA.
C—⅜" DIA.
D—¼" x ⅜"

A

B

C

HI-FI SPEAKER ENCLOSURE

THIS FOLDED exponential horn, in a 20-in. cube, has remarkable range of frequency response. Previous exponential horns have pleased the music lover and high-fidelity enthusiast, but they were either too high for use in a living room or, if they were low enough, they lacked high-note response. It is well known that high audio frequencies leave a speaker diaphragm as a narrow beam, and with earlier low speakers the beam was too low to reach the listener's ear.

A simply constructed acoustic prism solves this problem as shown in the accompanying diagrams. The speaker is inclined 30 deg., and the prism also bends the high notes 30 deg., so that you can hear the beam even if you are standing. A good 8-in. PM speaker is small enough to reproduce the high notes of fine music, yet large enough to move air for the bass tones. The bass tones come from the back of the diaphragm, and the exponential horn carries them around so that they emerge from the front of the assembly. Low tones bend readily as they have no beam effect.

Since no absorption is required, or desired, the efficiency is high, and ⅜-in. plywood is adequate for construction. All joints should be carefully glued and nailed. The 8-in. speaker should be an extended-range type with a power-handling ability of about 7 watts. From the 8-in. driver, the horn reproduces low notes as well as 15-in. speakers. Further, the use of a single reproducer eliminates crossover networks and intermodulation distortion. This distortion is present in many two and three-element loudspeaker systems. It is prevented in this design because the horn loads the single diaphragm. You will find that this

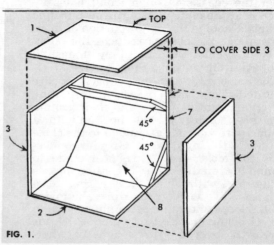

FIG. 1.

speaker-horn combination sounds as loud with 7 electrical watts input, as 28 watts to a speaker equipped with an infinite baffle (a tight box lined with absorbent material). You gain an additional advantage as your amplifier has less distortion at lower power outputs, and less than 7 watts will drive the horn so clearly that you will not have to turn up the gain on your amplifier.

Photos A, B and C show various views of the completed unit. The acoustic prism, which bends the high notes, is a series of parallel and horizontal sheets glued into the sidepieces, ⅜ in. apart. These sheets can be heavy cardboard, plastic or metal. Fig. 1 shows the first step in assembly with the right-hand side and top removed. The speaker panel, housing and braces are de-

tailed in Fig. 2. All dimensions can be easily checked in the material list. Fig. 3 is a cross section through the middle, showing the prism. Note that the back of the speaker housing is open to the horn. Fig. 4 shows the acoustic prism, partly and fully assembled. The front grille detail is quite simple as will be noted in photo A. Either heavy grille cloth or brown flock-coated grille screening may be used. This grille screening is galvanized wire mesh, flocked on both sides. Another grille material now available is Lumite-plastic grille cloth. It requires no backing and is of the wide-mesh basket-weave type.

Operating as an auxiliary speaker, this folded exponential horn can be used with any high-grade receiver or audio amplifier.

MATERIAL LIST

Item	Reqd.	Name	Dimensions Inches
1	1	Top	20 X 20 X ⅜
2	1	Bottom	20 X 19¼ X ⅜
3	2	Sides	20 X 19⅝ X ⅜
4	1	Speaker Panel	10½ X 8½ X ½; 30°, 30°
5	2	Sides, Speaker Housing	9 X 13 X ⅜ (See Fig. 3)
6	1	Slant Panel	8 X 19¼ X ⅜; 45°, 45°
7	1	Back	19¼ X 19¼ X ⅜
8	1	Slant Panel	12 X 19¼ X ⅜; 45°, 45°
9	1	Bottom Speaker Housing	9¼ X 10 X ⅜
10	1	Brace	1 X 19¼ X ½
11	2	Brace	1 X 9¾ X ¾
12	2	Prism Sides	7 X 9 X ⅜
13	2	Prism Braces	¾ X ¾ X 9¼
14	17	Prism Vanes	Cut to fit prism sides (Item 12)

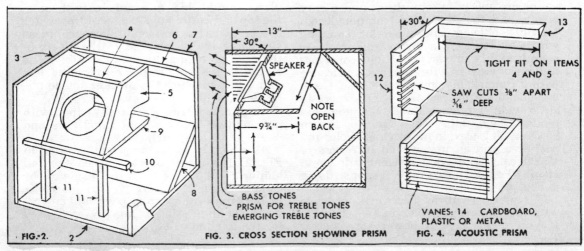

FIG. 2.

FIG. 3. CROSS SECTION SHOWING PRISM

FIG. 4. ACOUSTIC PRISM

BASS TONES
PRISM FOR TREBLE TONES
EMERGING TREBLE TONES

SPEAKER

NOTE OPEN BACK

13″
30°
9¾″

TIGHT FIT ON ITEMS 4 AND 5

SAW CUTS ⅜″ APART ³⁄₁₆″ DEEP

VANES: 14 CARDBOARD, PLASTIC OR METAL

A Four-Speaker Bass-Reflex Enclosure

HERE'S A LOUDSPEAKER system that's fun to build and a pleasure to listen to. It is specially designed for improving the sound quality of console radios and television receivers, but will also do full justice to low-cost hi-fi systems.

The system consists of four identical 5-in. speakers mounted in a bass-reflex cabinet of unusual design. Each speaker is mounted at an angle so that the high-frequency sound beams cover an angle of 120 deg. as compared to the 30-deg. dispersion angle of single speakers. Vertical spacing between the four units prevents interference between individual beams.

At low frequencies, the four small cones, acting in unison, can push around plenty of air, and the bass-reflex cabinet design provides efficient speaker-to-air coupling which makes even a low-power amplifier sound mighty impressive. Rigid construction provides a vibrationless enclosure with a remarkably smooth response. Don't use cheap surplus speakers and expect to get a wide frequency range. But good extended-range units, such as the Jensen P5TX models used in the original enclosure, will give you an upper limit in excess of 15,000 c.p.s. and good efficiency down to about 80 c.p.s. (measurable response down to 60 c.p.s.).

Cut out the required pieces in accordance with the dimensions given in Figs. 1 and 2. If you don't have a power saw, better

hunt up someone who has, because the dimensions are rather critical if a tight-fitting final assembly is to be obtained.

Inexpensive ⅜-in. fir or white-pine plywood can be used for the speaker-plate assembly and for the back and bottom of the cabinet. Birch plywood, ⅜ in. thick, is recommended for the top and sides, since this will take a good finish. The cleats fastened to the inside of the cabinet pieces should be ⅞₁₆ in. square and can be made from scrap lumber (not plywood).

Begin the construction with the speaker-plate assembly shown in Fig. 1. If all dimensions and angles have been cut correctly, the outside edges of the speaker plates should line up evenly with those of the top and bottom plates and of the center spacer. This is important because these surfaces will be fastened to the cleats in the cabinet during the final assembly. The cutout in the bottom piece is for the terminal strip to which the speaker and amplifier leads will be connected.

All panels must be securely joined with glue and nails. Any good wood glue and ¾-in. brads are satisfactory.

Assembly of the cabinet is illustrated in Fig. 2. The cleats are so placed that all nailing can be done from the inside of the cabinet. If the cleats are ⁷⁄₁₆ in. square, ¾-in. brads will get a firm grip without emerging from the ⅜-in. facing plywood used for the top and sides.

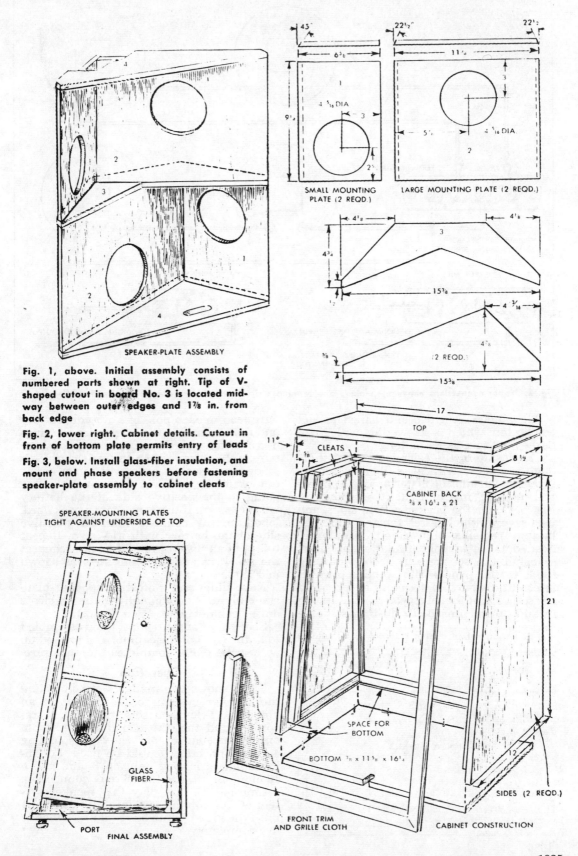

SPEAKER-PLATE ASSEMBLY

SMALL MOUNTING PLATE (2 REQD.)

LARGE MOUNTING PLATE (2 REQD.)

Fig. 1, above. Initial assembly consists of numbered parts shown at right. Tip of V-shaped cutout in board No. 3 is located midway between outer edges and 1⅞ in. from back edge

Fig. 2, lower right. Cabinet details. Cutout in front of bottom plate permits entry of leads

Fig. 3, below. Install glass-fiber insulation, and mount and phase speakers before fastening speaker-plate assembly to cabinet cleats

SPEAKER-MOUNTING PLATES TIGHT AGAINST UNDERSIDE OF TOP

GLASS FIBER

PORT

FINAL ASSEMBLY

TOP

CLEATS

CABINET BACK
⅜ x 16¼ x 21

SPACE FOR BOTTOM

BOTTOM ⅜ x 11⅝ x 16¼

FRONT TRIM AND GRILLE CLOTH

SIDES (2 REQD.)

CABINET CONSTRUCTION

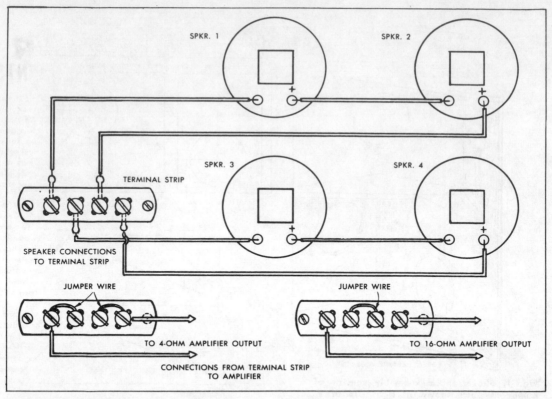

Fig. 4. Proper connections between speakers and terminal strip for matching 4-ohm or 16-ohm amplifier output

All panels are glued and nailed except the bottom which is screwed on with No. 4 flatheaded screws, ¾ in. long.

The inside of the cabinet must be thoroughly padded with glass-fiber or similar acoustical insulating material. Use a double thickness (1 in.) and cut it as shown in Fig. 5. Cover the back and both sides, and use several thicknesses for the top. The bottom remains uninsulated. Use large-headed tacks to hold insulation in place.

Install the speakers by front-mounting them to the panels with wood screws. It is essential that the speakers be properly phased so that their respective cones move in and out in unison. To do this, solder a

Fig. 5. Pattern of insulating material to fit cabinet

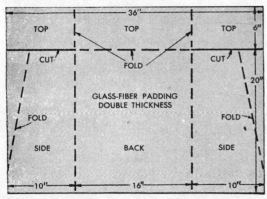

wire lead to each pole of a 1.5-volt battery and momentarily touch the voice-coil lugs of a speaker with the opposite ends of these wires (one wire to each lug). As contact is made, the speaker cone will move either out or in. If it moves out, label the lug going to the positive side of the battery with a + sign. If the cone moves backward, label the lug connected to the negative side of the battery with a + sign. Repeat this with all speakers and then interconnect the speakers and terminal strip as shown in Fig. 4.

Now glue and nail the speaker-plate assembly to the diagonally mounted cleats on the cabinet sides. (See Fig. 3.)

Some front angle trim, cut and assembled to fit the front of the cabinet and backed up with grille cloth, completes the enclosure.

Operation

Fig. 4 shows two methods of connecting the speaker system to the output of an amplifier. Television sets, radios, tape recorders and the like usually have 4-ohm output impedances, and the corresponding 4-ohm connection should be used. For hi-fi amplifiers having only an 8-ohm and a 16-ohm output, use the 16-ohm connection.

Caution: Do not play this speaker system at full volume (preferably not at all) until the glued joints have had a chance to dry completely.   ★ ★ ★

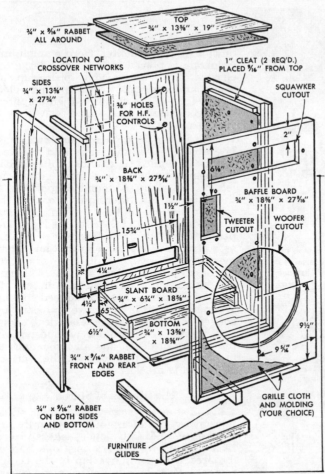

SPEAKER CONSTRUCTION HINTS

Solid, air-tight construction, except for specially prepared openings, is prerequisite in any high quality enclosure. All parts, except back, should be joined with a good wood glue. Glue rubber stripping to all inside edges which contact back cover when the latter is screwed in place. Screws may be used to hold parts together while glue is setting where screws do not show from the outside.

Dimensions of baffle-board cutouts depend on sizes of speakers employed. Countersink speaker-mounting holes so that screw heads do not interfere with application of grille cloth to front of baffle board. Anticipate eventual addition of tweeter and squawker by making the necessary cutouts and mounting holes, and covering any unused cutouts with wood blocks before grille cloth is installed.

Inside surfaces of top and both sides should be covered with 1-in.-thick acoustical insulating material, as shown.

Cover front surface of baffle board with black stain to prevent accentuated outline of speaker cutouts from showing through grille cloth.

THE BIG SWITCH TO STEREO

By Lothar Stern

IN AN ERA boasting such world-shaking advances as atomic power, supersonic aircraft and earth satellites, the mention of a mere phonograph record may seem trivial. In audio circles, however, and to music lovers the world over, the evolution of the stereo disc and the subsequent development of suitable playback equipment is just about the biggest thing that's come along since the advent of high fidelity. For here, at last, is a popular and popularly priced record which combines the perfection of high-fidelity sound with the directional effect and spaciousness of stereo—a combination which promises to remove the last barrier between reproduced music in the home and true concert-hall realism.

To anyone hearing stereo for the first time, the effect is truly dramatic. Almost like magic the entire orchestra seems to be spread out ahead. Gone is the "point source" effect associated with single-channel reproduction. As though a wall with a small hole in the center were suddenly removed from in front of an invisible orchestra, all instruments arrange themselves in their proper relative positions—an illusion so real that the reproduction almost rivals the original rendition as heard from the best seat in the auditorium.

The mechanics of stereophonic perception are simple enough. Consider, for example, the illustration in Fig. 1 which corresponds to ordinary single-channel, or

Fig. 1. In ordinary monaural or single-channel reproduction, all sounds from an orchestra are mixed and reproduced through a single speaker. A listener hears all sounds coming from a single point source

Fig. 2, above. When two microphone signals are mixed in one amplifier and reproduced by two speakers, the resultant sound is still a point source but seems to come from a position midway between the speakers. Fig. 3, below. True stereo reproduction requires two separate, independent sound channels

monaural reproduction. Here a single microphone is placed in front of a large orchestra. The microphone picks up all sound and converts it into a single electrical signal. This signal is then amplified and reconverted into sound waves by a loudspeaker.

But, while a good microphone can translate a complex sound wave into an exact electrical replica, it can not differentiate between sounds coming from either the left or the right. A sound originating at the extreme left, therefore, produces the same electrical output as an identical sound originating at the extreme right. The perception of depth is interpreted merely as a change of intensity so that an instrument playing at some distance away, regardless of its position, sounds as though the instrument were playing directly in front of the microphone at reduced volume. When all sounds of an entire orchestra are converted into a single electrical signal and reproduced through a loudspeaker, the feeling of depth and all indications as to the relative positions of the various instruments are lost.

The Illusion of Stereo

Fig. 2 shows a somewhat similar situation involving the use of two separate microphones and two loudspeakers. Here, each microphone covers only one half of the area with some overlap in the center region. Before being applied to the speakers, however, the two individual microphone signals are mixed in a common amplifier. Each speaker, therefore, receives the composite signal as if only one microphone were employed to cover the entire orchestra. This effectively nullifies any advantage gained through the use of two microphones, but it does produce some interesting results. Since each speaker now produces the same sound, a listener midway between the two receives exactly the same signal with his left ear as he does with the right, *just as he would if the sound source were directly in front of him*. But, while the apparent source of sound now shifts to a position between the two speakers, it still contains no trace of the original orchestral "spread."

In Fig. 3 we have the conditions necessary for true stereophonic perception. Again, two microphones and two loudspeakers are employed, but this time each microphone signal is individually amplified by a separate amplifier. As a result, a listener hears the left section of the orchestra reproduced by the left speaker and the right section by the right speaker. The center section which is picked up equally by both microphones produces the same sound from both speakers and seems to be coming from a point directly between the two, *just as though the listener were seated directly in front of the orchestra itself.*

Stereo in the Home

Stereo recordings have been with us for quite some time. In recent years all original recordings have been made on magnetic tape using two or more microphones. The output from each microphone is separately recorded on individual tape tracks and the multichannel-tape masters are used to produce commercial stereo and monaural tapes as well as single-channel discs. Today, anyone willing to invest in a stereo-tape player and pay the comparatively high price for stereo tapes can build up a sizable library of musical recordings which present the ultimate in the reproduction of recorded sound.

But sound on tape has not captured the fancy of the multitude of music lovers. The phonograph record still commands a lion's share of the high-fidelity market. And that is why the evolution of the stereo disc is causing such a stir in the musical world.

The concept of stereo sound on discs is not new. As far back as the late '30s a system was developed for recording two separate audio channels in a single record groove. The system used recorded the information received from one microphone in a lateral, left-to-right direction and the information from the other in a vertical, up-and-down direction. In playback, the

pickup cartridge separated the two channels and, feeding each signal to a different amplifier and speaker, produced true stereo sound. But the industry was not yet ready for stereo. Neither the quality of the record material, nor that of the cutting head permitted satisfactory recordings of this type and the system was shelved.

Later, an attempt was made to record stereo on discs by using two separate sets of grooves, each containing the information from a different microphone. This method required two separate and carefully ganged pickup cartridges and was so critical in adjustment that it, too, had to be quickly discarded.

After failure of the separate-groove discs, nothing was heard of stereo records for several years, but interest in stereo reproduction continued to rise. Stereo tapes became available and enjoyed increasing popularity. Radio stations began experimenting with stereo by simultaneously transmitting the same musical programs on AM and FM. The FM station broadcast the audio picked up by one microphone while, at the same time, the signals from another microphone were transmitted via AM. Stereo reception could be obtained by employing both an FM and an AM receiver. Broadcasts of this type are currently available in some sections of the country on a limited basis.

In the last year or two, a system of multiplexing two separate audio channels on a single FM carrier has received considerable attention. With this system, a single

Fig. 4. The Westrex method of cutting stereo discs: Signals from one microphone cause the cutting stylus to cut into the left groove wall, A, at a 45-deg. angle. Signals from the other microphone modulate right groove wall, B. Composite signal, C, causes simultaneous side-to-side and up-and-down groove variations

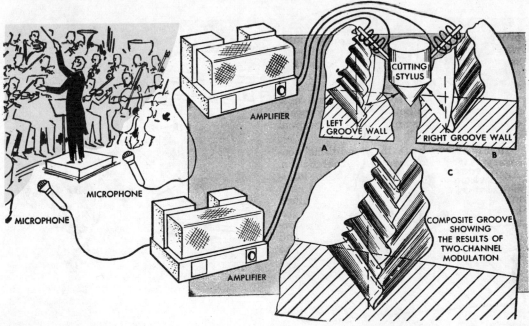

FM receiver in conjunction with an inexpensive multiplex adapter can provide stereo reception. But multiplexing, while seeming to provide the ultimate answer to stereo broadcasts, is still in the experimental stage. When and if this method will finally be adopted for popular stereo purposes still is a matter for speculation.

It seemed, for a while at least, that the public might be confronted with several types of stereo records, each requiring a different reproducing system. But this time the record industry, remembering the mistakes of earlier years, adopted a standard. By international agreement it was decided to use the system demonstrated by Westrex, the so-called 45-45 system, for cutting all stereo records.

How Records Are Cut

The Westrex method of recording is really a modification of the old lateral-vertical system. Instead of driving the cutting stylus in an exact vertical and lateral direction, however, the two applied signals cause the stylus to move diagonally, at 45-deg. angles. In the detail of Fig. 4, a signal applied to the left coil of the cutting head drives the cutter diagonally to the right, causing it to cut deeper into the record and, at the same time, displacing the groove in a lateral direction to the right.

A signal applied to the right-hand coil causes a similar excursion to the left. Thus, the two signals effectively modulate opposite walls of the groove and the result of combining the two actions produces a single groove which is displaced laterally as well as vertically from the norm.

The action of a typical stereo pickup cartridge is illustrated in Fig. 5. Here, use is made of two sensing elements which are mounted at 45-deg. angles. (Ceramic elements are shown here but the same theory also applies to magnetic cartridges. Both ceramic and magnetic units are currently available.) Each element produces maximum output voltage only when flexed in a direction perpendicular to its plane and is insensitive to signals cut the opposite direction. By utilizing the separate output voltages from the two elements, we recover the two separate signals initially supplied by the microphones. When these are applied to individual amplifiers and speakers, we have the necessary requirements for stereo reproduction.

Compatibility of Stereo Records

For complete compatibility, the stereo cartridge must be able to reproduce a monaural record as well as stereo discs. This requirement is met by present stereo cartridges without reservations. But, ideally, a stereo record should also be reproducible with a standard monaural cartridge. Here, the situation is somewhat more complicated. Normal monaural cartridges permit the stylus to move easily from left to right as is required for all monaural record

Fig. 5. Recovering two separate audio channels from single record groove requires two sensing elements in the pickup cartridge and two separate amplifier-and-speaker systems. Voltage output from each element varies with direction of stylus movement. Up-and-down motion produces equal but out-of-phase voltages

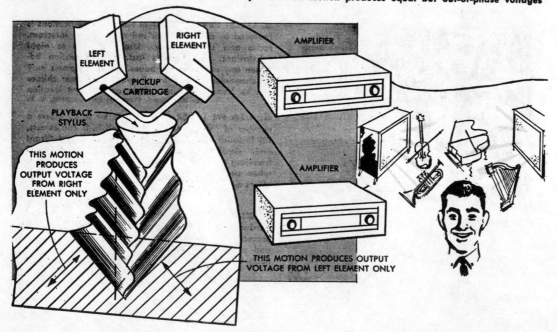

reproduction. Motion in a vertical direction, however, is often severely limited. It is conceivable, therefore, that such cartridges would cause the stylus to gouge out the vertical portion of a recorded stereo signal and would ruin the record for future stereo purposes. Obviously, the use of a monaural cartridge for playing stereo records is not recommended, but this is only

a minor disadvantage. Good monaural records are very plentiful and there seems to be little reason for anyone to invest in stereo discs unless stereo reproducing equipment is already on hand. The major problem, that of playing monaural records with stereo equipment, is satisfactorily resolved.

STEREO MUSIC AT LOW COST

AMID THE ENTHUSIASM caused by the appearance of stereo records comes the sobering realization that stereo reproduction in the home requires "two of everything." Not only two channels on the record itself, but two elements in the pickup cartridge, two amplifiers and two speaker systems are needed to extract the magic of stereophonic sound from the wiggly grooves of the stereo disc. To record fans who have already spent a good deal of money on their present phono system, this suggests a sizable investment for additional equipment which would prevent stereo from becoming an immediate reality. Fortunately, this is not necessarily true. Many homes already possess most of the required equipment for reproducing stereo records, so that the switch to stereo need not involve a major revision of the family budget.

Fig. 1 illustrates the equipment needed for stereo phono reproduction. Ideally, this would include a high-quality record changer or turntable, a stereo cartridge, two hi-fi amplifiers and two high-fidelity speaker systems. The words "high fidelity,"

however, are used here only to indicate the present ultimate in record reproduction. The stereo effect itself is rather independent of actual sound quality and may be enjoyed even if the equipment does not measure up to high-fidelity standards.*

In its simplest form, therefore, the advantages of stereo can be obtained by utilizing the amplifier and speaker of a monaural phono system in conjunction with the audio amplifier and speaker of any good radio or television receiver. Since many of these are already equipped with phono-input jacks, the entire conversion consists of replacing the present monaural phono cartridge with a stereo unit and adding a few pieces of wire—a job which can be both simple and inexpensive.

The real hi-fi fan will probably shudder at the mere suggestion of using a radio or TV set for playing high-fidelity records.

* Proof of this is given by the startling realism of stereo broadcasts involving the simultaneous use of FM and AM transmissions. Certainly, the ordinary AM receiver can not merit hi-fi status by any stretch of the definition. Yet the effects of such broadcasts are so dramatic that these are usually preferred to monaural broadcasts of true high-fidelity quality.

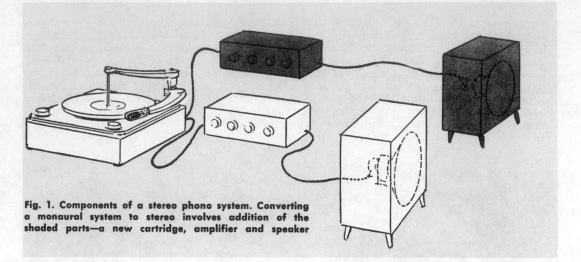

Fig. 1. Components of a stereo phono system. Converting a monaural system to stereo involves addition of the shaded parts—a new cartridge, amplifier and speaker

Such receivers, it is argued, do not have the wide frequency range required for good reproduction. Nor is their undistorted volume output sufficient for reproducing the full dynamic range of an orchestra. These arguments are unquestionably true. Yet while such units may be totally unsuited for monaural high fidelity, they can perform very well when used as the second channel of a stereo system which includes one hi-fi monaural unit. The use of two amplifiers now reduces the power requirements of each, so that both can usually be operated at a level within the capability of the inferior amplifier. Compared with true high-fidelity monaural reproduction, such a composite system may lose some of the extremely high and low frequencies, but the added stereo effect more than compensates for this loss.

When a radio or TV set is used as the second channel with an ordinary (nonhigh-fidelity) phonograph, the quality of reproduction will definitely be improved. This, added to the stereo effect, represents the most spectacular improvement in over-all performance that can be obtained at a relatively low cost.

While the actual conversion to stereo may not be difficult, it must be preceded by careful planning if optimum performance and versatility are to be obtained. Obviously, there would be little advantage in replacing the cartridge of an inexpensive table-model phonograph with a high-priced stereo unit. Conversely, it would be poor economy to replace a really good monaural cartridge with a mediocre stereo unit. Such a cartridge would not only compromise initial listening quality, but would itself have to be replaced during any subsequent improvement of the over-all system. The choice of stereo cartridge, there-

fore, depends primarily on the type of unit it is intended to replace.

Two Types of Cartridges

Basically, there are two types of phono cartridges; those which produce an output voltage due to the action of a magnetic field, and those which provide a signal voltage due to flexing of a crystal or ceramic element. Of the two, the magnetic units have generally been preferred by hi-fi fans interested in obtaining the best possible reproduction, and are often used in systems built up from individual components.

The ceramic cartridges are normally employed in medium-priced commercial systems. In addition to being slightly less expensive, these have a number of decided advantages. Compared with magnetic units they have a high-output voltage and require no equalization for various record characteristics. As a result, the amplifier with which they are used need not incorporate an equalized preamplifier and is far less expensive and less critical in design without compromising sound quality.

Replacing the Cartridge

In selecting a suitable replacement stereo cartridge, the above factors must be kept in mind. If the present cartridge is a crystal or ceramic type, it should be replaced with a similar stereo unit. If a magnetic cartridge is presently employed, a magnetic stereo unit, preferably by the same manufacturer, should be used. In such cases, however, the amplifier of the radio or TV set will not have the required gain or equalization for proper reproduction. A separate preamplifier must therefore be connected between the cartridge and the low-gain amplifier. (Some suitable commercial preamplifiers are available for about $11).

A normal method of mounting a monaural cartridge in a tone arm, and the necessary changes for a typical conversion are shown in Fig. 2. Most cartridges are fastened to the arm with two screws on standard ½-in. mounting centers. Since stereo cartridges are designed for this type of mounting, the change-over is easily accomplished. If the stereo cartridge is much thinner than the original one, a couple of spacers can be inserted, as shown, so that the stylus or turnover lever protrudes below the rim of the tone arm. Where the monaural cartridge has been mounted by another method, the changer manufacturer can usually supply a mounting adapter for the stereo cartridge.

Wiring Changes Are Simple

The necessary wiring changes, though simple, must be made carefully so that the mechanical action of the record player is not impaired. Principally, these consist of running another wire from the new cartridge to a terminal strip underneath the changer base plate, and adding a second output cable for connection to the second amplifier.

Fig. 2 shows the original wiring and the required changes for a typical Webcor changer. In these, a three-lug terminal strip below the base plate is used as a tie point for the cartridge leads and the output cable. Normally the red signal lead is connected to lug 1 and the black ground lead to lug 3. A jumper wire is soldered from lug 3 to ground lug 2. In the conversion, the jumper wire must be removed and the black ground wire, as well as the shield braid of the output cable moved directly to ground lug 2. The added cartridge wire is then routed through the tone arm along the same path and through the same cable clamps as the other two and is soldered to lug 3. The added output cable is soldered to lugs 2 and 3, and leaves the changer base or cabinet through the same hole as the original cable.

The wiring of other types of record changers or players follows the same general pattern. Where the original two wires consist of the center conductor and shield braid of a shielded cable, a similar shielded cable should be used for the added wire. In this case the new shield braid should be connected to the grounded terminal-strip lug. If the new stereo cartridge has four, rather than three, output lugs, the shield braid of the added wire must be connected to the second ground lug of the cartridge.

All connections to the cartridge must be made with clips soldered to the ends of the wire leads. Under no circumstances should any wire be soldered directly to the cartridge terminals.

For best bass response, a ceramic cartridge should be terminated with a high

Fig. 2. Replacing monaural cartridge with stereo unit requires extra cartridge lead and output cable. Four-terminal cartridges need another ground wire. Inset shows stereo cartridge in Garrard plug-in head

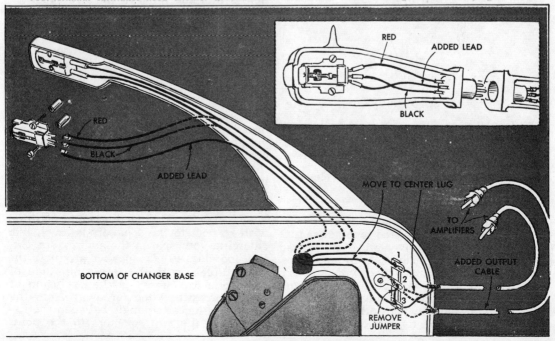

resistance, approximating 3 to 5 meg. The terminating resistance for the cartridge is the input resistance of the following amplifier. In radio or TV sets, this is usually a ½ or 1-meg. volume control. Such a control should be replaced, wherever convenient, with a 3-meg. unit. The stereo effect, which depends primarily on frequencies above 300 c. p. s., will not be affected by improper cartridge termination, but too low a value of amplifier input resistance will cause the loss of low audio frequencies which the amplifier and speaker may be capable of reproducing.

In anticipation of a great demand for stereo conversions, a number of commercial conversion kits are already available. Garrard, for example, offers kits which are tailored specifically for their changers, and "universal" kits, for most other changers or players, are available from major radio-parts distributors. Some manufacturers of complete phonographs provide kits of this type for their units and it is expected that many others will soon follow suit. (Most new changers and manual players, as well as the better phonographs, are factory wired for both stereo and monaural playback so that wiring changes at a later time are unnecessary.)

All stereo cartridges are compatible to the extent of being able to play both stereo and monaural records. For best monaural

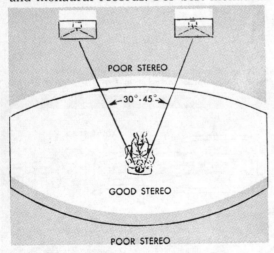

POOR STEREO

←30°-45°→

GOOD STEREO

POOR STEREO

Fig. 3. For best stereo, angle between loudspeakers and listener should be about 30 to 45 deg., but good stereo-listening area is relatively broad

results, however, both elements of the cartridge should be connected together so that the two individual signals are mixed and applied simultaneously to both amplifiers. This is easily accomplished with a s.p.s.t. switch. The switch may be mounted in any convenient location on the changer base or cabinet. One switch-terminal is connected with a wire to lug 1 of the terminal

strip beneath the changer mounting plate and the other to terminal 3. With the switch closed, both signals are applied to both amplifiers for monaural reproduction. For stereo, the switch is opened so that each amplifier receives only the signal from one cartridge element.

Most modern radios as well as some TV receivers are of the a.c.-d.c. variety. These, if not properly isolated, could present a serious shock hazard (See "Make Your TV Set Safe!," *Popular Mechanics*, Nov. 1957). Where such sets are used as the second channel for stereo, they should first be carefully investigated.

Normally, manufacturers are very particular in providing sufficient line-voltage isolation to eliminate such dangers, but some hazardous sets are in daily use. A qualified service technician can quickly determine if a particular set is safe, and any system incorporating one or more electronic components without power transformers should be "safety inspected" before being used.

Speaker placement for stereo perception has been the subject of much discussion. Despite recommendations regarding "phantom" speakers, third channels and a fearful list of prohibitions which suggest that no room is really ideal for stereo without much interior redecorating, good results are really quite easy to obtain.

Fig. 3 shows one possible arrangement where the two speakers are placed flat against the wall. Other arrangements, such as two corner speakers or one corner speaker and one "against the wall" baffle are also suitable. The important consideration is the placement of the two speakers so that their sound waves intersect the preferred-listening area at an angle of approximately 30 to 45 deg. This is the position which retains some unity of sound between the two halves of the orchestra, while preserving the directional effects that lend "life" and perspective to the real performance. Actually, the area for satisfactory stereo, as shown in Fig. 3, is quite broad. In fact, by adjusting the relative volume of the two channels, the apparent position of the orchestra can be shifted so that almost any section of the normal living room can simulate the best seat in the house.

Once the speaker locations and volume levels are fixed, changing your position with respect to the speakers is much like changing your seat in the auditorium. Sitting too close to one speaker produces the predictable result of hearing one side of the orchestra almost to the exclusion of the other; sitting too far away from the "stage" reduces the angle between the listener and the two speakers to the point where the stereo effect may be lost—much like sitting in the last row of a large auditorium.

If the angle between the listener and the speakers is too large, the directional effect is increased excessively. This may be highly effective for demonstrating such novelty recordings as ping-pong games and trains running through the living room, but can be very disconcerting when listening to a musical selection. An orchestra, after all, is an integrated unit and should not consist of two separate groups playing at opposite ends of the stage. And so, while speaker placement is not particularly critical, it can not be entirely disregarded.

Relative Volume Important

Good results can almost always be obtained by considering the speakers as the outer extremities of the stage, with the orchestra spread out between them, and facing the preferred listening area. Some experimentation with the relative volume of the two channels will result in best possible stereo perception for any specific location in front of the two loudspeakers.

Although reference was made earlier to "ordinary" (nonhigh-fidelity) phonographs, there is obviously a limit below which stereo conversion is neither practical nor desirable. The small, inexpensive portables, for example, just aren't suited for any kind of serious listening. There are, however, a host of larger table models and consoles which do deliver excellent sound quality. The performance of these, as well as that of the large number of monaural hi-fi systems in current use, can be greatly improved by dual-channel reproduction of stereo records.

Finally, it must be emphasized that the use of a radio or TV set as a second channel merely provides the means for an inexpensive transition from monaural to stereo sound. The physical separations between the two amplifiers introduces inconveniences when trying to obtain a balanced, over-all volume level from the two loudspeakers. Further, as the ear becomes accustomed to the magic of stereo, the true music lover will soon become aware of further improvements available through the use of a dual high-fidelity sound system. But it is doubtful that any subsequent change, regardless of cost, will equal the dramatic difference in sound caused by the low-cost, initial switch to stereo. ★ ★ ★

BUILDING AN EQUIPMENT CABINET

Designed with the do-it-yourselfer in mind, this cabinet includes all the features required for a complete, functional stereo-fidelity system. It's small enough (only 16¼ in. deep) to fit into most livingrooms and its contemporary styling blends in with virtually any type of furniture. Simple enough to be built by anyone familiar with the use of a power saw, it depends mainly on the matched grain of the wood itself for its distinctive appearance.

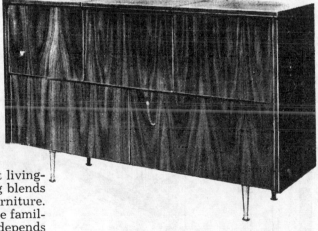

There's no dustcatching trim and no fancy fittings. Press-to-open touch latches eliminate the need for handles and its very simplicity is your assurance that, if you like it now, you won't tire of it in the years to come.

But let's take a closer look at the design.

Horizontally, the cabinet is divided into two sections. The upper section has three compartments — the lower one, two. The upper right-hand compartment is designated for a record player, concealed by a hinged top, while the identical left compartment can house a tape recorder.

The center section of the top is permanently fastened down so that it can be used as a resting place for a decorative center piece. Access to the center compartment is gained through a drop-leaf front panel so that there will be a minimum of stooping when manipulating the controls of the components (the preamplifier and radio tuner) mounted in this section.

Record storage is provided in the lower right hand section which, alternatively, could be employed as a speaker enclosure. There's ample space in the lower left hand compartment for a power amplifier or any other components or accessories which may be desired to round out the system.

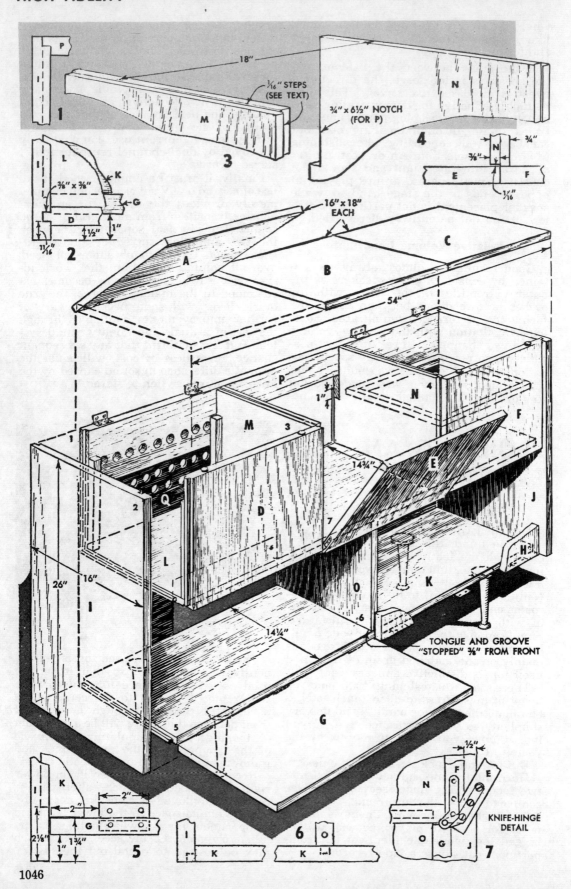

1

P

1

2

L

¾" x ⅜"

K

G

D

1"

½"

1"

¹¹⁄₁₆"

3

18"

¹⁄₁₆" STEPS
(SEE TEXT)

M

4

N

¾" x 6½" NOTCH
(FOR P)

N ¾"

⅜"

E   F

¹⁄₁₆"

16" x 18"
EACH

A   B   C

54"

P   N   4

M   3   F

14¾"   E

J

Q   D   7   1

2   H

L   O   K

16   6

I

26"   14¼"

5   G

TONGUE AND GROOVE
"STOPPED" ⅜" FROM FRONT

5

K

2"

2"

G

1"   1¾"

2⅛"

6

I   K

K

7

N   F
C   E
½"
O   G   J

KNIFE-HINGE
DETAIL

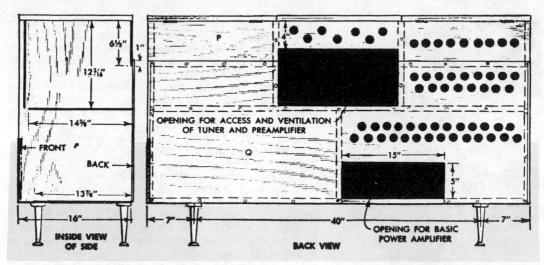

Side and back views of cabinet. Heavy, black lines in side view are grooves and rabbets cut in side pieces

without a considerable increase in size. If you already have a set of components, check the dimensions to make sure that everything will fit properly. It's a relatively simple matter, in the initial layout, to allow for an extra few inches in any direction.

Almost anyone handy with tools can put together some sort of cabinet. It's the choice of lumber and the attention paid to construction details which spells the difference between a professional job and one which looks like the homemade variety. We'll try to point out some of the pitfalls but the main thing is—work slowly, carefully, accurately. It's faster to measure twice and be sure you're right than to waste a piece of material and start over in the event of an error.

Choice of Lumber. Before you can order your materials you'll have to decide what type of lumber you want. This cabinet was made of ¾-in. walnut-veneered plywood which takes an excellent finish. To match the other furniture, you may prefer some other veneer. They're available in a great many types and patterns. A visit to your lumber or plywood dealer is recommended so that you can personally select your exact requirements. Matching the grain pattern of the exposed pieces is important. Take a close look at the front-view photograph of the completed cabinet. It isn't by accident that the "flames" of the upper panels coincide with those of the lower ones. It was planned that way.

The patterns of some veneers may be confusing and it is sometimes difficult to pick just the right combination. One good method is to cut out full scale tissue paper templates of the necessary veneered pieces (see Table 1) and to move these around on the matched veneer surface until the best

possible solution has been worked out.

Employ the factory-cut edges of the plywood sheet as one edge of as many pieces as possible. This gives you a straight edge to use as a guide on your bench saw. If you're careful, you should be able to cut all the face pieces from a single 4 x 8-ft. sheet of veneered ply, but some of the more difficult patterns may require a second sheet.

Now trace the templates on the wood surface with chalk or a soft pencil, being careful not to score the surface. Since the face veneer is only 1/28th in. thick, it is easily damaged beyond satisfactory repair. Label each piece with the code number coinciding with that in Table 1 and in the "exploded view" drawing.

You'll need a sharp handsaw, or a portable power saw, to rough-cut the individual pieces from the large plywood sheet. Be careful here—the underside of the thin veneer chips easily when cutting across the grain. Unless there's plenty of space between the pieces it's a good idea to "score" the underside of the wood deeply with a sharp knife near the "finish" line. Any chipping will then end at the scored line.

Finishing cuts on the individual pieces should be made on a bench saw, but even here care must be taken to avoid chipping. The use of a planer (hollow ground) blade helps, but doesn't eliminate it altogether. The best way is to accurately set the rip fence of the saw for the final cut and score the underside of the piece by running it through the saw with the blade clearing the table by a mere 1/16th in. Then, when you finally cut off the waste, with a second pass, you'll have a clean edge which requires no sanding.

Before you touch a blade to the wood,

Careful setting of saw blade and rip fence makes cutting of tongues a simple matter

Stopped grooves are cut with dado set or by repeated passes with regular blade—chisel is used to square stopped end

Bumper tacks recessed in top edge of front panels cushion the impact of dropped lids

Below: Veneer tape glued to exposed plywood edges gives solid lumber appearance

carefully study the construction details of the exploded view and the side and rear views. Since complete, step-by-step instructions can't be given here, it will pay you to become thoroughly familiar with the various parts of the cabinet and with the assembly details. We can, however, point out a few details which will help clarify the construction.

General Construction. Tongue-and-groove construction, with rabbets for the lid-hinge support piece (P) and bottom piece (K), is used throughout. This provides a sturdy cabinet while eliminating the need for unsightly and hard-to-install cleats. All joints are made with a good wood glue (see list of materials) which, when dry, makes a stronger and neater union than either nails or screws. All exposed plywood edges are covered with Weldwood flexible wood trim (to match the surface veneer) to give the completed cabinet the appearance of being made from solid lumber.

Careful inspection of the drawings reveals that, wherever a tongue-and-groove joint is used, the tongues are ⅜ in. less than the total length or width of the panel and the grooves are correspondingly "stopped." This adds gluing surface, thereby increasing the strength of the joint. The rabbets in bottom piece (K) and the corresponding rabbets in side pieces (I) and (J) are similarly treated.

Special attention should be paid to compartment separators (M) and (N). Detail 3 shows the cutting details for these pieces. Note that the ¾ x 6½ in. notch in the rear permits flushmounting of lid-hinge-support (P) with the back edges of the side pieces. A 1/16-in. step in the top edge of both (M) and (N) raises the permanently fastened lid (B) slightly above the two outside lids. This small difference is compensated for in the front by rubber bumpers fastened to the top edges of (D) and (F). In the rear, the outside lids are leveled by careful recessing of the hinges.

The 1/16-in. steps in the front edges of (M) and (N) provide the slight amount of clearance needed for proper operation of the touch-latch used in conjunction with drop-door (E).

Looking at the rear view, the holes and cutouts in lid-support (P) and back (Q) are for ventilating purposes. Electronic components get hot during operation and require adequate air circulation. The number of holes and the pattern isn't important. Remember, however, that each compartment housing a heat-producing component must be furnished with a cool-air intake at the bottom and a hot-air outlet at the top. The more material cut away, without weakening the panel, the better.

After all parts have been cut to size, dry-fit all joints—that is, assemble all unhinged parts. This is the time to check for accuracy of fit and to correct any discrepancies—not after glue has been applied. You'll probably need some help for this, unless you have enough bar clamps to hold the cabinet together. Always protect the stock from damage by clamps with wood blocks. Check everything carefully. After glue has been applied, it may be too late.

Satisfied with the fit, you can start the final assembly. Try to have everything you need in readiness beforehand—glue, a damp rag with which to

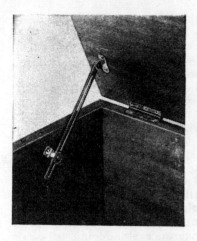

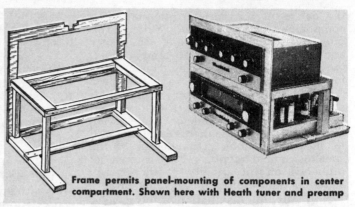

Frame permits panel-mounting of components in center compartment. Shown here with Heath tuner and preamp

Left: Friction lid-supports limit travel of left and right lids

wipe off the excess, sufficient bar clamps, and a try square to check for squareness of the assembled parts. Use plenty of glue between the joined pieces—enough so that it oozes out all along the edges as the joint is brought under pressure. The excess, however, should be wiped off, before it has had a chance to harden.

Best starting procedure is to lay the end pieces (I) and (J) on edge and join them to bottom piece (K). Wood screws may be used, through the bottom piece, to hold these parts together. They won't add much to the strength of the union, but they will eliminate the need for an unwieldy set of clamps. If screws are to be used, be sure to predrill pilot holes (after checking for squareness) before glue is applied.

Horizontal divider (L) is next, followed by front panels (D) and (F). Again, make sure that all parts match perfectly.

The rest is easy. Like the bottom piece, hinge support (P) may be fastened to the sides with screws since these won't show from the front. Dividers (M), (N) and (O) are next, followed by lid (B). The latter may need to be trimmed so that it just bridges the stepped-up edges of (M) and (N).

Now it's time to tape all exposed edges. Contact cement is recommended for this job, but this takes special care. You only get one chance, since the cement makes an immediate bond. Make sure that the tape lines up evenly with the entire surface before making contact. Otherwise you'll ruin a lot of tape. Trim the excess tape with sharp knife or razor blade and finish with fine garnet paper.

Hinges for lids (A) and (C) are recessed in the top edges of (P) and underneath the lids. Properly installed, they will raise the back of these pieces $\frac{1}{16}$ in., to be flush with the back of center lid (B). The outside lids are leveled at the front with rubber bumps installed on the top edges of (D) and (F). The bottom doors (G) and

(H) are then hinged in a similar manner.

Knife hinges are used for the drop-door (E). Remember, however, that all doors and lids must be taped before being installed. A bit of jockeying, even some edge trimming, may be required to obtain a close fit between these and the adjacent stationary panels.

Installation of the $\frac{1}{4}$-in. plywood back (Q) and the various items of hardware completes the construction project. The hardware consists of three friction lid supports (one for each of the hinged lids and one for the center drop door), four reversible lid supports (two for each of the bottom doors), three touch latches and a set of brass legs with mounting plates. The instructions supplied with the touch latches should be followed carefully to assure proper operation of the three doors.

A word about "finishing." The appearance of even the best cabinet can be utterly ruined by a poor job of finishing. The way you finish your cabinet depends, of course, on the rest of your furniture. You may wish to stain or just varnish the outside, or you may decide to paint the whole works. We won't try to second-guess your requirements by furnishing instructions here. Anyway, there's plenty of available literature on the subject and we suggest you visit your library unless you've had plenty of previous experience in this line of work.

Looking Ahead

For all practical purposes, the cabinet is finished. There still remain a few odds and ends, but these will have to wait until you have selected your equipment. For example, you'll have to provide corner posts or some sort of frame to which the mounting boards of the record player and tape recorder can be fastened (see "exploded view") and you'll have to drill holes in various separator panels through which the cables of the various interconnected components can be passed. Finally, you may want to "panel mount" the tuner and amplifier in the center compartment, though these components could be installed merely by setting one on top of the other.

But there are instances where the equipment cabinet becomes more than a mere housing for the electronic components. In cases where a loudspeaker is to be mounted in the main cabinet, the design of the speaker compartment can have as great an influence on the quality of the overall sound as that of any other component.

Normally, the installation of the speaker in the same cabinet with other electronic components is frowned upon by the confirmed audiophile. Small speakers in limited-size enclosures, it is argued, can not reproduce the lowest bass tones with the same efficiency as their larger counterparts. Further, vibrations set up within a speaker enclosure could adversely affect the performance of the record player and other components mounted in a common cabinet. But these arguments are only partly valid.

Today it is possible to buy speakers especially designed for small enclosures, and some of the so-called "bookshelf" systems are among the most highly rated units in the field. The problems of interaction between speaker and other parts usually can be resolved by careful isolation. While a separate speaker enclosure is definitely preferable, where space is a factor a built-in speaker can give excellent results.

The storage compartment of the cabinet, behind one of the lower drop doors, has ample volume for adequate housing of 8", 10" or 12" speakers. The installation of a complete monophonic speaker system will, of course change the appearance of the cabinet to some extent. Since such speakers must radiate outward into the living room, the speakers are front-mounted on the panel which, in turn, must be covered with grille cloth to protect the speaker cone. Though the adjacent storage compartment is not altered, it is probably best, from an appearance standpoint, to carry the grille-cloth pattern to the adjacent door as well, framing the edges with a suitable molding or trim.

For stereo it is possible to use a system whereby only the low frequencies are produced by the speaker in the cabinet. The high frequencies, together with the stereo information, can be reproduced by two small, wall-mounted speakers, one on either side of the main cabinet. In such cases it is possible to mount the low-frequency speaker in the bottom of the compartment, facing the floor, so that the appearance of the cabinet need not be altered.

TABLE 1 – LIST OF MATERIALS

1 SHEET VENEER PLYWOOD, ¾" x 48" x 96", (Veneer two sides, matched one side)

CODE	DESCRIPTION	SIZE	REMARKS
A, B, C	TOP LIDS	16" x 18"	
D	LEFT FRONT PANEL	12¾" x 17⅝"	⅜" x ⅜" tongue in left edge, stopped ⅜" from bottom
E	CENTER DROP DOOR	12¾" x 18"	
F	RIGHT FRONT PANEL	12¾" x 17⅝"	Same as D but tongue in right edge
G, H	BOTTOM DROP DOORS	13¼" x 26¼"	
I, J	LEFT AND RIGHT SIDES	16" x 26"	See side view and detail drawings for groove and rabbet dimensions
P	BACK HINGE-SUPPORT	6½" x 53¼"	⅜" x ⅜" rabbet on each end. See rear view for cutout

1 SHEET ¾" FIR PLYWOOD

CODE	DESCRIPTION	SIZE	REMARKS
K	BOTTOM	14¼" x 53¼"	⅜" x ⅜" stopped rabbet each end, ⅜" x ¼" stopped groove in center, see details 5 & 6
L	HORIZONTAL PARTITION	14¾" x 53¼"	⅜" x ⅜" stopped tongue each end, ⅜" x ¼" stopped grooves for M, N, O
M, N	TOP PARTITIONS	12⁵⁄₁₆" x 14¾"	⅜" x ¼" stopped tongue bottom edge, see details 3 & 4 and text
O	BOTTOM PARTITION	13"h. x 14¼"d.	⅜" x ¼" stopped tongue top and bottom edges

1 SHEET ¼" FIR PLYWOOD

CODE	DESCRIPTION	SIZE	REMARKS
Q	BACK PANEL	20½" x 53¼"	See rear view for details. Screw to rear edges

Weldwood flexible wood trim (veneer tape), 9 rolls, @ 1" x 8'; Weldwood plastic resin glue—mix as directed—for all glued joints; Weldwood contact cement for flexible wood trim; 1" x 2" (open) butt hinges (10); 1 pr. knife hinges (IR & IL) for center drop door; friction lid supports (1 for each lid, 1 for center drop door); Stanley reversible lid supports, (2 for each lower door); brass legs (6") with mounting plates; rubber tack bumpers (4).

A HIGH-FIDELITY STEREO AMPLIFIER (CHANNEL)

By Otto Fried

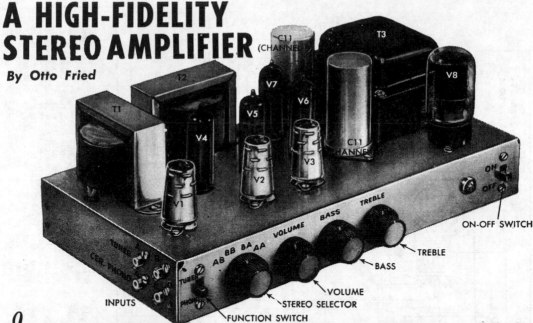

INPUTS · FUNCTION SWITCH · STEREO SELECTOR · VOLUME · BASS · TREBLE · ON-OFF SWITCH

*I*F YOU LIKE MUSIC but have so far resisted the temptation to scrap your present phonograph in favor of high fidelity—don't listen to stereo! But, if you already have exposed yourself to the stereo record, you may as well start planning the location of your two speakers—for, no doubt, you will have succumbed to the spell of three-dimensional sound and, whatever your past resistance to hi-fi, it will have been shattered by the magic of stereo.

But stereo, particularly high-fidelity stereo, is likely to be expensive. The dual amplifier and speaker requirements for stereophonic sound reproduction are not compatible with low cost, and the price of a really good stereo system is considerably higher than that of a comparable monaural unit. Money-saving short cuts are possible, of course. For little more than the cost of a stereo cartridge, almost any good monaural phono system can be converted to stereo by employing the amplifier and speaker of a suitable radio or TV set as the second channel (see "Stereo Music at Low Cost.") the inadequacies of such conversions, both from a standpoint of fidelity and operating convenience, will soon become apparent. The only uncompromising path to money-saving high-quality stereo is to dust off the tool box and build some of the necessary components yourself.

The amplifier described here, actually two amplifiers in one, combines stereo flexibility with true high-fidelity performance. While not "cheap," its construction cost is far below that of commercially assembled units with similar specifications, and its design is such that a more experienced hobbyist should have little difficulty in duplicating the original model.

No tricky circuitry here. No critical adjustments, hard-to-get parts or added frills which increase costs and complicate operation. Just a straightforward circuit of a dual amplifier, using a common power supply, with sufficient power to fill even the largest living room with clean, undistorted sound.

The principal difference between a stereo amplifier and a monaural one is the fact that the former has two complete and independent amplifier channels. There are, however, other differences which contribute to operating convenience and stereo flexibility. These are associated with the input switching arrangement and can readily be seen from the schematic diagram on page 1052

Note that the amplifier has four input jacks. Two of these, labeled TUNER and CER. PHONO, are associated with the A amplifier channel while their counterparts are associated with channel B. The TUNER jacks are intended to receive the output plugs from separate AM and FM tuners, and the CER. PHONO jacks receive the two separate output cables from a ceramic phono cartridge.

With switches S1 and S2 in the positions shown, one TUNER input jack is connected to amplifier channel A and the other to channel B. This permits the reception of stereophonic broadcasts which are available in many sections of the country on a limited but regular basis. With S1 in the CER. (down) position, the two elements of a stereo phono cartridge are connected to

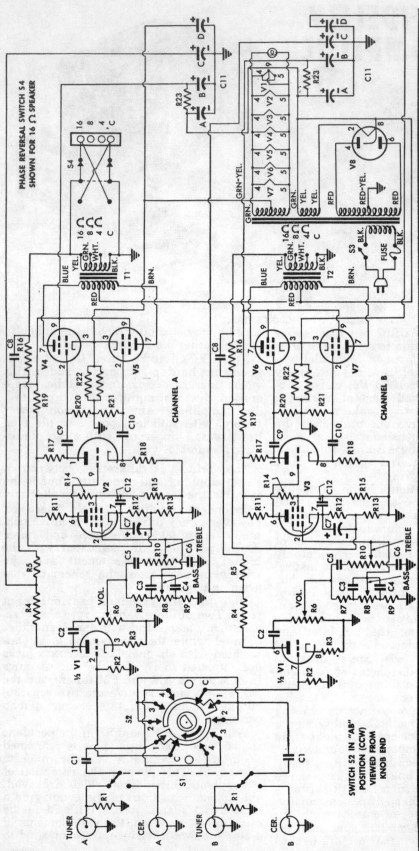

LIST OF MATERIALS

RESISTORS: (All resistors are ½-watt ± 10% unless otherwise specified. K = 1000 ohms, M = 1,000,000 ohms. 2 sets of the following values are required) R1,R15—100K; R2—2.7M; R3—6.8K; R4,R7—220K; R5—470K; R6, R8,R10—1M potentiometer, audio taper (requires dual, individually variable controls such as Mallory Concentric Midgetrols or equivalent; R9—22K; R11—2.2M; R12,R19—10K; R13—47; R14—1M; R16—2.7K; R17,R18—270K; R20,R21—330K; R22—165. 4 watts (2 330-ohm, 2-watt resistors connected in parallel); R23—2.2K, 2 watts.
CAPACITORS: (All are disk ceramics unless otherwise specified. Values given in mfds. 2 sets of the following values are required) C1—.02; C2,C12—0.1; 400-v. tubular; C3—.001; C4—0.01; C5,C8—0.00047; 400-v. tubular; C7—50.0, 10-v. electrolytic; C6—0.05, 400-v. tubular; C11—4-section electrolytic, sections A, B, C are 40 mfd./450-v., section D is 40 mfd./25-v.
TUBES: V1—12AU7/ECC82; V2,V3—6CQ8; V4,V5.—V6,V7—7189/6BQ5A; V8—5V4GA.
TRANSFORMERS: T1,T2—output, (primary impedance—8000ct, sec.-4, 8 and 16 ohms), Triad type S-31A; T3—power (plate-700vct 200 ma., filaments—5v./3a. and 6.3 vct./6 a.) Thordarson type 22R07.

SWITCHES: S1,S4—d.p.d.t. slide switch; S2—2 pole, 5 position rotary switch, shorting type (5th position lug not used); S3—s.p.s.t. slide switch.
MISCELLANEOUS: Chassis, 2 x 7 x 13-in. steel or heavy-gauge aluminum; 9-pin min. tube sockets, (4); 9-pin min. tube sockets with shields, (3); (all min. sockets are saddle type), octal tube socket; pilot-light assembly; No. 51 bulb; line cord with a.c. plug; phono-input jacks, (4); type 3AG, 2-amp. fuse and fuse holder; 4-term. output terminal strips, (2); No. 14 tinned bus wire; 4-lug terminal strips, (2); rubber grommets, (5); dual knobs for controls, (3); matching knob for switch.

PHASE REVERSAL SWITCH S4
SHOWN FOR 16 Ω SPEAKER

CHANNEL A

CHANNEL B

SWITCH S2 IN "AB"
POSITION (CCW)
VIEWED FROM
KNOB END

TUNER

CER.

TUNER

CER.

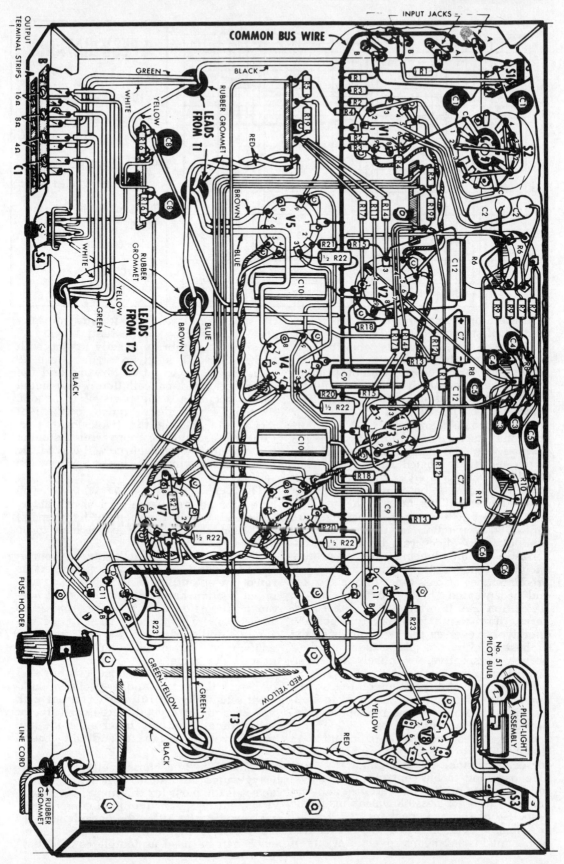

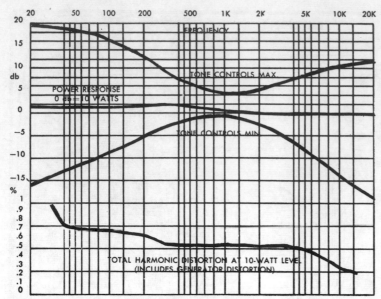

SPECIFICATIONS

RATED POWER—
10 watts per section

FREQUENCY RESPONSE—
20-20,000 c.p.s. ± 1 db

HUM AND NOISE—
68 db below rated power

TOTAL HARMONIC
DISTORTION—
See curve

SENSITIVITY—
0.3 volt

separate amplifier channels for the reproduction of stereo records. This same position gives excellent results when playing monaural records with the stereo cartridge. While monaural records cannot produce true stereo sound, the use of two amplifiers and speakers adds a pseudo-stereo effect which can be surprisingly realistic.

The stereo selector switch, S2, has four positions. Its function in the first or AB position has just been described. In the second position, labeled BB on the front panel, the switch applies the signal from the B TUNER jack to both amplifier sections simultaneously. This inserts the pseudo-stereo effect to the program of whatever tuner is connected to this jack. The pseudo-stereo effect can be further enhanced by unbalancing the separately variable tone controls, thus applying a predominance of bass tones to one speaker and accentuated "highs" to the other.

Position BA is often called "stereo reverse." For stereo material, this position effectively reverses the two halves of the orchestra, either to place them in their proper perspective, or purely for demonstration purposes.

Finally, the AA position of the switch applies the signal from tuner A to both amplifier sections to give monophonic reproduction from tuner A.

Other stereo requirements included in the amplifier are separate volume controls for each channel and independently variable bass and treble controls. These permit balancing of the two stereo signals and compensating for possible variations in the response of the two speakers.

A phase-reversal switch, S4, is included to permit instantaneous reversal of one of

the speaker voice coils. With any multiple-speaker system it is essential that all speaker cones vibrate exactly in step with each other. If a given signal were to cause one cone to move forward and the other backward, cancellation of the signal would occur in some parts of the room. Switch S4 provides a quick, convenient means for phasing the two speakers. A slow trip around the room while listening to a monaural signal source will leave little doubt as to which is the correct switch setting.

The performance of any amplifier can be evaluated from its electrical characteristics and, within the scope of its intended operation, this amplifier leaves little to be desired.

The performance curves and specifications table tell the story at a glance. At its rated power output of 10 watts, each amplifier section has *less than 1% total harmonic distortion over a range from 30 to 14,000 c.p.s.* This assures 20 watts of virtually undistorted power—more than enough for practically any application around the home.

A flat frequency response (within ± 1 db) over the entire audio spectrum, sufficient sensitivity for full power output with any ceramic or crystal stereo cartridge or radio tuner, and an inherent hum and noise level below normal audibility round out the details.

A 7 x 13 x 2-in. chassis, either steel or heavy-gauge aluminum, will conveniently house all the parts for this stereo amplifier. Placement of chassis-mounted components is shown in the title photograph and in the pictorial diagram. The parts themselves can be used as templates to determine the exact dimensions and positions of the necessary cutouts.

After installing the chassis-mounted parts, solder the heavy bus wire in place. This is grounded to the chassis at the input jacks and terminated at the upright electrolytic capacitors. These should be insulated from the chassis by means of their fiber wafers.

The rest of the wiring, although somewhat crowded in the vicinity of the controls, should present no problems. Start at the input jacks and work toward the power supply, making sure that each wire and part is well soldered to its proper connecting point. Follow the pictorial wiring diagram and use the schematic diagram to check your work after all wiring is finished.

Resistor R22 consists of two separate resistors connected in parallel. In the pictorial, the individual resistors of each parallel combination are labeled "½ R22," to avoid confusion.

A metal bottom plate should be used to cover the bottom of the chassis after all wiring has been completed and thoroughly checked. The bottom plate reduces hum pickup and prevents contact with dangerously high voltages appearing inside the chassis when the amplifier is turned on.

The amplifier should be turned on only after your loudspeakers have been connected to the terminal strips. Either 4, 8 or 16-ohm speakers may be used, but the phase reversal switch, S4, is wired, as shown, for a 16-ohm speaker. For an 8-ohm speaker, the wire from the junction of R16, C8 and the 16-ohm lead of T1 is connected directly to the 16-ohm terminal rather than S4 and the wire from S4 to the 16-ohm terminal is run, instead, to the 8-ohm terminal. The 8-ohm transformer lead is then soldered to the open lug of S4. Corresponding wiring changes must be made if a 4-ohm speaker is to be used.

As it stands, this amplifier was designed to handle the requirements of two radio tuners and a crystal or ceramic stereo phono cartridge. With the function switch, S1, in the CER. PHONO position, the input resistance to both channels is 2.7 megohms, the value of R2. While this value will generally provide good results with all cartridges of this type, manufacturers of some cartridges may specify other resistance values, or even a simple R-C network, for optimum performance. In such cases, R2 should be changed to conform with the manufacturer's recommendations.

Many high-fidelity enthusiasts prefer magnetic phono cartridges to crystal or ceramic units. This amplifier has neither the required gain nor the equalization needed for these low-output cartridges. It is a simple matter, however, to add a stereo preamplifier, or two inexpensive monaural units between the magnetic cartridge outputs and the CER. PHONO inputs of the amplifier. If this is done, the value of R2 should be changed to approximately 1 megohm. The preamplifiers need have no volume or tone controls because these functions are available in the main amplifier.

Now, if you already have a monaural hi-fi system but are planning to convert to stereo, the idea of retiring a perfectly good monaural amplifier in favor of a stereo unit just doesn't make sense. Furthermore, it isn't necessary. What you need is another single-channel amplifier, plus the switching provisions for stereo flexibility. In such a case, you can still build this amplifier, but you can save almost 50% of its construction cost.

Obviously, the B channel of the amplifier will not be needed and you can immediately omit V3, V6 and V7, plus all the associated circuit parts. V1 will still be needed, but no connections need be made to the second triode elements. In addition, the recommended power transformer can be replaced with one having a 120-ma. high-voltage rating for a further, substantial cost reduction.

The inputs and the switching circuits, however, should be retained. The wire lead from lug C of S2, normally connected to pin 7 of V1, should, instead, be connected to another phono jack which must be mounted somewhere on the chassis. A shielded cable, terminated on both ends with phono plugs, can then be connected from this jack to the high-impedance input jack of your present amplifier. This arrangement permits both amplifiers to be in use for stereo or monaural applications.

NOTE: Because of the relatively high power supplied by this amplifier, the chassis-mounted parts, as well as the chassis itself, will become quite warm after prolonged operation. This is no cause for alarm, but it does suggest the need for adequate ventilation when the amplifier is mounted behind a panel or in a cabinet.

Film Cans Store Hi-Fi Tape

Large 400-ft. 16-mm. film cans make excellent low-cost storage containers for recorded 7-in. magnetic-tape reels. Each can will accommodate two reels. The cover may be sealed with a strip of masking tape on which titles or other desired data may be written. The steel cans not only protect the reels from damage but also prevent accidental erasing by stray magnetic fields.

Hartwell M. Hughes, Inglewood, Cal.

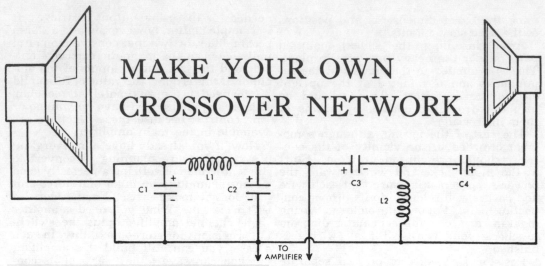

MAKE YOUR OWN CROSSOVER NETWORK

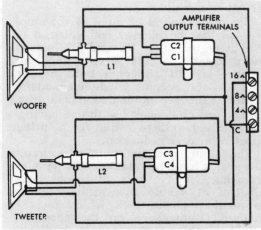

TABLE OF COMPONENT PARTS
SPEAKER VOICE-COIL IMPEDANCE

	3-4 OHMS	8 OHMS	16 OHMS
L1*	0.64 mh.	1.28 mh.	2.56 mh.
	Coil No. 6195	Coil No. 6199B	Coil No. 6318
L2*	0.16 mh.	0.32 mh.	0.64 mh.
	Coil No. 6196	Coil No. 6195	Coil No. 6195
C1-C2	20-20 mfd., 25wv.	10-10 mfd., 50 wv.	5-5 mfd., 25wv.
C3-C4	20-20 mfd., 25wv.	10-10 mfd., 50 wv.	5-5 mfd., 25wv.

* All coils are TV linearity or width controls made by J. W. Miller and available through leading radio-parts distributors.

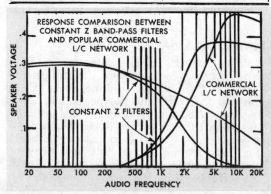

RESPONSE COMPARISON BETWEEN CONSTANT Z BAND-PASS FILTERS AND POPULAR COMMERCIAL L/C NETWORK

IF YOU'RE LOOKING for ways to improve the sound of your music system, take a critical look at your loudspeaker. Even if the other components are not of high-fidelity quality, chances are that the greatest improvement in sound can be obtained by concentrating on this portion of your radio, TV set or phonograph.

Single speakers, except for a few expensive hi-fi units, just aren't capable of reproducing the range of frequencies inherent in speech and music. The larger ones may adequately reproduce bass tones, but they can't handle the high frequencies which give brilliance and sparkle to music and a high degree of intelligibility to speech. Small speakers produce little or no sound at the low frequencies which provide the basic timbre of music.

Obviously, the solution rests in using two speakers, a large one (8 to 15-in. dia.) and a small one (3 to 5-in. dia.), each intended to reproduce a specific frequency range. And that's where the crossover network comes in.

The network is essentially a filter which divides the audio-frequency spectrum into two (or more) bands, sending each band to the particular speaker best equipped to reproduce it. In doing this, it must keep the low frequencies out of the high-frequency speaker (called tweeter) and the high frequencies out of the low-frequency reproducer (called woofer). Otherwise, the frequencies at opposite ends of the spectrum would interact, giving rise to a serious form of distortion.

The network shown here consists of two constant-impedance (Z) bandpass filters which do an excellent job of frequency separation. What's more, it is made of inexpensive parts which are available from most radio-parts dealers. Its characteristics, as compared with those of a particular commercial L/C filter, show a steeper slope near the crossover point and a smoother over-all response.

The filters consist of adjustable TV coils and aluminum electrolytic capacitors whose values, for various speaker imped- ances, are given in the table. Ordinary radios and TV sets are designed for speak- ers with 3 or 4-ohm voice coils, while hi-fi systems with separate amplifiers usually have provisions for matching any speaker impedance. The choice of filter parts, therefore, depends on your speaker selection.

For the specified parts values, the cross- over point (the frequency at which separa- tion becomes effective) is approximately 2000 cycles. This choice of frequency makes the network suitable for a number of high- fidelity woofer-tweeter combinations as well as for inexpensive replacement-type speakers.

The diagrams on page 1056 give details for connecting the parts and speakers, but you'll have to make a couple of adjust- ments to obtain optimum results. While precise adjustments require test instru- ments, such as an audio-signal generator and output meter, you'll find that your own ears do a pretty good job. Start by turning the screws of the TV coils about halfway into their forms and then listen critically to the resulting sound. If the midfrequency range (the soloist, for example) sounds a bit weak, either loosen the screw of L1 or tighten that of L2. If the midfrequencies seem accentuated, reverse this procedure. The idea is to make the over-all response as smooth as possible and a little experi- mentation can produce excellent results.

With the woofer properly housed in a suitable enclosure, a two-way speaker sys- tem can provide a worthwhile improve- ment in sound quality. This one-evening project, therefore, should prove to be interesting and informative as well as high- ly rewarding. ★ ★ ★

STEREO UPSTAIRS AND DOWN

By Lothar Stern

IF YOU'RE GOING IN for hi-fi, why not go all the way?

Right now, stereophonic hi-fi represents the ultimate in the reproduction of sound, with nothing better even remotely visible on the musical horizon. Perhaps you al- ready have it in your living room. Perhaps you're just planning it for your basement recreation room.

Why not put the two together? Stereo upstairs and down—with convenient con- trols to bring music where you want it, when you want it. This article tells you how it can be done, pointed up by the case history of a Park Ridge, Ill., family. They knew what they wanted and then put two and two together and came out with one —a single system that serves upstairs and downstairs to the satisfaction of all.

The Kaspers had just purchased a stereo system and they were eager to try it out. But an hour after the components had been unloaded from the family station wagon, they still stood unopened in the vestibule. In an adjoining room, the proud, new owners were settling their last remaining difference of opinion — upstairs or down?

Like so many of today's homes, the Kasper domicile boasts a comfortably fur- nished basement recreation room. Here, Ed spends most of his leisure hours, and here, it seemed to him, would be the ideal place for the stereo installation. But Vivienne had other plans. Most of her day was spent upstairs, and why shouldn't the system be installed where it would get the most use? The living room, she insisted, was the best place for it.

With the components waiting to be in- stalled, the dispute demanded an immedi- ate settlement and when a decision was reached, Ed had won his point. But not without a major concession.

The system was to be installed down- stairs, in a built-in bookcase which Ed had

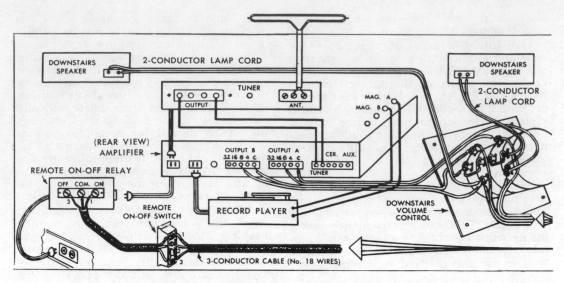

Wiring diagram of Ed Kasper's complete upstairs-and-down stereo installation.

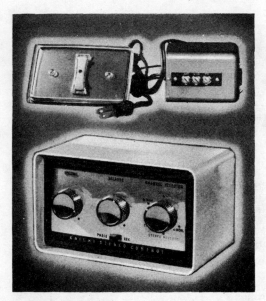

Principal additions to main stereo system are tiny Remcon relay (complete with wall switches), top, and Allied Radio's Knight stereo-remote-control kit

previously cleared specifically for this purpose. But provision would also be made for adequate reproduction upstairs, so that Vivienne could enjoy the new system while going about her daily tasks.

This promised to be a simple job. While two extra speakers would strain the budget a bit, the amplifier of the original system was deemed powerful enough to drive even two sets of speakers to better-than-normal listening levels. To meet Vivienne's stipulations, Ed would merely run cables from the upstairs speakers to the amplifier,

in order to obtain the sound in both places at once. And so the installation began . . .

Installing the components proved to be a simple matter. The thoughtful dealer had provided special color-coded interconnecting cables which removed all doubt as to what plugs were to go to which jacks. A couple of hours after the cartons were first unpacked, the system was turned on.

It worked perfectly. The unfamiliar controls took some getting used to, but, with the aid of the instructions, their mysteries were soon unraveled. By the end of the evening, the Kaspers were enjoying excellent results.

The extension speakers were ordered the following day.

Impedance matching. Adding extension speakers to a stereo system is simple.

When two speakers are connected to a single amplifier output, and both speakers have the same voice-coil resistance, the total speaker impedance is exactly one half that of the individual units. To match the amplifier properly, two 16-ohm speakers, for example, would be connected to the 8-ohm amplifier terminals, while two 8-ohm speakers would be attached to the 4-ohm terminals. Each speaker would then receive half of the total power delivered by the amplifier. So far as Ed was concerned, the most difficult part of the job was to locate a point in the basement ceiling where the wires could be passed to a suitable place in the living room.

After much deliberation, a single 4-conductor cable (two wires for each speaker) was run from the amplifier, along the ceiling molding, to the furnace room. From there, it passed through a hole in the ceiling to a recessed "planter" wall in the liv-

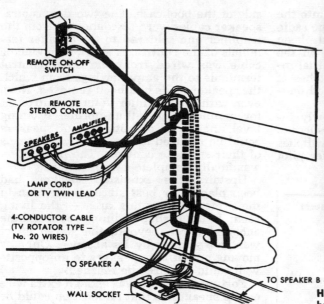

REMOTE ON-OFF SWITCH

REMOTE STEREO CONTROL

SPEAKERS   AMPLIFIER

LAMP CORD OR TV TWIN LEAD

4-CONDUCTOR CABLE (TV ROTATOR TYPE — No. 20 WIRES)

TO SPEAKER A

WALL SOCKET

TO SPEAKER B

Hiding wires between baseboard and carpet is hard on fingers but adds professional touch

ing room. Entrance to this room was gained through a hole in the baseboard where the four wires of the cable were split into two pairs, each running in a different direction to the two living-room speakers.

It was a job for the whole family. Even son Randy participated by pushing the cables out of sight between the baseboard and the wall-to-wall carpeting. When the set was turned on and the living room filled with music, everyone was elated.

But the elation was short-lived as the deficiencies of the installation became apparent. Not only was it impossible to balance both sets of speakers for optimum stereo perception in both places at once, but Vivienne soon tired of running downstairs before and after each telephone call to readjust the volume. There was much room for improvement.

Stereo remote control. It was not surprising, therefore, when, the following Saturday, Ed returned from a shopping trip and immediately disappeared into his workshop. Less than an hour later he reappeared, triumphantly exhibiting a stereo control unit he had just assembled from a kit of parts which, he announced, would solve the problem.

The Knight Stereo Control Kit seemed to have been designed specifically with Ed in mind. Not only did it permit the control of extension-speaker volume, it also provided a balance control for the extensions which was independent of the control on the main amplifier. In addition, there was a switch for reversing the connections to one extension speaker so that the pair could be properly phased, and another for choosing either stereo or monophonic operation. In short, the remote-control unit did every-

thing but turn the system on and off.

But even this last desirable function had been anticipated, for Ed had also bought a Remcon Remote Switch Kit which would permit him to do just that.

The switch kit consists of a small relay box containing a voltage step-down transformer and a low-voltage relay. The relay is momentarily energized at the touch of a remotely placed wall switch. Press the lower part of the switch and the relay contacts close to apply power to any device plugged into a receptacle on one end of the box. Press the top of the switch and the relay contacts open to shut off the power. Since all switching is done at low voltage, one or more remote switches may be connected to the relay box with ordinary cable, with no shock or fire hazard.

Again, the planter was removed from its shelf and two openings, one for the control kit and one for a remote on-off switch, were cut in the side wall just above the shelf. The previously installed speaker cable was cut at the point where it entered the living room and the four wires leading to the amplifier were connected to the "amplifier" terminals of the control box. The two 2-conductor lines leading to the extension speakers were fastened to the "speaker" terminals of the box.

Downstairs, a second on-off switch was fastened to the side of the bookcase and connected, with 3-wire cable, to the color-coded terminals of the relay box. A much longer 3-wire cable from this switch followed the route of the remote-speaker cable to the remote on-off switch upstairs.

Finally, the amplifier line cord was plugged into the socket of the relay box and that of the latter was plugged into the a.c. wall outlet. (The line cords of the radio tuner and record changer had been plugged into switched receptacles on the back of the amplifier during the initial installation.) When the on-off switches of the tuner and amplifier were turned on—nothing happened.

Then, Vivienne touched the newly installed on-off switch upstairs and—success. The pilot lights inside the remote switches glowed red; the tuner and amplifier pilot

---

Equipment Used in Ed's Stereo System

Initial System

Knight KN-734 Stereo Amplifier
Knight KN-120 Stereo FM-AM Tuner
Knight KN-2000 Speaker System (2)
Garrard RC88-4 Record Changer
G-E GC-7 Stereo Cartridge

Extension Speakers and R/C Equipment

Stephens 816/80FR Speaker System (2)
Knight Stereo Control Kit*
Remcon Remote Control Switch Kit with pilot-light switches and wall plates
Mosley 343-PK wall sockets with matching plugs (3)
Allied Radio No. 420005 Dual Volume Control
*Rated for stereo amplifiers furnishing up to 20 watts of power per channel.

---

lights lit up and, a few moments later, a previously tuned-in FM station came in loud and clear on both sets of speakers.

The remote-control unit worked like a charm. Upstairs the speakers could be balanced independently and the volume could be adjusted from maximum to a mere whisper. In the eyes of his family, Ed had gained the stature of an electronics genius.

Contentment reigned in the Kasper household until the following week end when trouble once more reared its ugly head. No sooner had Ed tuned in his favorite TV Western in the recreation room than Vivienne turned on the hi-fi upstairs.

Now anyone knows that two different programs in the same room just don't mix. Yet, when Ed turned down the hi-fi volume on the main amplifier, a squeal of dismay from upstairs told him that he had again incurred his wife's displeasure. Now, even with the upstairs volume control at maximum, the extension speakers were ominously silent. TV or hi-fi—that was the question.

Another trip to the radio store—this time for a dual-speaker volume control for the downstairs speakers, so that these could be operated at a level independent of the amplifier volume-control setting.

The control, Allied Radio part No. 420005, was mounted on a metal plate and installed next to the remote on-off switch on the side of the bookcase. The two downstairs-speaker cables were disconnected from the amplifier and soldered to the speaker terminals of the control. A short, 4-conductor cable was wired from the other control terminals to the amplifier lugs from which the speaker leads had been removed. Now, even with the amplifier volume control set for a much higher-than-normal listening level, the levels of both sets of speakers could be reduced independently by means of their separate controls. The installation was finally complete—well, almost.   •

Upstairs, the extension speakers had been placed for best stereo perception in the preferred listening area — the living room. In the L-shaped dining room and the enclosed porch beyond, the stereo effect was conspicuous by its absence. Only by moving one of the speakers to an opposite wall could this area be reached.

Fortunately there was enough extra wire on the speaker so that its location could be changed when the occasion demanded. But this practice soon produced a feminine veto. Not only did the wire, stretched across the carpet, present an unsightly appearance, it was downright dangerous to Randy who was wont to use the living-dining area as his personal speedway. Something had to be done.

Evaluating the situation, Ed found that the speaker location which would provide satisfactory stereo coverage for the dining area was near the point where the two speaker cables entered the living room through the planter wall. This made the solution simple and convenient.

At the preferred speaker location, Ed disconnected the wires from the speaker and fastened them instead to a Mosley type 343-PK transmission-line wall socket which, subsequently, was screwed to the baseboard. At the point where the cable entered the room it was cut and both ends connected to another socket. The latter was fastened to the baseboard directly over the entrance hole.

To the speaker terminals, Ed fastened a 4-ft. length of line cord terminated in a plug to match the previously installed sockets. It was now possible to move the speaker to either location and simply plug it into the nearby socket without resorting to long speaker leads. Even Vivienne conceded that this lent the finishing touch.

The system is not perfect. A change of radio stations, and a switch from radio to record changer still must be made from downstairs. But within these limitations, the remote installation offers all the advantages of two complete hi-fi systems—a low-cost means for obtaining stereo both upstairs and down.   ★ ★ ★

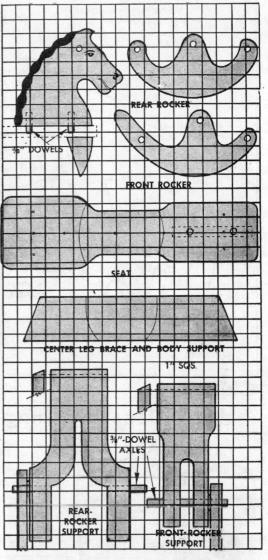

STAY-LEVEL ROCKING HORSE

By G. E. Hendrickson

EVEN THE YOUNGEST rider is in no danger of having this rocking horse throw him. The reason is that the two sets of rockers are so positioned that the body of the horse remains level at full gallop. Note how they are pivoted in much the same manner as a porch glider. All parts for the horse, including the rockers, can be cut from ¾-in. plywood, following the squared patterns on the facing page. Axles and rocker stops are lengths of ⅜-in. dowel. The stops are an added feature that limits the length of swing of the rockers, and also prevents the rockers from being inverted when the horse is dragged about by its youthful owners. On the front set of rockers, the rear stop is allowed to project about 3 in. outside each rocker to provide footrests for the rider, and also as a means of "driving" the horse.

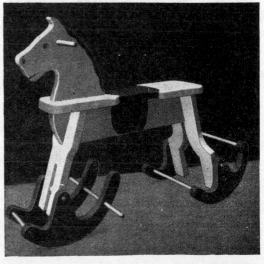

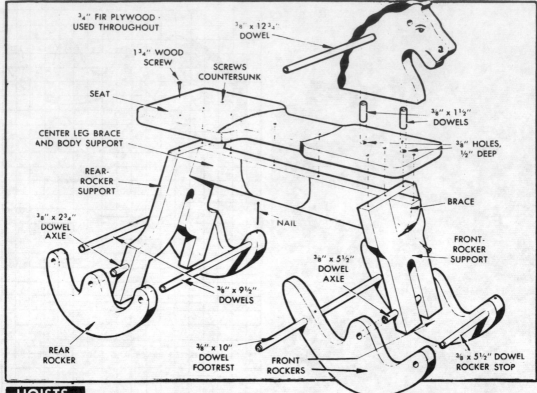

¾" FIR PLYWOOD ·
USED THROUGHOUT

⅜" x 12¾"
DOWEL

1¾" WOOD
SCREW

SCREWS
COUNTERSUNK

SEAT

⅜" x 1½"
DOWELS

CENTER LEG BRACE
AND BODY SUPPORT

⅜" HOLES,
½" DEEP

REAR-
ROCKER
SUPPORT

BRACE

⅜" x 2¾"
DOWEL
AXLE

FRONT-
ROCKER
SUPPORT

NAIL

⅜" x 5½"
DOWEL
AXLE

⅜" x 9½"
DOWELS

REAR
ROCKER

⅜" x 10"
DOWEL
FOOTREST

FRONT
ROCKERS

⅜ x 5½" DOWEL
ROCKER STOP

HOISTS

Hoist Uses Washing-Machine Motor, Gearbox

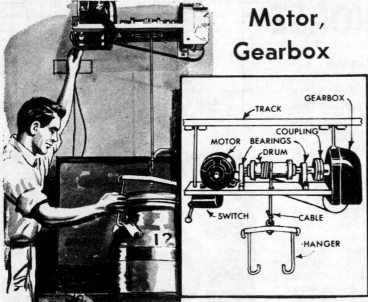

TRACK

GEARBOX

MOTOR

COUPLING
BEARINGS

DRUM

SWITCH

CABLE

HANGER

Although originally designed for lifting loaded milk cans from a cooler to a truck, this traveling hoist will prove handy wherever loads of a similar weight must be handled. A gearbox and electric motor from a washing machine are mounted on an angle-steel frame as shown in the detail.

To reduce any stress on the gearbox, a flexible coupling is used between it and the cable drum. A flexible coupling can be improvised by cutting a V-belt pulley in half along the center of the V-groove, then reassembling it with nuts and bolts, rubber washers being installed between the pulley halves. If a lathe is not available, the cable drum can be made by welding large washers to the ends of a length of steel pipe. The washers should prevent cable from sliding off the ends. It also may be necessary to weld still smaller washers to the large ones to reduce the hole to a size small enough to receive the drum shaft. It then is welded solidly to the drum ends. A switch is mounted on the angle frame below the motor, and the wire used to connect the motor to an outlet is long enough to allow the hoist to travel the full length of the overhead track. Trolley assemblies and track were purchased new.
Hobart Brothers Co., Troy, Ohio.

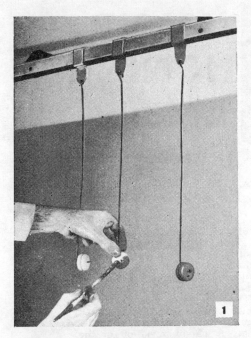

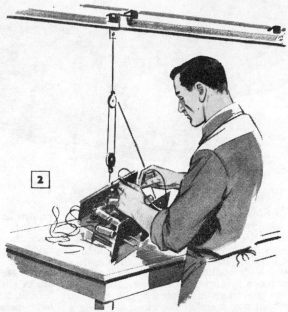

TRACK-MOUNTED HOIST FOR THE WORKSHOP

THIS HOIST when attached to the ceiling over your workbench in the manner shown in Fig. 2, provides the equivalent of a third hand for holding various work. To accommodate a number of lightweight pieces of work for painting or other purposes, U-shaped clips to which lengths of wire are attached are provided as in Fig. 1. The clips are forced from $\frac{1}{8}$ x 1-in. lengths of aluminum, allowing sufficient clearance for a sliding fit. Also, objects having a clamping device on them, such as the photofloodlamp in Fig. 4, can be clamped on the track when an overhead position is desired for the work.

The track is made from a $\frac{3}{4}$ x $\frac{3}{4}$ x 54-in. length of steel angle to which a $\frac{5}{8}$ x $1\frac{1}{16}$ x 54- in. length of hard maple is bolted as in Fig. 3. The track mounts consist of L-shaped brackets bolted on the back of the track and screwed to ceiling joists as indicated. The roller-equipped hanger for the hoist is made as detailed in Fig. 3. The rollers consist of two short lengths of $\frac{1}{2}$-in. rod center drilled to take $\frac{1}{4}$-in. bolts, and $\frac{1}{4}$-in. washers that are clamped against the roller ends when assembled to serve as flanges. The Z-shaped bracket from which the hoist is suspended is formed so that the lower flange is aligned vertically with the centers of the rollers. Any light-duty block and tackle may be used as a hoist, or it can be assembled from a length of rope and two single-pulley blocks equipped with beckets.

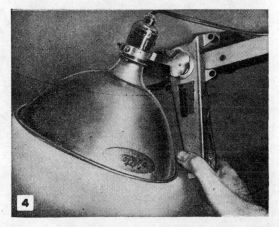

Below, photoflood lamp clamped on track provides ideal overhead lighting arrangement when photographing material or project displayed on workbench top

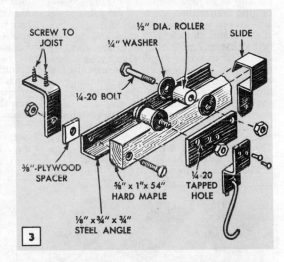

HAND HONING

has many uses

By Walter E. Burton

IN SMALL-SHOP PRACTICE, honing is simply the final step in either sharpening or dressing a cutting edge or finishing metal to a smooth surface before polishing or lapping. In metal finishing, honing has numerous applications where fit and appearance requirements do not call for the final operations of lapping or polishing. In present-day practice, both in sharpening a cutting edge and in finishing metals, hand honing is usually done with very fine abrasive stones which are available in a variety of sizes and shapes, grit sizes and degrees of hardness, Fig. 2. Not all of the abrasive stones pictured in Fig. 2 classify as hones, of course, as some are comparatively fast cutting and some are the combination type having one side coarse, the other fine. In sharpening a cutting edge, the main purpose of honing is to remove any roughness left from preceding operations done with stones of coarse and medium-grit sizes. The end result of the three-step procedure is a very smooth, keen cutting edge.

The bench stones, Fig. 2, commonly known as oilstones, generally are used in a fixed position, the work being moved over the surface of the stone in one of several uniform stroke patterns, back and forth, an overlapping circular movement, or a figure-eight stroke. When using the sticks, slips and hones, the work usually is held stationary and the abrasive is moved over the surface of the work or along the cutting edge. A handy variation of the abrasive stick is the engraver's pencil. It has practical applications other than the special purpose for which it was designed. For example, it's useful for finishing hard-to-reach areas of small parts such as jewel mountings, Fig. 1, and in instrument and model assembly where it is necessary to produce a bright finish without undue removal of material. Fig. 4 pictures another example where a small part is held in a collet chuck and hand finished with the engraver's pencil. A similar operation, using a slip, is being carried out in Fig. 3.

Figs. 8 and 9 picture important steps in sharpening a wood chisel. If the cutting

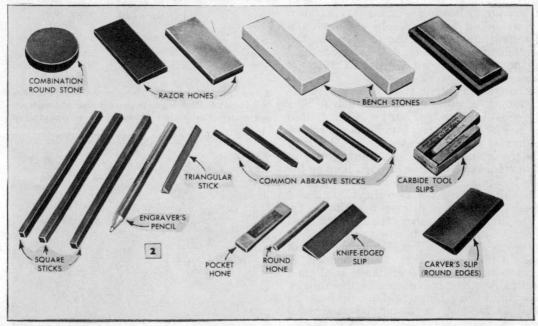

COMBINATION ROUND STONE

RAZOR HONES

BENCH STONES

TRIANGULAR STICK

COMMON ABRASIVE STICKS

CARBIDE TOOL SLIPS

ENGRAVER'S PENCIL

SQUARE STICKS

POCKET HONE

ROUND HONE

KNIFE-EDGED SLIP

CARVER'S SLIP (ROUND EDGES)

edge is very dull and nicked, rough grinding must be done to reshape the bevel and remove any nicks before the step pictured in Fig. 8 is carried out. Note in Fig. 8 that the blade is held with the bevel flat on the surface of the stone and also that it is held at a slight angle with the stone. This position gives better control as the sharpening strokes are made. The left hand applies pressure which should always be light. As this step proceeds to the point where grinding marks are removed from the bevel it will produce a wire edge, that is, metal at the extreme edge will be reduced in thickness to the point where it bends away from the surface of the stone. At this point the blade will cut fairly well but will not retain its edge for a normal time unless the wire is removed. This is done by inverting the blade, placing it flat on the stone and stroking very lightly.

To produce a very fine, keen-cutting edge, careful craftsmen go one step farther and dress the edge on a hard oilstone or slip. When doing this they place the bevel flat on the stone, then raise the blade very slightly so that the heel of the bevel clears the abrasive surface. Light stroking with the blade held in this position not only produces a razor-keen cutting edge, it also forms a narrow second bevel just back of the cutting edge to give added support. In all these sharpening operations, with the exception of rough grinding, a light oil should be used on the stone to float away the fine particles of metal removed in the sharpening and honing steps.

After rough-grinding the outside bevel on a gouge, carvers often finish the edge on a round-edge slip as in Fig. 10. Although in this case the slip is shown being held stationary in a vise, some craftsmen will

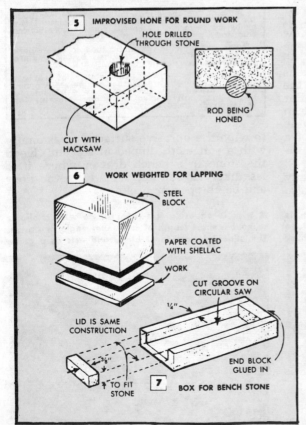

For a fine edge on a pocket-knife blade use a hard abrasive stick. Unless the edge is nicked or otherwise damaged, honing with the stick will suffice

Honing, or lapping, small gear wheels on a round bench stone removes burrs, dents or other imperfections and produces a fine finish. Use light oil on stone

prefer to use the slip freehand, holding the tool stationary rather than the slip.

Some jobs may require improvised methods, Figs. 5 and 6 being examples of special applications. For polishing rods and shafting drill a hole of the same diameter as the rod or shaft through an old oilstone, cut through with a hacksaw as in Fig. 5 and you have a handy hone for the job. In some instances it may be an advantage to weight the work uniformly rather than depend on finger pressure as in Fig. 12. This can be done as in Fig. 6, using a steel block to which the work is attached. This procedure, which is a form of lapping, utilizes a fine oilstone having a true surface.

To protect a fine, hard oilstone of the type shown in Figs. 8 and 9, which is ordinarily used at the bench, make a box, or holder, from hardwood as in Fig. 7. A few drops of glue will serve to hold the stone in the lower half of the box. Figs. 11, 13 and 14 are examples of hand operations where the work is held stationary and the abrasive is moved over the surface. For finishing a pocketknife blade to a keen edge, Fig. 11, cleaning up a worn lathe chuck, Fig. 13, or squaring the edge of a scraper blade, Fig. 14, these methods usually are satisfactory.

Keep the stone clean by wiping off any excess oil after using. It's a good idea also

TYPES OF OILSTONES USED IN HONING	
Hone* Material	Can Be Used to Hone**
	Knives and other edged tools
Silicon Carbide	Woodsman's edged equipment
	Iron castings
	Aluminum and brass parts
	Carbide tools
Aluminum Oxide	Woodworking and other shop tools
	High-speed-steel lathe bits
	Alloy-steel punches, dies, etc.
	Scissors
	Knives
Novaculite	Carving tools
	Razors
	Watch and clock parts
	Parts of models
	Gun-mechanism parts
	Workshop tools
	Carving tools
	Pocket knives
	Woodworking tools
	Leather-cutting knives
	Miscellaneous tools

Some of the above materials are made into honing wheels which are rotated in a jeweler's lathe or by other means at speeds considerably slower than for a grinding wheel of same size.

*The word "hone" is understood to mean here an abrasive stone called variously by such names as oilstone, sharpening stone and whetstone.

**Differences between the ability of various stones to hone different kinds of metals are not sharply drawn and, in general, it is possible to hone almost anything on any stone—allowing for variations in speed, finish, economy, etc.

to wipe the abrasive surfaces occasionally with a soft cloth dipped in solvent. Keep the stone in a bench drawer where it is less likely to fall accidentally to the floor and be chipped or broken. ★ ★ ★

If you drop a stone and break it, the broken parts are still useful. Here a section of a broken stone is being used to clean and polish a worn lathe chuck

A trick in squaring a scraper blade with a slip is to hold a short length of aluminum angle as shown. This slides along side of blade and acts as a guide

Is It a Good Buy?

BUILDER'S REPUTATION

Does the builder take pride in his product or is he more interested in the money he can make? Talk with owners of other homes erected by the builder. Was a qualified architect consulted in planning the house? Have storm sewers, other extras been provided?

BASEMENT

Does the basement have proper drainage? A good basement can be converted to a workshop, a rainy day playroom or a storage area. But be sure the basement isn't damp or easily flooded. Are the walls sealed against water? The stairway should be safe and well-lighted

NEIGHBORHOOD

Is it a new neighborhood with a future or an old area on the decline? Is it near slums or factories, or close to heavily traveled streets? Check the zoning laws—they may allow a rendering plant next door. Proper location can be most important in buying a house

TRAFFIC PLAN

Where do the doorways lead? Can the bedrooms be isolated from areas where other members of the family may be entertaining? Is the kitchen close to an outside entry or do you carry groceries through the living room? Study a copy of the floor plan of the house

KITCHEN AND BATH

Are the kitchen and bath up-to-date? Does the kitchen have adequate light and ventilation? There should be enough counter space and room for new appliances. The kitchen floors should be grease-resistant. Do you have to climb stairs to reach a bathroom? Is lavatory lighting adequate?

BEDROOMS

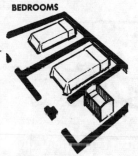

Nearly three fourths of all home buyers want at least three bedrooms; some prefer four. Bedrooms should have adequate ventilation and privacy. Space for the bed should not be broken by doors, windows, heat ducts or closets. Not more than two persons should sleep in same bedroom

STORAGE

Are the closets and cabinets designed for your needs? You may want separate storage areas for out-of-season clothing and clothes for current use. Are the closets lighted or do you have to grope in the dark? Will you need closets for toys or for household tools?

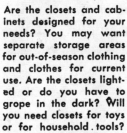

HEATING

Ask a heating contractor whether the furnace will be adequate for the size of the house and the climate. Also, will it be big enough if you add a room? Are heating ducts insulated? Trend is toward central air conditioning, so check the cost of adding a cooling unit

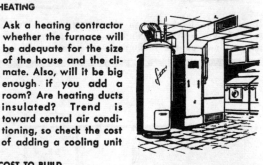

LANDSCAPING

Good lawn and shrubs add to the resale value as well as the appearance of a house. But shrubs should not be of the nuisance varieties that attract insects or make a mess of the yard. Yard should be adequate for fun and graded to drain water from house

COST TO BUILD

Bargains in real estate are rare but you may get more floor space per dollar in a bigger and older house. Find out what it would cost to build a new house to suit your personal needs. Then figure the cost of buying an older house and remodeling it to suit your taste

IS IT A GOOD

All home designs should start with a plan that meets the family's needs for good living. The arrangement of space and facilities in a house should be studied carefully before you build or buy

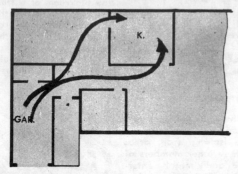

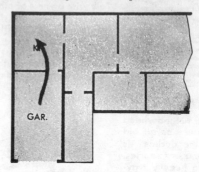

After you drive into the garage with groceries from the supermarket, how far away is the kitchen? If it's on the other side of the house, the plan is poor

Direct access from the garage or driveway to the kitchen, as illustrated above, can be found in the more efficient and desirable types of floor plans

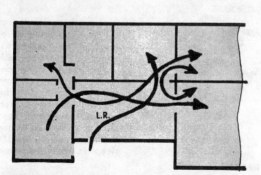

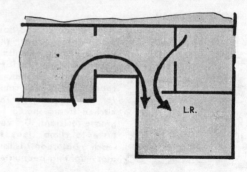

If all paths lead through the living room, it's a case of poor traffic planning. This room arrangement might give you the feeling you live on a freeway

In a better plan, the living-activity zone is in a "dead end" location. Access from the outside is fairly direct but the living room isn't a crossroad

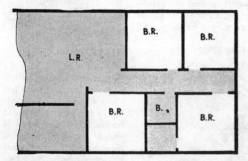

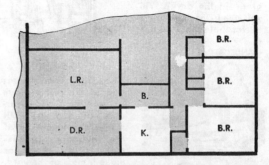

If there are small children in the family, it will be difficult for them to sleep when bedrooms are next to living-activity areas, as in the plan above

In a good floor plan, the sleeping area is isolated from the living-activity zone of the house. It permits adults to entertain without disturbing children

FLOOR PLAN?

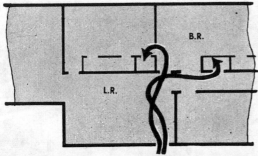

When visitors arrive on a stormy night, how far do you have to carry the dripping wraps before you can find a closet? Plan shown above would flunk this test

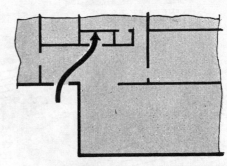

Good plan provides an entry closet near the outside door. Ample closet space in convenient locations is part of the secret of efficient space arrangement

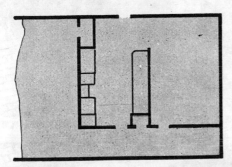

Kitchens should be planned to save steps but they also should provide room for eating facilities. Tiny kitchen above might reduce resale value of house

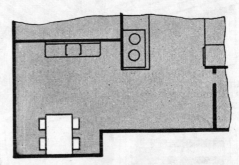

This plan has a larger kitchen and includes family dining space. Many surveys show majority of home-owners eat at least part of their meals in kitchen

Bedroom arrangement below makes poor use of available space for closets and requires long, narrow hallway

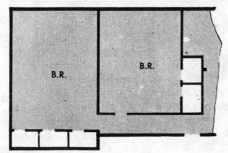

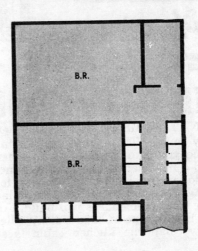

Plan at right shows how closet space can be gained in the bedroom zone by more effective arrangement of the total area. The master bedroom also gains a dressing room

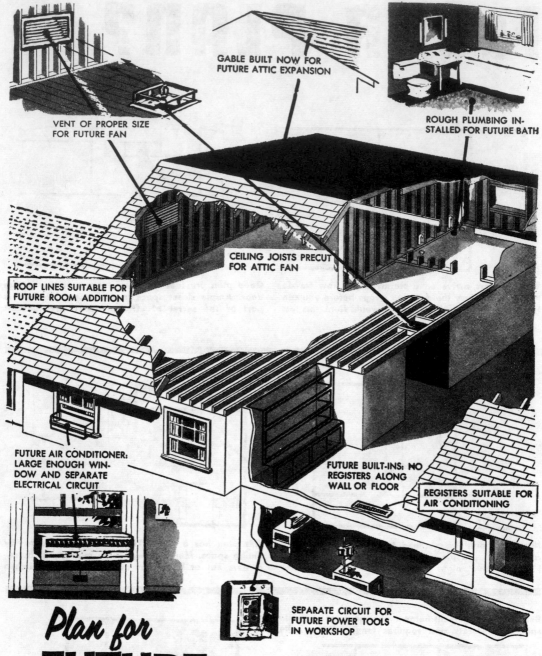

VENT OF PROPER SIZE FOR FUTURE FAN

GABLE BUILT NOW FOR FUTURE ATTIC EXPANSION

ROUGH PLUMBING IN-STALLED FOR FUTURE BATH

CEILING JOISTS PRECUT FOR ATTIC FAN

ROOF LINES SUITABLE FOR FUTURE ROOM ADDITION

FUTURE AIR CONDITIONER: LARGE ENOUGH WIN-DOW AND SEPARATE ELECTRICAL CIRCUIT

FUTURE BUILT-INS: NO REGISTERS ALONG WALL OR FLOOR

REGISTERS SUITABLE FOR AIR CONDITIONING

SEPARATE CIRCUIT FOR FUTURE POWER TOOLS IN WORKSHOP

Plan for FUTURE IMPROVEMENTS as You Build

ELIMINATE THIS, do without that, cut every corner. This is the discouraging experience you likely will undergo when you build a new home. There are just not enough dollars in the nest egg to pay for everything you want. But you can plan for future improvements as you build. For example, if you hope to have a dishwasher eventually, plan the kitchen cabinets so the dishwasher will simply replace one of the cabinet sections. Planning some built-ins in certain areas? Be sure there are no heat outlets, cold-air returns or electrical outlets in those spots. The house shown above has features taken from several different types of homes. Use the drawing as a check list in planning for the future —now. ★ ★ ★

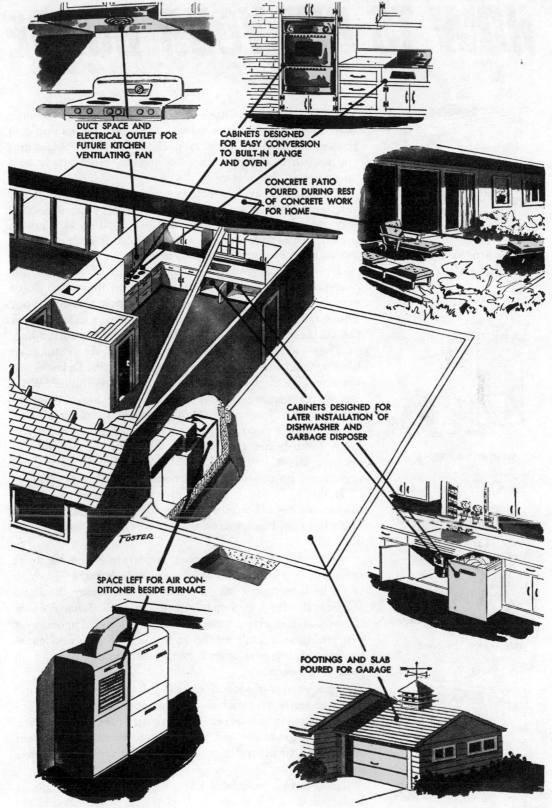

DUCT SPACE AND
ELECTRICAL OUTLET FOR
FUTURE KITCHEN
VENTILATING FAN

CABINETS DESIGNED
FOR EASY CONVERSION
TO BUILT-IN RANGE
AND OVEN

CONCRETE PATIO
POURED DURING REST
OF CONCRETE WORK
FOR HOME

CABINETS DESIGNED FOR
LATER INSTALLATION OF
DISHWASHER AND
GARBAGE DISPOSER

FOSTER

SPACE LEFT FOR AIR CON-
DITIONER BESIDE FURNACE

FOOTINGS AND SLAB
POURED FOR GARAGE

1071

HOW TO GET YOUR HOUSE

CLEAN OUT ATTIC, BASEMENT, GARAGE

CLEAN UP THE FURNACE

KEEP YARD IN TOP SHAPE

PAINT FRONT DOOR AND SHUTTERS

EACH YEAR millions of Americans play a gigantic game of musical chairs. Last year, for example, a restless 33 million citizens packed up their belongings and moved to a new home, leaving their old abode as a "new home" for others.

Perhaps you are perfectly happy in your present home; you may plan to stay there the rest of your life. This may well happen, but the odds are against it. Figures show that the "average" family—if there is such a thing— moves once every five to six years.

Even though you have no intention of selling your house at the moment, the information on these two pages may be useful in the future. These tips on selling your home come from real-estate brokers—professionals in the business of getting prospects to sign on the dotted line.

These experts say the first thing to do is take an hour's time to tour your home as a stranger. Drive down the street as though you were a prospective buyer. What is your first impression? Does the house look attractive and homey? Now walk through every room, analyzing all the home's good points and bad. List the assets—you know them better than anyone else—for the realtor. On another sheet list the liabilities, along with any good arguments he can use to overcome these drawbacks.

It doesn't usually pay to make major and expensive alterations to a house in order to sell it. Usually such alterations will not increase the selling price proportionately.

Inside the house, the most important thing to do is to *emphasize spaciousness throughout*. A buyer likes to think he is getting a lot of house for the money. You can increase the *feeling* of spaciousness in a good many ways. Clean out the attic, basement and garage, disposing of everything you don't intend to move with you and packing everything you won't need until you're settled in your new home.

Remove out-of-season clothing from the closets and pack or store it elsewhere. Uncrowded closets can convert a looker into a buyer. Remove all other out-of-season items from the house and yard, such as boating equipment and garden furniture in wintertime, skis and duck decoys in the summer.

Have a talk with the kids, if they're old enough to understand what's going on. If possible, find them a parking place for their bicycles outside of the garage, and insist that they keep their toys in their rooms whenever

IN SHAPE TO SELL

the house is being shown. Toys can give an appealing touch to a child's room, but the same toys underfoot can make the house seem crowded.

If your basement is dark and gloomy, make it seem larger by renting a sprayer and spraying the ceilings and walls a light color. Use a water-mixed vinyl or similar paint to get a good one-coat finish.

Suggest easy family living inside the house. If you have a fireplace, clean it out and lay some logs. To the buyer the sight will inspire a mental picture of a pleasant evening in front of the fire.

The most important room in the house is the kitchen, from the standpoint of selling. Glamorize it in any way you can. Give cabinets a new coat of paint. It may pay you to replace worn countertops.

REDECORATE KITCHEN

Repair the little things that the buyer is sure to notice. A loose porch step or a leaky faucet can profoundly affect the buyer's attitude, whether he knows it or not. Also, clean the furnace. For some obscure reason, men always look at the furnace of a home in the same way they kick the tires of an automobile.

When you show the house, have the windows sparkling clean and the drapes and shades open. This will make the rooms seem larger.

Outside the house, *suggest pleasant living, not work.* A lawn that needs mowing or a sidewalk that needs shoveling suggests hard work. Hire such work done if you must vacate the house before selling. If planting beds are overgrown and ragged, trim them back.

SPRAY-PAINT BASEMENT

Repainting the exterior is debatable, but one thing you can do is repaint the exterior doors, particularly the front door. It welcomes any visitor, including the buyer. Make it an appealing welcome.

Federal tax laws allow you to deduct all fix-up costs made within 90 days before selling your home. Keep receipts and a record of all such expenses.

Last but not least, if you turn the home over to a realtor, *let him show it without interference.* Selling is his business. He's much more likely to make a sale if you let him handle prospects himself. ★★★

LET REALTOR SHOW HOUSE

After checking patio wall with his pocket rule, building inspector explains to owner that wall must be lowered. It is a foot higher than legal limit allows, and it shields next-door neighbor's back yard

By **Richard T. Morris**
CHIEF BUILDING INSPECTOR,
CITY OF LOS ANGELES

as told to James Joseph

GET IN STEP WITH YOUR BUILDING CODE

In erecting roof and wall, homeowner unwittingly built a "room." This violates window minima in rooms off patio

Here, inspector discovers that center beam is unsupported. Two boards are hanging in midair

In yard above, the cabana wall is too high. Usually, back-yard walls may be no more than six feet in height. Furthermore, cabana is built too close to property line. This violates building code's side-yard law

HOME CRAFTSMEN by the thousands

—perhaps you among them—are right now pouring countless dollars and as many hours into home-improvement projects doomed to destruction.

Typical is the Illinois homeowner who labored a month of Sundays erecting a six-foot wall around his front yard. When irate neighbors complained, harried building inspectors had no choice but to ask him to lop off 18 decorative inches—to bring his craftsmanship within the 42-inch legal limit. He'd have conserved both muscle and money had he checked *first* with his local building office.

In New York, a homeowner converted his garage to a maid's quarters and ran afoul of a law common to most towns and cities. Unwittingly, he'd created a multiple dwelling in a neighborhood zoned for single-family homes. He was ordered to return the building to "original condition" —a garage. A moment's inquiry would have put his project in line with the building codes and saved him $3000.

More costly was the conduit-caused fire in Maryland which gutted a $30,000 home. Insurance sleuths voided the owner's policy—as they could by terms of its small print—when they discovered he'd installed the wiring without benefit of an electrical inspection. For $3—the price of a permit— he could literally have saved his house.

In California, a couple invested three

This vent for gas furnace was installed too close to valley flashing. Rainwater coursing along flashing might seep into vent and douse flame in furnace

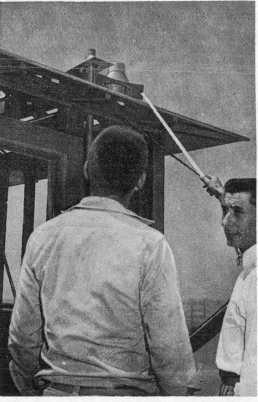

CHECKLIST FOR HOME BUILDERS

You'll probably need a building permit if:

1. Your home addition is valued over $100 (figuring *your labor* at going local rates).
2. The addition changes your home's use or "occupancy," say from a single to multiple-family dwelling.
3. You add a garage or convert the one you have to another use.
4. You wall in, roof or attach a patio to your house.
5. The pool you're building is deeper than 24 inches.
6. You build a retaining wall over four feet high.
7. You plan to install plumbing or electricity, either inside or outside your home.
8. Your barbecue's chimney is more than six feet high.
9. You drill a well or put in a lawn-sprinkler system.
10. You build a carport.
11. Your radio or TV antenna, tower or flagpole exceeds 45 feet in height.
12. The garden house you plan (lath house or pergola) has a floor area greater than 400 square feet.
13. Awnings or canopies extend 12 feet or more from your home's exterior walls.
14. You plan to install or alter street curbs or sidewalks.

weeks and $900 in a home-crafted room addition. Scarcely had they applied the last coat of paint than they received orders to demolish it. The new room, though expertly built, pre-empted the space which by law must be left between neighboring dwellings.

"Building codes?" shrugged the unhappy homeowners. "Why, we thought they applied only to contractors."

On the contrary, there's hardly a home project which isn't ruled, one way or another, by local building codes. True, you may not always need a *building permit*. But you always need to know the law—the *building code*.

What's more, if yours is among the 850 cities in 42 states operating under the "Uniform Building Code" (or the 150 southern municipalities using the "Southern Standard Code"), you'll likely need a permit *before* beginning any project which (1) changes the use or "occupancy" of your home; (2) costs more than about $100, figuring your own labor at local rates (some cities tab costs on the basis of $10 a square foot); (3) involves electricity or plumbing.

Free Information

Regardless of the project, it's a safe bet that before you pick up trowel or hammer you should pick up the phone and dial your local building office. Moreover, building inspectors have at finger tip a whole glossary of how-to-build-it information that's yours, free for the asking.

Maybe you're wondering whether the rafters of that detached garage you're planning should be two by fours or two by sixes. The building inspector knows, and advises you to buy two by sixes because he knows your local code.

What's the concrete formula for post-supporting piers under that patio roof you hanker to build? Within seconds the inspector's back on the phone with the answer: "One part cement, three parts sand, four parts gravel."

Or perhaps it's a retaining wall you're planning. The building office will give you the rough specifications, may even send an inspector out to the house to size up your problem. You pay nothing for do-it-yourself information, and but a modest fee for plan checking and building permits, if they're required.

How modest? Well, many building offices charge as little as $3 to check over plans for projects valued at $1000 and more. Once plans are approved, you pay another $5 to $6 for a permit, which gives you the green light to unlimber shovel and saw.

You've spent but $8 or $9, yet bought a bargain: the round-the-clock services of your building department.

As your project progresses, an inspector will check it over. He may suggest money-saving changes and labor short cuts. To-

Inspector notes cold joint in concrete foundation. Fault occurs when too much time elapses between pours

gether, you and the inspector will see the job through. Nor will you be asked to pay a cent more for all these services which, if you contracted them out, would likely run $10 to $15 per hour. Your original fee —$8 to $9 for the average home project— covers the works, and as many on-the-spot visits as you need to finish the job.

Unhappily, many home craftsmen who could most benefit from the inspector's years of do-it-yourself know-how neglect to ask his advice before taking tools in hand.

Recently, for example, I surveyed a residential tract whose $15,000 to $20,000 homes had been built within the past two years. Their owners, with incomes in the $6000 to $10,000 bracket, had money to spend—and they'd spent it putting up patios, fences and new room additions. Not one had bothered to apply for a building permit. Nor, for that matter, for construction advice. Small wonder that fully 11 percent of the home projects violated building codes, violated them enough to warrant citations.

One homeowner had installed a dozen light switches, every one of them illegal under the local code (they'd been ruled "not acceptable" by the fire marshal who blamed them for scores of fires).

Another had built a retaining wall with insufficient reinforcement to hold back a hill which threatened, even as I looked over the job, to bury his house.

Still another had crafted a barbecue in his front yard, a site illegal under most zoning regulations.

Looking out for homeowner's interests, inspector makes sure contractor understands window minima

"But," complained the householder, "it's my property, and I'll build my barbecue any darn place I please."

And people did, a short 25 years ago. They also built apartments next door to snug little bungalows. Nor was it uncommon for a 10-foot wall to rise, blocking both the view and light from a neighbor's house. You've seen such neighborhoods in the older parts of town. But you wouldn't want to live there, much less own one of the houses.

Building codes exist for your protection and safety—and for your neighbor's, too.

Recently, a homeowner hired a contractor to add a $5000 den. Luckily, before the contractor reached the plastering stage an alert inspector discovered that he'd set the room's girders on hollow concrete blocks. The added weight of the plaster, which often doubles the framed-in weight, would have crushed the blocks, wrenching the room out of shape and the plaster off the walls.

Winced the appreciative homeowner, "if it hadn't been for that inspector and the building codes, I'd have had nothing for my $5000 but a roomful of cracked plaster."

He might also have been left with a den whose windows (distorted in their frames) wouldn't open, and whose chimney, its flue lining cracked, might have set his house afire.

The inspector, and the rule book he carries, protect *you* from *your neighbor*, as well. In most cities the fellow next door can't build a barbecue without a spark-arrestor atop its chimney (sparks would threaten your home). Nor can he encroach upon your property line (he's got to leave a reasonable and specified "side yard" between his house and yours). Neither can he own a swimming pool unless he encloses it with a fence, its gate rigged with a kid-proof lock (thus, by law, he's required to protect *your* children from drowning as well as his own).

Set up in 1927 (and updated every three years), the Uniform Building Code is framed on the time-tested premise that if for safety's sake a brick chimney requires a fire-clay flue in Denver, the same lining is as necessary in Des Moines.

Manual for Homeowners

Most homeowners don't realize, however, that the Code is one of the most comprehensive do-it-yourself manuals ever compiled. It spells out specifically, for example, what kind of materials should go into your house, how its foundation should be laid, and the set back it must have from the street.

Nor is the code, as some have complained, either complex or contradictory.

On the contrary, it's written as much for the do-it-yourselfer as for the contractor.

Let's see, for example, what the Code has to say, in part, about windows—a section that's typical, and applicable to hundreds of home projects.

"Windows. All living rooms, kitchens and other rooms used for living, eating or sleeping purposes shall be provided with windows with an area not less than twelve square feet (12 sq. ft.) nor one-eighth of the floor area of such room. Not less than one half such area shall be openable."

Ironically, though the regulation is set down in plain language, it's one of the most frequently violated. Let's see why. Suppose you decide to add a den to your living room. The living room is 12 by 12 feet, or 144 square feet, and the contractor, abiding by the rules, installed 18 square feet of windows (1/8 the floor area, the legal minimum for a room this size).

But in cutting the door between the new den and living room you use half the room's former window area. You've violated the code, and also health and safety statutes. There's one obvious solution, of course: Install additional living-room windows, at least the minimum amount.

Just as commonly the window minima are violated when the owner of a U-shaped bungalow roofs and walls in what was once his patio and converts it into a den or bedroom. The windows in the three walls which now open onto the enclosed room are no longer "windows." Because they aren't, it's more than likely that the rooms they once brightened have less than minimum window area.

Are the window minima, and scores of minima like them justified? If you've been house shopping lately, I think you'll agree they are. You didn't carry a measuring tape as you went house to house, nor did you stop to measure window area. You didn't because you *knew* the house had been built to code specifications (thus had windows enough for light and health). Nor did you have to crawl beneath the house to check sewer connections. Neither did you chip off a hunk of foundation to have it lab-analyzed for strength. The code, in effect, had done that for you.

The code does more. In laying down zoning regulations, it protects your investment, insures that a foundry won't blight your neighborhood. Further, it guarantees that the neighbors won't turn their homes into motels or boarding houses. And, by the same token, neither can you.

Frequently, home owners run afoul of zoning laws because they don't understand the terms.

Front yard requirements: In a single-family residential zone (applicable to most of us) all homes must be set back a specified minimum and maximum distance from the front property line. In effect, front yards must have about equal depth (though this may vary under some codes as much as 10 feet).

Suppose that the minimum setback for houses in your block is 22 feet. Your house, however, is set 25 feet back from the front property line. You'd like to extend the dining room six feet into the front yard. Will the code permit a six-foot extension? Probably not, though you'd likely be allowed to add three feet, bringing your house within the 22-foot setback minimum.

Side yards: Most codes require that you have an open space—a side yard—between your house and the neighbors'. The side yard usually applies only to your house (but not, for example, to the garage). Some codes require a five-foot side yard (thus, 10 feet between houses). Some say the side yard must be no less than 10 percent of your lot width.

Your lot, let's say, is 50 feet wide. By the 10 percent rule, the open spaces on either side of your house must each be five feet wide.

More often than any other, homeowners violate the side-yard code. They extend den, patio, kitchen or dining room, closing this "breathing space" between their house and a neighbor's.

Rear yard: Just as the code specifies front-yard depth and width of side yards, it may also rule that your backyard be at least 25 feet deep (from the rear property line). Some codes specify a backyard "not less than 25 percent of the lot's depth."

There are exceptions, however, to even the code's most rigid edicts. The exceptions are necessary because, for one thing, there may be several types of lots—inside lots, corner lots, reverse corner lots and key lots—in the same block.

Side-Yard Construction

Regardless of lot type, some building may be permitted even in side yards. A carport, for example, is often permissible in a side yard so long as the structure is but one story high, not more than about 20 feet in length, and is entirely open on at least three sides (save for necessary supporting columns).

An attached garage may also be located in a front yard (though usually it must be set back at least five feet from the property line).

Cornices, sills, canopies and other architectural projections (but not bay windows) may often extend into a side yard. One code says, "but they may not project more than two inches for each one foot of side-yard width."

There's scarcely a project around the home which doesn't fall under your building code. You can, for example, fence your yard without getting a permit. Regardless, its height and placement must hew to the code. Generally you can build platforms, walks and driveways as long as they're not over two feet above ground nor constructed over the basement. You can put up flagpoles, towers and radio antennas, but they can't be over 45 feet high, nor attached to a building. You can build patios, yet they must comply with the code.

To help the homeowner comply, many cities have compiled easy-to-understand fact sheets. Among the dozen fact sheets available at no cost to the homeowner in Los Angeles, some detail minimum specs for low retaining walls, foundations and even one and two-story houses. One, for example, explains allowable fence heights on residential lots. Drawings simplify and interpret the code, telling the do-it-yourselfer all he needs to know about fences. (If yours is an "inside" lot set between adjacent lots, your front-yard fence may be no more than 42 inches high. But you may fence your backyard to a height of six feet).

Another fact sheet tells you how to build a detached garage. Drawings show how supporting posts should be centered, how many nails of what size must be used, and where. You're told, for example, that corner braces should be one by sixes. These are *minimum* requirements. If you want to use more than the required five eight-penny nails to secure the braces, you may. But you can't use less and stay within the code.

Instructions for Patio

Still another fact sheet for do-it-yourselfers explains how to put up a patio addition. Drawings indicate, for example, that you should use four by four-inch posts to support the patio's roof. And further, that the posts should be set on 12 by 12 by 12-inch concrete piers.

Building inspectors have made it unnecessary for you to thumb thru the 300 pages of the "Uniform Building Code." You're handed the rules on a single instruction sheet.

Nor does your building department stop there in catering to the fellow who hankers to build. Some inspection offices supply ready-made plans for projects ranging from two-story houses to fireplaces. You simply fill in the blanks with your project's dimensions and ask the inspector to approve them.

Filing for a building permit is almost as easy. Either by mail or in person you make application, detailing what it is you want to build. You may be told that your project doesn't require a permit (in which case, the inspector simply explains the code, hands you a fact sheet covering your project and sends you home to start work).

If a permit is required, you'll be asked to draw a plot plan (the scale usually ⅛ to ¼ inch to the foot). For simple home-projects (a breezeway, attached patio or remodeling) the building office may accept your own or a draftsman's plans, or plans from a magazine. Some offices, as I've mentioned, have plans already drawn which need only the insertion of your project's measurements. For elaborate or complex construction — anything "major" — you need an architect's plans and services.

For the average home project such as an attached patio, the building office will need a week for plan checking. If corrections are warranted, they'll be noted. And you'll be told to correct your drawings and return them for another look.

Once plans are approved and you've paid the plan-checking fee, you'll be issued a building permit. The permit fees, like local codes, vary. The average cost on a $1000 project shouldn't exceed about $6.

With your permit—your green light to build—you'll be given an inspection record card. The card is posted on your project, and must be available to the inspector.

Visits by Inspector

Modest home projects—a retaining wall, for example—may require only two visits by the inspector: one when you have the forms built and reinforcing steel installed, and another when the wall is finished.

Major projects require at least four checks of your workmanship and progress.

Foundation inspection is made *after* you've dug trenches for the foundation, have erected forms and installed reinforcing steel, but *before* you've poured concrete.

Framing inspection is made *after* all wood roof, wall and floor framing, fire-blocking and bracing are complete and all pipes, rough plumbing, chimneys, wiring and vents are in, but *before* you've placed any interior wall covering (rough-in plumbing and electrical work require, under most codes, the services of a licensed plumber or electrician).

Plastering inspection is made *after* all exterior, fire-resistive and structural plaster backing is in place but before you apply plaster or stucco.

Final inspection is made *after* your project is completed and ready for occupancy.

Nor should the home craftsman be vexed if the inspector spots a code violation and asks that it be corrected. The fact is that licensed contractors and professional craftsmen who've been years at their trades are almost as often found in error as the fellow putting up his first project. The inspector isn't infallible either.

Classic is the swank men's club in Oakland, Calif., which was completed some years ago, ready for tenants, before it was discovered that the contractor had forgotten to install bathrooms (nor had the building inspector been more perceptive).

More recently, a contractor putting in massive concrete piers for a multimillion-dollar university building couldn't savvy the architect's logic in designing some one size, and some another. Unhappily for the over-zealous construction man, the architect was on firm engineering ground. The contractor built all the piers alike—a boner far more costly than any homeowner's.

The fact is that homebuilders are often excellent craftsmen. Yet too often they transgress the code, jeopardizing the very projects on which they've spent months of effort and hundreds of dollars.

Not long ago I was summoned to a home on the complaint of a neighbor who objected to "what the people next door have done to their garage."

The people next door had done wonders. They'd converted the garage to a paneled den, its glass doors opening onto a patio.

They'd also broken half a dozen laws. They hadn't bothered to get a building permit (their project's evaluation exceeded $100). Just as unwittingly, they'd violated one of the most basic of residential codes: Having converted their garage, they'd literally put the family cars out on the street. Yet the code demanded garaging of one kind or another for the car.

Even after they'd paid a fine for building without a permit, the homeowners had to choose between returning the garage to original use or investing in a detached garage. Luckily, they had space enough for the detached unit. But the fine, construction corrections and the new garage cost them hundreds of dollars.

To get in step with their codes they'd have needed to spend only a dime—the price of a phone call to their local building office. ★ ★ ★

One of the biggest headaches for homebuilders, the warping and peeling of vulnerable exterior roof overhangs, can be solved with aluminum soffit. Economical and easy to install, the aluminum soffit will not rust, rot or warp, and is immune to termites. And, best of all, it leaves no ugly paint peelings

HE RAISED THE ROOF
—to add four bedrooms

This is how the Schroeder's simple two-bedroom home looked before they decided to add a second story

WHEN CAL SCHROEDER and his family of Lombard, Ill., outgrew their small four-room house, they had two possibilities for expanding their living space. One plan, which Cal favored originally, was the addition of at least two rooms at the back of the house, eventually making it an L-shaped structure. Such an addition would give them the minimum of needed living facilities, but this type of expansion would just about ruin the playground area in their small back yard. The Schroeders have four young children. The other plan involved the expansion of this small house into a two-story structure, providing four bedrooms on the second floor.

At the outset, there seemed to be numerous problems connected with the idea of adding a second story to an existing one-story house. The family had to live and be

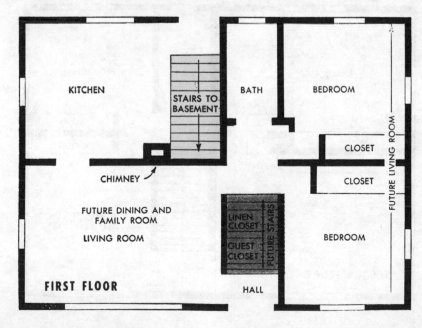

By
Donald R. Brooks

Floor plan of home before remodeling shows how easily it was altered. Former living room became a dining-family room and the new living room is in bedroom area

Look close and you'll see the lower part of this house. Second story has four rooms.

kept under adequate roof while the remodeling was under way. The work involved, through the eyes of inexperienced builders, seemed considerable and would most certainly stretch through the cold winter months. Normal living for the youngsters could not be interrupted during this rather long ordeal and this was of the utmost importance to Cal. He was determined to accomplish whatever changes were necessary without moving the family from the premises. This was not only a major factor from the standpoint of the children's well-being—the family finances made it highly advisable to avoid the expense of renting another home in town for the family during the time of remodeling.

The idea of adding a second story would leave their back yard intact and such an expansion would quite likely improve the

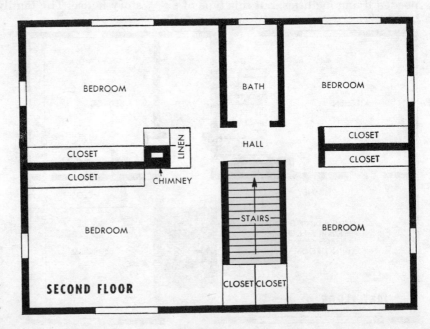

Stairs to the new second floor occupy space of former guest and linen closets. Bath was placed directly above first-floor bath to save on the plumbing costs of project

BEDROOM · CLOSET · CLOSET · LINEN · CHIMNEY · BEDROOM · BATH · HALL · BEDROOM · CLOSET · CLOSET · STAIRS · BEDROOM · CLOSET · CLOSET

SECOND FLOOR

So family could continue living in home during remodeling, old roof was left in place until new one was up

appearance of the house. But, how could such an amount of work be done without "exposing" present living facilities while the roof was raised"?

After much thought and planning, they decided to try adding an upper story and roof before removing the existing roof. There would be a chance of heavy rain while some roof openings existed when putting in additional floor joists to support the second-floor structure, but this risk seemed one with which they could cope.

Cal prepared his own scale plans for the addition and submitted them to the village for approval. His construction experience with a local telephone company was sure to be helpful, but there were many things to learn as he went along. The village approved the plans in a short time and materials were ordered to start construction.

New two by eight floor joists were first installed between the existing two by six ceiling joists. This required the cutting of small roof openings. To be sure of adequate

Floor joists for addition were placed between smaller existing ceiling joists. Old rafters were cut later

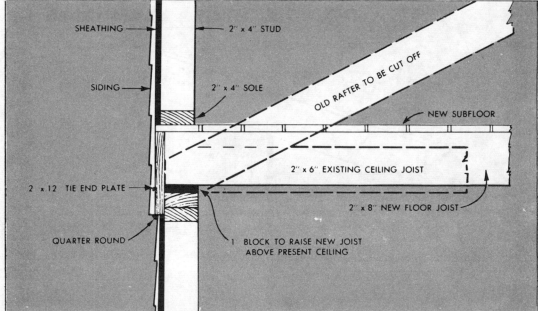

SHEATHING

2" x 4" STUD

SIDING

2" x 4" SOLE

OLD RAFTER TO BE CUT OFF

NEW SUBFLOOR

2 x 12 TIE END PLATE

2" x 6" EXISTING CEILING JOIST

2" x 8" NEW FLOOR JOIST

QUARTER ROUND

1 BLOCK TO RAISE NEW JOIST ABOVE PRESENT CEILING

Neighbors pitch in to help Cal Schroeder with the sheathing. Big overhang helps appearance of the house

clearance between the first-floor ceiling and the new floor joists, one inch block spacers were set under the new floor joists. A two by twelve tie-end plate was used to tie lower-story framing to the new upper-story structure. To the top of the tie-end plate a strip of new one by eight subflooring was nailed, then a two by four sole was toenailed in place. After this operation, the structure was ready for the second-floor two by four studs. The addition of sheathing gave a flush surface onto which

siding was nailed to cover the second-story section including the tie-plate end. A small quarter round was used to finish off the joint between the lower sheathing and the tie plate.

(The roof-rafter section and method of enclosing overhang is clearly detailed in the rafter illustration, although this method of construction can be varied according to individual preference and styling of the existing house.)

Detail shows how Schroeder joined the new roof to framing for second story. Roof has two-foot overhang

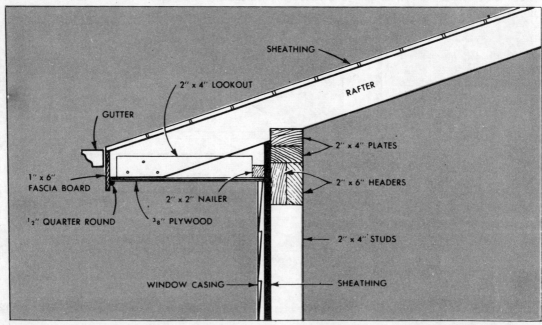

After completely enclosing the upper story, the old roof was dismantled. While the old rafters were not available for the new roof, they will become part of a small screened-in porch to be added to the back of the house at a later date. Sheathing taken off the old roof was conveniently nailed down as subflooring. Old rafters were cut off with a portable electric saw just below the level of the new two by eight floor joists.

The old guest closet (see floor plans) was eliminated completely and the space used for a stairway to the second floor.

This did not disturb the first-floor walls. The old living room became a dining-and-family room while the lower-floor bedrooms were made into one large living room across the end of the house.

With such carefully planned details, it was possible to raise the roof and complete the addition of four necessary bedrooms without interrupting family living. Important, too, is the economy realized as no foundation work was required and no major interior changes were necessary in order to acquire this completely new and valuable living area. ★ ★ ★

Remodeling Tips

ROOFS

Roofs seldom need replacing, but nearly all need repairs. Leaks should be stopped, and rotted or worn shingles replaced in patches wherever needed. Any redecorating inside will be ruined if water gets into the house afterward. Flat roofs can be made watertight with an inexpensive coating of tar and gravel; asphalt shingles are best for slopes.

EXTERIOR REPAIRS

Never cover wood siding with any new surface. It's wasteful. Besides, a coat of paint looks better anyway. Masonry should be pointed up and rotten wood replaced. Occasionally, an ancient portico or porch can be torn off economically if sagging, or if the looks of the house will be substantially improved. Any exterior work should be regarded with caution as any major outside building changes are expensive. Do not put in more than you can get out.

STRUCTURAL CHANGES

Go easy here, but keep a careful eye on the essentials. Rotten wood in sills or studs should be replaced. The cause (usually poor outside drainage) should be removed. Masonry foundations should be repaired where necessary. To put a sway-backed house back on an even keel at low cost, set jack-columns on a firm base under the sagging beams and take up only a turn or two each day. If you try to do it all at once you will crack plaster. Disconnect all steam and water pipes so movement of the house won't snap old joints. Homes, Inc., straightened one house that had no firm basement floor for columns. Nine hydraulic jacks were used with nine men working them simultaneously. Two new 12 by 12 beams were placed under the house with the ends seated in prepared niches in the foundation wall. Then the house was lowered into place.

INTERIOR WALLS

Many old houses have crooked walls and plaster that is rough and uneven. Wall surface replacement is expensive. Wallpaper can cover a multitude of flaws. Cracks can be patched and papered over. Where walls are crooked, the effect can be dispelled by intelligent use of wallpaper patterns. Striped paper run horizontally around a warped corner will hide the tilt. Large patterns are best. Where plaster is rough, use a heavy pebble-textured paper.

*Ask yourself this question
before investing time and money
in a home-improvement project:*

WILL IT INCREASE THE VALUE OF YOUR HOUSE?

THE NEXT TIME you plan to improve your home, ask yourself this question: Am I doing it merely to change the looks of things? If your answer is yes, then give your plans further consideration.

You don't want just a change—you want the time and money you spend to be an investment that will increase the value of your home.

For example, increasing the number of circuits in your home is a modest improvement that will make your house worth more if you should sell it.

On the other hand, removing bedroom ceiling lights and rewiring their wall switches to control bedside lamps is an improvement that is a matter of taste.

Some people prefer ceiling lights in bedrooms; some do not. The house is worth exactly the same either way.

Before beginning any home remodeling, whether it be indoors or outdoors, you should consider these three questions:

• Will the improvement increase your home's livability? The investment is not worthwhile unless you will enjoy it.

• Will it increase the house's market value if and when you sell? Well-chosen improvements can be worth more later than they cost right now.

• To what extent will the improvement increase maintenance? A large formal garden or an elaborate game room may increase property value, but excessive main-

Lightweight brick makes fireplace attractive. The brick is applied with a special adhesive, using a putty knife

Separating the living room from the entranceway are permanent dividers that are an excellent investment

tenance may outweigh this advantage.

After considering these questions, you must decide what improvements you want. One room in the house that should be given priority is the kitchen. Anything that will save work there will certainly increase the value of your home. Good investments are all of the latest mechanisms such as electric dishwasher, garbage disposer and built-in oven. A counter-top range is a definite asset, providing extra storage space beneath. New cabinets add color and storage space. An exhaust fan helps keep the kitchen fresh, especially after cooking and baking.

An attractive bathroom is always of value to your home. Plenty of counter and cabinet space is a big asset in a bathroom. Convenient in any bedroom is a closet lavatory, complete with wash bowl, mirror cabinet and storage space.

If your house has a fireplace, it should be made as attractive as possible. Prospective buyers like a large, eye-appealing fireplace. One method is to cover the surface with a thin brick that can be put on with adhesive. The cost is small compared to the significant increase in value.

If yours is a large living room, dividers can conveniently adapt it for two room purposes, while adding shelves or storage.

Outdoor fencing—for privacy and wind protection, for appearance, for protecting children and pets — increases the value of your property

Most-for-your-money home has a modern bathroom complete with good lighting, electric heater

Bathroom capacity of a home can be increased by installing a lavatory in the master bedroom closet

Outdoor landscaping poses less of a planning problem because time works with you. Bare-root trees and one-gallon shrubs are inexpensive and soon grow to be worth many times their cost.

Often during outdoor planning you may find that appearance means more than livability or minimum maintenance. This is because a home that is attractively landscaped draws admirers and instantly adds to the value of your home. Proper shrub-

bery and permanent rather than annual plantings mean a better looking front yard the year around. Permanent sprinkler installed in the lawn not only are convenient but are an excellent investment.

There are innumerable ways to improve the back yard, but most effective in increasing property value are conveniences such as patios, masonry barbecues and roofed, screened-in patios. An outdoor pool may be expensive, but today it is a

BACK-YARD IMPROVEMENTS

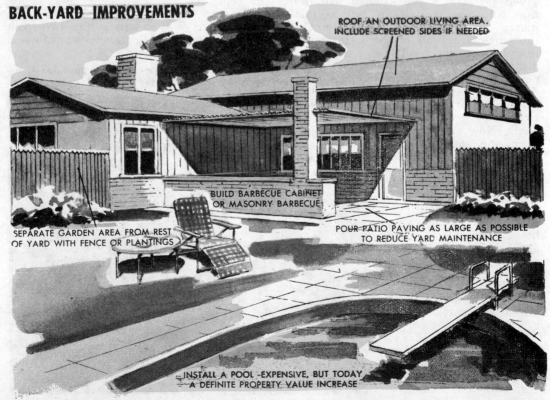

ROOF AN OUTDOOR LIVING AREA. INCLUDE SCREENED SIDES IF NEEDED

BUILD BARBECUE CABINET OR MASONRY BARBECUE

SEPARATE GARDEN AREA FROM REST OF YARD WITH FENCE OR PLANTINGS

POUR PATIO PAVING AS LARGE AS POSSIBLE TO REDUCE YARD MAINTENANCE

INSTALL A POOL—EXPENSIVE, BUT TODAY A DEFINITE PROPERTY VALUE INCREASE

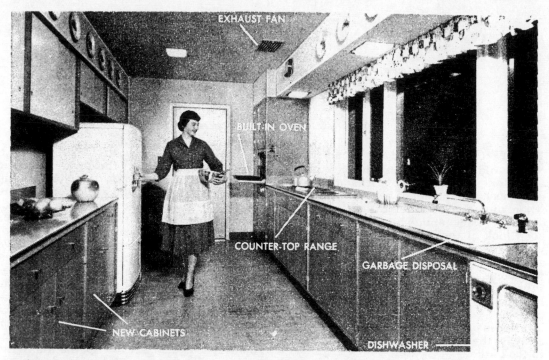

EXHAUST FAN

BUILT-IN OVEN

COUNTER-TOP RANGE

GARBAGE DISPOSAL

NEW CABINETS

DISHWASHER

Facilitating kitchen work with dishwasher, garbage disposer and built-in oven adds much to value of house

definite property-value asset. All of these items are part of the outdoor way of life now so popular. Any homeowner making these improvements will be paid well for his labor.

When you sit down to plan your home improvements, remember to ask yourself whether you're merely making change for change's sake or if you are increasing the value of your home. ★ ★ ★

FRONT-YARD IMPROVEMENTS

PRESERVE SIDING AND TRIM WITH PAINT FOR THE TYPE OF MATERIAL

TUCKPOINT BRICKWORK

ASPHALT OR CONCRETE THE DRIVEWAY

INSTALL SPRINKLERS IN LAWN

REPLACE ANNUALS WITH PERMANENT EASILY MAINTAINED PLANTINGS

NEW FACES
For Old Homes

By W. Clyde Lammey

BETTER LIVING need not mean selling the old house and buying or building a new one. Present-day prices and building costs can dim a lot of new-home dreams when you get around to putting the figures down in black and white. Take another good look at the house you live in before you make any decision. Add up the floor area and then compare with present costs for rooms of the same size at $10 to $20 a square foot. You may be in for a surprise. It could be, on the basis of this simple calculation, you will decide that while the interior is passably comfortable and livable as it is, the exterior could be a lot easier to look at.

If you buy an old house with an eye to remodeling, the trick in getting your money's worth is to appraise correctly its possibilities beforehand. Take time to study the exterior from grade to ridge line, keeping in mind that on many old homes the removal of the wide cornice alone will materially change its appearance. Mentally take off the front porch or veranda, relocate the front door, remove a dormer or two, visualize a fresh coat of paint and already you have a new house in place of the old. Now study the "befores" and "afters" below and on the three following pages to see what owners did to change the exteriors of several typical old homes. Note especially the changes made in the full two-story house pictured before and after in the center and upper views on the opposite page. Relocation of the dormer gave better utilization of the attic space and removal of the gable-end cornice overhangs and the installation of drop siding had the effect of widening the structure. Removal of the porch and relocation of the front door, which opens on a concrete stoop, provided for better distribution of living-room space, also served to maintain the balance of architectural details when shutters and side porch were added.

The house pictured in the before view at the lower right and below in the after view presents a somewhat different problem because of its rooms-in-line construction. Again the unattractive porch was removed and the gable extended to house the entryway. The louver fence, masonry planter and a new entryway and door alter the original so completely that it appears to be an entirely new structure.

The four views on pages 1092 and 1093 picture remodeling jobs carried out by the owners themselves. The two before views show what they started with and a careful study of the larger illustrations will show

AFTER

BEFORE

View at the right, center, is the "before" of the old home shown above after remodeling. Compare the two illustrations and note how few structural changes were necessary to modernize the exterior. Relocation of the porch and careful use of drop siding give the effect of lowering the height

Below, right and left, the home pictured in the before view is typical of many built from 40 to 60 years ago. Looks rather unpromising as it stands, but note what the owner did in view at left. Enclosing side yard with a louver fence and remodeling the front changed the house from old to new

AFTER

BEFORE

AFTER

Owners of these two homes, pictured in the befores below, did the work themselves. Owner of the smaller home needed more room and the additions planned and carried to completion are shown in the view above. Many homes of this type will permit similar alterations, creating greater livability and higher valuation

BEFORE

BEFORE

AFTER

how well they succeeded. The owner of the small house needed more room; upper view shows how he added to the existing structure. The width of the lot permitted expansion of the floor area in both directions but the height of the plate above grade required dual-pitch roof extensions to give the proper ceiling height in the additions. In this job the chimney was rebuilt to provide a second flue for a fireplace in the living room. The house in the lower before view was a very old one, but was found to be sound structurally. Remodeling required very little change in the interior. Because of this the owner concentrated all effort on modernizing the dated exterior. What he did is clearly shown in the larger view below. First, the porch was removed and the garage attached, the flat roof deck over the garage being finished with a plain railing. Then vertical siding was carried across the entire width at the height indicated. The original window openings were enlarged and new sash of modern design installed, including a large panel window in the living room. Then the single dormer and cornices were removed, the latter cut back flush with the walls and finished with fascia boards. An iron-railed concrete stoop and two coats of paint rounded out the job.

All the homes pictured were structurally sound to begin with and did not require any major alteration of the original framing in order to achieve the desired

Lower view, opposite page, is the before of the remodeled home pictured below. No major structural changes were necessary. So the flat-roofed garage was built on and topped with a plain railing. Cornices were removed and vertical siding was applied across the entire front and sides

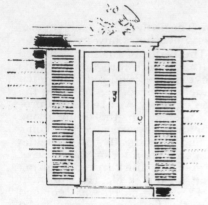

A new front entryway usually is a part of every remodeling job and manufactured units offer a wide choice of design. Shutters add pleasing detail

A recessed doorway has several advantages. Door itself is protected from weathering, it is less likely to leak and there are added decorative possibilities

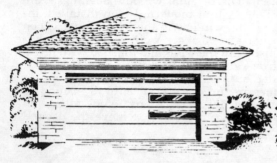

A modern door makes an old garage look new. These units are available ready-made in several styles which can be adapted to almost any building type

Due to variations in architectural lines a garage with a gable roof usually appears its best when fitted with a multiple-panel door of the type pictured

result. These are points to consider in any remodeling job.

The suggestions on this page are unit improvements that can be added to old or new homes. Garage and entry doors are manufactured units and come to you ready to install. The sketch at the left shows how one owner closed the "weather" side of the carport with closures woven from hardboard strips. The two sketches below show the addition of carports to existing small homes. ★ ★ ★

Above, a woven closure for "weather" end of carport added a pleasing appearance detail to this small home. Below, utilization of carport as a living area

When lot size permits, a carport is a practical addition to the small home. Has a definite appearance value. Note below how carport lengthens roof line

Above: Tailored to look like part of the house as originally built, this addition to the front of a story-and-a-half house, can be used for a den or for an extra bedroom and bath. Below: Similar addition on side of a two-story house is set back for appearance, and to retain usefulness of front side windows

REMODELING

WHEN YOU FEEL pinched for living space, and the basement or attic is not suitable or desired for added rooms, it may be necessary to build a room or two on the outside. Such an extension should match the rest of the house for best appearance.

Well-planned additions: Generally an added bedroom or den can adjoin a living room. Figs. 1 and 2 show examples. A dining room can be added as shown in Fig. 3. Where a large living room is used for dining space, and this is not desired, look into the possibility of transforming the present kitchen into a dining room, and then add a new kitchen. This can sometimes be located between the house and garage as shown in Fig. 4.

Foundation requirements: An addition to the outside of a house requires a substantial foundation brought to the same height as the house foundation. In cold climates it is usually best to have a foundation wall of poured concrete or of concrete blocks as

shown in details A, B and C of Fig. 5. For brick-veneer houses, the foundation walls are 10 and 12 in. thick with a portion of the wall often set back so that the brickwork can extend down to grade level as shown in detail D. For frame construction, foundation walls are usually 8 in. thick.

In warm climates an added room often can be supported by piers set on concrete footings. Readymade concrete piers are available in many localities. Piers also may be built up from bricks or concrete blocks. Where the latter are used each pier is held together by means of a perforated ¼ by 2-in. steel anchoring strip set vertically inside the blocks and imbedded in mortar. Foundation walls should always be extended to just below the depth of frost penetration. Where concrete piers are used, and they extend in the earth less than 3 ft., they should be cast integral with a footing, using ½-in. reinforcing rods.

Above: An addition like the one in Fig. 2, extended beyond the front of a two-story house can provide a sheltered entranceway and a guest closet in addition to an extra room. Below: Modern kitchen and attractive breezeway built between house and garage permit previous kitchen to be used for a dining room

Illustrations 1 to 4 courtesy Johns-Manville

Crawl spaces: Where the floor of an added room, to be level with the house floor, is raised any distance above grade, the crawl space under it should be made accessible. Where the floor is relatively close to the ground, the crawl space may have to be excavated to provide sufficient clearance, in which case the foundation walls should extend beyond the depth of the excavation.

Closed crawl spaces must be provided with adequate ventilation to prevent humid conditions caused by moisture evaporating from the ground. Excessive humidity in crawl spaces may cause exposed wood, including joists and flooring, to rot in a comparatively short time. It also causes other undesired conditions.

Laying out foundation lines: Whether you are installing a foundation wall or just pier supports for an added room, the first step is to accurately locate the position of

the added room by laying out foundation lines. Two walls will join the house wall at right angles. On most frame houses covered with siding or shingles, the exact location of such joining walls is variable. On brick-veneer houses, where the extension is to be of the same construction, wall joints between house and extension should dovetail together. To facilitate this, the outside edge of the new foundation should line up with vertical mortar joints of the house wall as shown in Fig. 6. The height of the added foundation should be the same as that of the house foundation.

With these details in mind, you stretch two chalk lines from the top edge of the house foundation, and at right angles to it as shown in Fig. 7. Often the lower strip of siding or some shingles must be removed for this purpose, as these generally overlap the foundation wall. The lines are located to represent the outside edges of the new foundation. The free ends are held by "bat-

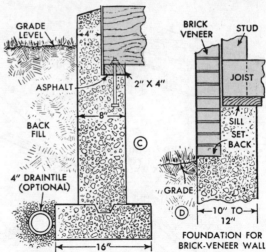

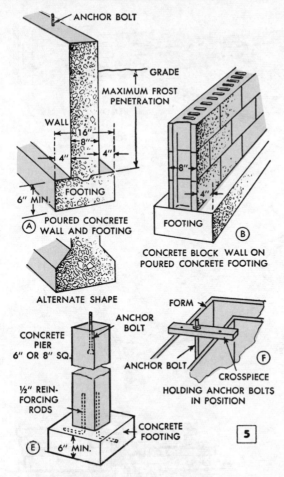

FOUNDATION FOR
BRICK-VENEER WALL

ter boards," arranged to roughly form a right angle about 3 or 4 ft. outside the corners of the new foundation. The batter boards are from 4 to 6 ft. long, and are nailed to posts securely driven into the ground. The upper edge of the boards must be the same height as the top edge of the house foundation, as found by pulling the chalk lines taut next to the posts, and bringing the lines level.

After the batter boards have been nailed to the posts, the lines are adjusted to come at right angles to the house wall. This is done by the triangulation method shown in Fig. 7, using a 1 by 4-in. straight board, cut off or marked to exactly 10 ft., and also marked to indicate 6 and 8-ft. spans. With this measuring stick you mark off 6 ft. on the house wall and 8 ft. on the taut line. When the line is adjusted so that the 10-ft. dimension comes exactly between the marks on the house and line, the latter will be at right angles to the house. The adjustment of the line is made by moving it along the batter board. When the right position has been found, the batter board is marked with pencil or a very shallow groove. This assures retaining the correct position

when temporarily removed while digging trenches. The lines will be parallel if the adjustments were carefully made. A third line then is stretched across the two from the batter boards. The three lines must be at right angles to each other.

A plumb bob, suspended from the intersection points of the lines, will indicate the outside corners of the foundation, and is used when positioning the forms. The inner edges of the foundation may be indicated similarly with chalk lines. In laying out foundations, the lines and batter boards often are placed higher than the top of the foundation, and vertical measurements then made from the lines to foundation height. This keeps the lines out of the way while building forms.

Foundation trenches and forms: Where earth is firm and compact, such as clay, it may be dug out for shallow foundations, in which case the sides are undercut at the bottom to footing width. Wooden forms then are required above grade only as shown in Fig. 8. In loose soil where the form must extend below grade, as in Fig. 9, you dig trenches 20 to 24 in. wide. A long-handled, pointed shovel is most convenient for this purpose. Instead of using plank forms as indicated in Figs. 8 and 9, you may be able to borrow or rent preassembled forms faced with exterior-type plywood or tempered hardboard.

Footings: Footings on which most house foundations rest should extend from 4 to 6 in. on either side of a foundation and should be 8 to 12 in. high. They are usually cast separately on undisturbed, compact earth. A groove about 2 in. deep and 4 in. wide, with beveled edges, as shown in Fig. 5-A, often is formed in the top of a footing. This serves to interlock the footing and foundation wall. However, the footing and wall can be poured integrally, in which case the

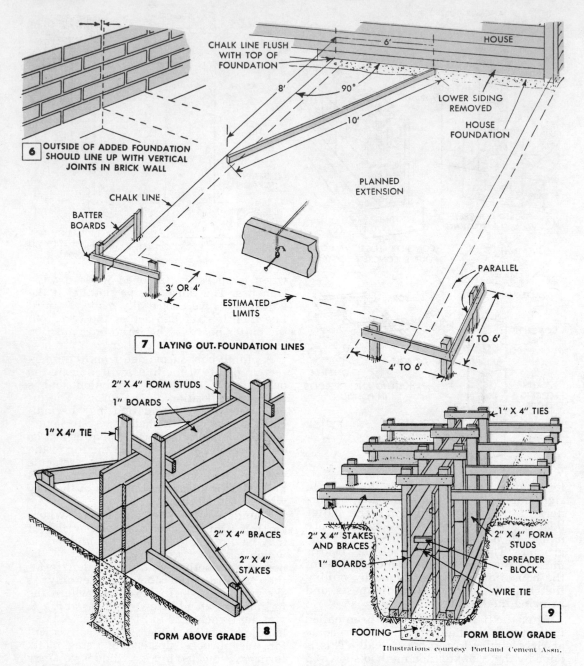

6 OUTSIDE OF ADDED FOUNDATION SHOULD LINE UP WITH VERTICAL JOINTS IN BRICK WALL

CHALK LINE FLUSH WITH TOP OF FOUNDATION

6'

HOUSE

8'

90°

10'

LOWER SIDING REMOVED

HOUSE FOUNDATION

PLANNED EXTENSION

CHALK LINE

BATTER BOARDS

3' OR 4'

ESTIMATED LIMITS

PARALLEL

4' TO 6'

4' TO 6'

7 LAYING OUT FOUNDATION LINES

2" X 4" FORM STUDS

1" BOARDS

1" X 4" TIE

2" X 4" BRACES

2" X 4" STAKES

FORM ABOVE GRADE **8**

1" X 4" TIES

2" X 4" STAKES AND BRACES

1" BOARDS

2" X 4" FORM STUDS

SPREADER BLOCK

WIRE TIE

FOOTING   FORM BELOW GRADE **9**

Illustrations courtesy Portland Cement Assn.

top of the footing form on either side of the wall must be closed.

Concrete for foundation walls: Use a 1 : 2¾ : 4 mix of portland cement, sand and gravel or crushed stone respectively. About 5½ gals. of water are required for each sack of cement when slightly moist sand is used. A rather stiff mix is preferred. The concrete is put into the forms in layers not deeper than 6 in. If possible, the entire wall should be cast in one continuous operation. If the work must be interrupted, as for an overnight period, you roughen the concrete surface with a stiff broom before it hardens. Then, before adding more concrete, wet the surface, and butter it with a ½-in. layer of mortar consisting of 1 part of portland cement and 2½ parts of sand. In many communities it is possible to get ready-mixed concrete which saves you the work of mixing it yourself.

Details of foundation walls: The upper edge of the added wall should come flush with the house wall. Allow for suitable vent openings. Such openings are framed in the forms if the walls are of poured concrete. You install ⅜-in. anchor bolts, from 12 to 20 in. long, so the thread ends will project above the wall to hold the sills or sole

FIG. 10

Photo courtesy Insulite Division, Minnesota & Ontario Paper Co.

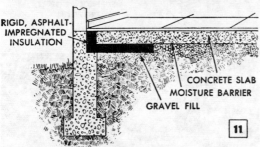

RIGID, ASPHALT-IMPREGNATED INSULATION

CONCRETE SLAB
MOISTURE BARRIER
GRAVEL FILL

PERIMETER INSULATION FOR CONCRETE-SLAB FLOORS

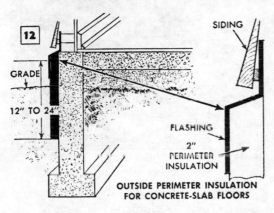

SIDING

GRADE

12" TO 24"

FLASHING

2" PERIMETER INSULATION

OUTSIDE PERIMETER INSULATION FOR CONCRETE-SLAB FLOORS

plates of the walls. The bolts are spaced from 6 to 8 ft. apart, starting near corners as shown in Fig. 13. They are held in position in the forms while pouring the concrete, by means of wood crosspieces laid across the forms as shown in Fig. 5-F. The bolts should project about 3 in. above the top of the wall for a single-thickness sole plate or sill, and 4½ in. for one of double thickness.

In a wall of concrete blocks, anchor bolts are similarly used. The mortar or concrete in which the bolts are imbedded is supported underneath by pieces of sheet metal inserted between the second and third courses from the top. In this case the bolts should be at least 16 in. long so that they will extend below the first course and possibly below the second. Fig. 10 shows a concrete-block foundation wall being coated with white waterproofing paint.

Concrete slab floors: Where a crawl space under an added room is not desired, and the floor level is just a little above grade level, you can have a concrete slab floor. This is generally 4 or 5 in. thick, and may be laid as soon as the foundation forms can be removed. Sometimes it can be laid integrally with shallow walls.

The earth around and under a slab floor should be well drained. It should be compact since loose earth or fill will settle and no longer support the slab. A 4-in. layer of coarse gravel, crushed stone or broken clay tile is spread on the compacted earth as indicated in Fig. 11. Cinders should not be used as these deteriorate. If gravel is used the "fines" are removed to prevent upward movement of water by capillary attraction. The gravel is tamped down firmly. Along the inside edges of the walls it should be 2 in. lower than elsewhere to accommodate perimeter insulation necessary in localities subject to frost.

Perimeter insulation: This prevents floors along walls from becoming cold and being subject to condensation of moisture. Rigid, asphalt-impregnated insulation, which is waterproof, is made for this purpose. It should be 2 in. thick or may consist of two 1-in. thicknesses. Extend the insulation along the entire inside edge of the foundation as shown in Figs. 11 and 14. Set strips on edge along the wall, then lay others horizontally to a 24-in. width.

Cover the gravel fill with strips of 55-lb. asphalt-saturated felt such as roll roofing. Overlap the edges 4 to 6 in., and seal them with roofing cement. After placing a ½ by 4-in. strip of resilient expansion-joint material where the new floor joins the house wall, as indicated in Fig. 14, you lay the concrete. Place welded wire-mesh reinforcing (40-lb. size) midway in the concrete while laying it.

To insulate an existing concrete slab floor such as a floor of a porch that is to be enclosed, apply 2-in. perimeter insulation on

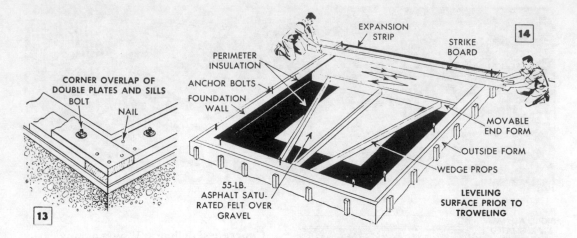

CORNER OVERLAP OF
DOUBLE PLATES AND SILLS
BOLT
NAIL

13

PERIMETER
INSULATION
ANCHOR BOLTS
FOUNDATION
WALL

EXPANSION
STRIP
STRIKE
BOARD

14

MOVABLE
END FORM
OUTSIDE FORM
WEDGE PROPS

55-LB.
ASPHALT SATU-
RATED FELT OVER
GRAVEL

LEVELING
SURFACE PRIOR TO
TROWELING

the outside of the foundation as shown in
Fig. 12. It should extend downward from
12 to 24 in., depending on the severity of
frost. The exposed portion above grade can
be protected and concealed with sheet-
metal flashing, preferably aluminum.

Laying concrete slab floors: For slab
floors you use a 1 : 2¼ : 3 mix. The floor is
laid and finished in sections as shown in
Fig. 14, for which a movable end form, held
in position with wedge props, is used. The
concrete surface is leveled with a "strike
board." This is laid across the forms at the
edges and is worked back and forth with a
saw-like motion while progressing. For a
smooth finish, the surface of the concrete is
troweled with a steel trowel as shown in
Fig. 15, just after the water sheen on the
surface has disappeared. Avoid overtrow-
eling as this results in surfaces that dust
and craze readily. For a rough surface you
use a wood float.

Uncovering the house wall: Now you can
uncover part of the house wall, as shown in
Fig. 10. You can remove both the wall covering and the sheathing at this time, or you
can leave most of the sheathing intact until
you are ready to attach the wall frames of
the extension.

With the aid of a plumb bob you mark a
vertical line on the house wall, in line with
the outside edge of the foundation of the
extension. If the house is covered with siding, you saw through this and also through
the sheathing. If the line comes over a stud,
saw on the side toward the portion of the
wall covering to be removed. If the wall is
shingled, remove these to the first joints
outside of the lines, away from the added
wall as shown in Fig. 10. On a brick-veneer
house, the opening is made to the first brick
joints outside of the lines, which would be
about ½ and 4½ in. on alternate courses.

Attaching sills or sole plates: Carefully
examine the house framing just above the
foundation. It may have a single or a dou-

FIG. 15   Photo courtesy Portland Cement Assn.

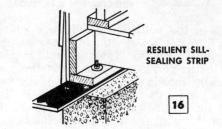

RESILIENT SILL-
SEALING STRIP

16

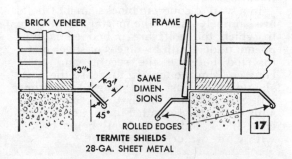

BRICK VENEER

3"
3"
45°

FRAME

SAME
DIMEN-
SIONS

ROLLED EDGES

17

TERMITE SHIELDS
28-GA. SHEET METAL

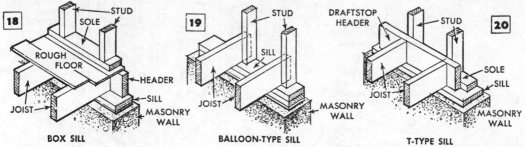

18 STUD / SOLE / ROUGH FLOOR / HEADER / SILL / MASONRY WALL / JOIST

BOX SILL

19 STUD / SILL / JOIST / MASONRY WALL

BALLOON-TYPE SILL

20 DRAFTSTOP HEADER / STUD / SOLE / SILL / JOIST / MASONRY WALL

T-TYPE SILL

Illustrations courtesy U. S. Federal Security Agency, Office of Education

ble sill, which should be duplicated on the extension. Also notice the type of sill construction and the width of the floor joists. Bore the sills or sole plates to fit the anchor bolts. The sills are set back from the outer edge of the foundation a distance equal to the thickness of the sheathing. For brick-veneer construction, they are set back a distance equal to the width of the bricks plus that of the sheathing unless the foundation is stepped for the brickwork. In case of concrete slab floors the sole plates of the walls are anchored to the foundation.

Tight foundation joint: Seal the joints between sills or sole plates and the foundation to prevent air leakage. You can use mortar spread on the foundation, pressing the sill on it and tightening the anchor bolts just enough to keep the sill level at the right height. A ½-in. sill-sealing strip of resilient, asphalt-saturated material, Fig. 16, is preferable to mortar. This also conforms to irregularities of the foundation.

Termite shields: In localities where termites are troublesome, you install sheet-metal shields between the foundation wall and the sills or sole plates as shown in Fig.

17. The shields extend horizontally from the wall and downward at a 45-deg. angle. The exposed edges should be rolled as a safety precaution.

Joists and bridging: When sills are laid in a mortar seal, allow 24 hrs. for this to harden before installing joists. Mark the joist locations at 16-in. centers on sills of opposite walls. The joists should be the same width as those of the house so the floors will come flush. For box-sill construction, Fig. 18, you nail headers to joists with 16-d. nails. Also toenail the joists and headers to the sills with 10-d. nails, spaced about 16 in. apart. Headers are not used in the "balloon" type of sill construction, Fig. 19, in which case the joists come almost to the outer edge of the sills. The joists are toenailed to the sills and the studs are nailed to joists and to sills. In T-sill construction, Fig. 20, a header is placed between joists and studs. If joists have a span of 10 ft. or more you need bridging to add stiffness to a floor.

FIG. 21

Photo courtesy Insulite Division, Minnesota & Ontario Paper Co.,

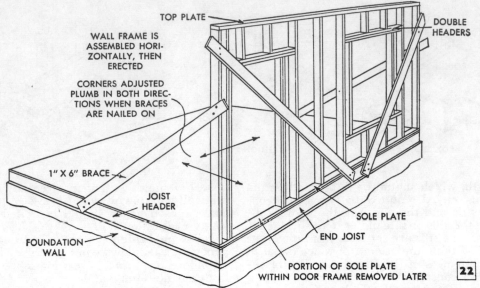

WALL FRAME IS ASSEMBLED HORIZONTALLY, THEN ERECTED

CORNERS ADJUSTED PLUMB IN BOTH DIRECTIONS WHEN BRACES ARE NAILED ON

TOP PLATE

DOUBLE HEADERS

1" X 6" BRACE

JOIST HEADER

FOUNDATION WALL

SOLE PLATE

END JOIST

PORTION OF SOLE PLATE WITHIN DOOR FRAME REMOVED LATER

22

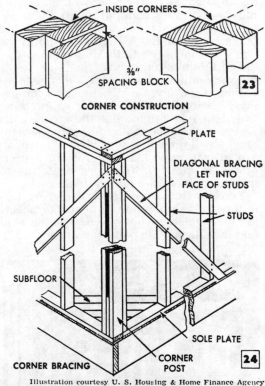

INSIDE CORNERS

⅜" SPACING BLOCK

23

CORNER CONSTRUCTION

PLATE

DIAGONAL BRACING LET INTO FACE OF STUDS

STUDS

SUBFLOOR

SOLE PLATE

CORNER BRACING

CORNER POST

24

Illustration courtesy U. S. Housing & Home Finance Agency

Floor insulation and vapor barrier: If the space below the floor is unheated and is ventilated, you will need insulation and a vapor barrier where cold weather is experienced. Most batt-type insulation is combined with a vapor-barrier covering, and has a projecting edge to facilitate nailing it to joists.

Subfloor: In box-sill construction, you lay the subfloor before erecting the wall frames. A subfloor may be laid across the joists at right angles, or diagonally at 45 deg., which provides greater rigidity. Details on laying subfloors are given in Section 16.

Erection of wall frames: Wall frames of an added room are shown erected in Fig. 21. First make the frame for the wall that is parallel to the house wall. Preassemble the frame in a horizontal position, spacing studs 16 in. on centers and end-nailing them through the plates with 16-d. nails, two at each end. Then swing the assembled frame into place, adjust it plumb in both directions and attach braces to hold it in this position as shown in Fig. 22. After erection, the sole plate is fastened down with 16-d. nails driven into the floor framing. The supporting braces are not removed until the frame is joined to others.

The corners of wall frames should provide nailing bases for both inside and outside wall coverings. Two types of corners so planned are shown in Fig. 23. Extra rigidity for wall framing at corners is provided with diagonal bracing of 1 by 6-in. stock mortised into and nailed to the studs as shown in Fig. 24.

Cutting back at eaves: Before erecting the side-wall frames, remove the roof gut-

FIG. 25

FIG. 26

Photo courtesy Insulite Division, Minnesota & Ontario Paper Co.

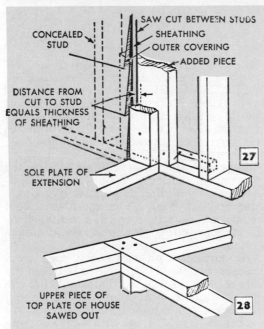

CONCEALED STUD

SAW CUT BETWEEN STUDS
SHEATHING
OUTER COVERING
ADDED PIECE

DISTANCE FROM CUT TO STUD EQUALS THICKNESS OF SHEATHING

SOLE PLATE OF EXTENSION

27

UPPER PIECE OF TOP PLATE OF HOUSE SAWED OUT

28

ter. some roof shingles, and cut the eaves back to the wall framing of the house. Projecting rafters are cut off flush with the top plate of the house wall. Asphalt shingle strips are relatively easy to remove without damaging them as shown in Fig. 25. On wood shingles it is necessary to cut the nails instead of prying them out. Section 6 includes methods of removing shingles. As the opened roof allows rain to get inside, which may cause damage, use a waterproof tarpaulin to cover the opening

Joining side-wall frames to house: Where a side wall of an extension is a continuation of a house wall, you nail the last stud to the corner framing of the house. Should the opposite side wall come directly over a stud in the house wall, it is similarly nailed to it. Where the wall of an extension joins the house wall at a location between studs as in Fig 27, a 2-in, upright, 6 or 8 in. wide, is inserted in the house wall, which provides a nailing base for the inside and outside wall coverings. Next, you nail on extra top plates. These join the house wall as shown in Fig. 28, and are overlapped at corners as shown in Fig. 24.

Wall sheathing and roofing: Install window and door casings and then cover the wall framing with sheathing as shown in Fig. 26. Installation of window and door casings, and the application of sheathing, can be done after the roofing has been completed. Sheathing and siding carefully removed from the house can be used to cover part of the extension usually. Ceiling joists and the roof framing are then added as shown in Fig. 29, nailing the rafters to the ceiling joists and also toenailing them to the top plate. Next, you apply the roof sheathing, roofing felt, flashing and shingles. Then it is usually advisable to add a vent in the top of a gable or in the roof besides one at the cornice of an added roof to assure adequate ventilation in the space between the ceiling and roof.

Wall and ceiling insulation: Outside walls and ceiling are then thoroughly insulated, using Batt-type insulation which is tacked

FIG. 29

or stapled to the inside surfaces of the studs and ceiling joists after the wiring has been installed. The vapor-barrier side of the insulation should always face the inside of the house.

Finishing details: Wood sheathing is covered with building paper before applying the outside covering such as siding or shingles. Siding is nailed on in such a way that the nails enter studs. Shingles are nailed directly to wood sheathing and in some cases directly to insulating-board sheathing by means of special self-clinching nails. Generally, however, shingles applied over insulating sheathing require horizontal furring strips as a nailing base.

Before finishing the inside, a doorway between the house and the added room must be provided. Also, an existing window may have to be removed. If window opening is located where a door is wanted, you merely increase the height of the opening and change its width as may be necessary.

For interior walls you can use any of the various wallboards which come in the form of panels or planking this dry-wall construction. You can also have the walls plastered, which is sometimes preferred, to match existing walls in the adjoining room. The trim is applied last.

Extensions on two-story houses: In adding a two-story extension to a house, the same general methods of procedure are followed as already described for a single-story addition. Adequate ventilation should be provided for an extended attic and it should be made accessible. Insulation then is installed over the second-floor ceiling as it is not needed between the first and second floors.

Attached garages: In building an attached garage, the same general procedure is followed as in building an extension having a concrete slab floor. A garage floor should be sloped slightly toward a center floor drain connecting to the house drainage system.

A ventilated passageway such as a breezeway should be provided between the garage and the house. This prevents the entrance of car fumes into the house and also helps to minimize tracking in dirt. An overhead garage door with compensating springs is convenient to use and is relatively easy to install, following the instructions such as are generally furnished by manufacturers.

Before building an attached garage it is highly important to investigate local building codes. These often call for special fireproof construction as, for example, a metal-covered door between the garage and the house. A garage ceiling may be brought to come flush with the first-floor ceiling. If suitable joists are used, an extra room can be built above.

BEFORE

AFTER

ONE-MAN REMODELING JOBS

By W. Clyde Lammey

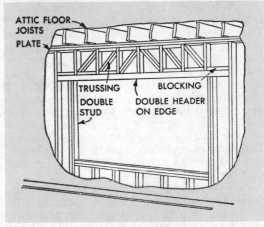

OFTEN IT TAKES only a simple change in architectural detail to bring a dated house right up to the day before tomorrow in appearance and livability inside and out. In some older structures you may wish to retain certain desirable characteristics of the old and add only a touch of new. Many older homes, especially those built within the last 50 years or so, are either square with a hip roof, or some variation of the common L-shape with gables and valleys in the roof design. Usually they are built full two-story with an attic and a dormer, or dormers, of unattractive detail and

BEFORE

AFTER

doubtful utility. Some old homes — often more than a half century old—have very attractive boxed and molded cornices and front-corner trim of a distinctive design.

Typical examples of these types are shown in the upper and lower views on the preceding page. The home in the lower before-and-after views was "up dated" to the owner's satisfaction by painting the exterior in an attractive color combination and adding a room-width window to make the interior more livable and the exterior more attractive. The old square home in the before-and-after views at the top of the preceding page was face-lifted by removing the ponderous porch and adding three multi-tipaned windows and a door framed in reeded columns and a broken pediment. No other part of the structure was altered, either inside or out. The change in appearance not only adds inestimably to the value of the property, but also lends something to pride of ownership as well.

These two are typical one-man remodeling jobs, that is, they can be handled by the owner himself, even when he has only a limited amount of spare time for the work. The nature of the procedure on either job is such that the entire project need not be completed in a day or a week. It can be worked out a window or a door at a time. When working alone on such projects as installing windows and doors, keep a waterproof tarpaulin handy so that you can cover the opening quickly should a sudden shower catch you with the job unfinished. The same precaution is carried out when it is necessary to remove or alter a dormer and reroof the opening.

Before you cut large openings in walls, especially in full two-story structures, it is necessary to plan the installation of a suitable header to support the weight above the opening. Framing in a large window is an example and the detail on the preceding page shows one recommended method. It is used when framing in a large sash in either a one-story or two-story structure, unless the building is balloon-framed, as were many of the older two-story homes. In this type of framing the studs extend from the sill, or sole, as the case may be, to the rafter plate at the second story. Then it's the usual practice to cut the studs over the opening and support the ends on a header built up by spiking two 2 x 10s together and then placing edgewise. The ends of the header are carried across to full-length studs beyond the limits of the rough opening. Truss bracing like that detailed is not ordinarily installed.

Small one-story homes generally lend themselves to modernizing by simple exterior changes. The one pictured before and after at the top of this and the opposite

BEFORE

This home is typical of many built 50 or more years ago. Enclosed porch is probably a later addition

BEFORE

It would be hard to judge the age of this house, but it has been around a long time. Below, this small home of later type lends itself to simple remodeling

BEFORE

A new enclosed porch of modern design, new wide siding, attic louvers, a flower box and new plantings got this result — put the original structure in a new age group in value, appearance and in livability

Above, note the before at the left and the after above. It's the same house, an outstanding example of what can be done with an old structure in good condition.

Below, the "picture window" replacement not only "upgrades" the exterior appearance of a small house, it also gives a feeling of greater space in the interior

Sometimes a window is unattractive because of its proportions or location. Here's an example of what novel ornamental shutters will do for such a defect

When nothing else seems suitable, a stone planter usually will do the trick. It's easy to build and even when there's nothing growing in it, it's still attractive

Above, a fence is hardly a remodeling job in itself, but it may supplement the work nicely. Below, same thing is true of yard divider. It has a number of practical uses, depending on location and purpose

page is a good example of what can be done. Note especially the change in appearance alone made by wide siding and the rebuilding of the existing porch. In this case it was found advisable to remove the imitation brick exterior, make a few minor repairs and add attic louvers before rebuilding the enclosed porch and finishing the job with wide siding. The only major structural change in this job is the porch, which was rebuilt completely in order to achieve the desired harmony of line and exterior detail.

The larger home pictured in before-and-after views in the center illustrations on the preceding pages is something special. At first sight it looks like an undertaking beyond the capacity of one man to carry out even though he might be skilled in the work. But look at the illustrations a little more closely and you will see that the only major changes are the building of an attached two-car garage and the half porch which replaces the original and is a continuation of the garage roof line. The dormer was removed to straighten the roof line of the main structure. The owner replaced the original window sash on the second story and added two new windows downstairs. Then he added new siding and ornamental shutters, removed one chimney and rebuilt the other. In this case the question to be decided is not so much whether one man can handle the job, but whether he has sufficient time to devote to it. With one man making all the moves necessary to carry out such a project it's going to be a long time between start and finish. A lot of time can be saved by subcontracting such jobs as pouring the garage floor and rebuilding the chimney. Hiring an architect to plan the job for you is money well spent. He can save you both time and effort, even on jobs less involved than the one in question. Savings realized by doing the work yourself will be considerable.

Often a small home of more recent type can be greatly improved in appearance and livability simply by changing a window or door or adding an open porch. The small home pictured in the before-and-after views at the bottom of the preceding pages is an example. The "picture" window gives a feeling of greater space in the living room and at the same time has the effect of lengthening the structure. The porch can be anything desired, open like that shown, a carport, or enclosed with screen or glass.

In addition to remodeling the structure itself, there are other architectural details, or "applique," which can be included as a part of the job, or independent of it. The sketches on this page suggest four such applications. In these details placement determines beauty and utility. ★ ★ ★

More Storage SPACE

IN YOUR HOME

By Ed Packer

Shell-type cabinet over radiator or behind door provides storage for mops, brooms and an ironing board

LACK OF STORAGE SPACE, a problem in many small apartments and in some homes, often can be solved by installing shell-type cabinets and by the use of drawers and fixtures located in areas not normally considered usable for storage. The area above a radiator or behind a door in a kitchen, for example, is an excellent location for a high, shallow cabinet, Fig. 1, that will accommodate brooms, mops and an ironing board. This cabinet is a shell type, which means that it consists of a frame of 1 x 2 lumber over which is nailed ⅛-in. hardboard. The frame is nailed or screwed directly to the wall and, if possible, should be positioned so that the nails or screws are driven into the 2 x 4 studding.

Fasten to Studding

In some cases it may be necessary to add one or more cross pieces at the back of the frame through which screws can be driven into the studding, to assure that the cabinet is firmly attached to the wall. Corner angles can be used to brace the frame of a cabinet that does not seem rigid enough. The wall forms the back of the cabinet, and in some cases the ceiling will be the top. If a cabinet is located in the corner of a room, the adjacent walls can be used as the back and one side of the cabinet. Shelves in the shell-type cabinets are cut from ¼-in. plywood and are supported on ¼-in. rods fitted in aligning holes drilled through the vertical front members of the cabinet and through the back members. If

it is desired to make the shelves adjustable, drill a line of holes at each location. Fitting the rods in different holes permits quick adjustment of shelf spacing.

Portable Clothes Pole

Cramped quarters also present problems in doing housework, such as when ironing shirts, dresses and other garments that must be hung on coat hangers rather than being folded for storage. A portable clothes pole is the answer to this problem. The pole is a length of light tubing or heavy curtain rod with a hole drilled in each end. Long S-hooks, bent from coat-hanger wire, have one end fitted in the holes in the pole and the other end slipped into holes drilled in the top edge of a door-frame, as shown in Fig. 2.

Bathroom Drying Rack

When hand laundry is done in a bathroom washbasin, a convenient self-storing" drying rack can be located above or near the basin if the side of a cabinet or a closet wall is near the basin. As indicated in Fig. 3, the telescoping rack is a length of tubing or pipe which slides inside a pipe of larger diameter. The latter is screwed into a pipe flange that is screwed to the cabinet or wall. Because pipe threads are tapered, it will be necessary to retap the threads in the flange from the flat side if the flange is used as shown in the detail.

When the rack is mounted on a cabinet the larger pipe should be located close to the underside of a shelf so it does not interfere with items on the shelf below. If the pipe is run through a closet wall it should be located so as not to interfere with the clothing, or may be positioned so it can be used as a clothes pole in the closet.

Bedclothes Storage

Storage for bed linens and blankets can be provided in a bedroom without using any floor space by installing a shell-type cabinet between a wall and the ceiling. The ceiling forms the cabinet top, one wall is the back and adjacent walls can form the cabinet ends. Hardboard doors can be hinged at the top to swing up against the ceiling, but a neater, more convenient closing can be had by making sliding doors as detailed in Fig. 4. Slides are simply wooden strips nailed to the inside edges of the cabinet framing. A trim strip across the front provides a finished appearance.

More Closet Space

Closets are another area where proper arrangement will add many cubic feet of storage space. Dustfree storage for hats and gloves can be provided by installing light-weight aluminum drawers on the bottom of an existing shelf, Fig. 5. Each drawer consists of an aluminum pan—its size is determined by the space available—to which are bolted lengths of aluminum angle as indicated in the left-hand detail. Slides for the drawers are made by screwing strips of wood and aluminum to the underside of the shelf as shown. Inexpensive cabinet

Portable clothes pole hangs from doorframe and saves steps when freshly ironed clothes, such as shirts, must be hung on clothes hangers as shown

Clothes-drying rack in bathroom is self-storing, consisting of pipe or tubing that telescopes into support pipe held in flange screwed to cabinet side

PULL-OUT PIPE

SHELF

PIPE CAP

PIPE FLANGE

SUPPORT PIPE

Storage for bed linens and blankets is provided by shell-type cabinet located between wall and ceiling

handles can be used for drawer handles. Overhead shoe storage in the closet is arranged by installing a shelf cut from a length of 1 x 4 across the doorframe high enough to provide head clearance, as shown in the right-hand detail in Fig. 5. A "tree" is provided for each shoe by bending a length of coat-hanger wire in a U-shape to the dimensions shown in the detail. Each tree then is fitted in holes drilled in the shelf.

Storage Under Refrigerator

If a refrigerator is the small, apartment size it often can be placed on a platform, Fig. 6, so that space below the platform can be used for storage. This type refrigerator usually is low enough so that raising it about a foot does not locate its shelves too high for easy reach. The platform on which the refrigerator is placed has three closed sides and can be made of 1-in. lumber, well braced, or from a strong packing case that has one end removed. For convenient access to the space beneath the platform, a drawer, fitted with casters, is made. Again, a packing case could be used. A sheet of plywood is fastened to the

Closet space is fully utilized by installing drawer for hat and glove storage and overhead rack for shoes

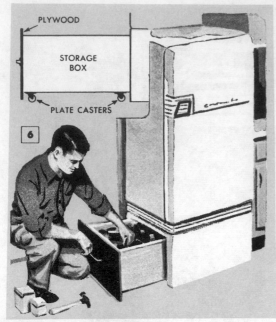

Drawer under raised refrigerator is ideal storage place for tools, shoe polish and miscellaneous items

outer end of the box to provide a neat appearance and a cabinet or drawer pull is screwed to the plywood. The drawer below the refrigerator is an ideal location for household tools, shoe polish and other miscellaneous items that are used only occasionally.

Shell-Type Base Cabinets

Shell-type cabinet construction also can be used for base cabinets. A sheet of ½ or ¾-in. plywood is used for the top and is supported on a 1 x 2 frame covered with hardboard. To assure that the top is well supported, screw the upper cross pieces of the cabinet to the wall in several places. If necessary, fit a vertical frame member from the floor to the top frame member at the back and sides of the cabinet to assure that the top is solid. Base cabinets located in such places as between a range and wall or between a range and an existing cabinet require only a top and door, since wall and range form the cabinet back and sides in one case, and the range, base cabinet and wall form the back and sides in the other. When building base cabinets, provide a toe space. ★★★

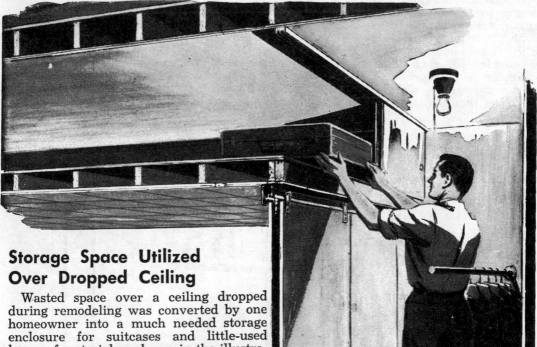

Storage Space Utilized Over Dropped Ceiling

Wasted space over a ceiling dropped during remodeling was converted by one homeowner into a much needed storage enclosure for suitcases and little-used boxes of material as shown in the illustration above. Working from inside the closet, which was added when the ceiling was dropped, the false joists were covered with hardboard, and sliding doors, also hardboard, were installed at the point of entry.

Presence of a closet is essential for access to the dead space. When a ceiling is lowered in a room that has a closet, it is only necessary to remove the part of the wall separating the dead space from the inside of the closet before installing hardboard flooring and sliding doors. The interior of the enclosure is painted white to assure adequate illumination.

Courtesy Masonite Corp.

FIG. 1

Photo courtesy Douglas Fir Plywood Assn.

Many bedrooms offer opportunity for spacious, reach-in wall wardrobes where well-organized arrangement makes full use of doors as well as space inside, and may eliminate need of separate vanity and chest of drawers

STORAGE SPACE

YOUR LACK-OF-SPACE problems often can be solved by simply reorganizing existing space to better advantage and greater convenience. This applies particularly to storage problems. A small floor area can be multiplied many times in shelf area that can be concealed in a cabinet. Storage cabinets may be built in permanently or they may be portable, permitting a change of location. Wall wardrobes or "storage walls" that open up completely with hinged, sliding or folding doors, provide quick and convenient accessibility.

In small bedrooms a wall wardrobe like the one shown in Fig. 1 practically eliminates the need of a separate vanity and chest of drawers. The boy's room shown in Fig. 2 has a built-in bunk with cabinet space under it, and is combined with a clothes closet at one end, a desk and book shelves at the other, and also conceals the clothes closet of an adjoining room. A window seat may be a continuation of wall cabinets as in Fig. 3, and provides a good storage place

for blankets during summer months. One of the most natural locations for built-in cabinets is the area under a low, sloping ceiling in an attic or on the second floor, where the floor space cannot be used to advantage for placing furniture. Fig. 4 shows a restricted space of this kind, and Fig. 5 shows how it was transformed by installing a cabinet. Fig. 6 shows a somewhat similar arrangement in which case the cabinet also included a drop leaf to serve as a desk, and a tier of open book shelves.

Wall wardrobes: Reach-in wall wardrobes provide more usable space than walk-in closets of the same size. Sliding or folding doors have an advantage in not requiring extra space for opening them. However, full-width swinging doors can be fitted with narrow shelves, Fig. 1, a midget vanity, Fig. 7, or with any of numerous attachments as shown in Fig. 8-B. The inside of wall wardrobes may include shelves, trays or drawers in addition to clothes-hanger rods. Tiers of drawers may open into the

FIG. 2

FIG. 3

Photos courtesy Western Pine Assn.

Bunk-and-cabinet combination of knotty pine, Fig. 2, and the cabinet and window seat having storage space below for blankets, Fig. 3, utilize space otherwise wasted. Low headroom of sloping roof, Fig. 4, prevents good furniture placement; can be used to much better advantage by cabinets and drawers as in Fig. 5

FIG. 4

FIG. 5

room directly, or may be concealed behind the cabinet doors.

Where a cabinet must be made shallow because of limited space, it is best to use extension clothes-hanger rods installed at right angles to the wall as shown in Fig. 8-A. Where more space is available, it is better to have the hanger rod parallel to the wall as shown in Fig. 1. This arrangement requires a minimum of 22 in. for the inside width of the cabinet. An outside width of approximately 24 in. is often used for wardrobe cabinets as the sides then can be cut from standard 4-ft. panels of plywood or wallboard without any waste. About 2 ft. of hanger-rod length is considered minimum allowance per person. Floor-to-ceiling height in cabinets generally permits the installation of two shelves above the clothes-hanger rod. The shelves should be accessible through doors at the top.

FIG. 6

Photos courtesy Douglas Fir Plywood Assn.

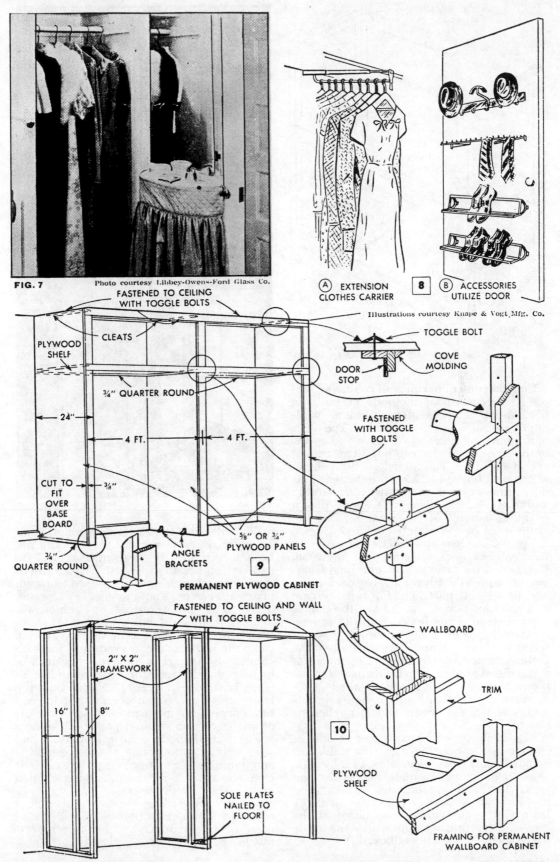

FIG. 7

Photo courtesy Libbey-Owens-Ford Glass Co.

Ⓐ EXTENSION CLOTHES CARRIER   8   Ⓑ ACCESSORIES UTILIZE DOOR

Illustrations courtesy Knape & Vogt Mfg. Co.

FASTENED TO CEILING WITH TOGGLE BOLTS

CLEATS

PLYWOOD SHELF

¾" QUARTER ROUND

24"

4 FT.   4 FT.

CUT TO FIT OVER BASE BOARD

¾"

¾" QUARTER ROUND

ANGLE BRACKETS

⅝" OR ¾" PLYWOOD PANELS

TOGGLE BOLT

DOOR STOP

COVE MOLDING

FASTENED WITH TOGGLE BOLTS

9

PERMANENT PLYWOOD CABINET

FASTENED TO CEILING AND WALL WITH TOGGLE BOLTS

2" X 2" FRAMEWORK

16"   8"

SOLE PLATES NAILED TO FLOOR

WALLBOARD

TRIM

10

PLYWOOD SHELF

FRAMING FOR PERMANENT WALLBOARD CABINET

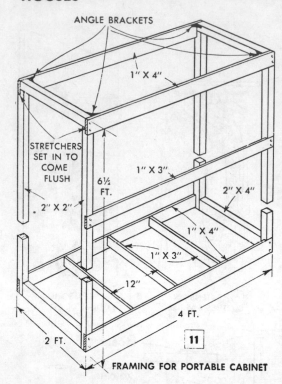

ANGLE BRACKETS

1" X 4"

STRETCHERS
SET IN TO
COME
FLUSH

6½ FT.

1" X 3"

2" X 2"

2" X 4"

1" X 4"

1" X 3"

12"

4 FT.

2 FT.

11

FRAMING FOR PORTABLE CABINET

FIG. 12   Photo courtesy Western Pine Assn.

FIG. 13   Photo courtesy Morgan Co.

Construction of permanent cabinets: Simple and economical methods of building permanent cabinets of plywood or wallboard are shown in Figs. 9 and 10. The walls of a room may serve as the back and as one or both sides of the cabinet. The ceiling and floor of the room enclose the cabinet at top and bottom. This arrangement cuts down the cost of materials considerably and is much less expensive to build than a portable cabinet of the same size as the latter must be completely enclosed.

Fig. 9 shows the construction of a permanent cabinet made of ⅝ or ¾-in. plywood. Because of its structural strength no framing is required. Plywood is used for the end panel and partition, for the shelving and the four doors. At the top the panels are nailed to cleats fastened to the ceiling, for which toggle bolts or other types of screw anchors are used. At the bottom the panels are fastened to the floor by means of small metal angles, or to cleats nailed to the floor. After the shelves are installed on ¾-in. quarter-round or regular shelf-supporting molding, the front trim is applied as shown.

Fig. 10 shows a less expensive cabinet of similar size consisting of ¼-in. wallboard or hardboard on a framework of 2 by 2-in. stock. Plywood of ¼-in. thickness also can be used for covering material. Where wood planks such as knotty pine are used, the framework must have crosspieces at the center. For a finished appearance the inside may be covered with wallboard.

Portable cabinets: Portable cabinets must be made rigid. Generally they should not be longer than 4 ft., not wider than 2 ft., and not higher than 6½ ft. These dimensions permit them to be passed through doorways easily. Those made of ⅝ or ¾-in. plywood do not require any framework, and can be made strong and rigid if assembled with glue and screws. However, a complete frame is always required for such cabinets if they are to be covered with wallboard or hardboard. Construction of framework is shown in Fig. 11. Notice how the front and rear crosspieces are set in, and how corners are made more rigid by means of angles. Prefabricated portable cabinets are also available in a variety of styles and sizes. Fig. 13 shows one of these which is adaptable to a number of applications. It comes as a knock-down kit, to be assembled and finished by the user.

Cabinet doors: Two doors are used generally for cabinet sections 4 ft. wide; separate doors for upper and lower compartments. Five-ply, ¾-in. plywood is most

FIG. 14

FIG. 15   Photo courtesy makers of Armstrong linoleum

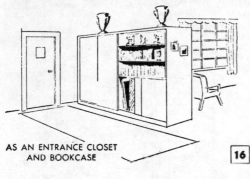

AS AN ENTRANCE CLOSET
AND BOOKCASE

16

resistant to warping. Door stops and catches for swinging doors may be placed along the top edges, and the doors should come flush with the trim.

Varied designs and applications: Cabinets of the kind described can be built on either side of windows. You can vary the length of a permanent cabinet to suit available wall space. A vanity, chest or desk can be located between two cabinets, or at one end as shown in Fig. 12. Where bedroom floor space is at a premium, cabinets can be recessed to take the heads of beds or other pieces of furniture as shown in Fig. 14.

A storage wall built between a bedroom and a bathroom is shown in Fig. 15. The center portion is a vanity backed with a large mirror and illuminated with a flush ceiling fixture. On one side is a wardrobe for clothes, which is accessible from either the bedroom or bathroom through sliding doors. On the other side tiers of drawers are located, both in the bathroom and bed-

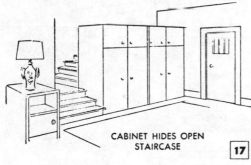

CABINET HIDES OPEN
STAIRCASE

17

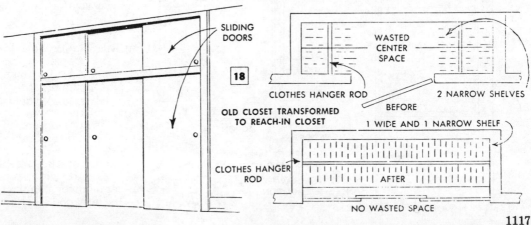

SLIDING
DOORS

18

OLD CLOSET TRANSFORMED
TO REACH-IN CLOSET

CLOTHES HANGER ROD

WASTED
CENTER
SPACE

2 NARROW SHELVES

BEFORE

CLOTHES HANGER
ROD

1 WIDE AND 1 NARROW SHELF

AFTER

NO WASTED SPACE

FIG. 19 Photo and illustration courtesy Masonite Corp.

FIG. 20 Photo courtesy Holcomb & Hoke Mfg. Co. Inc.

room. When not needed they are concealed behind sliding doors.

Cabinets of the wardrobe type also can be used to advantage in other parts of the house. Where the front door of the house opens directly into a large living room, a portable cabinet can function as an entrance closet. Fig. 16 shows two cabinets placed end to end. One is an entrance closet. The other has horizontally divided compartments, the upper one fitted with bookshelves and the lower one arranged for storage. The latter should accommodate card tables as shown. Often entrance cabinets can be located to conceal part of a stairway as shown in Fig. 17.

Changing walk-in closets: Shallow walk-in closets can be made much more convenient, and their capacity can be increased as

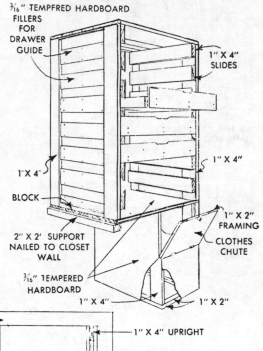

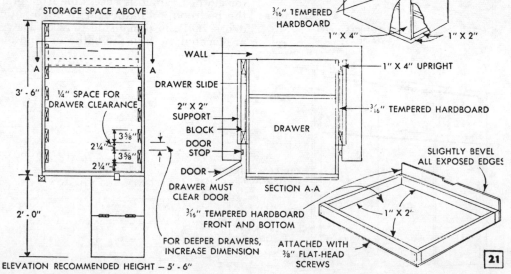

FIG. 22

Photo courtesy Masonite Corp.

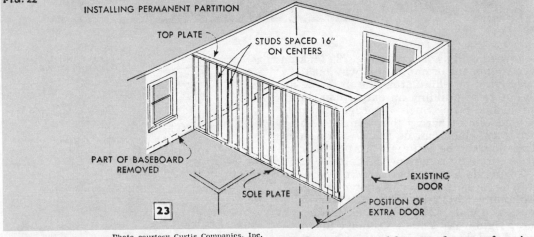

INSTALLING PERMANENT PARTITION

TOP PLATE

STUDS SPACED 16"
ON CENTERS

PART OF BASEBOARD
REMOVED

SOLE PLATE

23

EXISTING
DOOR

POSITION OF
EXTRA DOOR

Photo courtesy Curtis Companies, Inc.

much as one-third by simply transforming them to reach-in closets as shown in Fig. 18. Instead of using hinged doors requiring free floor area for swinging, sliding or folding doors are preferable. Fig. 19 shows a folding door on a somewhat wider closet, previously inconvenient because of its length. The folding door also offers better illumination and ventilation.

Hall linen closets also can be improved by installing sliding trays as shown in Fig. 20. Construction is detailed in Fig. 21. Notice that tempered hardboard is used for drawer bottoms as well as for covering. A clothes chute to the basement can be provided on a first floor by simply cutting and boxing an opening between two joists. This requires cutting through both the finish and subfloor, and through the basement ceiling.

Two rooms for one: Where an additional bedroom is needed for greater privacy, you can divide a large one into two by installing

FIG. 25

Photo courtesy Johns-Manville

a storage wall as shown in Fig. 22. Making two rooms out of one in this way makes a big saving by eliminating the probable alternative of building an extra room in an unfinished attic. Such a storage wall may extend almost across the room, leaving a doorway which can be fitted with a door. The room can be restored to its original size at any time by removing the cabinet.

To divide a room permanently, you install a regular partition as shown in Fig. 23. Although 2 by 2-in. stock may serve for studs and plates, 2 by 4-in. stock produces a more rigid wall. You first remove the baseboard and shoe molding, and also any molding at the ceiling. After marking the location of the partition, nail the sole plate to the floor. You can attach the top plate directly under the plaster of the ceiling. If it crosses joists or comes under one lengthwise, you fasten the plate to these with 16-d. nails. Where the partition plate comes under a space between two joists, you use toggle bolts or screw anchors.

The end studs are toenailed to the plates and fastened to the walls. Then other studs are installed at 16-in. centers. ____ is then applied, followed by trim. Such a wall on 2 by 4-in. framing may have recessed portions to accommodate shelves for books or knickknacks.

Utilizing other waste space: For putting things out of sight, yet readily accessible, there are many other spots in the average house that can be put to profitable use. Perhaps the area under a stairway is just the place for an extra powder room. Don't

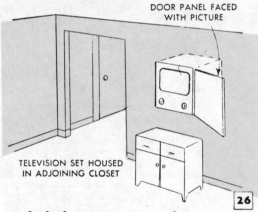

DOOR PANEL FACED WITH PICTURE

TELEVISION SET HOUSED IN ADJOINING CLOSET

26

overlook the opportunities that many corners offer for the installation of attractive corner cabinets such as the one shown in Fig. 24. Walls of attic rooms may be recessed as in Fig. 25 for wide pieces of furniture such as a day bed, vanity, desk, radio, phonograph or television set.

One method of saving the space in a living room or den, which is usually sacrificed to accommodate a television set, is to locate the set in an adjoining closet as indicated in Fig. 26. For this an opening must be made in the wall at the desired height for the screen, controls and speaker grille, and perhaps located over the present radio set. The opening is framed and may be closed when not in use by providing a single or a double door. It can also be concealed by means of a picture, in which case offset hinges are used, the framed opening then being extended about 1 in. from the wall surface.

YEAR-ROUND CHECK LIST
FOR HOUSE AND YARD

JANUARY

Repair furniture.
Fix faucet leaks.
Change furnace filters.
Prune fruit trees.
Inspect plant mulching.
Feed the birds

FEBRUARY

Build yard furniture.
Repair awnings.
Start plants in flats.
Make root cuttings.
Prepare hotbed.
Prune trees, grapevines.
Fertilize lawn.
Plan garden, flowers.
Order garden seeds

MARCH

Repair screens.
Check yard tools.
Buy grass seed.
Check garden hose.
Repair trellises.
Check electric cords.
Paint and paper

APRIL

Check roof for leaks.
Sharpen mower.
Plant trees and shrubs.
Seed, top-dress lawn.
Clean attic, garage.
Hang birdhouses.
Clean planting borders.
Check electric fans.
Paint lawn furniture.
Repair fences

MAY

Clean fireplace (put wood ashes on garden).
Edge sidewalks and flower borders.
Set out transplants.
Have air conditioner serviced.
Oil all appliances

JUNE

Clean yard incinerator.
Spray shrubs.
Treat lawn with weed killer.
Check locks and the operation of windows

JULY

Paint trim.
Check flashing.
Tuck-point brick.
Clean chimney.
Fertilize lawn again.
Spray evergreens.
Check extinguishers.
Check basement humidity

AUGUST

Clean and check furnace (Change filter, oil motor and fan, follow factory instructions).
Finish outside painting.
Water lawn on schedule.
Stock up on fuel.
Fertilize garden

SEPTEMBER

Have TV and radio sets checked (antennas, grounding wires, etc.).
Oil and clean kitchen ventilating fan.
Reseed spots in lawn.
Store electric fans in dustproof bags.
Repair storm windows

OCTOBER

Turn off and drain outside faucets.
Store garden hose.
Water evergreens.
Prepare shrubs for winter

NOVEMBER

Test weather stripping.
Screen shrubs and young trees from rabbits.
Clean rain gutters

DECEMBER

Prepare for Christmas:
Make outside decorations.
Finish workshop projects early.
Check tree lights, stand, outside lights.
Fireproof tree or have extinguishers handy.
Recheck extinguishers

Let the artist have his way. He can't hurt that papered wall if it's covered with clear sheet plastic

20 WAYS TO "KIDPROOF"

By E. R. Haan

HIGH-SPIRITED youngsters are a joy to have around the home and their antics are a real source of amusement—until they begin to expend their energies on the walls and furniture. When you're stuck with scratched furniture, marred woodwork, kicked-in screens and torn and scribbled-up books, your admiration for Junior's vitality will be somewhat dimmed. Attempts at reasoning and scolding won't sink in for long, so the next best thing you can do is to prepare for the onslaught, set up the barricades—in other words, make your house as thoroughly "kidproof" as possible.

Those Worried Walls

For example, in an artistic mood young Rembrandt will find the walls irresistible and there's nothing will ruin ordinary wallpaper better than pencil and crayons.

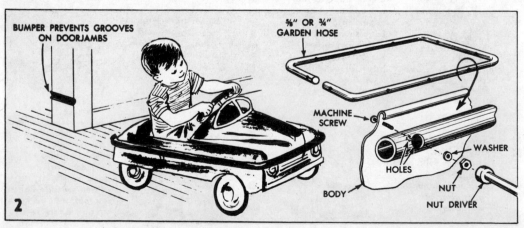

BUMPER PREVENTS GROOVES ON DOORJAMBS

⅝" OR ¾" GARDEN HOSE

MACHINE SCREW

WASHER

HOLES

NUT

NUT DRIVER

BODY

Someday he may write the great American novel; meantime you'd better make those lower shelves off limits

YOUR HOME

Though washable paper is best for nurseries and playrooms, ordinary wallpaper can be given a coat or two of waterproofing lacquer. This keeps the paper from absorbing grease, jelly and other substances which seem to be part of a child's natural covering. Walls in play areas also may be covered with clear plastic, Fig. 1, tacked or taped in place and extending four feet or so from the floor — just above the little fellow's reach. The plastic won't be as noticeable as you think.

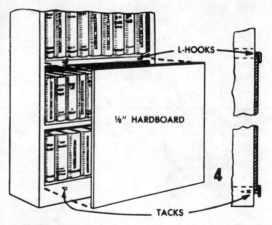

Open fireplaces are an open invitation to crawlers

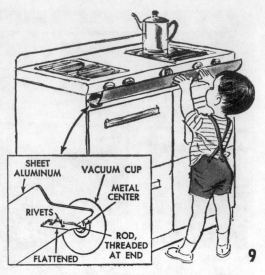

Foiled again! dad covered the knobs on the stove

Of Tots and Wheels

Wheeled toys may be considered another weapon in Junior's war against furniture and walls. Here, bumpers of rubber tubing or garden hose will save the day. These are best placed all around the vehicle at the outermost points and may be secured with small machine screws as shown in Fig. 2. A screen enclosed porch also will come in for a lot of abuse, especially on rainy days when the porch becomes a playground. Stopping the front wheel of a tricycle can make old screen out of new in a matter of minutes. Guard rails can be made easily with solid, steel curtain rods fitted into screw-type brackets placed two or three feet from the floor, Fig. 5. These cannot be removed even by the most enterprising of children.

Boy, Book and Trouble

The little fellow shown in Fig. 3 has obviously developed a literary bent, but unfortunately it won't be long before his enthusiasm gets out of hand. Torn and scribbled pages are, of course, a foregone conclusion. Patient mothers may spend part of each day with the child "reading" him stories and pictures. But what to do when she's not around and those lower shelves become a temptation? One way around this is to conceal the lower shelves behind removable panels of hardboard or plywood. The lower edges may be set to rest on tacks, as shown in Fig. 4, while the upper edges are held by L-hooks which turn to permit removal of the panel.

Fireplaces are another hole in the wall into which youngsters love to crawl, much to mother's consternation, but there's no reason why it can't be closed up when not

10

A hinged door on the toolchest keeps kids out

11

Top shelf's the best place for paint and varnish

in use. Simply nail together a frame of 2 x 4s which fits snugly inside of the fireplace opening and cover this with hardboard, Fig. 6. It can be quickly removed when you're set for a cozy evening around the fire.

Nail It Down

With their seemingly inexhaustible supply of energy and a craze for creeping, crawling and climbing over everything, it would seem that the only way to keep everything from going to ruin would be to nail everything down. A table completely set with place setting and all, for example, just begs for that toddler to come along and pull the whole works down on the floor. This can't happen if a piece of tape is used with tacks and a safety pin, as in Fig. 7, to "pin" that cloth down. The little guy in Fig. 8 is in for a bad bruising, but it won't happen a second time if dad will attach an angle bracket to the shelf and screw it into a wall stud. His brother in Fig. 9 has seen mother light the stove time and again and those little knobs are just too much for him —he's got to try them. Fortunately, someone had foresight enough to cover the controls and knobs with an aluminum guard fitted onto suction cups, as illustrated.

The shiny tools in dad's workshop too, will eventually become a source of fascination. But, it's when dad's away that the tots will want to play and the results can be havoc. A hinged door like the one in Fig. 10 can be locked, keeping the cabinet's contents out of the hands of unwelcome guests. The wise fellow in Fig. 11 stores his paints, varnish and the like on a shelf high enough to elude even the most ingenious and persistent of children. To play it double safe, better put your ladders away where the gang can't find them.

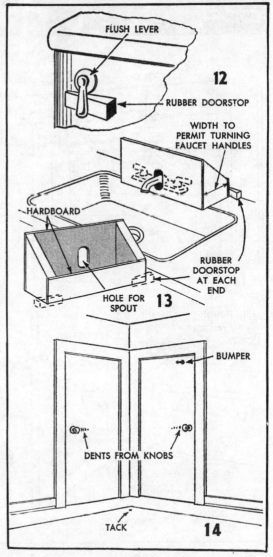

FLUSH LEVER

12

RUBBER DOORSTOP

WIDTH TO PERMIT TURNING FAUCET HANDLES

HARDBOARD

RUBBER DOORSTOP AT EACH END

HOLE FOR SPOUT

13

BUMPER

DENTS FROM KNOBS

TACK

14

15

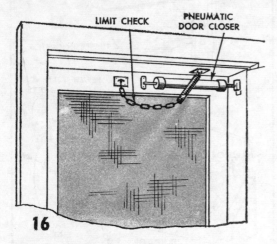

16

LIMIT CHECK   PNEUMATIC DOOR CLOSER

What's the lifespan of a glass-topped coffee table with kids around? Don't press your luck to find out. Play it safe and cover it with a piece of hardboard

Water, Water Everywhere

And then there's running water. Ever watch a small child wrapped up in the fascination of running water? Sooner or later he'll want to get his hands in it, then float his toys and away we go until no source of water is sacred. One couple, harried to the point of exasperation, couldn't find a way to keep little miss trouble from dropping toys into the toilet bowl. Things got worse when she learned to flush it. Two or three plumbing bills later, dad hit on the idea of wedging a rubber door stop behind the flush lever—tight enough so that it could only be removed by an adult, Fig. 12. The kitchen sink too attracted

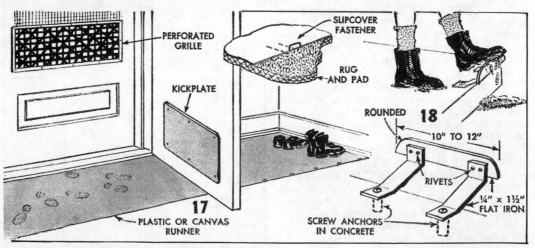

PERFORATED GRILLE

KICKPLATE

SLIPCOVER FASTENER

RUG AND PAD

ROUNDED   **18**

10" TO 12"

RIVETS

¼" x 1½" FLAT IRON

17

PLASTIC OR CANVAS RUNNER

SCREW ANCHORS IN CONCRETE

little miss trouble and she was forever "washing dishes" and making a general wet mess of things, herself included. Of course, there was always the danger she would scald herself with the hot water. The solution? A hood made of hardboard as shown in Fig. 13. The back portion of the hood was wedged between the faucet housing and the wall using two rubber door stops. This still left enough room for an adult to be able to reach in and turn the faucets on and off.

In and Out With a Bang

Doors, of course, are little more than a nuisance to six- and seven-year-olds and must be opened with as much haste and violence as possible—resulting in cracked plaster in the wall behind the door and marred finishes where doors are installed in a corner, as shown in Fig. 14. Since a word to a child is soon forgotten, the only answer is to locate a door stop at the top of one of the doors and to place resilient covers on the doorknobs. A tack placed on the corner of the rug will keep running feet from kicking the rug back and trampling on it—the short way to ruin for many a fine floor covering. And, speaking of doors, there's many a pneumatic door closer that has been ruined by a gang of youngsters pushing the door past the closer's limits. This is best prevented with a chain and spring mounted as shown in Fig. 16.

The more delicate pieces of furniture, like glass-topped coffee tables, are naturals for free-swinging kids. Rather than take odds on how long the glass top will last, cover it with a piece of hardboard or plywood as is being done in Fig. 15. Cellophane tape will hold it on and is easy to remove when company arrives and the kids are safe in bed.

WASHER   SCREW
DOORKNOB SHANK
HEAVY CORD OR FURNACE CHAIN.

19

No more whining at the screen door. Li'l Mike lets himself in with this handy door opener on the knob

20   PLASTIC COVERS

PLASTIC RUNNERS

HARDBOARD →

21

When Junior Leaves a Trail

The battle against tracked-in mud is best fought with a plastic or canvas runner fastened to the rug with slipcover fasteners, as shown in Fig. 17. A metal mud scraper, Fig. 18, anchored to one side of the porch will work wonders, once you've taught the kids to use it. And to protect the screen and the door finish, there's no substitute for a grill and a kickplate to absorb the blows most kids find a necessary part of entering the house.

It's All in the Game

Of course, the mess kids make is a natural part of their learning and growing.

After all, these little people *do* live in a world of adults and have a hard time adjusting to it. Take our little friend Mike, in Fig. 19; the door certainly wasn't designed with him in mind. A little ingenuity on dad's part, plus a screw, a washer and a length of cord brought the problem down to a toddler's size. Plastic covers are best for protecting fabric-covered furniture, Fig. 20, and plastic runners protect the floor when learning to eat means throwing the food around, as witness our friend in Fig. 21, or when play means using paints, ink, etc. Then again, rolling toys run better if the rug is covered with a sheet of hardboard. ★ ★ ★

Latticework Relieves Plain Exterior-Wall Area

Bare, unbroken, exterior-wall areas between widely spaced windows in a house can be made interesting by the addition of latticework designs similar to those shown. Such a design also will serve to make the house appear longer, lower and "tied to the ground," an effect long considered very desirable in a house by most architects. Made from ¾ x 1-in. stock, the members used in the overlaid design are half-lapped and joined with nails and waterproof glue. The latticework is completed by finishing with several coats of exterior paint, either in the same color as the windows or in a contrasting color. If 1-in. blocks are inserted between the latticework and the wall of the house, the former can be used as a trellis, thus providing an additional decorative effect for the wall.

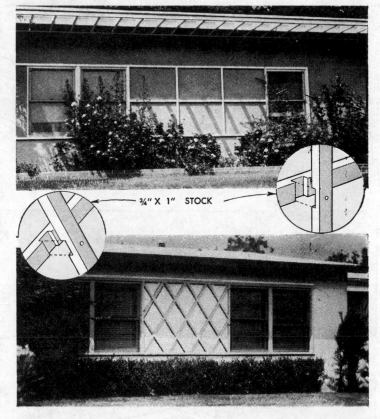

¾" X 1" STOCK

Avoid letting newspapers, magazines, handbills and mail accumulate at your entrance during an extended absence. Such "advertising" practically invites prowlers inside to strip the premises at their leisure

Outsmarting the Housebreaker

By Enno R. Haan

RETURNING TO FIND your home ransacked can take all the enjoyment out of a vacation or an evening out. Unfortunately, many persons actually invite such theft by advertising their absence without realizing it. The chances of having your home burglarized can be minimized by a few common-sense precautions.

First: Avoid telltale clues that advertise your absence and thus invite housebreakers, who usually prefer to work when occupants are gone. Second: Make provisions to mislead and confuse would-be intruders as they usually try to avoid needless complications, trouble and risk. Third: Lock all doors and windows whenever you leave and install additional fastening devices as may be necessary. The average housebreaker prefers places that are easy to enter. Fourth: Inform the police of your vacation absence so they can check up daily. Also ask neighbors to keep an eye on the place for any signs of activity. Fifth:

Leave your jewelry and other valuables in a bank safety-deposit box, in a burglarproof safe or with trusted relatives or friends. Although these measures, or any others, do not make a home burglarproof, they are nevertheless effective deterrents. A burglar-alarm system may be installed also as an added preventive measure.

Lights, Shades and Radio

A dark house having the front entrance or porch light on as in Fig. 8 is a dead giveaway that the occupants are absent for the evening. A dimly lighted front hall or living room does not fool a smart prowler. A lighted bathroom is much more effective, but it's even better to have the house illuminated as usual. Most of the window shades and drapes should be open so that neighbors can notice the presence of an intruder. **Leaving your radio turned on during a few hours' absence does not cost much and suggests that someone is home,**

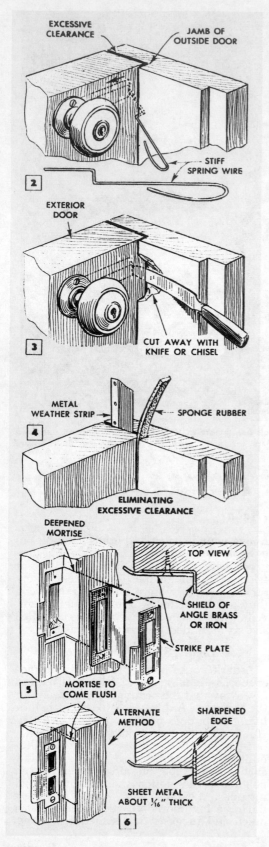

Old-time naive habit of "hiding" key under mat or in mailbox is like handing it to a burglar as he habitually checks these places first for easy entry

provided that the prowler cannot look into rooms completely. However, some rooms should not be entirely visible from the outside as this enables a prowler to check whether the house is unoccupied.

Clues of Absence at Doors

Accumulated newspapers, magazines, circulars, etc., at your front door and stuffed in the mailbox, Fig. 1, betray absence. Thus alerted, a prowler can move in with comparative safety. To prevent such evidence, have your newspaper deliveries discontinued during your absence and have the mail held at the post office or forwarded to you. Then ask a neighbor to pick up circulars and packages and remove "have called" signs sometimes hung on doorknobs.

An array of milk bottles at a back door is another urgent invitation to a prospective prowler. A note left for a milkman to discontinue milk may be read by someone else first. Use the telephone to cancel milk deliveries. **Also avoid newspaper comments on a pending trip; no one will read this with greater personal interest than a housebreaker.** Don't leave door keys under mats, Fig. 7, in mailboxes or other hiding spots for the convenience of other members of the family. These are the first places that prowlers investigate for easy entry. Have each member of the family carry a separate key without any address attached.

Making Door Latches Hard to Open

Many door latches can be opened easily by using a length of spring wire, as in Fig. 2, a thin knife blade or a screw driver. This will be more difficult to do if excessive clearance between the door and jamb is eliminated by installing weather stripping as shown in Fig. 4. However, leave the normal 1/16-in. clearance between the door and jamb to allow for expansion. Most outside doors have rabbeted doorjambs but it's easy to cut away some of the wood with a jackknife or chisel to permit inserting a thin blade as in Fig. 3, to pry the latch

Leaving an entrance lamp lighted, but the rest of the house dark and quiet when you're out for the evening, is another "polite" invitation to prowlers

loose. To prevent such jimmying, you can install a piece of angle brass or steel as in Fig. 5, or a piece of flat steel sharpened at one edge and driven into the jamb as in Fig. 6.

Interior doors sometimes serve as entrances to dwellings as, for example, the doors in the hallway of an apartment building that give access to the apartments; also the doors between houses and attached garages that are left open or unlocked. Inside doors generally have stop strips nailed or screwed to the jambs and these can be pried up to get at the door latch. To make such doors more foolproof, eliminate excessive clearance between the stop and door by relocating the stop strips. Then attach them more securely with ring-type drive nails, two or three of which should be located near the lock. You can also install shields as shown in Figs. 5 and 6.

A crude but effective method of jimmying a door open is to insert the end of a crowbar, or similar tool, between the door and the jamb and apply brute force to disengage the latch from the striker plate. This method of entry can be made difficult by providing additional holding devices that do not respond to this action.

Install Locks Having Dead Bolts

Entrance doors should have foolproof cylinder locks equipped with dead bolts or dead latches. These cannot be pried open with a wire or knife like an ordinary latch. A dead bolt on a cylinder lock, such as the mortise-type entrance lock shown in Fig. 9, works independently of the doorknobs. The dead bolt can be opened or closed from the inside with a turn button and from the outside by means of the door key. Tubular-lock sets, such as shown in Fig. 10, have a latch only but this can be deadlocked to give the same security as a dead bolt.

Adding Auxiliary Fasteners

In many homes only the front entrance is provided with a tamperproof lock and

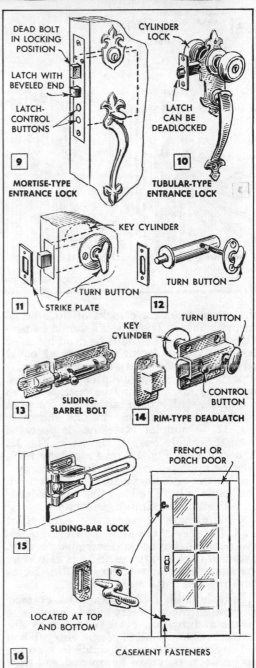

9 — MORTISE-TYPE ENTRANCE LOCK
DEAD BOLT IN LOCKING POSITION
LATCH WITH BEVELED END
LATCH-CONTROL BUTTONS

10 — TUBULAR-TYPE ENTRANCE LOCK
CYLINDER LOCK
LATCH CAN BE DEADLOCKED

11 — STRIKE PLATE
KEY CYLINDER
TURN BUTTON

12 — TURN BUTTON

13 — SLIDING-BARREL BOLT
KEY CYLINDER

14 — RIM-TYPE DEADLATCH
TURN BUTTON
CONTROL BUTTON

15 — SLIDING-BAR LOCK

16 — FRENCH OR PORCH DOOR
LOCATED AT TOP AND BOTTOM
CASEMENT FASTENERS

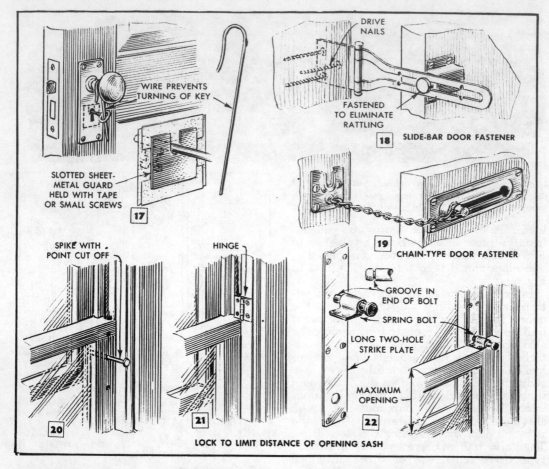

WIRE PREVENTS TURNING OF KEY

SLOTTED SHEET-METAL GUARD HELD WITH TAPE OR SMALL SCREWS

17

DRIVE NAILS

FASTENED TO ELIMINATE RATTLING

18 SLIDE-BAR DOOR FASTENER

19 CHAIN-TYPE DOOR FASTENER

SPIKE WITH POINT CUT OFF

20

HINGE

21

GROOVE IN END OF BOLT

SPRING BOLT

LONG TWO-HOLE STRIKE PLATE

MAXIMUM OPENING

22

LOCK TO LIMIT DISTANCE OF OPENING SASH

the other doors have locks of little or no security value. These doors should be provided with separate bolts or dead locks, or other auxiliary locking devices of equal effectiveness. A sliding bolt of the tubular type is least conspicuous as it is housed inside the door. It may be operated from the inside with a turn button and from the outside with a key, as the one shown in Fig. 11. A simpler style that is operated from the inside only is shown in Fig. 12. A barrel bolt, Fig. 13, or a rim-type latch may be operated from the inside and outside as the one shown in Fig. 14, or from the inside only. The kind that can be deadlocked offers maximum protection.

An alternate arrangement consists of a bar fastener of the kind shown in Fig. 15. For doors that open onto screened porches, patios or decks, extra security is gained by installing casement fasteners, Fig. 16, at both top and bottom of the doors.

Built-in milk and package boxes near kitchen-entrance doors may provide a means of intrusion even though they are themselves too small to permit entry. When not equipped with an adequate lock on the inside door, they can be opened and then may permit manipulation of a wire hook to open the door. In some cases it is even possible to extend an arm through an open milk box and reach the lock of the door.

Practically no security whatever is offered by bit-key locks that are often found on back doors. Leaving the key in the lock on the inside offers no protection as it can be pushed out or gripped by a special tool and turned. About the only way to prevent the key from being turned is to hold it with a stiff-wire hook as shown in Fig. 17. To prevent the key from being pushed out, you can insert a slotted, sheet-metal guard under the keyhole escutcheon, or plate, as is also indicated in Fig. 17. Screen door hooks are no deterrent to a prowler as he simply slashes the screen to loosen the hook.

Locking Partly Opened Doors

Bar fasteners and chain fasteners, Figs. 18 and 19, that are commonly used to keep out intruders when a door is partly open, are installed so that a person outside cannot loosen them by reaching inside. Spirally grooved drive nails should be used to fasten parts that attach to the jamb. Or, flat-headed wood screws can be used, the slots being filled with solder after installation, which prevents their easy removal with a screwdriver.

Secure Window Fasteners

When doors are hard to open, prowlers turn to windows that are not easily observed by neighbors. Double-hung windows—those having an upper and lower sash—can be locked effectively by means of the usual crescent-type sash locks installed at the parting rails. However, they provide no security when the sash are left partly open for ventilation. Therefore, it is advisable to fit windows with supplementary locks that limit the distance that the sash can be opened. Some of these locks can be opened easily from the outside with a length of wire or a flat blade. The homemade arrangement shown in Fig. 22 consists of a spring bolt which engages holes in a strike plate. The latter is screwed to the upright of the upper sash. It is difficult to open from the outside, particularly if the bolt has a groove at the end as shown in the detail. The groove should engage the edge of the strike plate automatically when either sash is opened the maximum distance. The reason for a long strike plate extending to the top of the sash is to prevent the sash from being marred by the bolt sliding over its surface. The bolt also enters the lower hole automatically when the window is closed, and thus assures a locked window even though the center lock may be forgotten. Figs. 20 and 21 show two other methods of locking partially opened windows.

Outswinging casement windows having crank-type adjusters cannot be opened easily when they are closed or slightly open—not far enough to permit inserting a heavy-wire tool or an arm to reach in and turn the crank. Casement windows that swing inward can be held by means of regular casement fasteners like doors as shown in Fig. 16, or by means of bar fasteners. The latter will hold the windows locked when they are completely closed or slightly open. Using chain locks or hooks and eyes for this purpose does not eliminate movement and rattle.

Hooked screens in front of windows offer no protection at all as it is so easy to slit them and then open the window. Basement windows are likely to be inadequately locked. Second-story windows often are accessible from the low roof or deck of a porch or garage, or by means of a ladder conveniently acquired by the prowler on the premises. With this in view, it's best to keep a ladder inside the house or in another locked building. ★ ★ ★

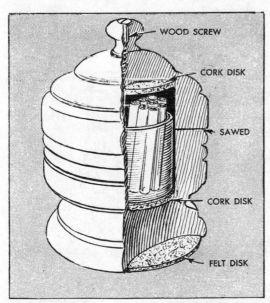

CIGARETTE HUMIDOR — WOOD SCREW, CORK DISK, SAWED, CORK DISK, FELT DISK

Cigarette Humidor

CIGARETTE HUMIDOR

A crown finial, removed when modernizing a stairway newel, or a similar turning cut from an old pedestal table, forms an unusual cigarette humidor. After the turning is sawed in two, as shown in the detail, use an expansive bit to drill both the top and bottom sections to receive a glass container. The latter is simply a jar or tumbler which has been cut slightly shorter than the length of the cigarettes. The rim of the container, which should extend about ¼ in. above the edge of the hole in the bottom section, is ground smooth.

FARM OR COTTAGE WATER SYSTEM

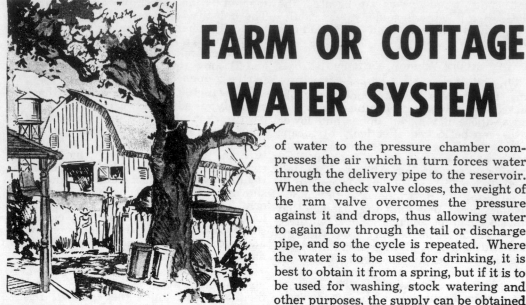

MANY rural homes and summer cottages can be furnished with running water from a near-by spring or stream even though its daily flow is modest, by installing a hydraulic ram. This is a pump which takes advantage of a small water fall to lift a portion of the water to a considerable height. Theoretically, a hydraulic ram should lift one half of the water available twice the height of the fall or 1/20 of it twenty times the height of the fall. But the actual efficiency of rams is less and varies considerably. Fig. 1 shows the working parts. Under normal conditions, the ram valve is open, thus allowing water to flow through the ram. As water flows, its velocity increases until the valve is lifted and quickly closed. Since water in motion possesses energy, a considerable pressure is developed. This pressure opens the check valve, thus admitting a quantity of water to the pressure chamber. When enough water has entered to relieve the excess pressure, the check valve automatically closes, thus preventing water from flowing back. At this instant a small volume of air enters through the breather hole to replenish the air dissolved and carried away by the water. Upon the next stroke of the ram this air will be forced into the pressure chamber. The addition of water to the pressure chamber compresses the air which in turn forces water through the delivery pipe to the reservoir. When the check valve closes, the weight of the ram valve overcomes the pressure against it and drops, thus allowing water to again flow through the tail or discharge pipe, and so the cycle is repeated. Where the water is to be used for drinking, it is best to obtain it from a spring, but if it is to be used for washing, stock watering and other purposes, the supply can be obtained from a small stream.

We shall first explain simplified methods which will enable anyone to determine how much water can be lifted from a spring to the location where it is to be used, and

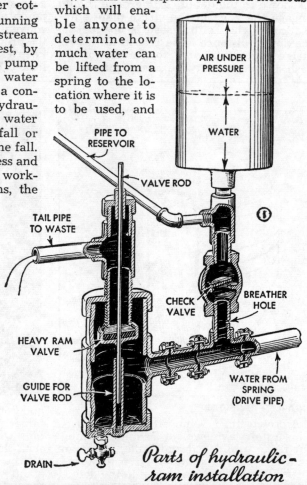

Parts of hydraulic-ram installation

AIR UNDER PRESSURE

WATER

PIPE TO RESERVOIR

VALVE ROD

TAIL PIPE TO WASTE

CHECK VALVE

BREATHER HOLE

HEAVY RAM VALVE

WATER FROM SPRING (DRIVE PIPE)

GUIDE FOR VALVE ROD

DRAIN

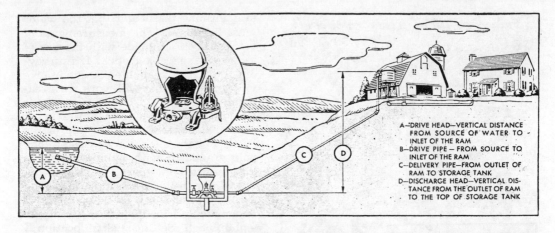

A—DRIVE HEAD—VERTICAL DISTANCE FROM SOURCE OF WATER TO INLET OF THE RAM
B—DRIVE PIPE — FROM SOURCE TO INLET OF THE RAM
C—DELIVERY PIPE—FROM OUTLET OF RAM TO STORAGE TANK
D—DISCHARGE HEAD—VERTICAL DISTANCE FROM THE OUTLET OF RAM TO THE TOP OF STORAGE TANK

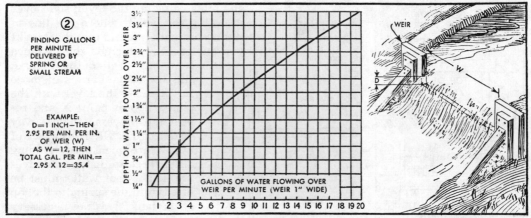

② FINDING GALLONS PER MINUTE DELIVERED BY SPRING OR SMALL STREAM

EXAMPLE:
D=1 INCH—THEN
2.95 PER MIN. PER IN.
OF WEIR (W)
AS W=12, THEN
TOTAL GAL. PER MIN.=
2.95 X 12=35.4

First measure distance D, which is the depth of water flowing over the weir, by the method shown in Fig. 3. Locate this value at the left-hand side of the chart, follow across to the curve, and then drop down where the amount of water in gallons per minute for each inch of weir length is given. Multiplying this number by the length of the weir in inches gives the total amount of water passing over the weir per minute

then illustrate methods of surveying the spring and determining the other necessary values. Then the spring must be surveyed first to find whether it will deliver enough water. To do this it is dammed as shown in Fig. 2, so that all of the water flows over the edge of the board or "weir." The weir must be perfectly level and so arranged that no water can flow under or around it. The flow should be slow and free from turbulence. The depth of the water flowing over it is measured as shown in Fig. 3. First drive a stake a couple of feet above the weir, the top of both stake and weir being level, which can be determined by the method shown in detail A. Then the distance from the top of the stake to the surface of the water is measured as in detail B. We can now determine the amount of water in number of gals. per min., by referring to Fig. 2. To illustrate the method we will assume that the depth of water flowing over the weir is one inch. We locate one inch on the left-hand side, following across to where this line meets the curve, and drop down to read a trifle below 3, say 2.95, as the gals. per min. for each inch of weir. Next we multiply this by the length of the weir which we will assume to be 25 in., giving a total of 73.75 gals. per minute. As the flow of springs varies with the seasons, it is necessary to estimate the minimum flow if this is not known. Let us assume that the flow during the dry season is 10 gals. per min. This value can, of course, be determined during the dry season by the weir method as explained.

Next, it is necessary to determine how high the ram will have to pump water to fill the supply reservoir, which may be located in the attic or other convenient place. Some use an outside tank. Fig. 4 shows a practical arrangement for the water-supply system. The reservoir or supply tank should be large enough to hold an entire

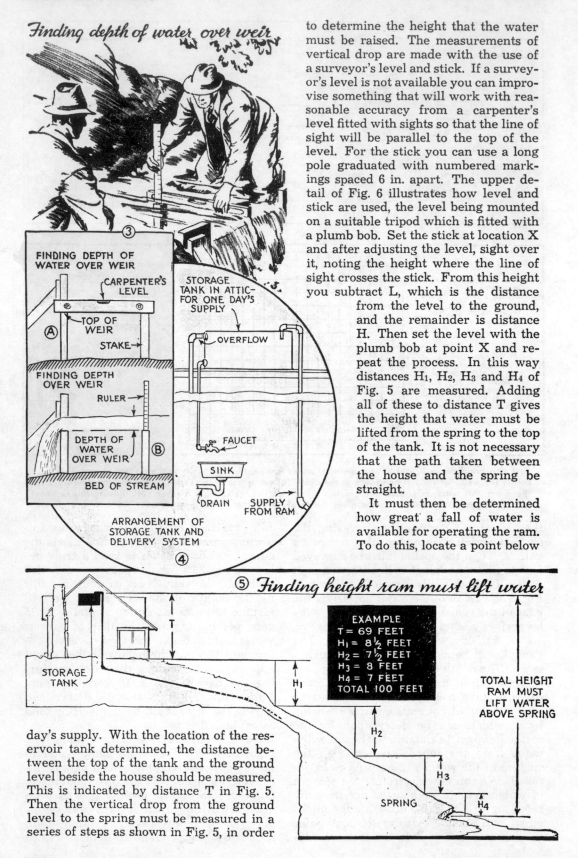

Finding depth of water over weir

③
**FINDING DEPTH OF
WATER OVER WEIR**

CARPENTER'S
LEVEL

Ⓐ
TOP OF
WEIR

STAKE→

**FINDING DEPTH
OVER WEIR**

RULER →

DEPTH OF
WATER
OVER WEIR

Ⓑ

BED OF STREAM

STORAGE
TANK IN ATTIC·
FOR ONE DAY'S
SUPPLY

OVERFLOW

FAUCET

SINK

DRAIN

SUPPLY
FROM RAM

ARRANGEMENT OF
STORAGE TANK AND
DELIVERY SYSTEM
④

to determine the height that the water must be raised. The measurements of vertical drop are made with the use of a surveyor's level and stick. If a surveyor's level is not available you can improvise something that will work with reasonable accuracy from a carpenter's level fitted with sights so that the line of sight will be parallel to the top of the level. For the stick you can use a long pole graduated with numbered markings spaced 6 in. apart. The upper detail of Fig. 6 illustrates how level and stick are used, the level being mounted on a suitable tripod which is fitted with a plumb bob. Set the stick at location X and after adjusting the level, sight over it, noting the height where the line of sight crosses the stick. From this height you subtract L, which is the distance from the level to the ground, and the remainder is distance H. Then set the level with the plumb bob at point X and repeat the process. In this way distances H_1, H_2, H_3 and H_4 of Fig. 5 are measured. Adding all of these to distance T gives the height that water must be lifted from the spring to the top of the tank. It is not necessary that the path taken between the house and the spring be straight.

It must then be determined how great a fall of water is available for operating the ram. To do this, locate a point below

⑤ *Finding height ram must lift water*

STORAGE
TANK

T

EXAMPLE
T = 69 FEET
H_1 = 8½ FEET
H_2 = 7½ FEET
H_3 = 8 FEET
H_4 = 7 FEET
TOTAL 100 FEET

H_1

TOTAL HEIGHT
RAM MUST
LIFT WATER
ABOVE SPRING

H_2

H_3

SPRING

H_4

day's supply. With the location of the reservoir tank determined, the distance between the top of the tank and the ground level beside the house should be measured. This is indicated by distance T in Fig. 5. Then the vertical drop from the ground level to the spring must be measured in a series of steps as shown in Fig. 5, in order

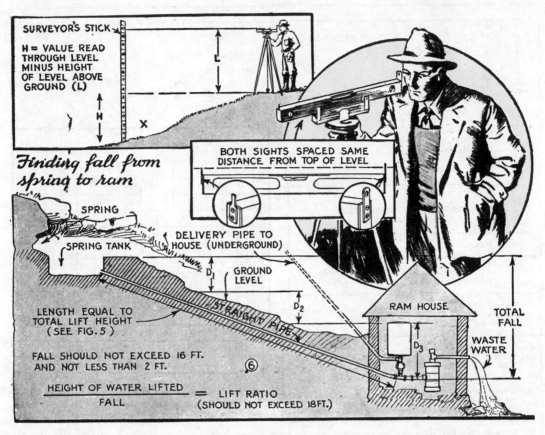

Finding fall from spring to ram

SURVEYOR'S STICK

H = VALUE READ THROUGH LEVEL MINUS HEIGHT OF LEVEL ABOVE GROUND (L)

BOTH SIGHTS SPACED SAME DISTANCE FROM TOP OF LEVEL

SPRING

SPRING TANK

DELIVERY PIPE TO HOUSE (UNDERGROUND)

GROUND LEVEL

STRAIGHT PIPE

LENGTH EQUAL TO TOTAL LIFT HEIGHT (SEE FIG. 5)

FALL SHOULD NOT EXCEED 16 FT. AND NOT LESS THAN 2 FT.

RAM HOUSE

TOTAL FALL

WASTE WATER

$$\frac{\text{HEIGHT OF WATER LIFTED}}{\text{FALL}} = \text{LIFT RATIO (SHOULD NOT EXCEED 18 FT.)}$$

Besides measuring the vertical drop from the top of the reservoir tank to the spring, the additional drop from the spring to the ram, located not over 16 ft. below the spring, should be measured in the same way, using the level system shown in the upper details

the level of the spring from which the waste water from the ram can easily drain away. The straight pipe-line distance between the spring and the ram should be about the same as the vertical height to which the ram must lift the water. To continue with the example, we will assume that the top of the supply tank was found to be 100 ft. from the spring. This means that a pipe at least 100 ft. long will have to be run from the spring, straight but sloping downward, to a place below the spring where the ram will be located. Having determined the ram location, which should not be less than 2 ft. nor more than about 16 ft. below spring level and 100 ft. or more from the spring as shown in Fig. 6, we are ready to find the fall or head available for pumping water. This is the vertical height of the spring above the ram location and is found with a surveyor's level and stick as previously explained. We will assume our survey shows that the total fall (Fig. 6) is 14 ft. Then from Fig. 7 it is easy to determine whether a spring

will pump as much water as is required. Assuming that the ram will be located 14 ft. vertically below the spring, Fig. 6, we deduct 2 ft. to allow for frictional loss in the drive pipe. This leaves 12 ft. as the fall available for pumping water. We will also assume that the requirements are 550 gals. of water per day. Referring to Fig. 6, we add the lift to the fall and multiply this by the number of gals. per day, that is, 550 multiplied by 114 or 62,700. Next, according to G of Fig. 7, the fall available for operating the ram, which is 12 ft., is multiplied by 14.4 which equals 172.8. We must next determine the efficiency of the ram by referring to Fig. 9. To do this we divide the height the water is to be lifted above the ram, or 114 ft., by the fall from the spring to the ram, or 14 ft., to get the lift ratio. In this case 114 divided by 14 equals 8. We locate this at the left side of Fig. 9, example A, follow across to the curve and down to the bottom and read 45 percent as the efficiency. Multiplying this by 172.8, as shown in Fig. 7, we get

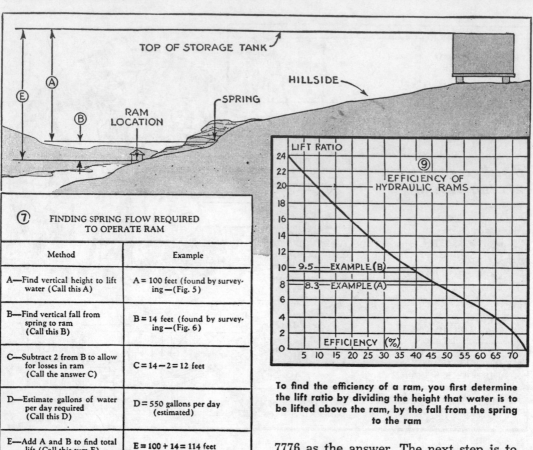

To find the efficiency of a ram, you first determine the lift ratio by dividing the height that water is to be lifted above the ram, by the fall from the spring to the ram

⑦ FINDING SPRING FLOW REQUIRED TO OPERATE RAM

Method	Example
A—Find vertical height to lift water (Call this A)	A = 100 feet (found by surveying—(Fig. 5)
B—Find vertical fall from spring to ram (Call this B)	B = 14 feet (found by surveying—(Fig. 6)
C—Subtract 2 from B to allow for losses in ram (Call the answer C)	C = 14 − 2 = 12 feet
D—Estimate gallons of water per day required (Call this D)	D = 550 gallons per day (estimated)
E—Add A and B to find total lift (Call this sum E)	E = 100 + 14 = 114 feet
F—Multiply D by E (Call this product F)	F = 550 X 114 = 62,700 foot gallons per day
G—Multiply C by 14.4 and this product by efficiency of ram (Fig. 9) (Call this G)	Since efficiency = 45% (Fig. 9) G = 14.4 X 12 X 45 = 7776
H—Divide F by G to find gallons per minute required of spring	H = 62,700 ÷ 7776 = 8 gallons per minute required from spring

⑧ FINDING GALLONS OF WATER PER DAY AVAILABLE FROM SPRING

Method	Example
I—Multiply 14.4 by gallons per minute from spring (Call this product I)	Spring delivers 10 gallons per minute and the fall is 14 feet. Water must be lifted 100 feet above spring. I = 14.4 X 10 = 144
J—Multiply I by C (See Fig. 7) and by the efficiency (See Fig. 9 for C) (Call this product J)	Since C = 14 − 2 = 12 and efficiency 45% J = 144 X 12 X 45 = 77,760
K—Divide J by E to get gallons pumped per day (See Fig. 7 for E)	K = 77,760 ÷ 114 = 682 gallons per day

7776 as the answer. The next step is to divide the first product, or F, by the second product G, or 62,700 divided by 7776, which equals 8 gals. per min. as the amount of water which the spring will have to supply in order to furnish the required amount of water.

If the spring supplies 12 gals. of water per min. during the dry season, we will be safe in installing the ram. But if, after making these determinations, it should be found that the spring will not deliver sufficient water, the next thing to do would be to figure how much water could be pumped per day during the dry season. Fig. 8 illustrates the method of making this calculation. Then, after you have found that there is sufficient fall available to operate a ram, the job of figuring the exact size required, and how to install it, comes next. This is thoroughly covered in the following pages, which also contain workable methods of making parts cheaply from pipe fittings. Hydraulic rams are made in a number of sizes and varieties; their advantage over home-made rams is that they have been developed for long use and minimum trouble.

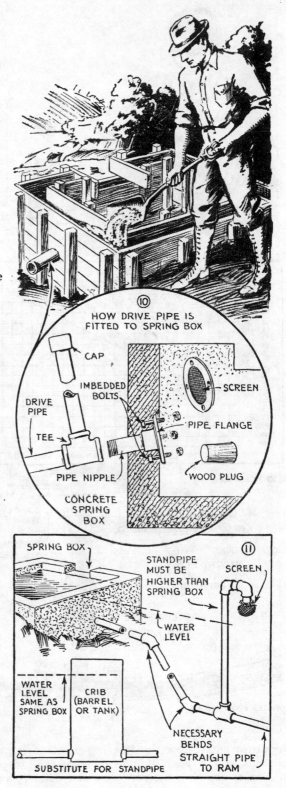

AFTER surveying the spring or stream we will now proceed with the design and construction of a ram. The initial step is to find the size of the drive pipe, that is, the pipe which runs from the spring to the ram. The chart shown in Fig. 12 makes this easy. First refer to the bottom of the chart and locate the number corresponding to the gallons of water per minute which must be furnished to the ram. Continuing with the example that was followed earlier, which re quired 8 gals. per minute, we locate 8 gals. per minute at the bottom of the chart, draw a vertical line to the curve, and at the point where this line crosses the curve, draw a horizontal line to the left-hand side of the chart and find that a ram-pipe size between 1¼ and 1½ in. will be required. Accordingly, we will select the nearest larger standard pipe size, or a 1½-in. pipe. The delivery pipe that runs from the ram to the supply tank should be one half this diameter, or in this case, ¾ in. In all cases where the size of pipe required comes out a fraction under standard size of pipe, then the next larger standard size should be used. In no case should the smaller size be used as this would tend to reduce the rate of flow to an extent which would probably interfere with the satisfactory performance of the installation.

Fig. 10 shows a method of attaching the drive pipe to the crib or spring box. The spring box, preferably of concrete, should be constructed so that all of the water, or a sufficient amount of it, flows into the box. The side from which the excess water is to be allowed to overflow should be made a few inches lower than the rest of the box so that the surplus will flow in the proper direction. The pipe from the ram should enter the side of the box as shown. By this means all of the water issuing from the spring can be used for operating the ram during dry seasons. If the tem-

10 HOW DRIVE PIPE IS FITTED TO SPRING BOX

CAP — IMBEDDED BOLTS — DRIVE PIPE — TEE — PIPE NIPPLE — CONCRETE SPRING BOX — SCREEN — PIPE FLANGE — WOOD PLUG

11 SPRING BOX — STANDPIPE MUST BE HIGHER THAN SPRING BOX — SCREEN — WATER LEVEL — WATER LEVEL SAME AS SPRING BOX — CRIB (BARREL OR TANK) — SUBSTITUTE FOR STANDPIPE — NECESSARY BENDS — STRAIGHT PIPE TO RAM

further flow, after which the cap on the vent pipe is unscrewed so that the draining of the pipe is assured. Then drain cocks at the ram and pressure tank are opened to allow all water in the installation to drain off.

The ram pipe should be run straight from spring to ram, if possible. If this is impossible, one of the methods shown in Fig. 11 may be used. The standpipe must be of the same or of larger diameter than the drive pipe and must extend vertically to a height a few inches above the level of the water in the spring tank. This pipe has a "goose neck" at the top to prevent the entry of dirt. A screen should also be placed over the open end to prevent insects from entering. Similar cautions are required in the use of the crib which may be used as a substitute for the standpipe.

Having determined the pipe sizes and laid out the ram line, we are ready to construct the ram. Fig. 13 shows details for the assembly of an effective type of ram which can be made from ordinary pipe fittings. Note that all of the dimensions are figured from the diameter and length of

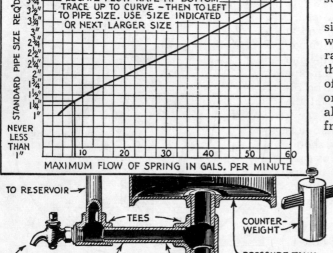

⑫ FINDING SIZE OF DRIVE PIPE

STANDARD PIPE SIZE REQ'D.

4"
3¾"
3½"
3¼"
3"
2¾"
2½"
2¼"
2"
1¾"
1½"
1¼"
1"

NEVER LESS THAN 1"

LOCATE FLOW RATE AT BOTTOM TRACE UP TO CURVE – THEN TO LEFT TO PIPE SIZE. USE SIZE INDICATED OR NEXT LARGER SIZE

10   20   30   40   50   60

MAXIMUM FLOW OF SPRING IN GALS. PER MINUTE

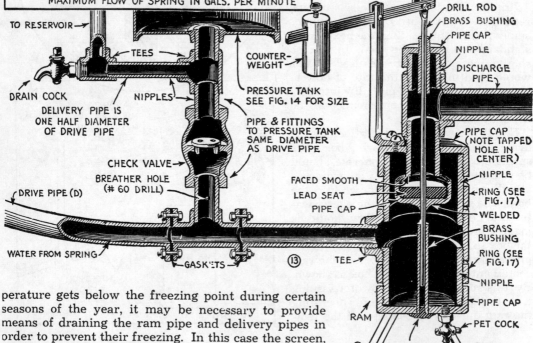

TO RESERVOIR

TEES

DRAIN COCK

DELIVERY PIPE IS ONE HALF DIAMETER OF DRIVE PIPE

NIPPLES

COUNTER-WEIGHT

PRESSURE TANK SEE FIG. 14 FOR SIZE

PIPE & FITTINGS TO PRESSURE TANK SAME DIAMETER AS DRIVE PIPE

CHECK VALVE

BREATHER HOLE (# 60 DRILL)

DRIVE PIPE (D)

WATER FROM SPRING

GASKETS

⑬

TEE

FACED SMOOTH

LEAD SEAT

PIPE CAP

DRILL ROD

BRASS BUSHING

PIPE CAP

NIPPLE

DISCHARGE PIPE

PIPE CAP (NOTE TAPPED HOLE IN CENTER)

NIPPLE

RING (SEE FIG. 17)

WELDED

BRASS BUSHING

RING (SEE FIG. 17)

NIPPLE

PIPE CAP

PET COCK

RAM

PLUGGED AND WELDED

perature gets below the freezing point during certain seasons of the year, it may be necessary to provide means of draining the ram pipe and delivery pipes in order to prevent their freezing. In this case the screen, which ordinarily covers the pipe opening at the spring box, is removed and a wood plug inserted to prevent

the ram pipe as shown in Fig. 14. The pressure tank should have a capacity in gallons approximately equal to the volume of the drive pipe. Applying the simplified formula given in Fig. 14 to our example, we first multiply the diameter of the drive pipe by itself. Thus for a 1½-in. drive pipe, we get 2.25. Next we multiply this by the length of the drive pipe in feet, assumed to be 100 ft. and then by 0.041 to find the size of the pressure tank in gallons. Performing this operation, we get 2.25 times 100 times 0.041 equals 9.2 gallons. A 10-gal. expansion tank of the kind used on hot-water heating systems will be satisfactory. The tank selected should not be smaller than 9.2 gals. and not much over 15 percent larger.

The ram proper is made from sections of pipe and fittings whose diameters are four times the diameter of the drive pipe. Therefore, in our example, we must use 6-in. pipe and fittings for the ram. The ram discharge pipe should be 1½ times the diameter of the drive pipe. All

DESIGN DATA TO DETERMINE SIZE OF PIPE, ETC. FIG. 14	
Procedure	Example
First: Find drive-pipe diameter from Fig. 12. Call this "D"	As 8 gal. per min. is flow from spring, Fig. 12 shows drive pipe should be 1½ in.
Second: Find diameter of delivery pipe. This should be ½ D	½ of 1½ gives ¾ in. for size of delivery pipe. Never use pipe less than ½ in.
Third: Find size of pressure tank in gallons. This is D times D times the length of drive pipe times .041	1½ times 1½ times 100 (length of drive pipe) times .041 equals 9.2 gal. required size of pressure tank
Fourth: Find size of pipe and fittings for ram. This should be 4 times D	Drive-pipe dia. 1½ in. times 4 gives 6 in. for size of ram pipe and fittings
Fifth: Find size of pipe and fittings for discharge pipe. This is 1½ times D	Drive-pipe dia. 1½ in. times 1½ gives 2¼ in. for size of discharge pipe and fittings.

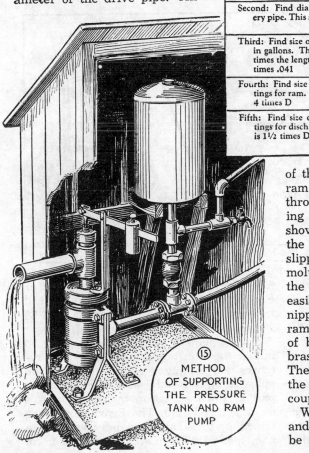

⑮ METHOD OF SUPPORTING THE PRESSURE TANK AND RAM PUMP

of these values are given in Fig. 14. The ram valve is made by drilling a hole exactly through the center of a pipe cap and pressing a length of drill rod through it as shown. The drill rod should be welded to the pipe cap as shown to prevent it from slipping. Next, the pipe cap is filled with molten lead as indicated. The purpose of the lead is to form a soft bed which can easily seat on the end of the faced pipe nipple which extends from the top of the ram. This rod is guided by the top insert of brass tubing and a similar length of brass tubing in the bottom cap of the ram. The drill-rod end which projects through the top pipe cap should be drilled and coupled to the counterbalance, Fig. 16.

When these parts are properly assembled and the ram installed rigidly, which can be done as shown in Fig. 17, it will be

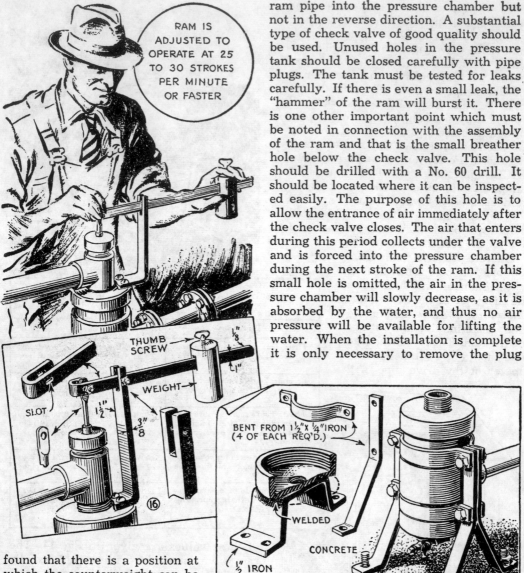

RAM IS ADJUSTED TO OPERATE AT 25 TO 30 STROKES PER MINUTE OR FASTER

THUMB SCREW

⅛"

1"

WEIGHT

SLOT

1½"

3/8"

⑯

BENT FROM 1½"X ¼" IRON (4 OF EACH REQ'D.)

WELDED

CONCRETE

½" IRON

BOLTS IMBEDDED

⑰ TWO METHODS OF RIGIDLY FASTENING THE RAM

ram pipe into the pressure chamber but not in the reverse direction. A substantial type of check valve of good quality should be used. Unused holes in the pressure tank should be closed carefully with pipe plugs. The tank must be tested for leaks carefully. If there is even a small leak, the "hammer" of the ram will burst it. There is one other important point which must be noted in connection with the assembly of the ram and that is the small breather hole below the check valve. This hole should be drilled with a No. 60 drill. It should be located where it can be inspected easily. The purpose of this hole is to allow the entrance of air immediately after the check valve closes. The air that enters during this period collects under the valve and is forced into the pressure chamber during the next stroke of the ram. If this small hole is omitted, the air in the pressure chamber will slowly decrease, as it is absorbed by the water, and thus no air pressure will be available for lifting the water. When the installation is complete it is only necessary to remove the plug

found that there is a position at which the counterweight can be located so that merely touching the lever arm will cause the valve to close or open. The exact location of the weight will be found after the ram has been installed. A length of pipe may be connected to the discharge "tee" in order to guide the tail water away from the ram house. In no case should this pipe be bent or should fittings be used, as bends would slow down the flow of water and interfere with operation. This, and a good method of mounting both the ram and pressure tank, are shown in Fig. 15.

The check valve between the drive pipe and pressure tank, Fig. 13, should be arranged so that water can flow from the

from the ram pipe in the spring box or crib, and adjust the counterweight until the ram operates at between 25 and 30 strokes per minute or faster.

If a homemade ram does not stand up under the constant hammering and requires too frequent replacement of the valve, it might be advisable to improve this part of the installation by substituting a manufactured ram. The instructions contained in these articles apply whether a homemade or manufactured ram is used.

SIMPLE ICEBOAT

It's made boy-size and it can be boy-built, but there's no reason why you can't make it grown-up size by merely increasing the dimensions

THIS SPEEDY little iceboat has the advantages of unobstructed vision, low center of gravity and spring action to absorb shocks from rough ice. These characteristics make it especially suitable for iceboating on ponds, small lakes and rivers. With the mast unstepped it is compact enough to be carried on top of a car, and light enough to be towed by hand like a sled.

The frame or chassis consists of only two parts, the runner plank and the body plank. The runner plank is bent as shown in Fig. 1, by soaking the piece overnight or steaming it an hour or more and placing in a rough form until it dries and sets. Spruce is the best wood for the runner plank, although selected white pine will do if the former is not available. Figs. 1, 2 and 3 detail the simple construction clearly.

Runners, Figs. 1 and 3, are of steel, ground to a V-shape on the running edge. Forward end of the frame is carried on a coil spring mounted as in the lower left-hand detail in Fig. 3. Upper end of the steering shaft turns in a bushing cut from brass tubing. Rear runners are bolted to hardwood blocks which are attached to the ends of the curved runner plank. The mast, you'll note, is tapered above the step and is held in position when stepped by a transverse pin. Shrouds or stays are made from 1/8-in. steel cable and fitted with turnbuckles. When rigging the craft, draw the stays only moderately tight. This precaution allows the leeward stay to go just slightly slack when in use, which gives better control of the sail and prevents any undue strain on the mast. Unbleached

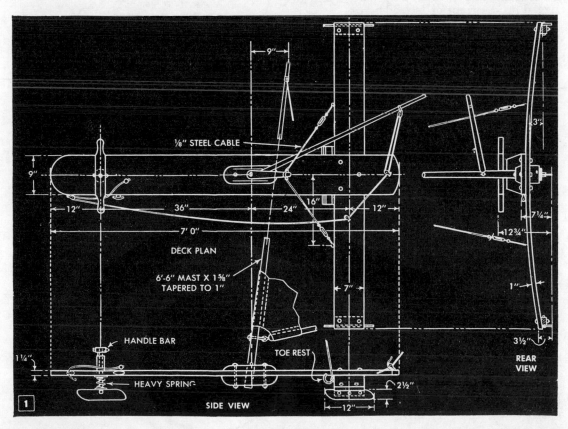

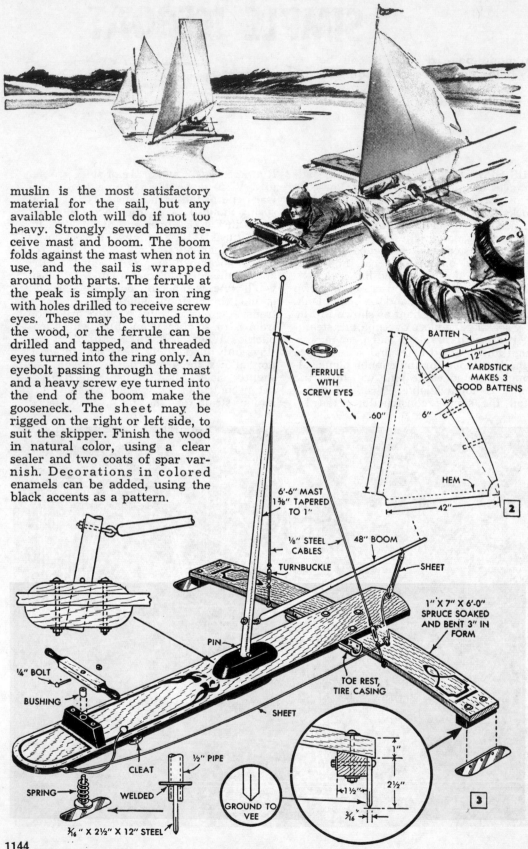

muslin is the most satisfactory material for the sail, but any available cloth will do if not too heavy. Strongly sewed hems receive mast and boom. The boom folds against the mast when not in use, and the sail is wrapped around both parts. The ferrule at the peak is simply an iron ring with holes drilled to receive screw eyes. These may be turned into the wood, or the ferrule can be drilled and tapped, and threaded eyes turned into the ring only. An eyebolt passing through the mast and a heavy screw eye turned into the end of the boom make the gooseneck. The sheet may be rigged on the right or left side, to suit the skipper. Finish the wood in natural color, using a clear sealer and two coats of spar varnish. Decorations in colored enamels can be added, using the black accents as a pattern.

FERRULE WITH SCREW EYES

BATTEN

12"

YARDSTICK MAKES 3 GOOD BATTENS

.60"

6"

HEM

42"

2

6'-6" MAST 1⅝" TAPERED TO 1"

⅛" STEEL CABLES

48" BOOM

TURNBUCKLE

SHEET

1" X 7" X 6'-0" SPRUCE SOAKED AND BENT 3" IN FORM

PIN

TOE REST, TIRE CASING

¼" BOLT

BUSHING

SHEET

CLEAT

½" PIPE

SPRING

WELDED

GROUND TO VEE

1"

2½"

1½"

³⁄₁₆"

3

³⁄₁₆" X 2½" X 12" STEEL

Farmers and Gardeners:

Your Insect Enemies And How to Fight Them

By Kenneth Anderson
Drawings by F. David Hewitt

SCIENTISTS BELIEVE insects were swarming over the earth hundreds of millions of years before the first humans. And some predict insects will still be thriving when the last man has left this planet. In the meantime, you are surrounded by a virtually infinite number of tiny predators who will steal your food and clothing, wreck your house and furnishings or send you to the hospital with a serious disease. *Popular Mechanics* asked entomologists of the U. S. Department of Agriculture to name the 20 most destructive insects in this country. They are illustrated on these pages as they appear in various stages of their development. The egg-laying adults frequently are winged, like moths and beetles, and bear little resemblance to the wormlike larvae which hatch from the eggs. The young of other insects may be nymphs which look like the adults but are much smaller. The larva changes into an adult while in the cocoon of the pupa stage, and the life cycle continues. For the most effective use of the insecticides listed, study the manufacturer's instructions, or consult your local agricultural agent. Specific information about applying the chemical killers varies according to such factors as the stage of development of the plant or insect, the season, or even the time of day.

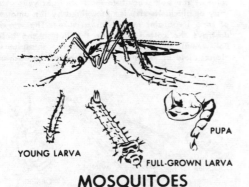

MOSQUITOES

People have been slapping at mosquitoes for centuries. The six-legged carriers of malaria, yellow fever, encephalitis and other diseases have, in effect, told man where he could build his cities and plant his crops. Some 2000 species of mosquitoes have been found. They breed in water—salt, fresh or foul—and a small amount of water will sustain a big swarm. DDT is recommended, but dieldrin or toxaphene is needed in some cases

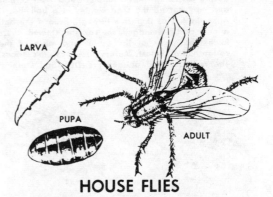

HOUSE FLIES

Much more than a simple nuisance, the house fly may carry germs of typhoid fever, dysentery, yaws or tuberculosis. Flies cannot exist without decaying organic matter in which to breed but can travel up to 13 miles to find it. And the number of off-spring one female can produce in a season is the figure 191, followed by 18 zeros. Some flies, like some mosquitoes, are DDT-resistant. Recommended killers: chlordane, lindane, toxaphene, methoxychlor

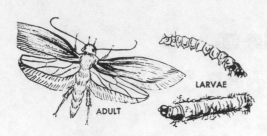

CLOTHES MOTHS

Fabric pests, like the webbing clothes moth, cause up to a half-billion dollars damage each year. A full-grown clothes-moth larva is about one half inch long, has a white body and dark head. The moth is yellowish or buff, with a wingspread of a half inch. Adult clothes moths do not flit about lights, but hide in dark areas. The larvae eat articles that contain wool, mohair, down, hair or feathers. Control chemicals: DDT, EQ-53 and chlordane

GRASSHOPPERS

Members of a large order including legendary Old World locusts and Mormon crickets, grasshoppers have been known to destroy 75 percent of the farm crops in an area of 17,000 square miles. Despite extensive control measures, they cause an estimated $18,000,000 damage yearly. Most destructive U.S. species include differential, migratory red-legged and clear-winged grasshoppers. These insects can be killed by using aldrin, chlordane or toxaphene

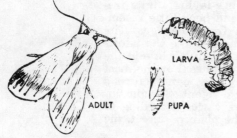

PINK BOLLWORM

From India, where it was first found, the pink bollworm has spread to the world's major cotton producing areas. The larva relishes cottonseed kernels and may eat all the seed kernels in a boll. But it ruins the lint as it passes through. Even if the boll is only partly damaged, the cut and stained fibers lower the grade of the cotton and much of the cottonseed oil is lost. Mature larva has pink stripes. The recommended poisons are DDT and Guthion

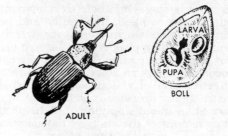

BOLL WEEVIL

About 10 percent of the cotton crop is destroyed each year by this insect which slipped across the Rio Grande River from Mexico in the 1890s. The color of the boll weevil varies from light yellow to gray or black. Its size is determined by the amount of food it obtains in the larval stage. The weevil destroys the cotton buds or the lint in the boll. Boll-weevil poisons include: Endrin, toxaphene, aldrin, dieldrin, Guthion, Malathion and heptachlor

LEAFHOPPERS

As flies spread diseases among humans, leafhoppers carry plant diseases. Leafhoppers transmit viruses which destroy peaches, cranberries, beans, grapes, potatoes and sugar beets. The potato leafhopper also attacks alfalfa and red clover, damaging up to one fourth of these crops in the Eastern states. Besides spreading diseases, leafhoppers damage plants by sucking juices from the leaves. DDT, methoxychlor, Malathion are recommended insecticides

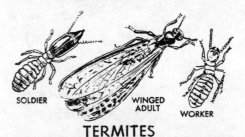

TERMITES

These insects are so destructive in some regions that railroads use metal ties. Termites can eat wood because of tiny organisms in their intestines that help digest cellulose. Subterranean termites attack wooden parts of buildings from nests in the soil, where they get the water necessary .for their existence. Recommended soil poisons to be used around building foundations include DDT, chlordane, dieldrin, sodium arsenite, and lindane

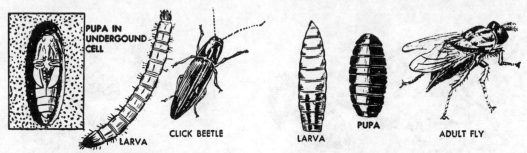

LARVA · CLICK BEETLE · LARVA · PUPA · ADULT FLY

PUPA IN UNDERGOUND CELL

WIREWORMS

Ranging in color from white to orange, with dark heads and tails, wireworms are the larvae of click beetles. They attack any vegetable or field crop, from tomatoes to potatoes, but feed only on the underground parts of the plants. The larvae bore holes in the larger stems, roots and tubers and cut off smaller underground stems. Wireworms in Western states are killed by DDT, but in Eastern states, chlordane is the recommended insecticide

SCREW-WORMS

Canniballike screw-worms feast on the flesh of living warm-blooded animals. The adult fly, which is bluish-green in color and three times the size of a house fly, lays its eggs in cuts and scratches on livestock. If the wounds are not treated, the screw-worms eventually will kill the animal. This insect causes about $20,000,000 damage each year. Scientists are using atomic radiation to sterilize the adult screw-worm flies so their eggs won't hatch

LARVA · ADULT

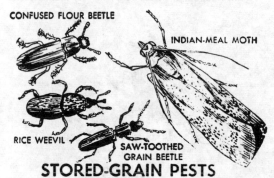

CONFUSED FLOUR BEETLE · INDIAN-MEAL MOTH · RICE WEEVIL · SAW-TOOTHED GRAIN BEETLE

SPRUCE BUDWORM

Spruce-budworm larvae tunnel in old needles of spruce and fir trees, then bore into opening buds. In one outbreak in Canada, Maine and Minnesota, budworms destroyed 225 million cords of pulpwood. During a recent rampage in Oregon, they defoliated three million acres of Douglas fir. The adult moth is grayish-brown and the larva changes from yellowish-green to reddish-brown as it becomes full-grown. Foresters apply DDT to feeding budworms

STORED-GRAIN PESTS

Annual worldwide losses to stored-grain insects are measured in millions of tons. The weevils, beetles and moths that you may find in your pantry are the same kind that infest grain elevators. Many of the pests are so small that their presence in stored grain is not detected until they have multiplied several times. Cribs and granaries can be treated with DDT, methoxychlor or pyrethrin powders. Kitchen cabinets should be sprayed with DDT

LARVA · ADULT · PUPA

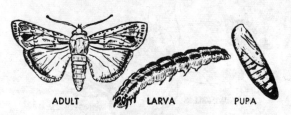

ADULT · LARVA · PUPA

CORN EARWORM

Most destructive of ear-corn insects, the green or brown corn earworm causes more than $50,000,000 damage each year to field and sweet corn. It also attacks cotton, tomatoes, alfalfa, beans, peanuts and tobacco. The moth lays eggs on the corn silks and the larvae follow the silks down into the ear after they hatch. The full-grown larvae leave the ears and go into the soil where they enter the pupal stage. Poisons include DDT and methoxychlor

ARMY WORMS

Offspring of night-flying moths, army worms get their name from the fact that vast hordes of the larvae sometimes go on warlike rampages which wipe out entire fields of grass or grain. They also attack sweet corn or cabbage, and the fall army worm destroys peanuts, other legumes. The larva has a striped body and may be 1½ inches long. Recommended insecticides are DDT, TDE, toxaphene, chlordane, aldrin and dieldrin applied by spraying

1147

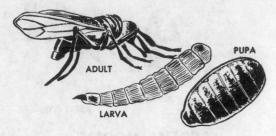

LIVESTOCK FLIES

Horse flies, stable flies and horn flies cause annual losses of $245,000,000 by tormenting livestock. Milk cows give less milk and beef cattle produce less beef when irritated by these pests. Horn flies and horse flies are bloodsucking insects like the black flies that kill animals in swarm attacks. Cattle protected by DDT gain 50 pounds per month more than untreated cattle. Other controls include pyrethrins, thanite, Malathion, lethane, methoxychlor

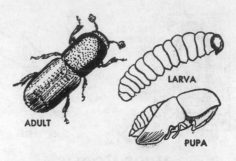

BARK BEETLES

One outbreak of bark beetles in the Black Hills wiped out a billion board feet of pine. In Colorado, a swarm of bark beetles once killed 400,000 trees in a mass attack. They breed in timber damaged by fire or storm, then attack healthy trees nearby. The beetles bore through the bark and construct tunnels and egg galleries in the soft wood tissue. Bark beetles are killed by chlordane, ethylene dichloride and DDT applied to the beetle-infested area

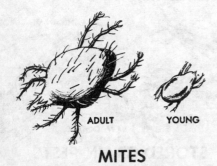

MITES

Not true insects, mites are tiny eight-legged sucking pests that attack people, plants and animals. Chiggers are mites that annoy humans and the little "red spiders" that stunt the growth of plants also are mites. Some members of the family cause mange in farm and wild animals. Others infest poultry, reducing egg production and weight of broilers. Most mites are controlled by sulphur, parathion, demeton, Malathion, Aramite or toxaphene

CATTLE GRUBS

Cattle grubs, the larvae of heel flies, hatch from eggs fastened to the hair of cattle. The grub bores into the skin, tunnels through the tissues of the animal for months, then cuts another hole in the hide to leave the host and enter the pupa stage. Both meat and hides of grub-infested cattle bring a lower price when the animals go to market. The total annual loss is $100,000,000. Rotenone and Dow E7-57 are recommended insecticides for this pest

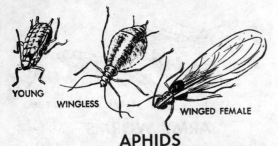

APHIDS

Also known as plant lice, aphids attack almost every kind of plant. They cut into plant tissues and suck the juices. Aphids also spread plant diseases. The green peach aphid alone transmits 50 kinds of plant viruses. Adults produce both winged and wingless offspring, with winged, migratory types increasing in numbers as colonies become crowded. Recommended insecticides include DDT, TEPP, Malathion, demeton, rotenone and nicotine sulfate

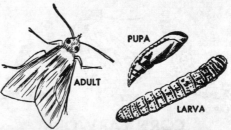

EUROPEAN CORN BORER

Since its ancestors arrived in America in a shipment of broomcorn 40 years ago, the European corn borer has spread to the Gulf Coast and the Rocky Mountains. One of the most injurious enemies of field and sweet corn, it caused nearly $350,000,000 damage in one year alone. The pink or brown larvae tunnel through all parts of the corn plant, from the brace roots to the tassels. Borer is killed by DDT, ryania, heptachlor, toxaphene

SPRING-BRONZE STRIPPING

ZINC-RIB STRIPPING

DOOR-BOTTOM STRIPPING →

ADHESIVE-BACKED FELT STRIPPING

IT PAYS TO
WEATHER-STRIP

Heat is a costly item and when allowed to escape through windows and doors it's like money pouring through a hole in your pocket. Weather stripping will help "plug the hole" and save up to 37 percent of the total heat loss in an average five-room home.

By Wayne C. Leckey

DO YOU KNOW there is a hole equivalent to the size of a saucer in every non-weather-stripped window in your home? That's what the 21 lineal ft. of $\frac{1}{16}$-in. clearance crack around a double-hung sash equal, and it's through this crack that a large amount of heat goes out and dirt-laden air comes in. Tests by the Weather-strip Research Institute show that a 15-m.p.h. wind against a non-weather-stripped window admits more than 45,000 cu. ft. of air—cold and damp—every 24 hrs.

Weather-stripping doors and windows is a job most any handy homeowner can do himself. Of the many different types of window weather stripping, the zinc rib-strip type is perhaps the most permanent, although it does require more work to install than, for example, the stick-on type pictured in Figs. 7 and 8. Special grooving

planes and routers are used by professional installers, but the man with a home shop can cut grooves with a saw and drill press.

To install zinc rib-stripping on double-hung sash, first carefully remove the window stops, take out the lower sash and set it aside. Next, remove the left-hand parting bead. This is a $\frac{3}{8}$ x $\frac{3}{4}$-in. wooden strip that forms a channel for the upper sash and which normally is a press fit in a groove in the window frame. In most cases, this bead is stuck with paint and requires careful prying to get it out. With this strip removed, the upper sash can be lifted out. Fig. 4 shows how each sash must be grooved and rabbeted for the zinc strips. A plain strip is used along the bottom of the lower sash, while a corrugated strip is used across the upper sash. In each case, a $\frac{5}{32}$-in. groove is cut in the edges of the sash to fit

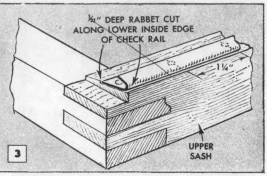

Interlocking hook strips are nailed to beveled check rails to seal opening between upper and lower sash

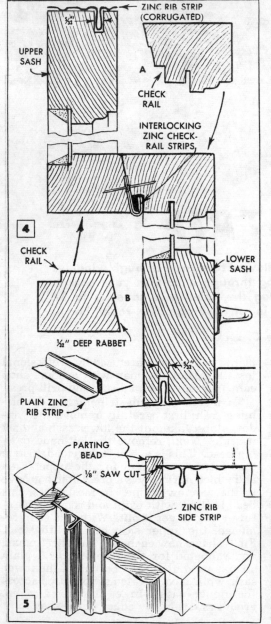

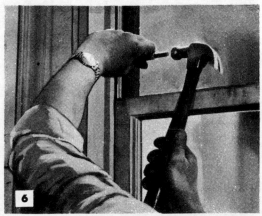

over the lip of the weather stripping. A circular saw is used to cut the grooves in the manner shown in Fig. 1.

Similar grooves are cut in both sides of the upper and lower sash to ride on corrugated strips placed vertically and tacked to the sides of the frame as in Fig. 5. Here you'll notice, too, that a saw cut is made 1/8 in. deep in the inside face of each parting bead to help anchor the strips in place.

A portion of the upper ends of the zinc side strips must be cut out so they will clear the sash-cord pulleys. Where the side strips meet the head and sill strips, the ends of the side strips have to be cut at a 45-deg. angle so the ribs of the head and sill strips will pass under. Nail the head strip to the frame, spacing the nails 3 in. apart.

The interlocking hook strips along the check rails, Fig. 4, are nailed in rabbets. The shallow rabbet in the beveled face of the upper check rail, detail B, can be cut easily with a circular saw, but the stepped rabbet in the lower sash, detail A, requires cutting with a router bit in a drill press and with the sash supported at an angle. The sectional drawing, Fig. 4, shows how the two strips hook snugly together when both sash are closed. Figs. 2 and 3 show how the large hook strip is nailed flush across the edge of the upper sash. The other strip is nailed similarly.

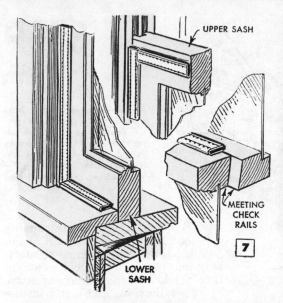

Figure 7 — labels: UPPER SASH, MEETING CHECK RAILS, LOWER SASH

Adhesive-backed felt weather stripping is pressed on and pulled off like masking tape. Ideal for apartment and home renters. Provides an effective seal

The upper right-hand side strip is held with a nail at the top and one at the bottom and with a nail above and below the pulley slot. Now to replace the sash: Place the upper left-hand side strip in its groove and slide both the sash and strip into the frame, adjusting the side strip to fit over the head strip. Nail as before, Fig. 6, and replace the parting bead. To replace the lower sash, fasten the right-hand side strip in place by inserting the flange of the strip in the saw cut in the parting bead and drive one nail at the top and one at the bottom inner edge of the strip. Install the lower left-hand side strip in the same way as the upper sash, replace the inside stops and finally nail the sill strip in position.

Spring-bronze weather stripping is used to weather-strip doors and is nailed to the jambs of the doorframe so the contact edge is about $\frac{1}{8}$ in. from the edge of the stop, Fig. 9. The important thing is to get the strip stretched properly so there are no buckles in the contact edge. Put on the head strip first, spacing the nails 1 in. apart to avoid buckling and resulting air leakage. Next, miter the upper end of each side strip and then fasten with a nail near the top and another 1 in. below. Stretch the bronze strip by driving an awl or ice pick through it near the lower end and into the wood. Press downward on the awl to stretch the strip, leaving the awl in the wood. Drive one nail at the middle, one at the bottom and two in between. Complete the nailing 1 in. apart as before. After the strip is nailed, the flange must be adjusted up or down so it touches the edge of the door at all points. If it must be raised slightly, run a dull-pointed tool along the crease of the strip a couple of times with an even, firm pressure. ★ ★ ★

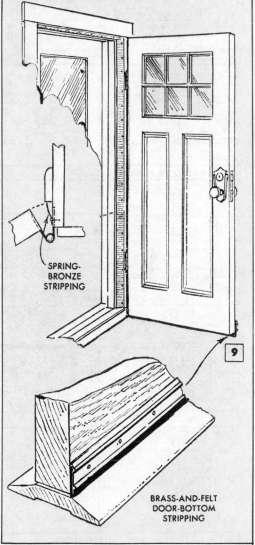

Figure 9 — labels: SPRING-BRONZE STRIPPING, BRASS-AND-FELT DOOR-BOTTOM STRIPPING

STOP

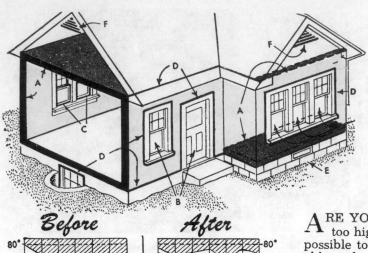

A—Insulation and vapor barriers; B—Storm sash and doors; C—Weather stripping on all sash and doors; D—All cracks calked; E—Wall encloses unheated space under floor; F—Vents above ceiling insulation

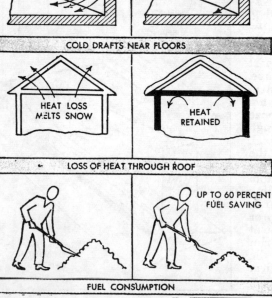

Before   *After*

HEAVY LINE, AVERAGE   TAKEN DURING SAME WEATHER

SEVEN-DAY RECORD OF TEMPERATURE VARIATIONS

RECORD OF TEMPERATURE AT VARIOUS HEIGHTS

GREATLY REDUCED

COLD DRAFTS NEAR FLOORS

HEAT LOSS MELTS SNOW   HEAT RETAINED

LOSS OF HEAT THROUGH ROOF

UP TO 60 PERCENT FUEL SAVING

FUEL CONSUMPTION

ARE YOUR heating costs running too high and is it difficult or impossible to heat your home comfortably and uniformly in cold weather? In older homes installation of storm sash, weather stripping, and insulation and calking can reduce heat losses through the walls, ceilings and windows of the structure as much as 60 percent. Aside from the substantial saving, you will have a more comfortable, healthful home.

Insulation: Insulating values of different types of wall construction are given in Fig. 3, details A to J inclusive. Good insulating materials, properly installed, will last the life of the building and are resistant to fire, moisture and insect attack. There are four basic types, or kinds, of insulation — the loose-fill type, flexible batts, blanket and quilted forms, and the rigid-board and reflective metal-foil types. Many porous insulating materials are faced with a vapor barrier. Others require the installation of a separate barrier to prevent the passage of moisture.

Where to insulate: About 25 percent of the heat loss from the average uninsulated house is through the roof. Snow melts quickly from an uninsulated roof, even though the temperature is well below the freezing point.

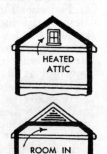

UNHEATED ATTIC   HEATED ATTIC

ROOM IN ATTIC   ROOM IN ATTIC

1

THOSE HEAT LOSSES

If it is desirable to insulate only a part of the house at one time, start with the top-floor ceiling or the roof, Fig. 1. Note also the details above and at the left. If you don't need a heated attic, insulate the ceiling, Fig. 2; if a warm attic is desired, insulate the roof. Rooms built in attics should be insulated above and on all sides facing unheated spaces. Next in importance to the roof or ceiling are the exterior walls. Include walls that separate living quarters from unheated spaces such as an attached garage or an attic stairway. Also insulate floors over unheated spaces such as garages, basements and the areas between the ground and floor as shown by Fig. 4.

Importance of vapor barrier: If you live where the average January temperature is 35 deg. or less, condensation of moisture may occur if you insulate without vapor barriers. Moisture-laden air inside the house slowly penetrates the plaster and insulation and condenses to water or ice when it comes in contact with the cold inner surface of an exterior wall or roof, Fig. 6, A. Results of condensation are rotted wood, peeling paint, damage to inside walls and ceilings, and damage to insulation. To prevent this, install vapor barriers between the insulation and the heated interior of the house, Fig. 6, B. A vapor barrier may be a membrane (such as asphalt-saturated paper or felt, metal foil and waterproof wall covering) or simply vapor-resistant paint (such as aluminum paint, most lead-and-oil paints and spar varnishes). Ordinary tar paper and roofing felts are not suitable for this purpose. Insulation faced with vapor-barrier coverings, Fig. 5, can be installed directly between the studs or joists. The vapor barriers should also be used where air from a basement or crawl space can get into walls and pass upward to the attic. Walls of attic stairways must not be overlooked, and doors to attics should be weather stripped, painted or varnished, and sometimes insulated, too.

Venting spaces over insulation: When you insulate, be sure to ventilate the space

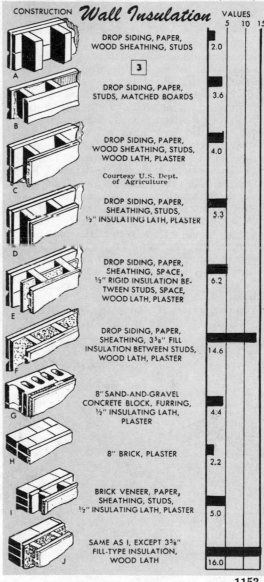

2

Courtesy Celotex Corp.

CONSTRUCTION *Wall Insulation* VALUES
5   10   15

A	DROP SIDING, PAPER, WOOD SHEATHING, STUDS	2.0
B	DROP SIDING, PAPER, STUDS, MATCHED BOARDS	3.6
C	DROP SIDING, PAPER, WOOD SHEATHING, STUDS, WOOD LATH, PLASTER	4.0

Courtesy U.S. Dept. of Agriculture

D	DROP SIDING, PAPER, SHEATHING, STUDS, ½" INSULATING LATH, PLASTER	5.3
E	DROP SIDING, PAPER, SHEATHING, SPACE, ½" RIGID INSULATION BETWEEN STUDS, SPACE, WOOD LATH, PLASTER	6.2
F	DROP SIDING, PAPER, SHEATHING, 3⅝" FILL INSULATION BETWEEN STUDS, WOOD LATH, PLASTER	14.6
G	8" SAND-AND-GRAVEL CONCRETE BLOCK, FURRING, ½" INSULATING LATH, PLASTER	4.4
H	8" BRICK, PLASTER	2.2
I	BRICK VENEER, PAPER, SHEATHING, STUDS, ½" INSULATING LATH, PLASTER	5.0
J	SAME AS I, EXCEPT 3⅝" FILL-TYPE INSULATION, WOOD LATH	16.0

3

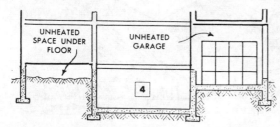

UNHEATED SPACE UNDER FLOOR

UNHEATED GARAGE

4

Courtesy United States Gypsum Co.

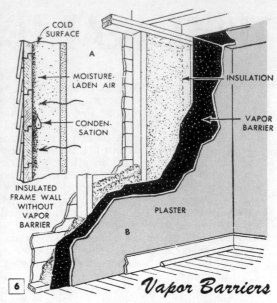

Vapor Barriers

above insulated ceilings to minimize condensation on the underside of the roof. Fig. 7, A to F inclusive, shows several methods of doing this with louvers, roof vents and cornice vents. The area of the vents should be equal to at least 4 sq. ft. for every 1000 sq. ft. of attic floor area.

How much insulation? More insulation is needed in homes where winters are severe than where the climate is mild. For best results the thickness of insulation will depend on the kind of insulating material, the house construction, inside temperature to be maintained and other variable factors. It's best to consult a reputable dealer or contractor in your community who can advise you concerning the kind and quantity of insulation to install.

Loose fill: Loose-fill insulation comes in bags or bales. To cover a ceiling first install a vapor barrier, if necessary, directly on the ceiling. Cut the barrier to fit snugly

around all obstructions to minimize air leakage. Wedge it between joists or attach it to them with cleats nailed to the joists as in Fig. 8, A. Pour in the fill to a 4-in. thickness, Fig. 9, distributing it evenly with an improvised strike board that straddles the joists, Fig. 8. If the attic is floored, remove some of the floor boards, Fig. 8, B, so that the material can be distributed uniformly. If the area is finish-floored, it will be necessary to have a contractor blow the fill in. When this is done use water-resistant paint or wall covering on the underside of the ceiling to serve as a vapor barrier, if the climate requires it.

Insulating frame, stucco or brick-veneer walls of existing houses with loose fill generally is a job for a contractor as he has the equipment required to blow in the material as in Fig. 11. Strips of siding or other wall covering are removed temporarily and holes bored in the wall sheathing, Fig. 10.

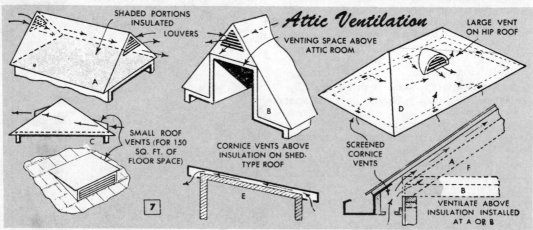

Attic Ventilation

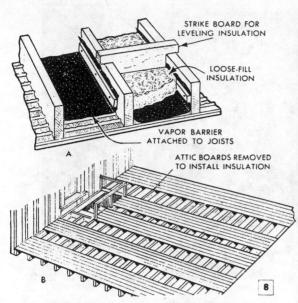

STRIKE BOARD FOR LEVELING INSULATION

LOOSE-FILL INSULATION

VAPOR BARRIER ATTACHED TO JOISTS

ATTIC BOARDS REMOVED TO INSTALL INSULATION

A

B

8

9

Courtesy Celotex Corp

Loose-Fill Insulation

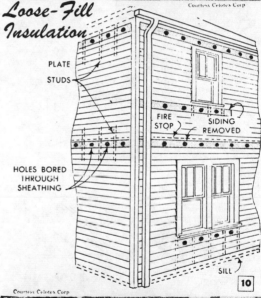

PLATE

STUDS

FIRE STOP

SIDING REMOVED

HOLES BORED THROUGH SHEATHING

SILL

10

Courtesy Celotex Corp

11

Be sure that all spaces are filled, including those under windows and fire stops.

Flexible insulation: Insulation in the batt, blanket and quilt forms comes in widths that fit snugly between studs, joists and rafters, and in lengths up to 48 in., or in rolls up to 100 ft. The thickness varies from ½ to 3⅝ in. When using flexible insulation, cut it to fit snugly around obstructions, placing it with the vapor barrier facing the inside of the house. Fill all spaces and push the ends of the batts together snugly. When insulating a sloping roof with batts or blankets, start at the eaves and work up as in Fig. 12. Make U-shaped barrier pockets to seal the spaces between rafters where they join the plate, tacking the pockets to the plate and to sides of the rafters as in Fig. 13, A. The lower end of the insulation fits in the pockets, which may fit tightly against the roof boards unless air is circulated from cornice vents. In this case space is left above the pockets and batts as shown in Fig. 13, B, and at A and B, detail F, in Fig. 7. The air space at B is left when only the floor is insulated. Detail C, Fig. 13, shows how quilt-type insulation is fastened with strips to the plate and rafters. If the vapor-barrier facing on batts has flanges at the ends, these should overlap each other. The side flanges are tacked or stapled to the rafters. Where a portion of the roof serves as a room ceiling, the wall covering will come directly against the vapor-barrier facing of the batts as in Fig. 13, D. When installing flexible insulation in walls, start at the bottom, filling all spaces between studs, and cut the batts or blankets as

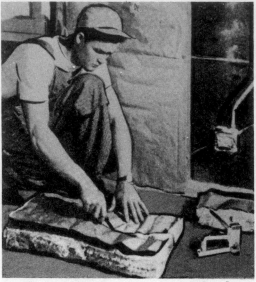

Courtesy Celotex Corp.

Courtesy United States Gypsum Co.

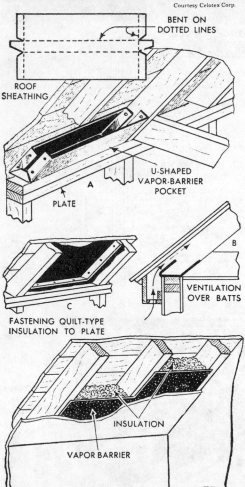

BENT ON DOTTED LINES

ROOF SHEATHING

U-SHAPED VAPOR-BARRIER POCKET

PLATE

A

VENTILATION OVER BATTS

B

FASTENING QUILT-TYPE INSULATION TO PLATE

C

INSULATION

VAPOR BARRIER

PLASTER

D

13 *Flexible Insulation*

necessary to fit snugly into corners and against obstructions. If you encounter water pipes in exterior walls, place the insulation between them and the sheathing.

Rigid insulating board: When remodeling or adding a room in an attic, you have the opportunity to use rigid insulating board, Figs. 14 and 15. It also has a structural value, some forms being used as sheathing, some as a plaster base, and others having a finished surface to serve as a wall covering. The board ranges from 1/2 to 1 in. in thickness and comes in sheets 4 ft. wide and up to 12 ft. long. It also is available in smaller panels or in squares. The edges of panels or squares may be square, beveled, rabbeted or tongue-and-groove. Small panels are arranged horizontally and are staggered so that the joints of adjacent rows come on different studs as in Fig. 15, A. As the panels usually have interlocking edges, no horizontal nailing supports are needed between studs. Large sheets should extend from floor to ceiling as in Fig. 15, B. When shorter sheets are used, cross supports for nailing are necessary. Nail sheets to the center supporting studs first then at the edges. Space the nails 4 to 6 in. apart and about 3/8 in. from the edges, using special nails available for the purpose. When rigid insulating board is used between studs, joists or rafters, it is cut to fit snugly and nailed to 1-in. strips. It also is used under floors—either subfloors or finish floors—leaving a 1/8-in. space between sheets to allow for expansion.

Insulating masonry walls: To insulate a masonry wall, first coat it with asphalt dampproofing compound. Then nail the insulating board to 1 x 2-in. furring strips spaced 16 in. on centers as in Fig. 16. Use

Courtesy Celotex Corp

Courtesy Celotex Corp

expansion sleeves or other screw anchors for attaching the furring strips to concrete. Thin blanket insulation can be inserted between the strips before attaching the board to obtain added insulating value.

Reflective foil: Reflective foil comes separate or as a facing on other forms of insulation and also as a facing on plasterboard. In insulating value it is roughly equivalent to ½-in. insulating board when exposed to an air space not less than 1 in. wide, Fig. 16. The foil also is an effective vapor barrier. Since it does not absorb heat like other forms of insulation, it is particularly useful in warm climates. Several sheets separated by air spaces also may be used. A small amount of dust on the foil does not greatly reduce its reflective power.

Storm sash: A properly fitted storm sash provides a dead-air space between it and the regular window, which acts as insulation. Tests at the University of Illinois have proved that a 20-percent fuel saving is possible in most homes when they are completely equipped with tight storm sash and storm doors. Another result is a 1 to 2-deg. temperature increase at the floor level. Besides saving heat, storm sash reduces condensation on windows.

If you cannot equip the entire house at one time, start by installing storm sash on the sides facing the prevailing wind direction. The inside surface of storm sash should fit tightly against the blind stop of the window casing, Fig. 18, but the sash should have ⅛-in. clearance around the edges, detail A, to compensate for swelling. If surface irregularities of contacting surfaces of sash and casing prevent a tight fit, you can seal the joint by using felt or sponge-rubber strips glued in a rabbet cut

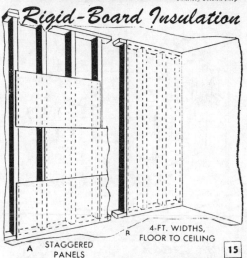

Rigid-Board Insulation

4-FT. WIDTHS, FLOOR TO CEILING

A STAGGERED PANELS

RIGID-BOARD INSULATION

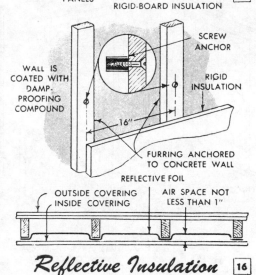

SCREW ANCHOR

WALL IS COATED WITH DAMP-PROOFING COMPOUND

RIGID INSULATION

16"

FURRING ANCHORED TO CONCRETE WALL

REFLECTIVE FOIL

OUTSIDE COVERING INSIDE COVERING

AIR SPACE NOT LESS THAN 1"

Reflective Insulation

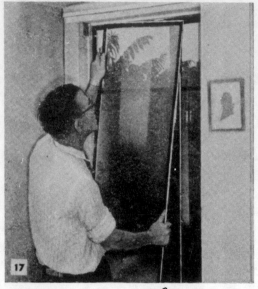

17

along the edge as in detail B. Edges of 1⅛-in. sash frames are rabbeted to make them fit old-style ¾-in. casings, as in detail C. Storm sash for double-hung windows is available in full length or in sections, Fig. 19. Divided sash can be passed through a window and hung from the inside of the house, eliminating the need of a ladder. To hold storm sash in place, use sash hangers at the top and hooks and eyes at the bottom. Where ventilation is desired, use sash adjusters to hold the sash open or lock it when closed. As an alternative you can use ventilating openings in the lower rail.

The metal-framed storm sash for metal casement windows are applied from inside, Figs. 17 and 20. As they generally cover individual window sections only, they do not stop condensation on the frames. To prevent this you can use a wooden sash to cover the entire window as in the right-hand detail of Fig. 20. The use of dual panes in windows as a substitute for storm sash is effective in reducing heat loss by conduction but does not prevent air leakage at the edges of the window frame or stop condensation on the frames.

Weather stripping: Many kinds of fabric, felt and rubber weather stripping are subject to wear and shrinkage which gives them only temporary value. Fig. 22 shows how to apply various kinds to a double-hung sash. Metal weather stripping, available in various widths, is easy to install and is permanent. Exposed ends are bent back slightly to avoid catching in the wood when the sash slides over them. Fig. 23 shows how this type of weather stripping is installed on a doorframe. Note that it is cut

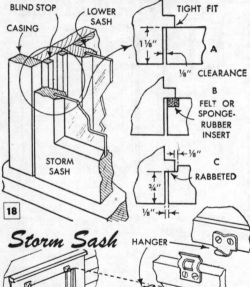

18

Storm Sash

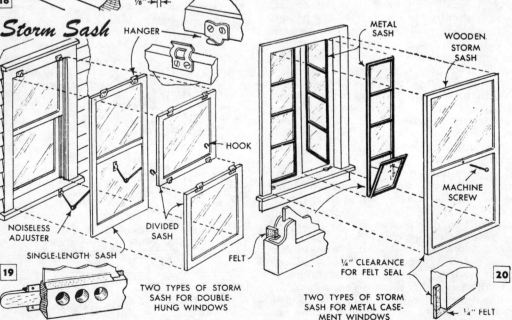

19   TWO TYPES OF STORM SASH FOR DOUBLE-HUNG WINDOWS

TWO TYPES OF STORM SASH FOR METAL CASE-MENT WINDOWS   **20** away at the striker plate. The threshold can be fitted with a wood or metal-backed felt weather strip but, for appearance and durability, a rigid metal weather strip consisting of two interlocking members is preferable. On wooden casement windows, felt or fabric weather strips go on the outside, but the flat-metal type is fitted in the same manner as on doorframes. If necessary, dress down edges of tight-fitting sash to provide clearance for the strips. On metal casement windows, the metal-framed storm sash usually has felt inserts which provide a tight seal and thus serve as weather strips. You can seal metal sash, however, by gluing rubber tape to the frame all around, using automotive rubber cement.

Calking: A fairly high percentage of heat is lost through spaces at window and door frames and through cracks at points where walls join roofs and foundations, or where pipes and conduits pass through walls. To reduce this loss fill narrow cracks with calking compound, using a calking gun as in Fig. 21 which forces the compound deeply into the cracks by pressure. Before calking, brush out loose particles of dirt from the crevices. Don't use the compound alone to fill wide cracks and openings as it will shrink and pull loose. Wide spaces must first be packed with oakum or jute before calking. Hammer this tightly in place with a blunt-edge tool so the filling is almost flush with the opening but leaves enough space to take a layer of calking compound as a final seal.

Curtain walls: If you have a basementless home built on piers instead of on a solid, continuous foundation and cold

Calking 21

weather makes the floor uncomfortable, a curtain wall may be 'the solution to the problem. This should have vents for cross circulation during warm weather and, if necessary, be provided with an entranceway. In cold climates both a curtain wall and adequate insulation under the floor are necessary. When batts or blankets are used between the floor joists, the vapor barrier should be laid face up. The batts can be given added support by nailing wallboard or wire mesh to the underside of the joists. Floors of basementless houses need not be insulated if the heating pipes or ducts pass through the crawl space, or if the space is insulated on all sides. ★ ★ ★

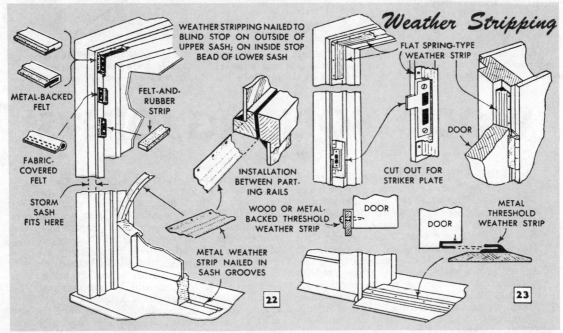

Weather Stripping

METAL-BACKED FELT

FABRIC-COVERED FELT

STORM SASH FITS HERE

WEATHER STRIPPING NAILED TO BLIND STOP ON OUTSIDE OF UPPER SASH; ON INSIDE STOP BEAD OF LOWER SASH

FELT-AND-RUBBER STRIP

INSTALLATION BETWEEN PARTING RAILS

WOOD OR METAL-BACKED THRESHOLD WEATHER STRIP

METAL WEATHER STRIP NAILED IN SASH GROOVES

FLAT SPRING-TYPE WEATHER STRIP

CUT OUT FOR STRIKER PLATE

DOOR

DOOR

DOOR

METAL THRESHOLD WEATHER STRIP

22

23

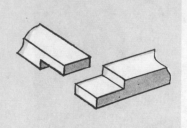

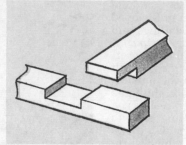

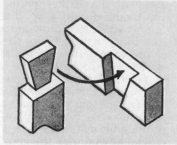

CORNER LAP. Ends of workpieces are halved and shouldered on opposite sides, joined at right angles

MIDDLE LAP. Used when joining rails to uprights where rails meet uprights. Joint is often pinned

DOVETAIL LAP. Through dovetail is half-lapped onto rail or upright. Often seen in old cabinetwork

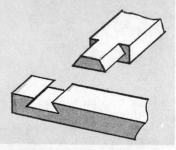

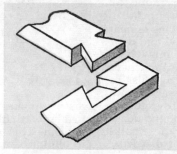

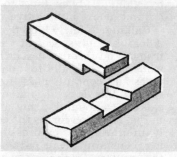

DOVETAIL LAP. Provides much greater strength than plain middle-lap joint. Should be glued, pinned

HOUSED DOVETAIL LAP. Used where end grain must be concealed in finished work. Should be glued

DOVETAIL LAP. Sometimes referred to as half dovetail lap. Easier to make than regular dovetail lap

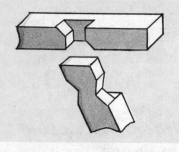

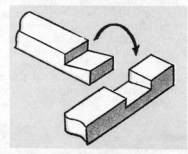

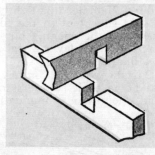

TIE LAP. Somewhat similar to half dovetail joint but usually is used when joining framing timbers

BEVELED TEE LAP. Same as beveled corner lap except that members are joined as in the middle lap

CROSS LAP—EDGEWISE. This cross lap is made with notches cut in from the edges of joining members

WOODWORKING JOINTS

By C. W. Woodson

HERE ARE COMMON variations of the half-lap joint, most of which are still used in light joinery and heavy framing. Nearly all of the joints detailed will be found in various types of old work. The half-lap joints are quite easily made with hand tools, proceeding as in steps A, B and C in the details on the opposite page. Some joints detailed are quite similar, others differ considerably in form from the true half lap, but require essentially the same procedures in cutting and fitting. Names of the joints detailed are those in common usage, but in some cases will differ with names given in older works on the subject of joinery. The strength of the lap joint in any form depends on close, accurate fitting. As a rule, the joints should be pinned or glued for maximum strength and resistance to lateral strain. Nearly all of the joints detailed are effective in joining either hard or soft woods in both cabinet framing and heavy structural framing. But here again it should be emphasized that maximum strength is attained by accurate fitting of the joining members as well as by a careful selection of the hard or soft woods used. ★ ★ ★

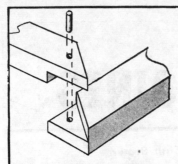

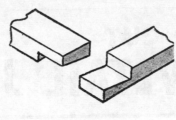

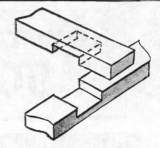

LAPPED MITER. Used when joining frames when it is desirable to have miter show only on one face

BEVELED CORNER LAP. A good joint to use where there is strain on one or both pieces. Should be glued

CROSS LAP. Workpieces are lapped flush at right angles. Parts must be true fit for maximum strength

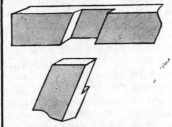

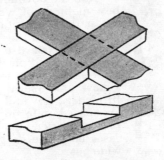

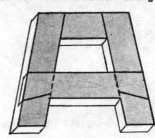

ANGLE HALF LAP. Same as middle lap except parts are joined at an angle. Snug fit is essential

ANGLE CROSS LAP. Members are half-lapped at an angle. Sawbuck table legs are type of this joinery

TRESTLE LAP. Joints are same as half-dovetail lap except that the shoulders are cut at an angle

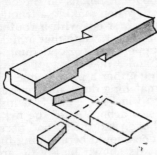

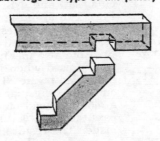

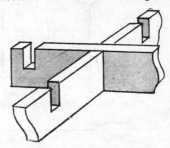

WEDGED HALF-DOVETAIL LAP. Used on framing that is assembled and disassembled frequently

ANGLE LAP WITH SHOULDER. Its main use is in heavy framing and as brace in heavy shelf bracket

EDGE LAP. Used when making open grilles or when assembling compartments in box or tool tray

HOW TO CUT
DOVETAIL JOINTS

By Sam Brown

SELF-LOCKING and as strong as the wood itself, the dovetail joint is one of the oldest and best methods of wood joinery. Most familiar is the multiple-dovetail joint used in drawer construction in all the better-grade cabinets, but the single dovetail also has many applications. Both single and multiple dovetails are made in a variety of sizes. Dovetails cut on an 11-deg. angle are almost universally used in present-day joinery. In modern dovetail cutting the sockets and pins are spaced uniformly, but in older types of joinery the pins varied in relation to the spacing. In some cases only one or two pins were used, even on wide boards.

Dovetail grooving: Figs. 1 to 14 inclusive picture and detail methods of cutting dovetail grooves and matching dovetail tenons on the circular saw and drill press. When making a frame, Figs. 1 to 5, the groove is first cut with a router bit on the drill press as in Fig. 1. Note that a high fence must be used to support the work adequately. Note also in Figs. 2 and 3 that this type joint can be used when joining either a plain frame or a paneled frame. The matching dovetail tenon is cut on the circular saw as in Figs. 4 and 5, using a molding head on the saw arbor. After the first pass the work is turned over and the second pass made. The resulting tenon should be a sliding fit in the dovetail groove. As shown in Fig. 6, an allowance must be made in the depth of the groove to provide clearance for the end of the dovetail.

A similar procedure is used when joining rails to square legs, or curved legs to a single round column as in Figs. 7 to 14 inclusive. When routing

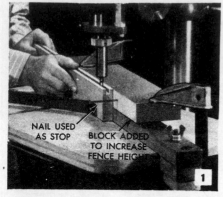

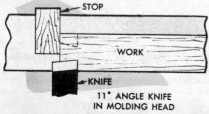

Details and photos at left and below show how to cut dovetail grooves and matching dovetail tenons. Joint is used when framing either plywood or raised panels. Groove is cut on drill press

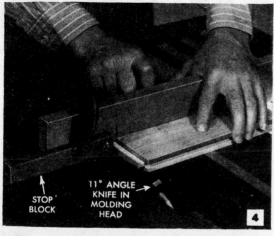

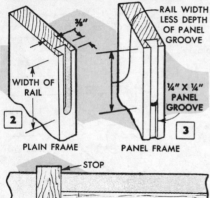

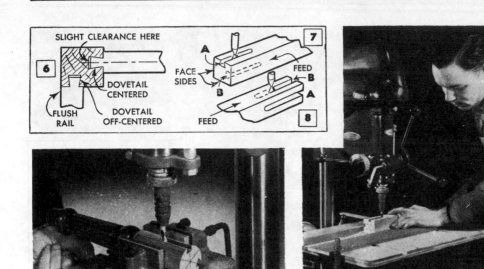

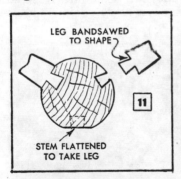

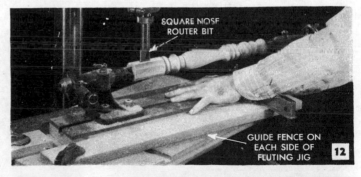

grooves on adjacent sides of the leg care must be taken to keep the proper sequence of operations so that the parts will assemble correctly. This is indicated in details A and B in Figs. 7 and 8. The grooves are run first with a straight router bit, then finished with the dovetail bit. Note in Fig. 6 how the tenon is offset when the construction calls for a flush rail.

Dovetail grooves in round work: When cutting dovetail grooves 120 deg. apart, Fig. 11, the work can be mounted between indexing centers as in Fig. 12. When there are four legs the surface is sometimes squared with a router bit as in Fig. 12, this being the first operation after turning. Dovetail tenons are cut on the curved legs as in Fig. 14. Note in Fig. 11 that the dovetail shoulders, or cheeks, are curved slightly so that they join accurately to the curved surface of the column. This can be done by bandsawing to the correct contour.

Dovetail dadoes and sockets: Dovetail dado cuts are made in a manner similar to

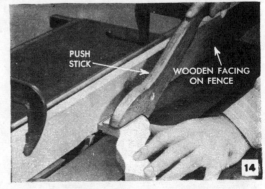

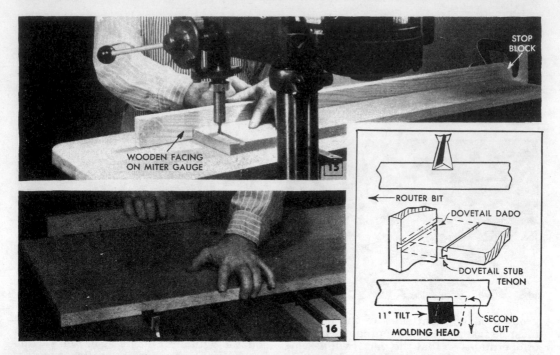

WOODEN FACING
ON MITER GAUGE

STOP
BLOCK

ROUTER BIT

DOVETAIL DADO

DOVETAIL STUB
TENON

11° TILT

MOLDING HEAD

SECOND
CUT

dovetail grooves except that the cut is made across the grain as in Fig. 15, using the drill-press setup pictured. Here a special table is bolted to the regular machine table and grooved for the miter gauge which is taken from the saw table to serve this purpose. A long wooden facing, carrying a stop, is screwed to the miter gauge. The dovetail tenon is cut as in Fig. 4. Another method of cutting the dovetail dado is shown in Fig. 16, using the molding head tilted 11 deg. as in the detail at the right of Fig. 16. Although the molding-head setup is much the faster of the two methods, it is subject to possible error as the stock must be reversed for the second cut. Accuracy requires that the edges of the stock be parallel.

Single dovetail joint: Sometimes referred to as a pocket dovetail, this joint is often

¼"
ROUTER BIT

STOP

SPACER

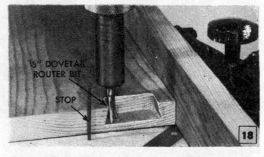

½" DOVETAIL
ROUTER BIT

STOP

Above, first cut in making a pocket is made with a straight router bit in the drill press. Note spacer strip. Below, single matching dovetail is made with molding head as in Fig. 4, except that stock is on edge

Above, after cutting pocket with straight router bit, job is finished with ½-in. dovetail router bit. Nail is used as stop in both operations. Below, in the finished joint dovetail should be snug fit in the pocket

STOP
BLOCK

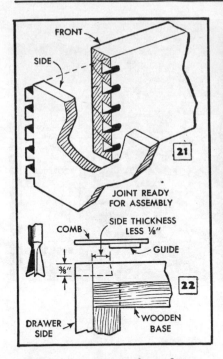

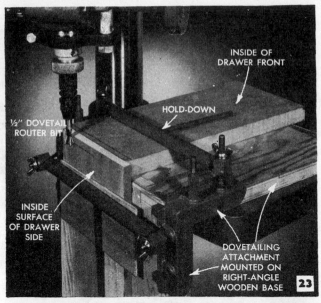

Multiple dovetails, such as used in drawer construction are the easiest of all to cut with the aid of the dovetailing jig shown

This is the jig assembled with two pieces of stock in place. In some cases a weight is needed to steady the sliding jig

The cut partially completed. Photo shows finger template which guides the dovetail bit. Joint is finished in one pass

used to join top rails to legs or panels in cabinet construction. This type of joinery was much favored by older cabinetmakers. Fig. 20 pictures a typical example. Usually it is best to cut the socket, or pocket, first. This is first cut square as in Fig. 17, using a ¼-in. square-nosed router bit. Use a spacer strip for the run-in cuts. The width of the spacer should be equal to the width of the pocket minus ¼ in. Then, using the same setup, a ½-in. dovetail bit will make the angular side cuts as in Fig. 18. The matching dovetail pin is made with the setup shown in Fig. 19. It is the same as that in Fig. 4, except that the cuts are made with the work on edge. Care must be taken to make an accurate layout.

Dovetail drawer joints: These are the easiest of all to cut as you use the dovetail jig pictured in Figs. 23, 24 and 25. When correctly set up this unit cuts the sockets and pins in one pass, a finger template, or comb, Fig. 22, guiding the bit for each cut. When the cuts are finished the parts join as in Fig. 21. No glue is used in the joint. Care must be taken when making the setup, Fig. 23. A weight, Fig. 24, helps to steady the sliding jig. Fig. 25 shows the completed cuts. ★ ★ ★

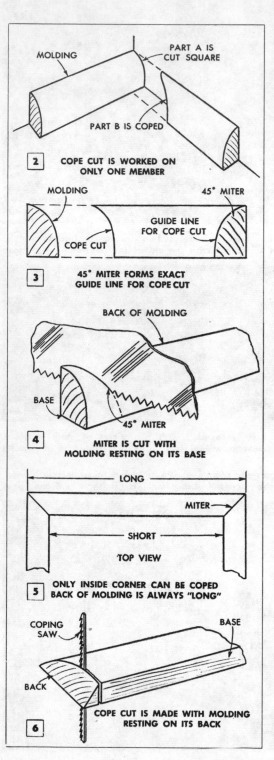

MOLDING

PART A IS CUT SQUARE

PART B IS COPED

2 COPE CUT IS WORKED ON ONLY ONE MEMBER

MOLDING

45° MITER

GUIDE LINE FOR COPE CUT

COPE CUT

3 45° MITER FORMS EXACT GUIDE LINE FOR COPE CUT

BACK OF MOLDING

BASE

45° MITER

4 MITER IS CUT WITH MOLDING RESTING ON ITS BASE

LONG

MITER

SHORT

TOP VIEW

5 ONLY INSIDE CORNER CAN BE COPED BACK OF MOLDING IS ALWAYS "LONG"

COPING SAW

BASE

BACK

6 COPE CUT IS MADE WITH MOLDING RESTING ON ITS BACK

CORNICE

BASE SHOE

1

How to Cut
COPED JOINTS

By Sam Brown

A COPED JOINT is made by cutting the reverse shape of the molding on one end of a piece of molded stock and then joining this to another piece at right angles, as in the corner of a room. The resulting joint has the same appearance as a mitered joint on identical pieces of molding but, in addition, has the advantage of not showing a crack between the joining members should the wood shrink after installation. Two common applications of the coped joint are the cornice mold and base shoe shown in the photo and detail, Fig. 1.

Basic procedure: Figs. 2 to 6 inclusive show the procedure in making a coped joint. First it is necessary to fix in mind the differentiation between the base and back of the molding. In the shoe mold shown in the detail, the narrow, flat side is the base and the wider, flat side the back. When the miter is cut, Fig. 4, the base is always down as indicated. In the crown molding, Fig. 7, the base is the flat side that fits against the ceiling. After cutting the miter on the shoe mold, the cope cut is made by following the miter line with a coping saw, the molding

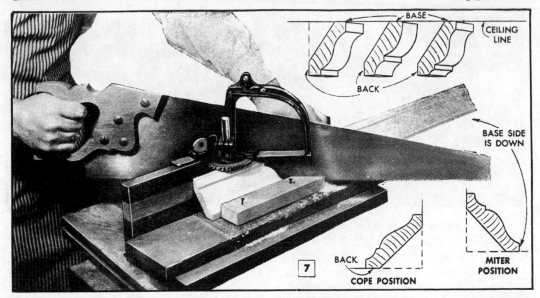

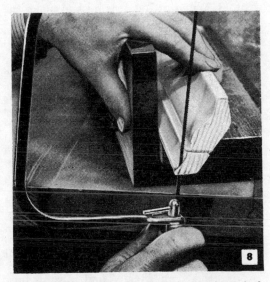

resting on the back as in Fig. 6. Care must be taken to follow the line of the miter precisely as otherwise the joint will not fit snugly when the parts are placed at right angles. The edge will be somewhat easier to follow if blackened by rubbing with a carpenter's pencil. Use a fine-toothed blade in the coping saw as it is easier to control.

Coping crown molding: Typical crown moldings are shown in Fig. 7. Many shapes and sizes are available. One of the most common applications of the crown mold is that of room trim, Fig. 1. Generally such cornices consist of one molding, but in some cases the cornice may be built up of several moldings of varying sizes. If the job is new to you and if you are working with moldings of fairly large size, then it's well to keep in mind that as a rule the predominating curve of the cornice molding generally gives the best appearance when placed at the top. The three sections in the upper detail, Fig. 7, are examples of this basic rule. However, the rule applies more specifically to one-piece molded cornices. Also, identifying two of the three flat surfaces as base and back is simply a convenient way of keeping the parts in order on a given job. The terms do not in any way designate the type of moldings used. It's a good idea to mark the moldings before you begin fitting as this will help to eliminate the possibility of error. After marking all pieces, follow the basic procedure in cutting —hold the base side down for the miter cut and place the molding with the back down for the cope cut. Note the cope and miter positions in Fig. 7, also Fig. 8. Cutting is done generally in a miter box as pictured, the molding being supported by a stop nailed or clamped to the bottom of the

Above, making the cope cut after mitering the end of the molding. Miter cut is guide for the cope cut. Below, checking the accuracy of the joint after coping. When coping the stock is slightly undercut

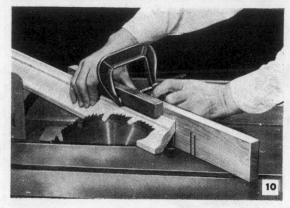

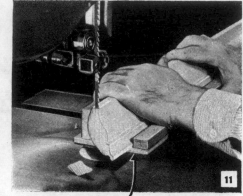

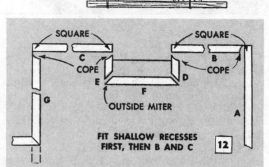

JIG FOR COPE CUTTING ON BANDSAW

Moldings can be mitered and coped on power tools, using the circular saw for the miter cut and the bandsaw and simple jig for the cope cut

box. If a power saw is used a stop is clamped to the crosscut guide as in Fig. 10. Coping cuts also can be made on a bandsaw by making a simple jig as shown in Fig. 11. When fitting, it is best to make the first cope cut on a short piece of waste molding so that the fit can be carefully checked as in Fig. 9. The accuracy in following the guide line formed by the miter cut determines the fit when the parts are placed together in their proper relation. Because of this, carpenters and interior trimmers usually undercut very slightly when coping, although some workmen prefer to do this as a separate operation, using a rotary file, or burr, driven by a flexible shaft or hand grinder as in Fig. 14. On some types of moldings the rotary file is suitable for undercutting.

Order of fitting: Although experienced carpenters and trimmers often fit moldings on the two long sides of a room and then cope both ends of the two shorter pieces to fit, less experienced workers usually will find it easier to fit the pieces successively around the room. Figs. 12 and 13 show how to proceed in this manner by coping one end of each piece and fitting mitered joints at outside corners. Fig. 13, details A to D inclusive, shows how to cope the molding in a square or rectangular room. Fig. 12, details A to F inclusive, shows how molding is fitted when an offset in the wall is involved. One thing to keep in mind while carrying out the installation in any room is that the molding has a "long" and "short" side after mitering, Fig. 5. When fitting the lengths of molding that have square-cut ends, avoid forcing into the corners as the pressure may break the plaster. If a piece must be coped and at the same time cut to length, the initial miter cut is made to the same length as would be required were the joint a simple miter. It's a good idea to make careful measurements of the walls before cutting stock. ★ ★ ★

SQUARE   SQUARE
C   COPE   B   COPE
E   D
G   F
OUTSIDE MITER   A
FIT SHALLOW RECESSES FIRST, THEN B AND C   **12**

SQUARE   COPE
COPE   A   USE SCRAP OF MOLDING TO START
B   COPE FIRST, THEN TRIM SQUARE TO LENGTH   D
SQUARE   C   **13**

Some workmen prefer to undercut the cope with a rotary file, or burr, driven by means of a hand grinder

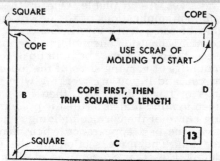

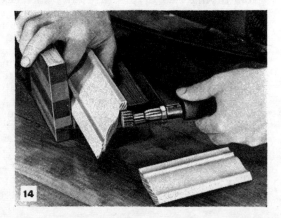

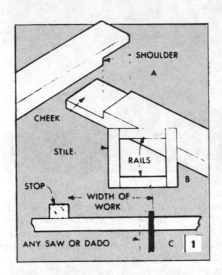

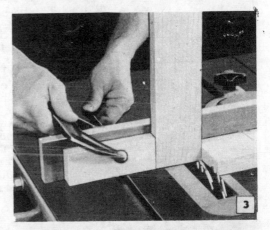

How to Cut Lap Joints

By Sam Brown

IF YOU MAKE your own screen frames or storm sash, frame hardboard panels or build a sawbuck table, you will need to make very accurate lap joints. The end lap is the simplest to make, either by hand methods or complete on the circular saw. The cross lap, or middle lap, requires a bit more care when making the setup. The same is true of the oblique lap, or angle lap, as it is sometimes called. When made accurately and then joined with glue and wooden pins, the end lap makes a strong, serviceable joint for the four corners of a frame such as that for a storm sash or screen. Where appearance of the finished job is of some importance it should be remembered that a frame assembled with lap joints at the corners generally looks best with the stiles unbroken as in Fig. 1, detail B. The assembly should be planned and the joints cut accordingly.

When making the end lap on a circular saw the stiles (vertical members) and the rails should be cut to final, or net, length. The shoulder cut is made with the saw blade or dado set to cut half the thickness of the stock. Be sure that this setting is accurate, then locate the stop block (a clamp also can be used, Fig. 5) and clamp it in position. Note that the stop is located from the far side of the dado head (or saw blade) and that the distance is equal to the width of the stock, Fig. 1, detail C, and also Fig. 3. If you use the miter gauge without a facing board, then the ripping fence

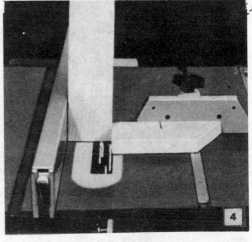

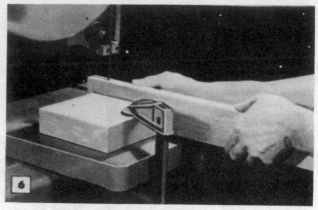

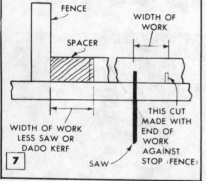

When there are several lap joints to make, you can speed up the job by making shoulder cuts with the saw blade, Fig. 5 above, and finish cheek cuts on bandsaw

FENCE

SPACER

WIDTH OF WORK

WIDTH OF WORK LESS SAW OR DADO KERF

SAW

THIS CUT MADE WITH END OF WORK AGAINST STOP (FENCE)

7

When making cross lap, an accurate spacer block is essential. Make one as in Figs. 8, 9

can be used as a stop, Fig. 4. The initial, or shoulder cut, then is made as in Fig. 2. When running the end lap on the power saw there are two ways of removing the waste. The first is by repeated passes over the dado head, shifting the stock after each pass, or by running the shoulder out first as in Fig. 5 and finishing with the cheek cut made on the bandsaw as in Fig. 6. The former method is perhaps the most accurate.

The cross or middle-lap joint is generally used to join two pieces of stock at the center to form a cross. When accurately made it's a strong, durable joint. Although the shoulder cuts can be made to pencil marks alone with reasonable accuracy, it's better to make the setup with a stop (the saw fence) and a spacer block. The spacer should be of a length equal to the width of the work less the width of the saw or dado kerf, Fig. 7. The best way to make a stop block is to remove the kerf width from a scrap piece of the work stock as in Fig. 8 and then nail the two pieces together as in Fig. 9. Fig. 10 pictures a block made in this manner being used to set the second shoulder cut, the first shoulder cut having been made with the fence used as a stop.

Cutting the oblique cross lap, Fig. 12, requires careful attention to detail when making the setup.

Both members of the joint are cut in the same way with the miter gauge at the same angle and on the same side of the saw table. Cut the stock to the net length and square across the ends. Do any additional cutting after the lap cuts have been made. Pencil the position of the joint on one member and mark the ends that are to be placed against the stop with the letter "S" for easy identification. The miter-gauge setting is the same as the angle of the work, Figs. 11 and 12. Note that the angle cuts to level the assembly, that is, the cuts made on the ends of the stock, are half that of the center angle, Fig. 12. If a spacer block is used, its length must equal that of the angle cut across the work less the width of the saw kerf, lower detail, Fig. 12. However, a somewhat better way is to pick off the spacing distance with inside calipers as in Fig. 13, and then use the caliper setting to space the cuts, one leg of the caliper bearing against the stop block as in Fig. 14.

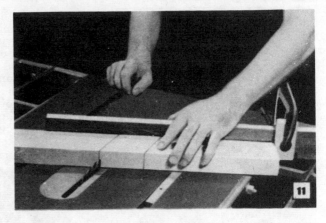

Figs. 15 to 18 inclusive show how to cut an end lap with rabbet. When cutting this joint keep one rule in mind: the rabbet depth must always be one half the thickness of the workpiece. Note the upper detail, Fig. 16, also Figs. 17 and 18. One good way to assure an accurate setting of the saw or dado for cutting the rabbet is pictured in Fig. 15. Make two cuts, one on each side of a piece of scrap stock of the same sectional dimension as the material to be joined. If the cuts are even as shown, the setting is correct. For convenience, the width of the rabbet is made the same as the depth as this permits sawing it with the same fence setting, Fig. 16. Otherwise cutting the end lap with rabbet is much the same procedure as cutting the ordinary end lap except, of course, the length of the cut portion on the rails is shorter by the width of the rabbet, Fig. 16, lower detail. Note also the cut pictured in Fig. 18.

Some forms of the lap joint require right and left-hand cutting. An example is the mitered end lap, Fig. 19. Figs. 20 to 24 inclusive picture the procedure. First, you cut the stock square and to the net length. Next, you cut a plain miter on the rails as in Fig. 20. When

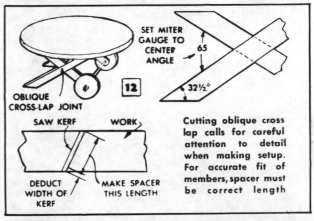

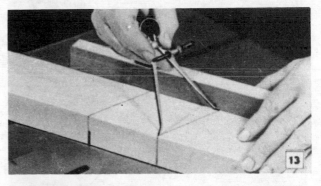

SET MITER GAUGE TO CENTER ANGLE — 65

32½°

OBLIQUE CROSS-LAP JOINT

SAW KERF — WORK

DEDUCT WIDTH OF KERF — MAKE SPACER THIS LENGTH

Cutting oblique cross lap calls for careful attention to detail when making setup. For accurate fit of members, spacer must be correct length

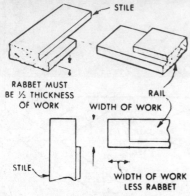

RABBET MUST BE ½ THICKNESS OF WORK

STILE

RAIL

WIDTH OF WORK

STILE

WIDTH OF WORK LESS RABBET

cutting the miters make sure that the stock does not creep along the miter gauge as the cuts are made. Then, with the saw blade set to cut only half the thickness of the stock, run a mitering cut on one end of all the stiles, Fig. 21. Now, with the blade at the same setting, swing the miter gauge to the opposite side of center and cut the miter on the opposite end of each of the stiles, Fig. 22. This requires resetting the end stop. As the final step in this series of operations you run a shoulder cut on

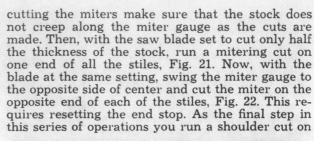

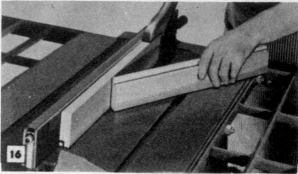

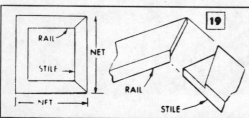

RAIL

STILE

NET

NET

RAIL

STILE

Mitered end lap is best of all lap joints appearancewise. When joined, stiles and rails appear as plain mitered at the corners. Care in making the setup on circular saw will assure accurate fit. Photos below and on opposite page picture the procedure

each of the rails as in Fig. 23, making sure that the stop (in this case the fence) is set to locate the cut at the precise corner of the miter. It's important to make sure of this setting; otherwise the joint will not fit properly. The last step is removing the waste from the shoulder cuts and this can be done with the dado, or faster still, with a molding head fitted with square cutters as in Fig. 24. The mitered end lap makes the neatest joint of all as the joints appear as regular miters when placed with the face side out as in the left-hand detail in Fig. 19. Before cutting any end lap, cross lap or mitered end lap be sure that all pieces are of uniform width and thickness. ★ ★ ★

Glue Sizing for Wood Joints

Furniture and picture-frame joints can be made more secure with an application of glue sizing on the surfaces to be joined before actually gluing them together. This practice is especially useful for joints where considerable end grain appears, as the sizing seals the pores against penetration by the glue used in joining the members. The sizing is made from the same glue used in fastening the pieces together but is diluted to a thin solution. Any excess remaining on the surfaces should be removed to permit an open joint.

Glue sizing may also prove useful in treating end-grain paneling, especially plywood. Applied to the bare wood, it limits penetration by the finishing material, creating less contrast between end-grain and cross-grain surfaces. Some finishes, however, will not adhere to glue sizing.

Walter E. Burton, Akron, Ohio.

Sanding Freshly Glued Joint Seals and Finishes It

To make a joint in a glued-up wooden workpiece less conspicuous, sand the surfaces before the glue has set firmly. Wood dust will mix with the glue to provide a filler that matches the wood. The sanding block assures that the joint is flush with the other surfaces.

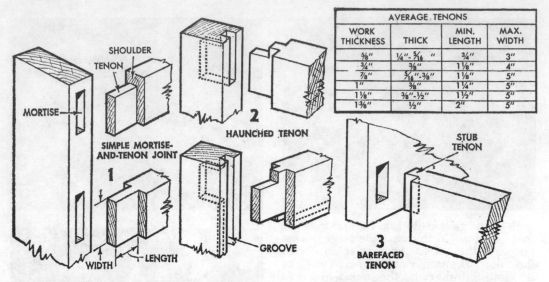

AVERAGE TENONS			
WORK THICKNESS	THICK	MIN. LENGTH	MAX. WIDTH
5/8"	1/4"-5/16"	3/4"	3"
3/4"	3/8"	1 1/8"	4"
7/8"	5/16"-3/8"	1 1/8"	5"
1"	3/8"	1 1/4"	5"
1 1/8"	3/8"-1/2"	1 1/2"	5"
1 3/8"	1/2"	2"	5"

HOW TO CUT MORTISE-

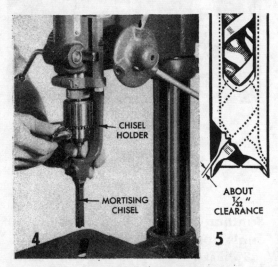

TWO TOOLS, a circular saw and a drill press, make you the boss of the strongest joint in woodworking—the mortise and tenon. Possessed of many variations, the simpler styles shown in Figs. 1, 2 and 3 are most useful. The simple mortise and tenon, Fig. 1, is used extensively in framework construction, such as kitchen cabinets. When the rail stock is narrow, a haunch (shoulder) often is added to prevent twisting, Fig. 2. The haunch also is used as an automatic "fill" for the groove in making paneled frames. When the groove is the same size as the tenon, all the stock is grooved as a first operation, after which the mortises and tenons are made. If the groove is narrower than the tenon, it should be run last, stopping the

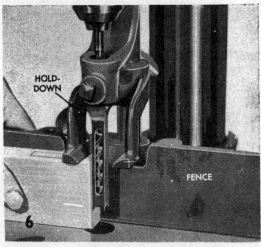

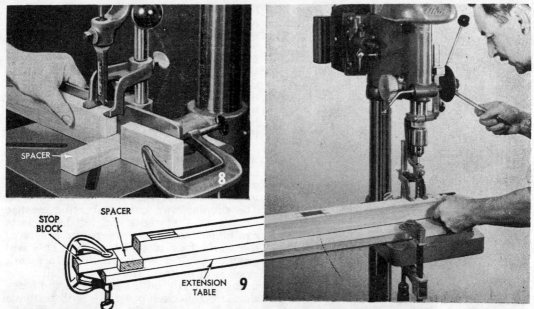

SPACER — 8

STOP BLOCK
SPACER
EXTENSION TABLE — 9

AND-TENON JOINTS
By Sam Brown

cuts short of the ends of the work. The barefaced tenon, Fig. 3, is often used in cabinet construction having plywood ends.

Average dimensions for tenons are given in the table. The general rule is to make the tenon thickness ⅓ to ½ the thickness of the work stock. Tenon width and length can vary greatly but the width should not exceed 5 in. If a wider tenon is needed, it should be divided into twin tenons with a space between to avoid a weak mortise.

The mortise usually is cut first because its width is nonadjustable, whereas a tenon can be sawed fat or thin as needed. Mortising is done on the drill press with the use of a mortising chisel fitted in a special holder. The chisel is mounted first, after which the bit is slipped inside of it, Fig. 4, and held by the chuck. A clearance of about 1/32 in. between chisel and bit is needed to prevent overheating, Fig. 5. The drill press should run at 1800-2800 r.p.m. for softwood; 900-1400 r.p.m. for hardwood.

A mark should be made on the work to show the required depth of cut (⅛ in. deeper than the tenon length) and the depth stop is set to maintain this depth, Fig. 6. From here on the procedure will vary with the job. Most work will have four or more similar joints to be made. When this is the case, the required guide marks should be penciled on one master piece, which is used in making the required drill-press and saw settings. All similar cuts should be made at the same time. Cutting similar mortises is done with the use of a stop block and spacer. The first chisel cut is set by a stop block, as in Fig. 7; the

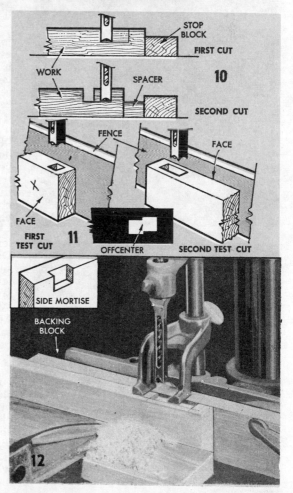

STOP BLOCK
WORK
FIRST CUT

WORK
SPACER
SECOND CUT
10

FENCE
FACE
FACE
FIRST TEST CUT
OFFCENTER
SECOND TEST CUT
11

SIDE MORTISE
BACKING BLOCK
12

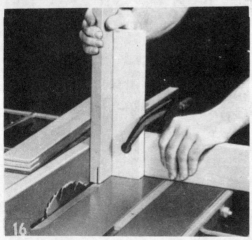

opposite end of the mortise is located by means of a spacer, Fig. 8. The width of the spacer is the length of mortise minus the width of the chisel, as can be seen in Fig. 10. After the two end cuts are made, the wood between can be cut out by taking successive bites of about ⅔ the width of the chisel. Extra working room needed for long work can be obtained by clamping a board to the drill-press table in front of the fence, Fig. 9.

Properly positioned, the face side of the work should be kept against the fence for all cuts. However, when you have right and left members, this is not practical unless you set up right and left-hand stops. The simpler way is to center the mortise exactly so that right and left-hand parts can be cut with the same setup, reversing the work, face in and face out. This will produce perfect work provided the work stock is of uniform thickness, which is the usual case. The initial setting of the fence should be checked carefully with test cuts made on a scrap of the work stock, Fig. 11. Make one cut with the face side out, then reverse to put the face side in and make a second cut. If the two show a jog, Fig. 11, it is obvious you are offcenter.

The side mortise, Fig. 12, is a housed joint rather than a mortise and tenon. However, it is cut with the mortising chisel and is often used in frame construction. It easily is cut by using a backing block and hold-in, as shown. A good amount of pressure is required in making all mortising cuts, but it should not be overdone. It is better to use a slow, steady feed and it is helpful to lift the chisel frequently. Cutting both end holes first, as shown, is recommended. If you use the alternate system of working from one end to the other, do not make the final cut less than ⅔ the width of the chisel; a narrow cut tends to "bend" the chisel or to force the work away from it.

All the tenon parts first are cut to net length, including the length of the tenons. Do this exactly, using a stop block for all similar parts. With the stock cut to net length, you can proceed with the tenons. When just a few tenons are needed, the system of flat sawing with the dado head, Fig. 13, is reasonably fast and perfectly safe. Even a single saw is not too slow for just a few pieces, although this cut normally is used only for the shoulders, Fig. 14. The minimum safe setup to saw the cheek cuts is a high fence and pushboard, as shown in Fig. 15. Somewhat better is the miter-gauge facing in combination with a clamped upright and the regular fence, as shown in Fig. 16. This gives support in all directions and is fast and safe. Naturally, if you do a lot of tenon work, it is worthwhile to make or buy a regular tenoning

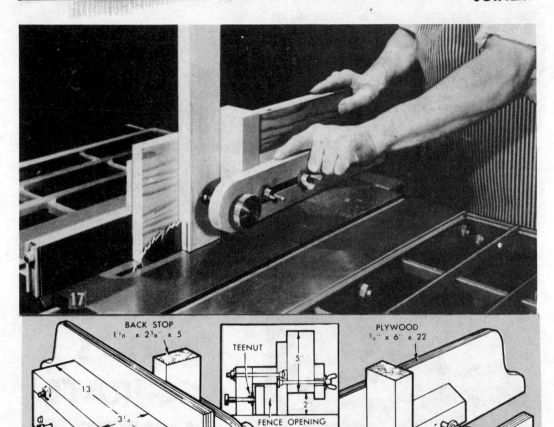

BACK STOP
1⅛ x 2⅜ x 5

TEENUT

5

FENCE OPENING

2

PLYWOOD
¾" x 6" x 22

13

3¼

⅛" TEENUT

TENSION
SCREWS

DOWEL
GUIDE PIN

TENSION
PLATE

BACK VIEW

18 TENONING JIG

PLYWOOD
CLAMP BAR
¼ x 2¼ x 9

jig. A good homemade fence-riding style is shown in Fig. 18. It is fitted with a tension plate so that it can be made an exact snug, sliding fit on the regular fence. Even without the clamp bar, Fig. 19, it is much better than the high fence and pushboard idea.

Tenons should be made a good press fit. Like other operations, all similar pieces should be cut at the same time. In the usual method of working, the stock is turned face out, face in for the two cheek cuts. This will produce uniform tenons provided the stock is of uniform thickness. Of course, you can make a test joint first, adjusting the fence carefully to make a tenon which is too large for an easy hand fit but goes together nicely with a few taps of a mallet. The cheek cuts are usually made first in order to preserve maximum end surface to ride on the saw table. The shoulder cuts are an easy job and can be set to length with the regular fence, Fig. 14, or as in Fig. 20 with a stop block fastened to the miter-gauge facing. ★ ★ ★

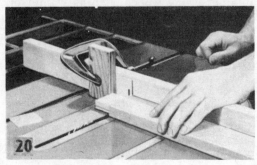

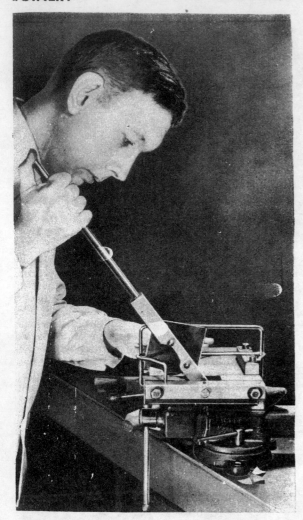

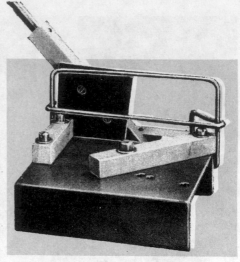

TRIMMER MAKES ACCURATE MITERS

By Walter E. Burton

ACCURATE MITER JOINERY is the mark of superior craftsmanship. Cutting a close-fitting miter joint on stock from ⅜ in. thickness up can be done quite easily with regular tools such as a miter box or a power saw. But working a miter joint on thinner materials is more difficult. Holding a true line even with a hollow-ground blade on a power saw or by hand with a fine-toothed dovetail saw is almost impossible on grainy woods such as walnut or oak. That's where a small miter trimmer comes in handy. It slices neatly through thin wood, cardboard, some plastics and also thin hardboard. When the pieces are fitted and glued you have a fine, hairline joint. This trimmer is designed for such light cuts on material up to about 1½ in. wide. The two-edged cutter is mounted on a lever, or handle. It pivots on a shaft mounted on one side of the base, which is a length of steel channel. The blade moves in an arc, giving a shearing cut.

The two guide fences are made of hard wood such as oak or maple. The longer one pivots from one corner of the base and its free end is bolted into one of several holes arranged in an arc. This allows miter cuts to be made at any one of several angles. The holes are drilled and tapped 5/16-18 while the hole in the fence for the index bolt is made slightly oversize so that fine corrective adjustments may be made with a protractor. If desired, a curved slot may be substituted for the bolt holes. This will allow the guide fence to be fixed in an infinite number of settings from 90 to 45 deg. The second and shorter fence is set at 90 deg. and is bolted to one side of the base.

The cutter arm is a section of steel bar with a portion cut away at the center. This cut-away portion provides blade clearance and insures against the arm striking the finger guards. The upper end of the bar is drilled to receive an 11-in. steel rod which serves as a lever extension. The rod is

Cutter is attached to a pivoted handle, or lever with edges in position to give a smooth, shearing cut

Series of holes arranged in an arc allow various miter settings to be made ranging from 45 to 90 deg.

secured by means of two setscrews and its use makes the arm less bulky than if the bar were used alone. The handle carrying the cutter pivots on a $\frac{7}{16}$-in. steel rod which passes through holes in the base and the outside retaining bar. The rod and handle are in turn held in place by the retainer bar bolted to the base with hardwood spacers. These spacers double as the pads on which the blade comes to rest.

The blade itself is a piece of $\frac{1}{16}$-in. tool steel almost square in shape. Its two cutting edges enable the trimmer to cut in two directions—on the pull or the push stroke. Thus, the end of a workpiece may be squared to 90 deg. by placing the work against the stationary fence guide and by swinging the arm up and back.

The blade is almost, but not quite square. This is because at the end of the arc in which it is swung its cutting edges must come to rest squarely on the cutting pads. The exact angle of the cutting edges is found by cutting a blank of steel measuring $3\frac{1}{4}$ in. square. Mount this blank temporarily on the cutter arm and swing the

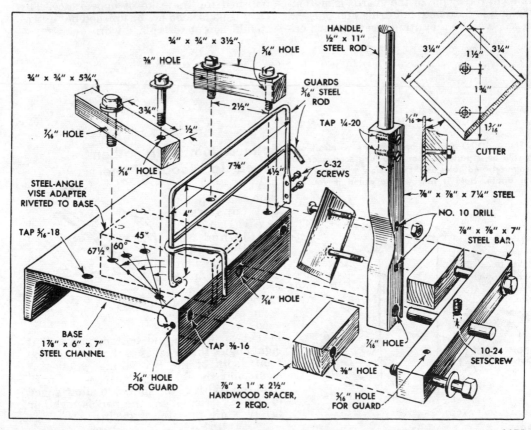

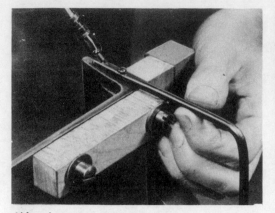

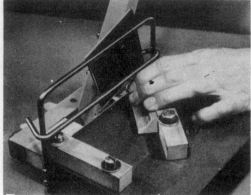

Although not essential, the trimmer is fitted with hand guards as a safety feature. Guards cover cutting edges through arc of travel in either direction

Here's the trimmer in use making a 45-deg. cut on a common type of molding. Note also that trimmer has a fixed fence located at 90 deg. for convenience

arm so that an outer blade corner is in line with the base. Scribe a line to indicate where the cutting edge is to be ground.

The cutter arm should swing between the base and the retainer bar without appreciable play. It may be necessary to place shims of thin cardboard or sheet metal between the bar and the hardwood spacers to prevent binding. Washers placed between the arm and the base will keep the knife edges from striking the metal base.

The finger guards may be bent from 3/16-in. steel rods. One of the guards is stationary and is flattened and drilled on one end to receive two mounting screws which en-

gage threaded holes in the base. The other end fits into a hole drilled into the base. The other guard is a floating piece which normally rests on the fence guide bolts. This guard is easily removed to accommodate thicker, heavier work. To provide a means of holding the trimmer firmly while it is in use, a steel angle is riveted to the underside of the base. This allows the trimmer to be clamped in a vise. The base and cutter arm may be lacquered or enameled in an attractive color and the guide fences polished for the sake of appearance. The cutting pads need not be finished but extras should be cut to replace worn ones. ★ ★ ★

WHEN A JOINT OPENS between the crossrail and the stile of a paneled door, two long screws driven in counterbored holes as shown below will draw it up tight again. Hold it first with a clamp if you can

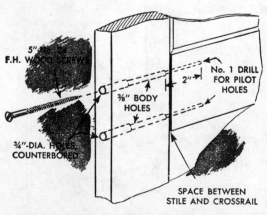

5" No. 2² F.H. WOOD SCREWS

No. 1 DRILL FOR PILOT HOLES

2"

3/8" BODY HOLES

3/4"-DIA. HOLES COUNTERBORED

SPACE BETWEEN STILE AND CROSSRAIL

Splined Joints Strengthen Glued-Up Wooden Panels

A wood panel, such as a table top, that consists of several boards butt-joined and glued together, will be considerably stronger if the joints are splined. Splines of 1/4-in. plywood are used, and should

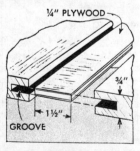

1/4" PLYWOOD

3/4"

1 1/2"

GROOVE

be cut so the top and bottom grain is at right angles to the edges of the boards. The total depth of the two spline grooves at each joint should be at least 1/8 in. more than the width of the spline, to allow space for excess glue. Clamp the panels together firmly while the glue is drying.

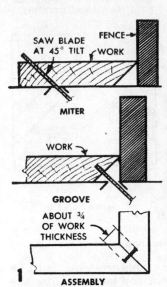

SAW BLADE AT 45° TILT · FENCE · WORK

MITER

WORK →

GROOVE

ABOUT ¾ OF WORK THICKNESS

1 ASSEMBLY

When the stock is joined along the edge, the miter cut is run with the saw blade tilted to 45 deg. Then the cut faces are grooved for splines

Cutting the MITER JOINT

By Sam Brown

NOTHING PLEASES the eye of the craftsman more than a neatly worked miter joint which leaves the grain of the wood unbroken at the corner and shows nothing more on the surface than the fine line indicating where the parts were joined. A good, tight-fitting miter joint is quite easy to produce, either by hand with a simple miter box or with a power saw. About all it takes is careful attention to setups and procedures.

When mitering the corners of a boxlike structure, the 45-deg. cuts are made along the edges of the stock as in Figs. 1 and 2, and to add strength and rigidity the joint is splined, Fig. 1. The joint can be made complete on the circular saw with the blade tilted to 45 deg.

The crosscut miter is perhaps the most common type of miter joint. It is worked with the saw blade set at 90 deg. and the miter gauge set at 45 deg. Two work positions are possible in each table groove, as shown in Figs. 3 and 4. The open position, Fig. 3, is preferred by most craftsmen as it tends to keep the hands away from the saw blade. The closed position offers somewhat better support but is not as safe because the feed hand is behind the blade—the area where most saw accidents happen.

There is seldom any need to use the closed miter-gauge position. If the work can be turned over, face to back, both ends can be cut without disturbing the position of the miter gauge, Fig. 7. It can be seen that the same edge is toward the miter

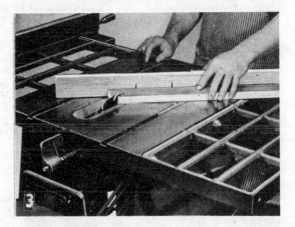

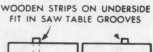

WOODEN STRIPS ON UNDERSIDE
FIT IN SAW TABLE GROOVES

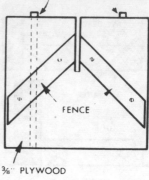

FENCE

⅜" PLYWOOD

MITER TABLE

When making crosscut miter cuts on strips of equal length, use a stop on ripping fence for accuracy

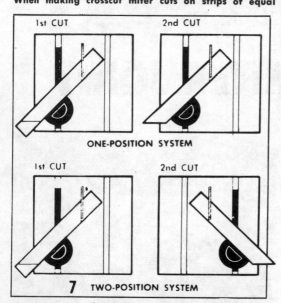

1st CUT   2nd CUT

ONE-POSITION SYSTEM

1st CUT   2nd CUT

7 TWO-POSITION SYSTEM

gauge for both cuts, but the work must be face up for one cut and face down for the other. This, of course, can't be done with moldings and various jobs where the work must remain face up. In this case, the open position is used for both cuts but the miter gauge must be turned to the opposite 45-deg. position and used in the opposite table groove, as shown in Fig. 7. If you are doing a lot of molding work, the auxiliary miter table shown in Fig. 6 is useful as it permits right and left-hand cuts at will. The simplest type of miter cut occurs when pieces are cut from a long work strip. Both right and left cuts can be made by simply turning the work alternately edge-for-edge and face-to-back, Fig. 5, using the same miter-gauge position throughout, and without reversing the work end-for-end.

Grooving for splines on crosscut miters can be done freehand with the aid of a

First splining groove is run with stock in this position. Note use of hold-in to keep stock against fence

Opposite end of stock is spline-grooved with piece in this position. Use special care in making cut

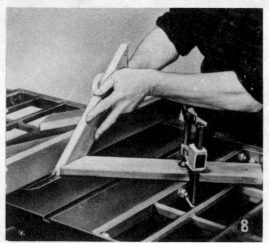

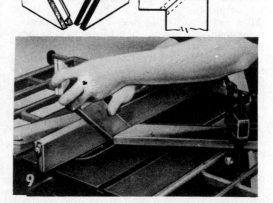

SPLINE

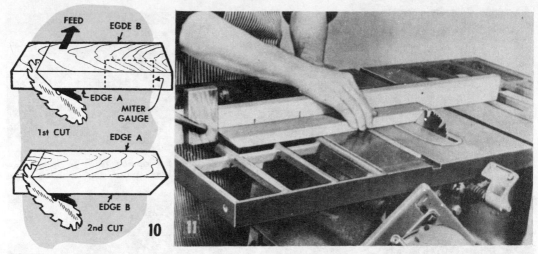

When crosscut mitering as in Fig. 11, use a stop to assure accuracy. For second cut turn stock, Fig. 10

spring hold-in. One end of each work piece can be cut in an open position, Fig. 8, but the other end must be worked in the objectionable closed position, Fig. 9. Only the shallow depth of the cut, rarely exceeding ⅜ in., makes this kind of freehand sawing practical and reasonably safe. Splines of ⅛-in. plywood will usually fit the saw kerf if sanded lightly on both sides. For exact control of the saw kerf width, the well-known trick of slipping a piece of paper between the arbor flange and saw blade is worth keeping in mind; the slight wedging action of the paper will make the saw wobble slightly and cut a slightly wider groove than normal. The spline stock is usually cut square and is fitted slightly beyond the inside corner of the joint, as in the right-hand detail, Fig. 9.

A second type of common crosscut miter is done with the work flat on the table but with blade tilted, Figs. 10 and 11. In work of this kind the miter gauge is in the 90-deg. position and can be used in either table groove as desired, with a slight preference for the right-hand position because this puts cut-off waste pieces under the blade. Both ends of the work can be cut with the same miter gauge position; the face side of the work is up for both cuts but the edges reverse, Fig. 10. It is necessary that the stock be of uniform width, since non-parallel edges would cause inaccuracy in cutting.

Other than the conventional wood fastenings (splines and dowels), there are mechanical fasteners for several types of miter joints. One in common use is known as the clamp nail, which draws the members of the miter joint firmly together, Fig. 13. A special thin blade cutting a 22-gauge kerf is required to cut the spline groove. For narrow work, one method is to cut the kerfs with a band saw, Fig. 12. This is worked with the miter gauge and with end

Miters on narrow stock are often joined with clamp nails. Bandsaw blade cuts a kerf of the right width

Clamp nails have flanges shaped to draw the mitered faces tightly together to form strong, rigid joint

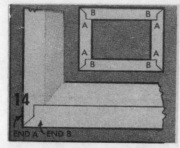

In making a rabbeted miter joint cut all parts square to net length

Run a test piece with shoulder ½ the work thickness. Use miter blade

Set ripping fence to locate saw blade exactly flush with work face

Beginning with end A, Fig. 14, make a shoulder cut with blade in waste

Follow with successive cuts to clear waste just beyond miter line

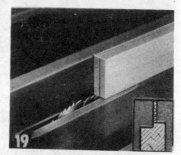

Using the test piece set the ripping fence at ½ work thickness

Make shoulder cut on end B, Fig. 14. Repeat on all ends marked B

Tilt blade to 45 deg. and miter corners on all ends marked B

Make same mitering cut on all ends marked A. Note use of test piece

and depth stops as shown. The average bandsaw blade produces a kerf of just the right width. The width of the average clamp nail is $9/16$ in.; a saw kerf $5/16$-in. deep will accommodate and also will allow just the right clearance.

There are many special types of miter joints but the extra work in cutting them tends to limit their use to choice pieces of cabinet work. One such joint, excellent for cabinet bases and similar work, is the rabbeted miter, Fig. 14. Its main feature is the rabbet which provides a square butting corner easily assembled with glue or nails. In an average assembly with four work pieces, the A and B ends of each work piece go together as shown in Fig. 14. Cutting this or any other fancy cabinet joint requires care in making exact saw settings. Follow the step-by-step procedure shown in Figs. 14 to 22.

In all miter work done on the circular saw it is very important to have the miter gauge and saw set at 45 deg. This is simply a matter of checking. Before you start work on the actual job, run cuts on scrap stock and test with a square. If the cuts check true, you are all set to begin work. If not, adjust the miter gauge setscrews or change the settings of the tilt stop.

In all types of miter work it also is important to use a sharp saw blade to give a clean, true cut. If you use a circular saw to make the cuts, it is best to use a hollow-ground blade which runs without set in the teeth. The hollow-ground blade does not chip the lower edge of the stock, which is important when the piece must be reversed or turned over to make a second miter cut. Never crowd the blade. Run all cuts slowly. Hold the stock firmly to prevent creeping.

★ ★ ★

Six Ways to Reinforce Joints on Woodwork

MAKE YOUR FURNITURE and other woodwork last longer and be more serviceable by reinforcing weak or loose joints. Of the many types of joints used in woodworking, the simpler ones shown here may be used either in new construction or in repairing loose joints in any existing construction.

A quick and sturdy repair for corners, when pieces are simply butted together, is to use two dowels. Drill two holes through the outer member and well into the adjacent member and drive in glue-coated dowels. These should be flattened slightly on one or more sides to allow air and excess glue trapped at the bottom of the holes to escape. Trim the dowels flush and refinish. For an extra-strong joint use three dowels.

For picture frames, and other articles having mitered joints where inconspicuous bracing is required, use a thin piece of wood. Saw a slot across the joint to take a thin wooden block snugly. Apply a thin coat of glue to both sides of the block, insert it and clamp until dry. The block should be trimmed to fit flush and a matching finish applied on the exposed edge before it is glued.

When a joint is weakened by rot or splitting and replacement is not warranted,

Above, members that are butted together are reinforced by drilling and fitting joint with dowels. Below, triangular block of wood fastened on inside surface of joint strengthens deteriorated members

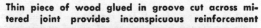

Thin piece of wood glued in groove cut across mitered joint provides inconspicuous reinforcement

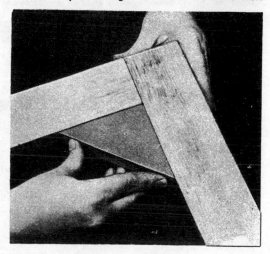

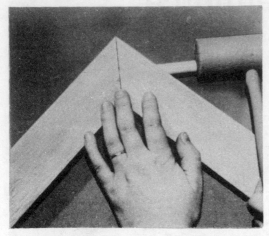

Above, for alternate repair of mitered joint glue dowel in hole drilled across joint at right angle

Metal brackets are easy to install on mitered joint, above, when appearance is secondary consideration. Below, triangles of thin plywood fastened on both sides of joint provide extra-strong reinforcement

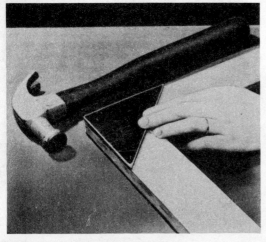

fit a triangular wooden block snugly on the inside surface of corner and screw it in place. Drill pilot holes in the block and corner members and use screws long enough to penetrate sound wood.

Another method of strengthening a mitered joint is to drill both pieces at right angles to the joint and drive in a glue-coated dowel. Where members are of sufficient width reinforce the joint with two dowels. Trim and finish dowel ends when the glue is dry.

To save time when reinforcing a mitered corner use metal angle brackets on screen doors, windows and other places where appearance is not too important; brackets can be painted over to make them less noticeable. Also, these brackets are suitable for strengthening purposes where a surface is out of view, such as in drawers and the underside of some tables and benches.

A very sturdy repair, and one that may be used when added thickness is no problem, can be made by gluing and nailing a thin plywood gusset over the corners of a joint. For added strength, gussets may be used on both sides of the joint. A sheet-metal gusset can be used where added thickness would prohibit this type of repair.

On a mortise-and-tenon joint subject to strain, such as the rungs on a chair, try locking the tenon with a small dowel. To do this, first glue and clamp the parts together. Then, at right angles to the joint, drill a hole through mortise and tenon, coat the dowel with glue and drive it into the hole to pin the end of the tenon tightly in the mortise. Trim away the projecting portion of the dowel, sand the surface smooth and refinish to match. Use of a hardwood block under hammer protects the dowel and surface of furniture. ★ ★ ★

When driving dowel for mortise-and-tenon repair use hardwood block to protect dowel and furniture

KERFING IS THE WAY
to bend wood without steaming

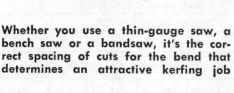

Whether you use a thin-gauge saw, a bench saw or a bandsaw, it's the correct spacing of cuts for the bend that determines an attractive kerfing job

KERFING provides a simple and practical method of bending wood without steaming, and consists of running in a number of saw cuts (kerfs) across the wood to reduce its mechanical thickness. Once used extensively in wooden casket construction, the operation is sometimes referred to as an "undertaker's bend."

The craftsman's usual approach to a kerfing job is to space the kerfs close together and cut the wood as thin as practical. For average work, ¼-in. center-to-center spacing of kerfs is used, while the uncut portion of wood can be as thin as ¹⁄₁₆ in. The job is set up as shown in Figs. 3 and 4, with a nail driven into the miter-gauge facing to space the cuts exactly. A thin-gauge saw is preferable, but good work can be done with any bench-saw blade.

Kerfing also can be done on the bandsaw, Fig. 6, a method which has the advantages of being faster and producing a narrower kerf than a bench saw. The advantage of the narrow kerf is that it can be closed completely when the work is bent and will make the job stronger. When bandsaw kerfing, you cannot make use of the spacing pin, but you can make an equally accurate measure by advancing each kerf as it is cut to a mark on the miter-gauge facing, as shown in Fig. 5. Note that the miter gauge is rotated about 6 deg. to allow the work to clear the bandsaw arm. A stop clamped to the saw table assures cuts of equal depth.

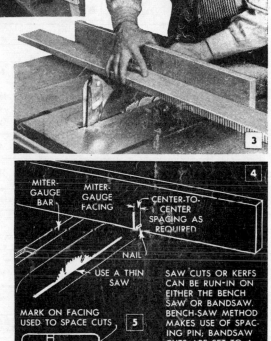

MITER-GAUGE BAR — MITER-GAUGE FACING — CENTER-TO-CENTER SPACING AS REQUIRED

NAIL

USE A THIN SAW

MARK ON FACING USED TO SPACE CUTS

STOP

SAW CUTS OR KERFS CAN BE RUN-IN ON EITHER THE BENCH SAW OR BANDSAW. BENCH-SAW METHOD MAKES USE OF SPACING PIN; BANDSAW CUTS ARE SET TO A MARK ON MITER-GAUGE FACING.

MITER GAUGE IS TURNED ABOUT 6° SO WORK CLEARS BANDSAW ARM

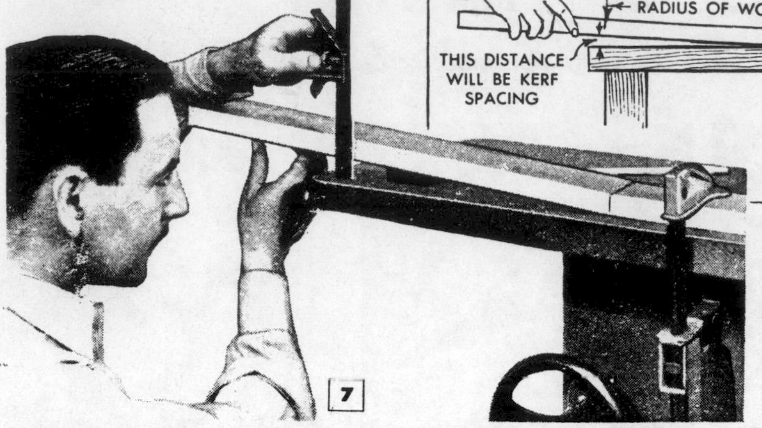

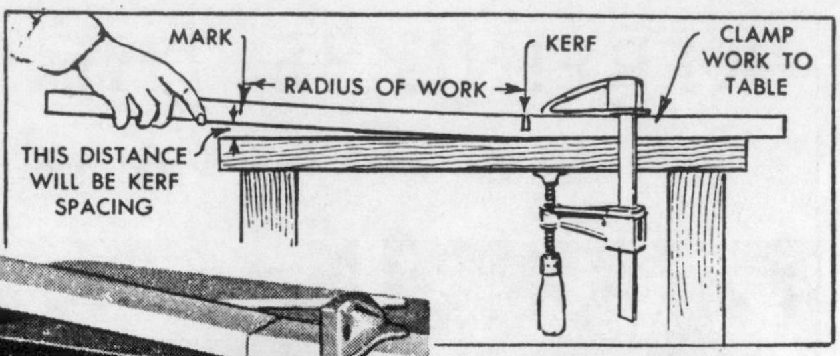
MARK
KERF
CLAMP WORK TO TABLE
RADIUS OF WORK
THIS DISTANCE WILL BE KERF SPACING

7

SPACING OF CUTS CAN BE DETERMINED BY A SIMPLE SETUP SHOWN. PULL UP GENTLY ON THE WORK AND MEASURE THE AMOUNT OF MOVEMENT AT WORK RADIUS THIS WILL BE SPACING. IT IS NOT NECESSARY THAT THE KERF CLOSE

8 KERFING TABLE

(1) TEST BEND	(2) NUMBER OF CUTS IN CIRCLE	(3) KERF TO CLOSE	SPACING OF CUTS (4) RADIUS OF WORK IN INCHES: 3	4	5	6	7	8	9	10	11	12	13	14	15	16
1/8"	258	.018 (1/64)	1/16	3/32	1/8	5/32	5/32	3/16	7/32	1/4	1/4	9/32	5/16	5/16	3/8	3/8
3/16"	171	.027 (1/32)	3/32	1/8	3/16	7/32	1/4	9/32	5/16	3/8	3/8	7/16	7/16	1/2	9/16	9/16
1/4"	129	.036 (1/32)	1/8	3/16	1/4	1/4	5/16	3/8	7/16	1/2	1/2	9/16	5/8	11/16	3/4	3/4
5/16"	100	.047 (3/64) (AV. BAND SAW)	3/16	1/4	5/16	3/8	7/16	1/2	9/16	5/8	11/16	3/4	13/16	7/8	15/16	1
3/8"	83	.056 (1/16)	3/16	1/4	3/8	7/16	1/2	9/16	5/8	3/4	13/16	7/8	15/16	1	1 1/8	1 3/16
7/16"	72	.065 (1/16)	1/4	5/16	7/16	1/2	9/16	11/16	3/4	7/8	15/16	1	1 1/8	1 3/16	1 5/16	1 3/8
1/2"	63	.074 (5/64)	1/4	3/8	1/2	9/16	11/16	3/4	7/8	1	1 1/16	1 3/16	1 1/4	1 3/8	1 1/2	1 9/16
9/16"	56	.084 (5/64)	5/16	7/16	9/16	5/8	3/4	7/8	1	1 1/8	1 3/16	1 5/16	1 7/16	1 9/16	1 11/16	1 3/4
(5) 5/8"	50	.094 (3/32) (AV. CIRC. SAW)	3/8	1/2	5/8	3/4	7/8	1	1 1/8	1 1/4	1 3/8	1 1/2	1 5/8	1 3/4	1 7/8	2
11/16"	46	.102 (7/64)	3/8	1/2	11/16	13/16	15/16	1 1/16	1 3/16	1 3/8	1 1/2	1 5/8	1 3/4	1 7/8	2 1/16	2 3/16
3/4"	42	.112 (1/8)	7/16	9/16	3/4	7/8	1	1 3/16	1 5/16	1 1/2	1 5/8	1 3/4	1 15/16	2 1/16	2 5/16	2 3/8

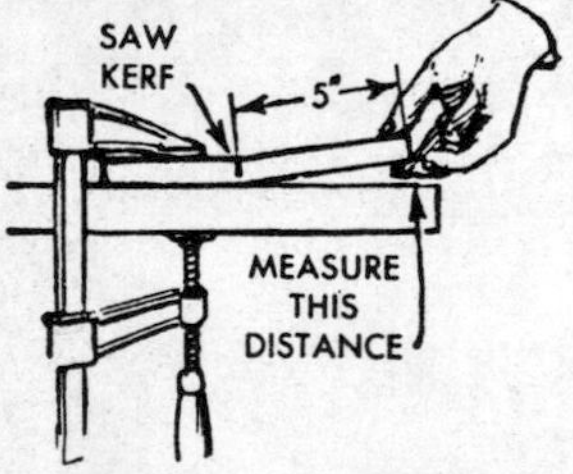
SAW KERF
5"
MEASURE THIS DISTANCE

1. Test bend is made on scrap piece being worked. Amount of lift at end is value used in first column. 2. This gives number of cuts in a circle. Half circle requires half as many cuts. 3. Width of saw kerf. This column applies only to 3/4-in. stock. Kerf can be wider but will not close. 4. Center-to-center spacing of kerfs. Cuts can be spaced closer but not wider. 5. Spacing in this line works out exactly and values are used to check work sizes not listed. A 6-in. radius needs twice the spacing of 3-in. radius. If test bend is 5/16 in., a 12-in. radius requires 3/4-in. spacing

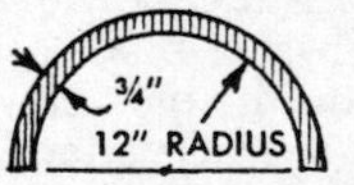
3/4"
12" RADIUS

HOW KERFING TABLE IS USED

Make a test bend as shown in drawing at extreme left. For maximum strength, leave as much uncut wood as possible. Gradually deepen cut until test piece can be bent 1/8 in. Then find 1/8 in. in column 1. On same line, column 2 shows 258 cuts needed for full circle, or 129 cuts for half circle. Under 12-in. radius column, 9/32 in. is the spacing required. Note in column 3 that the kerf needed to close is 1/64 in. wide. As this is not practical, a wider kerf is used, even though it will not close tightly when stock is bent. **Second example of same job:** If you want the kerf to close, start with the .047-in. bandsaw kerf in column 3. Then all the figures on this line will apply. Test bend must be 5/16 in. and spacing will be 3/4 in. Kerfing is done on the bandsaw as pictured in Fig. 5

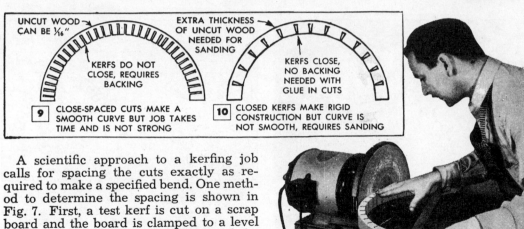

UNCUT WOOD CAN BE 1/16"

KERFS DO NOT CLOSE, REQUIRES BACKING

9 CLOSE-SPACED CUTS MAKE A SMOOTH CURVE BUT JOB TAKES TIME AND IS NOT STRONG

EXTRA THICKNESS OF UNCUT WOOD NEEDED FOR SANDING

KERFS CLOSE, NO BACKING NEEDED WITH GLUE IN CUTS

10 CLOSED KERFS MAKE RIGID CONSTRUCTION BUT CURVE IS NOT SMOOTH, REQUIRES SANDING

Sanding work is required when kerfs are wide-spaced

A scientific approach to a kerfing job calls for spacing the cuts exactly as required to make a specified bend. One method to determine the spacing is shown in Fig. 7. First, a test kerf is cut on a scrap board and the board is clamped to a level surface. Then the board is lifted and the amount of lift at the work radius is measured to determine the spacing required. While exact, this method is subject to considerable variance, for the deeper the kerf is made, the more the wood will bend and the wider the spacing will be. You are assured in all cases, however, that if one kerf allows the wood to bend a certain distance at the radius, further cuts will allow the same bend all around and will ultimately make a circle of the specified radius.

All of the various factors in kerfing are brought under control by the use of the kerfing table shown in Fig. 8. By referring to the table, you can control any of the factors which may be needed for a certain job. You can make the kerfs close for maximum flexibility, or determine the maximum thickness of uncut wood which can be left and still permit the bend. Any allowance made should lean to closer spacing than the table shows. The fault of wide spacing is that, while it permits the bend, the curve will form in a series of flat faces, Fig. 10, and may require sanding to bring it to a smooth curve. The advantage of wide spacing is that it allows the kerfs to close; if you run glue into the cuts before bending, the final product will be a bent piece of wood capable of standing alone. On the other hand, close-spaced kerfs, Fig. 9, consume time and the job is not strong. They must always be backed by a number of glue blocks as shown in Fig. 12.

After the kerfing is completed, the actual bending of the wood should be done gradually to avoid any danger of splitting. Give the work a comfortable bend and span a piece of wood across it to hold the shape, Fig. 13. After setting to this curve for an hour or two, the work can be given another bend. Sometimes it is necessary to sponge the work for about five minutes with warm water, as shown in Fig. 14. This will allow nearly double the bend possible with dry wood, a fact which should be kept in mind when determining the kerf spacing.

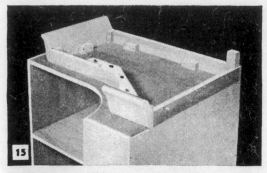

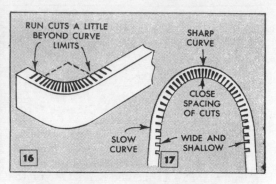

The thin-section method of producing bent work can be used for forming both inside and outside curves

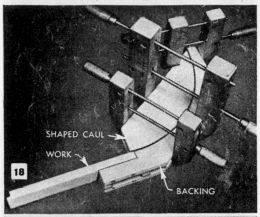

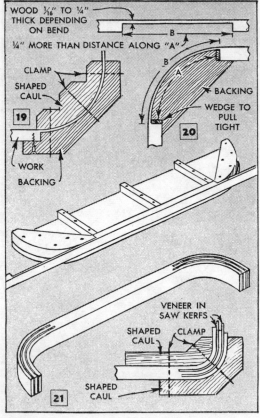

Kerf spacing is always uniform if the curve is uniform. On slight bends, however, the spacing may vary. Fig. 17 is an example—closely spaced cuts are used to make the sharp bend, while a few widely spaced cuts serve for the flat curve. Fig. 1 is an example of a flat bend where two or three cuts about halfway through the wood are enough to take the strain off the wood. The job shown in Fig. 2 makes use of a number of uniform and closely spaced kerfs cut very shallow; the idea is to reduce the effective thickness of the wood to make a more comfortable bend. Fig. 16 shows a quarter-round curve with kerfing extending beyond the curve limits.

An alternate to kerfing for most bent work is the technique of thinning the wood, as shown in Figs. 15 and 18 to 20 inclusive. Like close-spaced kerfing, this work always requires a backing, which, in this case, must be a solid block of wood or an equivalent built-up backing. The thin section is glued to the backing, necessitating the use of a shaped caul or pressure block in the clamping operation, as shown in Fig. 18. This is an example of an inside curve; Fig. 20 is an example of an outside curve. When one end of the thinned section is free, the shoulder is butted tightly against the backing block; when the work does not have a free end, it is more practical to cut the thinned section a little overlength to permit stretch-fitting with wedges.

Still another technique used for bent work is kerfing lengthwise with the work, as shown in Fig. 21. The cuts should be run in on the bandsaw with the use of a ripping fence and can be spaced to suit. Dependent on the sharpness of the curves and the number of kerfs, work of this kind may require some steaming. Strips of veneer are placed in the saw kerfs and the work is clamped without glue, using hot-water sponging or steam if needed. After the work has dried, the clamps are released and the permanent assembly made with glue. Although this method of bending is more work than the other systems, it has advantages in that the work will stand alone and the edge can be exposed.

KITCHEN NOVELTIES

JUST THE THING to brighten up the kitchen, these two wall novelties, representing little cottages, provide convenient storage for hot pads, pot holders and condiments. The salt-and-pepper shelf also includes a dinner gong and mallet.

To make the hot-pad holder, enlarge the design on paper ruled in 1-in. squares, transfer it to ¼-in. plywood and jigsaw the parts. Sand the sections smooth and fasten them together with brads. Then drill two holes for hanging the shelf, one at the top and the other at the bottom of the backboard. Cloth pot holders are hung from two screw hooks turned into the backboard below the hot-pad shelf. Thin felt washers glued to the back of the plywood hot pads will keep them from marring the surface of the table.

The shaker shelf is assembled in the same manner as the hot-pad holder, except for holes drilled in the eaves and front of the shelf for decoration. The gong is made from a tin-can lid having a finished edge, such as the lid of a shortening can. Dish the gong and give it a hammered finish before polishing it with steel wool, and then punch two holes near the edge for hanging it from the shelf. Finally, wax the gong or coat it with clear shellac and hang it with a length of cord attached to the underside of the shelf. The mallet is made of plywood and should be hung from a brass screw hook directly in front of the gong.

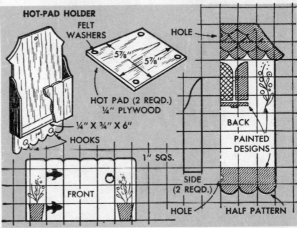

HOT-PAD HOLDER
FELT WASHERS
HOLE
5⅞" 5⅞"
HOT PAD (2 REQD.) ¼" PLYWOOD
¼" X ¾" X 6"
HOOKS
FRONT
1" SQS.
SIDE (2 REQD.)
HOLE
BACK
PAINTED DESIGNS
HALF PATTERN

Colorful designs similar to those shown in the diagrams may be painted on the plywood shelves with poster, or show-card, colors and then protected with a coat of clear varnish

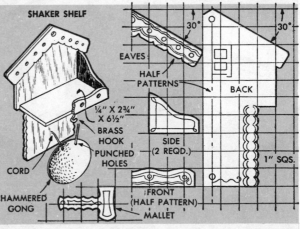

SHAKER SHELF
30°   30°
EAVES
HALF PATTERNS
BACK
¼" X 2¾" X 6½"
BRASS HOOK
PUNCHED HOLES
SIDE (2 REQD.)
1" SQS.
CORD
FRONT (HALF PATTERN)
HAMMERED GONG
MALLET

YOUR
MODERN
KITCHEN

In view above note step-saving arrangement for food preparation. Island counter acts as service counter to dining room, or as snack or breakfast bar, which may be serviced from kitchen

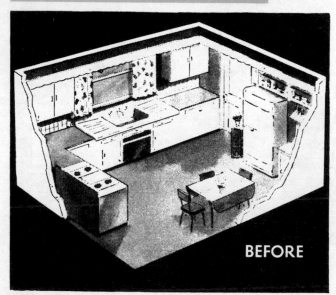

BEFORE

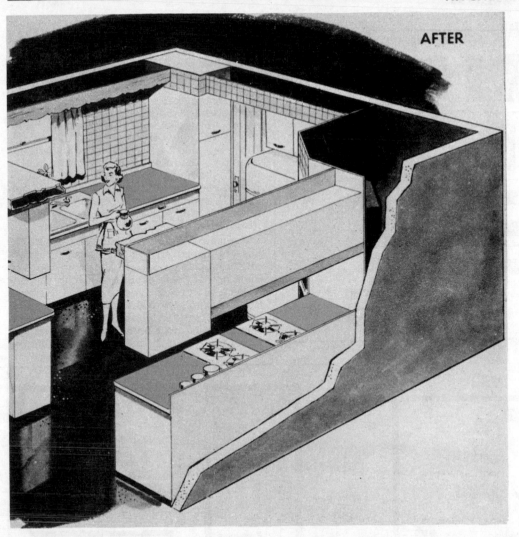

AFTER

MODERN, STREAMLINED KITCHENS are amazing improvements over those of grandmother's day, and even over those of 10 and 15 years ago. It is no wonder then, that the kitchen usually is the first room that is contemplated for major improvement. An old kitchen brought up to date with improved facilities means much less work and more pleasant surroundings. Modern equipment eliminates most of the stooping, reaching and stretching necessary in older kitchens. The biggest chore — dishwashing — now can be done automatically, and with a maximum degree of sanitation. It is only necessary to scrape off the leavings from plates and utensils, place them in a dishwashing unit, and turn on the switch. The cycles of washing, rinsing and drying follow each other without your attention.

Most older kitchens are inefficient because they are not arranged to conform with the natural sequences in which food is brought into the kitchen, stored and then prepared for consumption—a sort of production-line sequence. In such a kitchen countless steps and time are wasted. Another major fault of many older kitchens is the limited amount of storage and counter space, and the inconvenient location of dishes, utensils and supplies, which should be almost within arm's reach from the point where they are needed. Often an old kitchen can be made much more convenient by simply rearranging the existing facilities and adding more cabinet and counter space. The appearance of counters, as well as that of walls and floors, can be improved greatly by using durable, attractive coverings now available in many colors and designs.

The cost of modernizing a kitchen will vary with the number and kind of improvements installed. Where a large expenditure is made for equipment, you can make a saving by installing it yourself. You may also be able to build some of the cabinets, breakfast nook, snack bar, and other

1193

4 BASIC ARRANGEMENTS

U-SHAPED
Dead-end, U-shaped kitchens generally are the most efficient type of layout. They save many steps between, sink, range and refrigerator

L-SHAPED
This kitchen plan is next best, but household traffic may interfere with work areas in narrow rooms. This should be avoided wherever possible

CORRIDOR TYPE
Small rooms with a door at each end may require this arrangement. Often, distances between the three units are less than in L-shaped kitchen

SINGLE-WALL TYPE
Extremely narrow room may have cabinets and appliances all along one wall — least desirable arrangement

1 REFRIGERATOR   2 SINK   3 RANGE —
SEQUENCE MAY BE REVERSED

1

equipment yourself, which represents a further saving.

The first essential is good planning. After getting acquainted with the requirements of a modern kitchen, you plan to meet these in the space that you have available. Time spent in planning can eliminate many errors. Perhaps existing plumbing lines can be utilized without appreciable change. However, don't hesitate to have them extended to locations that are better suited to producing a more efficient kitchen. Added electrical outlets may also be needed. All work of extending the wiring and plumbing lines should be done prior to the installation of cabinets.

Four basic arrangements: Today's kitchens are based on the four basic arrangements shown in Fig. 1. You can approximate one of these even if the shape of your present kitchen cannot be altered. Keep in mind that in every kitchen there are three centers of activity: 1—storage, 2—preparation and cleaning, 3—cooking and serving. All of these centers include vital appliances

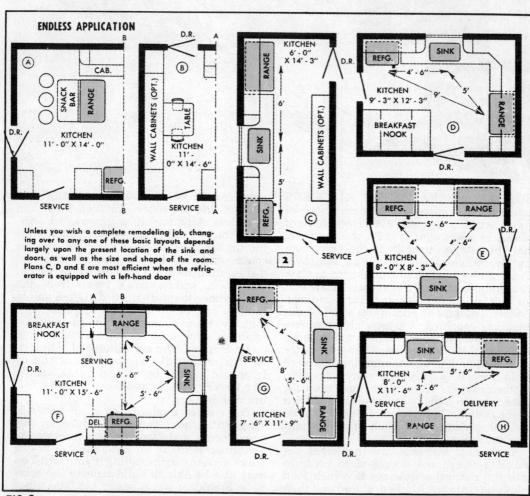

ENDLESS APPLICATION

Unless you wish a complete remodeling job, changing over to any one of these basic layouts depends largely upon the present location of the sink and doors, as well as the size and shape of the room. Plans C, D and E are most efficient when the refrigerator is equipped with a left-hand door

2

FIG. 2
1194

Many different kinds of materials are used in styling smart, modern kitchens for various effects. Walls may be of sparkling structural glass in color, or may be of beautifully grained wood for cozy, colonial effect

Youngstown Kitchens

The economy of today's average household does not include provisions for servants, but is based on the do-it-yourself idea. Accordingly, the food-preparation and food-consumption centers are brought close together

Western Pine Assn.

EVERYTHING ORDERLY AND OUT OF SIGHT

3 VEGETABLE DRAWERS

4 PULL-OUT CUTTING BOARD

5 PULL-OUT LAPBOARD

6 STORAGE COMPARTMENTS IN DRAWERS

7 CABINET FLOUR SIFTER

8 DISPOSAL CAN ON SINK DOOR

9 SLIDING TOWEL RACKS

10 PULL-OUT BREADBOX

and cabinets placed in a production-line sequence so that kitchen operations can proceed orderly from storage to the dining table. The line starts at the service door where food is delivered, and ends at the nearest point to where food is served. A, B and C of Fig. 11 indicate the paths of walking in a kitchen. It is important that these be as short as possible over the usual minimum of 4 ft. to save steps, especially distance B, between sink and range, where most walking is done.

By studying the typical kitchen layouts shown in Fig. 2, you'll find one that is most adaptable to the shape of your present kitchen. The new arrangement will depend largely on the location of the sink as extensive plumbing changes are expensive, although pipes can be shifted about 8 in. in either direction at small cost. A dead-end, U-shape kitchen generally is the most efficient. See Plan F of Fig. 2. Two alternate arrangements of one end are shown at A and B. If the room is less than 11 ft. wide, the two wall cabinets on the same wall as the window are eliminated and the width of base cabinets along this wall is reduced. Then the plan will fit an 8 or 9-ft. kitchen width but the alternate arrangements at A and B may not be possible. If your kitchen is 4 or 5 ft. shorter than the plan shown

at F, the breakfast space may have to be sacrificed.

Storage center: Counter space of at least 18 x 24 in. should be provided next to the refrigerator on the side where the door opens. This is for deliveries as well as for food to be removed from or returned to the refrigerator. Cabinet storage space

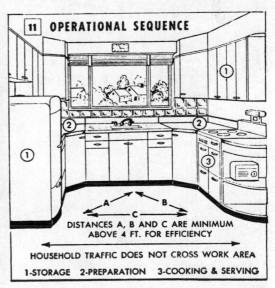

11 OPERATIONAL SEQUENCE

DISTANCES A, B AND C ARE MINIMUM ABOVE 4 FT. FOR EFFICIENCY

HOUSEHOLD TRAFFIC DOES NOT CROSS WORK AREA

1-STORAGE   2-PREPARATION   3-COOKING & SERVING

12

should be within arm's reach of this coun - er. If you have a home freezer cabinet, it should be placed next to the refrigerator if space permits. For vegetables and fruits, a near-by base cabinet should contain a tier of easy-sliding, ventilated drawers, Fig. 3. Flour, sugar, etc., can be kept in a drawer having metal containers as in Fig. 6. Or, you may prefer to keep flour in a sifter that slides into a wall cabinet as in Fig. 7. Some cereals and condiments may be kept in wall cabinets most convenient to points where food is prepared. Always keep in mind that supplies should be stored close at hand where they are first used.

Preparation and cleaning center: This includes counter space of not less than 24x36 in. at one or both ends of the sink. For cutting, you can install a slide-out hardwood leaf, Fig. 4, or a slide-out lapboard, 26 to 28 in. above the floor, for working in a seated position as in Fig. 5. Processing equipment is stored in drawers or on shelves of base cabinets along the preparation counter. Counter space where dishes are stacked for washing should not be less than 24x36 in. This may be the same counter used for food preparation. It will be on your right when facing the sink if you wash dishes, from stacking to storing, in a right-to-left sequence. Then the cabinets where dishes are stored should be at your left, so they can be dried and put into the cupboard. Cutlery goes into partitioned drawers near by, and cooking utensils preferably on easy-sliding shelves or drawers in base cabinets. Dishwashing equipment is stored under the sink and this space may include one or more sliding towel racks as in Fig. 9. Convenient disposal cans may be fitted on the sink-cabinet doors as in Fig. 8—one provided with a waxed-paper

KITCHEN STORAGE SPACE AND COUNTER REQUIREMENTS	1 bedroom (2 adults)	2 bedrooms (3 adults)	3 bedrooms (4 adults)	4 bedrooms (5 adults)	5 bedrooms (6 adults)
13					
Wall-cabinet shelf area (sq. ft.)	24	30	36	42	48
Base-cabinet drawer capacity (cu. ft.)	36	45	54	63	72
Counter area (sq. ft.)	16	20	24	28	32
Refrigerator capacity (cu. ft.)	5	6-8	6-8	8-12	8-12

This table based on usual occupancy of residence with provisions for moderate entertaining. Storage space is influenced also by frequency of food deliveries and unusual volume of entertaining, not included in these figures.
Data reproduced by courtesy of General Electric Co.

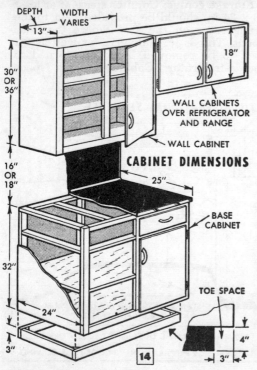

DEPTH — WIDTH VARIES — 13"
30" OR 36"
18"
WALL CABINETS OVER REFRIGERATOR AND RANGE
WALL CABINET
16" OR 18"
25"
BASE CABINET
CABINET DIMENSIONS
32"
24"
TOE SPACE
3"
4"
3"
14

15 SIZES AVAILABLE IN READY-MADE WOOD AND STEEL CABINETS (dimensions in inches)			
TYPE CABINET	WIDTHS	HEIGHT	DEPTH
Wall	15, 18, 21 24, 27, 30 36, 42	18, 30, 36	12, 13
Base	15, 18, 21 24, 27, 30 36, 42, 48	36	24 to 24¾
Counter			25 to 27
Corner wall units	24 and 26 on each wall	30, 36	13
Corner base units	29 and 36 on each wall	36	24 to 24¾
Sink units	18, 21, 24, 30 36, 42, 48, 54 60, 66, 72, 84	36	24 to 24¾
Utility	18, 21	84	13, 18, 21, 24, 24¾

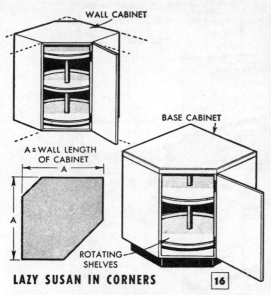

WALL CABINET

BASE CABINET

A = WALL LENGTH OF CABINET

A

A

ROTATING SHELVES

LAZY SUSAN IN CORNERS

16

17

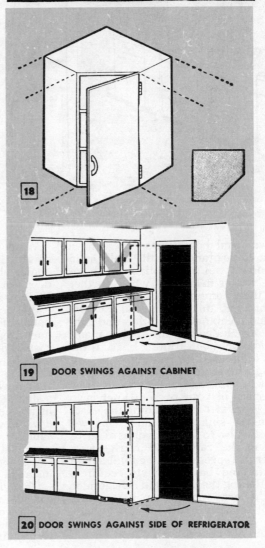

18

19   DOOR SWINGS AGAINST CABINET

20   DOOR SWINGS AGAINST SIDE OF REFRIGERATOR

bag to catch refuse, and the other for empty cans, jars and bottles. If you go beyond the manual dishwashing stage, you'll install an electric dishwasher and perhaps also a motorized disposal unit.

Cooking center: The cooking range should be located conveniently near the dining-room door, breakfast nook or both. A counter not smaller than 24x24 in. should be placed next to the range to facilitate transferring cooked food to serving dishes. Base cabinets near the range can hold some of the heavy cooking utensils. Bread and bakery goods are kept near the range in a special metal-lined drawer similar to the one in the drawing in Fig. 10.

Planning center is optional: If space permits, you can have a planning center. A drop-leaf table 30 in. high and a stool or chair that slides under it are provided as in Fig. 12. An open wall shelf holds a small radio and cookbooks so that the table can be pulled out into the room and used for other purposes. A shallow drawer keeps pads, pencils and bills out of sight.

Figuring storage space: When planning a new kitchen, first determine the storage and counter space needed. This varies with the size of the house and the family (see Fig. 13). Compare your figures with the measurements of base and wall cabinets given in Figs. 14 and 15 so that you can work out cabinet and counter dimensions to suit. Ready-made wooden and steel cabinets are available in the sizes given in Fig. 15. If the kitchen is larger than needed, only part of it may be required, leaving space for a breakfast nook or snack bar as suggested in Fig. 2, plans A, B, D and F. Corner space can be utilized to best advantage by using corner cabinets, available

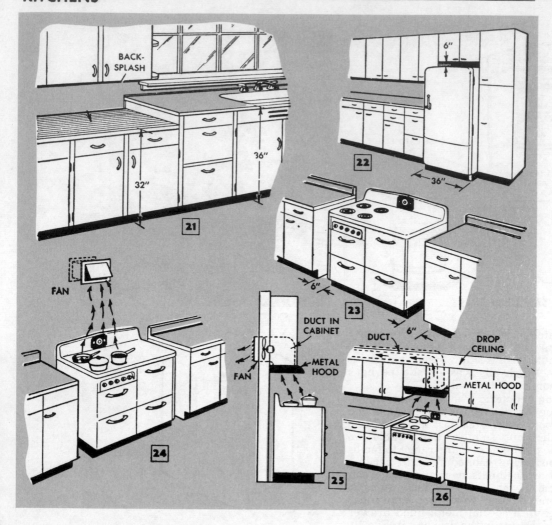

in both wall and base types. These have doors at a 45-deg. angle to the walls as in Fig. 18. Some types are available with rotating shelves, as in Fig. 16, which further increases their convenience. A utility cabinet for brooms, dust mops and vacuum cleaner, and a cabinet for clothes and rubbers, can be included in your kitchen plans. Also include a built-in ironing board if the kitchen is to be used for ironing.

Planning with scale models: An excellent method of crystallizing a plan is to draw the floor space of your present kitchen to scale, say ½ in. to 1 ft., including the exact position of the sink, doors and windows. Then cut out, also to scale, cardboard strips representing the range and refrigerator, and two strips representing the total length of the wall and base cabinets required. After positioning the range and refrigerator at the right locations, cut up the cabinet strips to fit between and adjacent to them. Clearance between counters facing each other should not be less than 4 ft.

Windows and doors: Sometimes, for best results, it may be advisable to have a carpenter change the location of a window or door—or just the direction the door swings. Windows in frame houses are easier and less expensive to change than those in brick houses. For adequate illumination, the window area of a kitchen should not be less than 20 percent of the floor area. One counter at least, preferably the preparation and cleaning counter, should be well lighted from a window. Most women prefer to have a sink at a window but this is not essential in a well-planned, efficient kitchen. Windows never should be "boxed in" by wall cabinets. A much better appearance results when cabinets are spaced about 9 in. from the window edges and rounded shelves are installed as shown in Fig. 17.

Changing the position of a door entails considerable mess. A door should not swing into a work area or interfere with the use of cabinets and appliances as in Fig. 19. Nor should a door swing against an open

Modernized, streamlined kitchens are great improvements over those of grandmother's day; an old kitchen brought up to date with improved facilities means much less work and more pleasant surroundings to work in

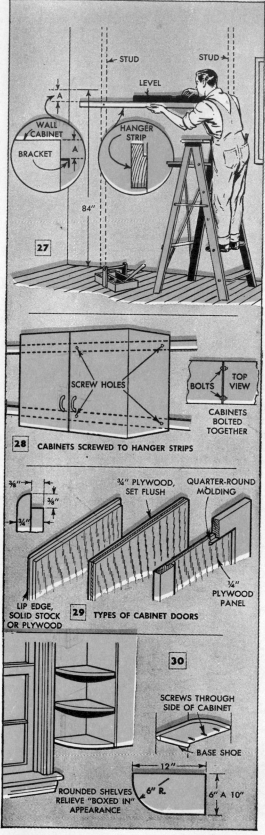

CABINETS BOLTED TOGETHER

28 CABINETS SCREWED TO HANGER STRIPS

LIP EDGE, SOLID STOCK OR PLYWOOD

29 TYPES OF CABINET DOORS

ROUNDED SHELVES RELIEVE "BOXED IN" APPEARANCE

Illustration courtesy A. J. Lindemann & Hoverson Co.

Wall or cabinet oven has an infra-red ray broiling unit, a stainless-steel front and automatic controls

wall which should be used for a necessary cabinet. A door may swing against the end of a cabinet or appliance as in Fig. 20. Two doors are preferred to three, especially in small kitchens. If possible, they should be located so that household traffic will not cross kitchen work areas, as indicated by the arrow in Fig. 11 and also in the floor plans A, B and F in Fig. 2.

Cabinet heights, clearances, spacing: Base cabinets should have toe space 4 in. high and 3 in. deep to facilitate working at counters without leaning. Standard height of base cabinets is 36 in. although the food-preparation counter, or part of it, may be lower to suit the user. A 32-in. height here suits the average woman. Glued-up hardwood tops are available as shown in Fig. 21. There should be a clearance of 15 to 18 in. between counters and wall cabinets.

Wall space over sinks and counters should be protected with a backsplash, Fig. 21, not less than 4 in. high and preferably extending from the counter to the wall cabinets. When planning cabinets, a space 36 in. wide generally is allowed for a refrigerator, with a 6-in. clearance above it, Fig. 22. Most kitchen ranges are of the 36 or 39-in. size. Normally, a 42-in. space is allowed to accommodate them but if the range is set between cabinets, or a cabinet and a wall, this allowance is not enough to permit cleaning the sides of the range. A 6-in. space at each end as shown in Fig. 23 is better. A 30-in. wall cabinet may be set over an electric range with the usual 18-in. clearance. Gas ranges, however, require at least a 30-in. clearance because of their greater fire hazard. This still permits the use of 18-in. wall cabinets over them, if necessary, but none at all is preferable.

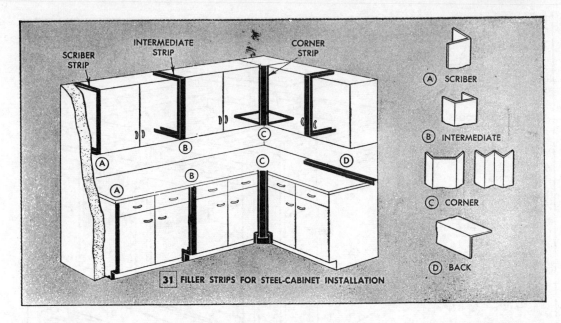

SCRIBER STRIP

INTERMEDIATE STRIP

CORNER STRIP

(A) SCRIBER

(B) INTERMEDIATE

(C) CORNER

(D) BACK

31 FILLER STRIPS FOR STEEL-CABINET INSTALLATION

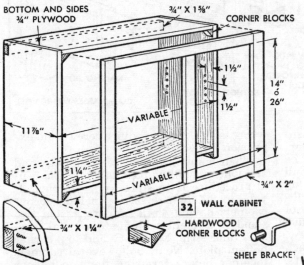

BOTTOM AND SIDES ¾" PLYWOOD

¾" X 1⅝"

CORNER BLOCKS

1½"

14" or 26"

1½"

VARIABLE

11⅞"

1¼"

VARIABLE

¾" X 2"

¾" X 1¼"

HARDWOOD CORNER BLOCKS

SHELF BRACKET

32 WALL CABINET

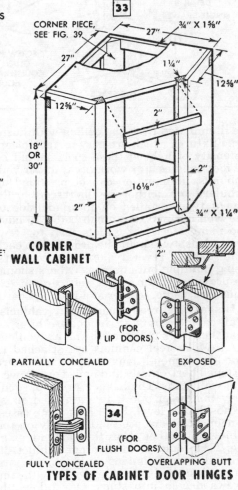

33

CORNER PIECE, SEE FIG. 39

¾" X 1⅝"

27"

27"

1¼"

12⅝"

12⅝"

2"

18" OR 30"

16⅛"

2"

2"

¾" X 1¼"

2"

CORNER WALL CABINET

PARTIALLY CONCEALED

(FOR LIP DOORS)

EXPOSED

FULLY CONCEALED

34 (FOR FLUSH DOORS)

OVERLAPPING BUTT

TYPES OF CABINET DOOR HINGES

Kitchen ventilation: An exhaust fan gives a complete change of air in a few minutes to eliminate cooking odors, excess heat and humidity. Air exhausted by the fan is automatically replaced by fresh air drawn in through an open window, or air coming from other rooms. Often an exhaust fan is located over a service door. However, if the range is against an outside wall, a better place for the fan is directly above the range as in Fig. 24. Two other arrangements are shown in Figs. 25 and 26. Prefabricated hoods equipped with exhaust fans are available in various sizes.

Lighting fixtures: It's advisable to have a center ceiling light for general illumination of 10 foot-candles. A control switch should be located at each important entrance. Sink, range and breakfast table can

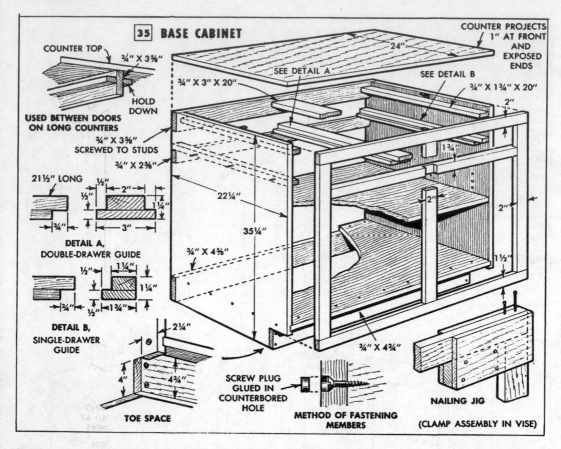

35 BASE CABINET

COUNTER TOP

¾" X 3⅝"

HOLD DOWN

USED BETWEEN DOORS ON LONG COUNTERS

¾" X 3⅝" SCREWED TO STUDS

¾" X 2⅝"

21½" LONG

DETAIL A, DOUBLE-DRAWER GUIDE

DETAIL B, SINGLE-DRAWER GUIDE

TOE SPACE

SCREW PLUG GLUED IN COUNTERBORED HOLE

METHOD OF FASTENING MEMBERS

SEE DETAIL A

SEE DETAIL B

COUNTER PROJECTS 1" AT FRONT AND EXPOSED ENDS

24"

¾" X 3" X 20"

¾" X 1¾" X 20"

22¼"

35¼"

¾" X 4⅝"

¾" X 4¾"

NAILING JIG

(CLAMP ASSEMBLY IN VISE)

be illuminated from the ceiling with flush-type fixtures which are easy to keep clean. Intensity of light at these spots should be 40 foot-candles. For work areas under wall cabinets, illumination can be provided by tubular lamps, either the fluorescent or filament type installed on the underside of the wall cabinets. It's much better to have too many electrical outlets than too few, and at least two should be provided on each wall. Locate several along the counters, using multiple outlet strips. Others should be provided at the range, refrigerator, exhaust fan, radio, toaster and ironing board.

Installing ready-made wall cabinets: Wall cabinets of 30-in. height are hung so that their tops will come 84 in. above floor level. Most steel cabinets are attached to wooden or metal hanger strips which are fastened horizontally and nailed or screwed into wall studs. The hanger strips, particularly the upper one if two are used, must be absolutely level, Fig. 27. In some cases, hanger strips are used individually on the cabinets; in other cases they extend, as in Fig. 28, to hold more than one cabinet. In still other installations, the cabinets are screwed directly to the walls with the screws driven into studs. On hollow tile walls, toggle bolts are used for fastening,

whereas brick walls require screws and expansion sleeves.

When hanging metal wall cabinets, and also when installing base cabinets, the usual procedure is to start from a corner. If your installation does not include corner cabinets having 45-deg. doors, fasten two standard straight cabinets to a metal "corner" filler strip, Fig. 31, C, and to a corner bottom plate. Next, bolt, several cabinets together before screwing them to hanger strips or wall. Steel cabinets are sometimes provided with removable knockouts for bolts used to fasten the cabinets together. If not, holes must be drilled. Wooden cabinets generally are fastened together with screws. Before screwing the cabinets permanently, check with a level to see that the front and sides are plumb. Often it is necessary to use shims behind the cabinets where plastered walls are uneven.

Avoid locating a refrigerator next to a corner wall cabinet as it will interfere with opening the cabinet door. Avoid having a cabinet butt tightly against an end wall, as this would interfere with the operation of doors. This also applies to base cabinets. The needed clearance space between cabinet and wall is concealed by using a "scriber" filler strip, Fig. 31, A. If the wall is

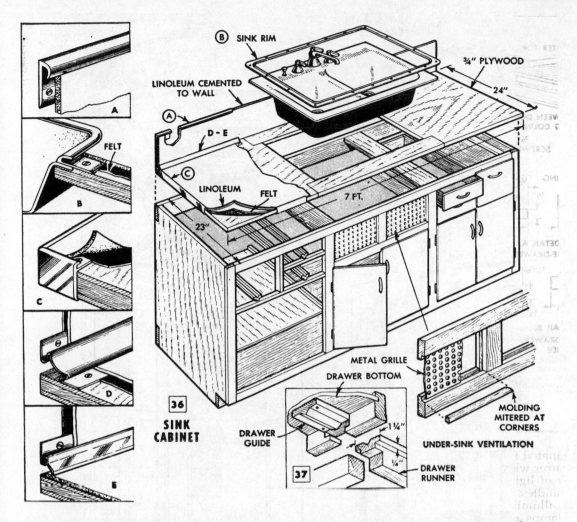

uneven, the strip is held in position, scribed to conform to the wall surface and then cut accordingly with tin shears and fastened in place. On metal wall cabinets having sides that do not conceal the hanger strips, "back" filler strips, Fig. 31, D, are added for concealment. A spacing of 6 to 10 in. is recommended between wall cabinets and windows where rounded shelves, Fig. 30, are used. When it is necessary to fill a gap of a few inches between cabinets to stretch them, an "intermediate" filler strip, Fig. 31, B, is used. These strips come in various widths.

Base cabinets and counters: Installation of base cabinets is started at corners the same as with wall cabinets. If the corner space is not to be used, two straight-type cabinets can be butted together at right angles and a corner filler strip added at the front. Then a counter support cleat is nailed or screwed to the wall studs. Corner space can be utilized with special cabinets having parallel-to-wall or 45-deg. fronts, in which case no corner strips are needed.

The cabinets are fastened together, shimmed with wooden wedges to get them perfectly level on uneven floors, then screwed to wall studs. A base shoe will hide the exposed crack where the cabinet is raised above the floor.

A base-cabinet assembly also can be "stretched" to desired length by either inserting a narrow tray cabinet or else using one or more "intermediate" filler strips between the cabinets. A single counter can extend over the entire assembly although, in some packaged units, individual cabinet counters are provided. Where counters butt against sinks, wedge-shaped filler strips coated with sealing compound assure waterproof joints. Backsplash on sinks and counters may be integral with them, may be attached as separate units, or may be provided by covering wall with linoleum.

Building your own: Cabinet construction is simplest if ¾-in., 7-ply plywood is used together with solid stock lumber. White pine is good, and so is birch or gum. Thin plywood or hardboard requires additional

1205

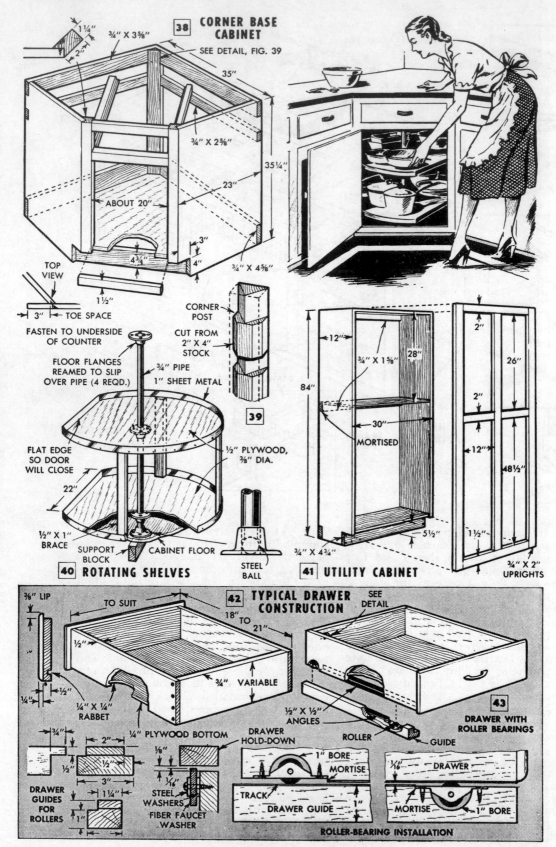

38 **CORNER BASE CABINET**

SEE DETAIL, FIG. 39

1¼"

¾" X 3⅝"

2"

35"

¾" X 2⅝"

35¼"

23"

ABOUT 20"

3"

4¾"

4"

¾" X 4⅝"

TOP VIEW

1½"

3" — TOE SPACE

CORNER POST

CUT FROM 2" X 4" STOCK

39

FASTEN TO UNDERSIDE OF COUNTER

FLOOR FLANGES REAMED TO SLIP OVER PIPE (4 REQD.)

¾" PIPE

1" SHEET METAL

FLAT EDGE SO DOOR WILL CLOSE

22"

½" PLYWOOD, ⅜" DIA.

½" X 1" BRACE

SUPPORT BLOCK

CABINET FLOOR

STEEL BALL

40 **ROTATING SHELVES**

41 **UTILITY CABINET**

12"

84"

¾" X 1⅝"

28"

30"

MORTISED

5½"

¾" X 4¾"

2"

26"

2"

12"

48½"

1½"

¾" X 2" UPRIGHTS

42 **TYPICAL DRAWER CONSTRUCTION**

SEE DETAIL

⅜" LIP

TO SUIT

18" TO 21"

½"

¾" VARIABLE

¼"

½"

¼" X ¼" RABBET

¼" PLYWOOD BOTTOM

½" X ½" ANGLES

ROLLER

GUIDE

43 **DRAWER WITH ROLLER BEARINGS**

¾"

2"

½"

3"

1¼"

DRAWER GUIDES FOR ROLLERS

1"

⅛"

1/16"

STEEL WASHERS

FIBER FAUCET WASHER

DRAWER HOLD-DOWN

1" BORE

MORTISE

TRACK

DRAWER GUIDE

1"

1/16"

DRAWER

MORTISE

1" BORE

ROLLER-BEARING INSTALLATION

framework and entails considerable joinery. Simple screwed or nailed joints, coated with glue where possible, give adequate strength, although dowels produce stronger joints where narrow stock is butted together. Flat-headed screws are concealed in holes counterbored and drilled for the screw body. A pilot hole should be drilled for the thread portion of the screw, and the screw coated with soap for easy driving. Plugs, cut from dowels that fit the holes tightly, are glue-coated and driven to come flush with the surface. Crack filling, sanding and painting will conceal them entirely.

Making wall cabinets: The top, bottom and sides of wall cabinets, Fig. 32, are 11⅞ in. wide to get four widths, including waste for saw cuts, out of a standard 48-in. plywood panel. Before assembling, the inner faces of the side members are drilled for shelf brackets. Note that the front framework is made separately of solid stock and fastened with glue and 6 or 7d finishing nails. Butt joints of narrow stock can be assembled flush at the sides with the nailing jig shown in Fig. 35, using a C-clamp to hold the joining pieces together tightly. Then two 10d finishing nails are driven in, slightly toed toward each other, and the heads are sunk about ½ in. deep with a nail set. For extra rigidity, hardwood corner blocks are glued and screwed in place. When cabinets extend to the ceiling, the portion above the 84-in. height should have separate doors.

In the corner wall cabinet shown in Fig. 33, the sidepieces of the doorframe are hardwood, rabbeted, glued and screwed to the side panels. Corner posts for wall and base cabinets are made as shown in Fig. 39. Top and bottom of the cabinet extend 1 in. into the doorframe so that ¾-in. inserts will fit flush with the front.

Rounded shelves to flank windows are detailed in Fig. 30 Three types of modern cabinet doors are shown in Fig. 29 and five types of hinges are shown in Fig. 34. In fitting the doors, allow ⅟₁₆ in. all around the opening for clearance.

Construction of base cabinets: Baseboards are removed for installing base cabinets detailed in Figs. 35 and 38. Toe space should be 4 in. high and 3 in. deep. If desired, the cabinet floor may be set into ⅛-in. grooves in the sides for added rigidity, the floor being glued and screwed through the sides. As with wall cabinets, the front framework is made separately and, after it is attached, the drawer guides, hold-downs and counter-support crosspieces are installed. An alternate arrangement for drawer guides, using a single V-shaped guide for each drawer, is shown in Fig. 37. For ventilation under a sink, metal grilles are advised, and counters can be screwed

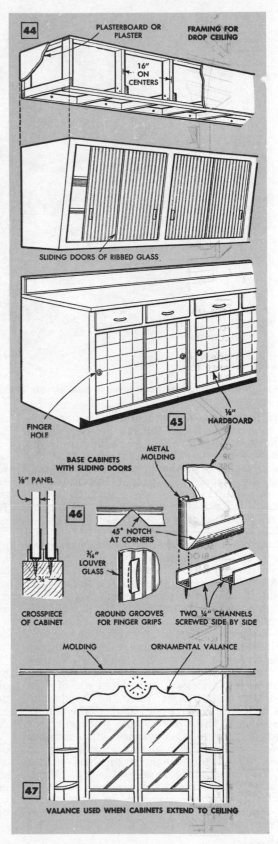

44 PLASTERBOARD OR PLASTER — FRAMING FOR DROP CEILING — 16" ON CENTERS

SLIDING DOORS OF RIBBED GLASS

45 — ½" HARDBOARD

FINGER HOLE

BASE CABINETS WITH SLIDING DOORS

METAL MOLDING

⅛" PANEL

46 — 45° NOTCH AT CORNERS — ¾₆" LOUVER GLASS

¾"

CROSSPIECE OF CABINET — GROUND GROOVES FOR FINGER GRIPS — TWO ¼" CHANNELS SCREWED SIDE BY SIDE

MOLDING — ORNAMENTAL VALANCE

47 — VALANCE USED WHEN CABINETS EXTEND TO CEILING

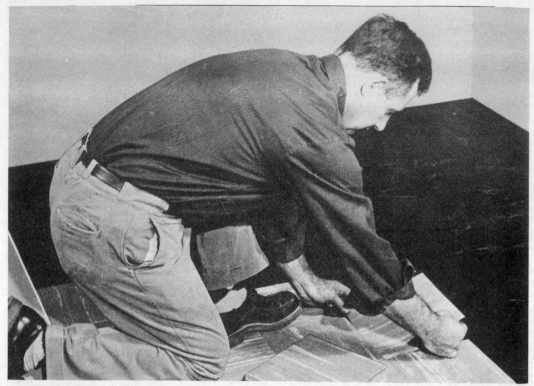

Armstrong Cork Company

An attractive linoleum floor covering will set off kitchen cabinets to good advantage and is easily laid

to the base units by using angle brackets.

As corner base cabinets, Fig. 38, are too large to pass through doors, they must be assembled in the kitchen. Note that the doorframe is similar in construction to that of the corner wall cabinet. Rotating-shelf units, called Lazy Susans, Fig. 40, are labor-savers. Floor flanges, reamed out to slip over ¾-in. pipe, serve as bearings. A steel ball carries the weight. Three or four braces between the shelves and a block under the cabinet floor are required.

Drawer construction is shown in Fig. 42. A clearance of 1/16 in. at the top and at each side of a drawer prevents binding. Utility cabinets usually extend to the top of wall cabinets. Fig. 41 shows construction.

Roller bearings for drawers: For easy-action drawers, you can use rollers and tracks as shown in Fig. 43. One roller is recessed in each side of a drawer at the back, and another is recessed in the front end of each guide. The guides must be hardwood. Tracks are ½-in. metal angles. The rollers project slightly beyond the track surfaces for clearance. Fiber washers at the drawer tops are arranged to rotate on screws to minimize friction against the hold-downs.

Covering counters and table tops: Materials used for this purpose include linoleum, plastics and ceramic tile. In some states building codes specify what to use. Linoleum is laid over felt, Fig. 36, both the felt

and linoleum being cemented with water-proof cement.

To apply sheet plastic, you spread special adhesive on the clean, dry counter or table top, and also on the underside of the plastic sheet. Let the adhesive air-dry from 40 min. to 2 hrs. The temperature should be 70 deg. F. Test the cement for dryness by pressing a piece of heavy wrapping paper on the surface. It should pull free without picking up any of the cement. Then place a piece of wrapping paper over the cement, and lay the plastic sheet, already cut to exact size, over this. (The plastic can be cut with a fine-tooth saw held at a low angle to prevent chipping along the edges.) Then pull out the paper and press plastic down into firm contact with counter. See detailed instructions on page 1210.

A variety of moldings in anodized aluminum, stainless steel and plastic can be obtained for installation at edges and corners of counter-covering materials. Types of moldings are shown in Fig. 36, details A to E.

Sliding cabinet doors: To make sliding doors of ⅛-in. tempered hardboard, you cement panels of this material in stainless-steel channels as shown in Fig. 46. By making 45-deg. cutouts, the stock can be brought around corners neatly. Metal channels of large size serve as slides. Bezels frame the finger-grip holes. Sliding doors

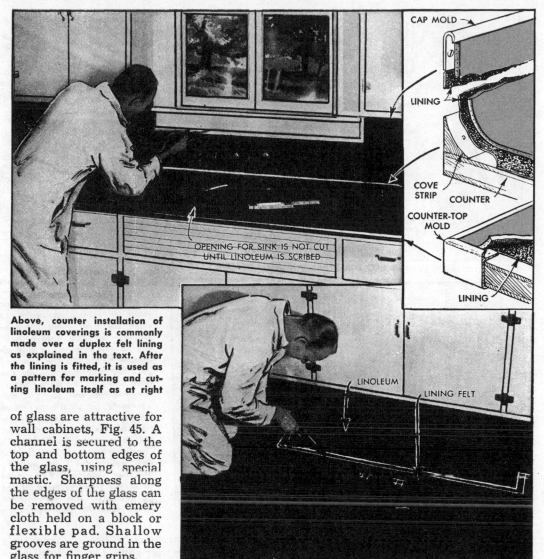

CAP MOLD

LINING

COVE STRIP

COUNTER

COUNTER-TOP MOLD

LINING

OPENING FOR SINK IS NOT CUT UNTIL LINOLEUM IS SCRIBED

LINOLEUM

LINING FELT

Above, counter installation of linoleum coverings is commonly made over a duplex felt lining as explained in the text. After the lining is fitted, it is used as a pattern for marking and cutting linoleum itself as at right

of glass are attractive for wall cabinets, Fig. 45. A channel is secured to the top and bottom edges of the glass, using special mastic. Sharpness along the edges of the glass can be removed with emery cloth held on a block or flexible pad. Shallow grooves are ground in the glass for finger grips.

Valances and drop ceilings: When cabinets extend to a ceiling on either side of a window, a valance as in Fig. 47, greatly improves the appearance. A drop ceiling or soffit, to close the waste space over wall cabinets, should be installed before the cabinets are put in place. The framework, Fig. 44, is nailed to ceiling joists and wall studs.

Counter tops: Covering the counter tops of cabinets calls for the best-quality linoleum and careful workmanship. It's common practice to lay the linoleum top over a felt liner, which provides not only a good cementing base but also a template for cutting the linoleum accurately. Start the job by installing all metal trim. Then, if the linoleum is to extend up the wall to provide a splash back, apply a flexible plastic cove strip in the corner between the counter top and the wall. Next, fit a length of liner felt

½ in. short at the corners, edges and metal trim. Do not cut out for the sink well; this will be taken care of later. After rough-cutting the felt, fasten it securely with thumbtacks so that it will not move during the scribing operation which is to follow. Be sure that the felt is pushed tightly against the cove strip. Set the scriber (dividers) to approximately a 1-in. opening and scribe up to all edges except the sink well and the front edge of the cabinet. Now, remove the felt and spread it over the linoleum. Tape it in place to prevent movement. Then, with the same divider setting, retrace all scribed lines to transfer the outline to the linoleum. Next, place the felt back on the counter top and fit it carefully to the flanged metal trim. Then cement in place using a moistureproof cement. Cut the lino-

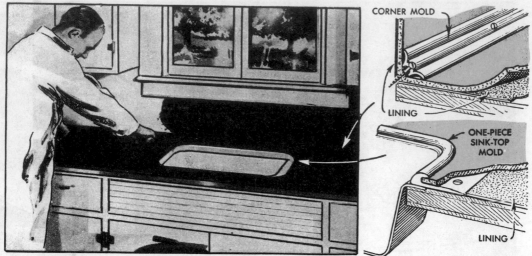

CORNER MOLD

LINING

ONE-PIECE SINK-TOP MOLD

LINING

DAMPPROOF CEMENT IS USED FOR BOTH LINING AND LINOLEUM

THE LINOLEUM IS UNDERSCRIBED TO FIT THE SINK MOLDING

The upper detail above shows an alternate back-corner treatment for linoleum counter tops which is somewhat easier to work out than using the continuous top and splash back over a corner cove. In this alternate treatment, the top and back are applied separately, the back being butted to the top in a right-angle butt joint. A corner mold of plastic or metal finishes the joint. The lower detail above shows the fitting of the covering to the sink well. The linoleum is cut out for the sink well about 1 in. oversize and then underscribed to a neat fit in the sink-top molding (as at the left). The underscriber saves time in this operation

leum to the scribed lines, spread moisture-proof cement over the felt and roll the linoleum in place. Make certain of a good contact over the cove strip in the corner. Go over the entire linoleum surface with a rolling pin to assure perfect contact. Underscribe the overhanging front edge and roll it down last. Cut out the sink well with a sharp knife about 1 in. oversize. Then underscribe to a neat fit in the sink-top molding. For this particular work the underscriber saves a lot of time where neatness is so essential. Finish all counter tops with paste wax rubbed to a high polish.

Other coverings: Other counter coverings besides linoleum are of course available, the most popular of which are the plastic laminates. These are as easily installed as linoleum. Begin by removing the old material from the counter and scraping or sanding it clean and dry. Then, cut the laminate to the exact size of the counter top, sawing at a low angle with a fine-toothed saw to avoid chipping the edges.

For long straight cuts, use a carpenter's saw. For irregular shapes and where convenient, use a coping saw. Use cellulose tape or masking tape to hold the trimmed sheet of laminate in place while making the sink cut-out. You can make a rough cut-out first, sawing at least two inches away from the line of the final cut with a keyhole saw. Then make the final cut with a coping saw. To apply the bonding cement, pour it on the under side of the sheet of laminate and spread evenly. Work at a temperature of not less than 70 degrees with most cements and allow to air-dry for not less than 40 minutes nor more than 2 hours. (Instruction sheets and special spreaders are supplied with many laminate kits.) Test the cement for proper dryness by pressing a piece of wrapping paper on the surface. The paper should pull free without picking up any of the cement. Then place lightly on the counter a piece of wrapping paper large enough to cover it completely. Slide the laminate into place over the paper and

Alsynite Company of America

Armstrong Cork Company

1211

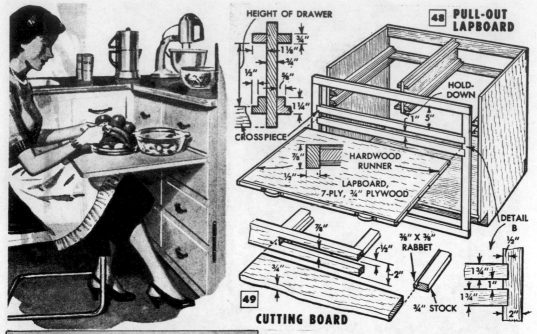

48 PULL-OUT LAPBOARD

HEIGHT OF DRAWER

¾"
1⅛"
¾"
½"
⅝"
1¼"

CROSS PIECE

HOLD-DOWN

1" 5"

⅞"
½"
HARDWOOD RUNNER

LAPBOARD, 7-PLY, ¾" PLYWOOD

DETAIL B
½"

49 CUTTING BOARD

⅞"
½"
¾"
2"

⅜" X ⅜" RABBET

¾" STOCK

1¾"
1"
1¾"
2"

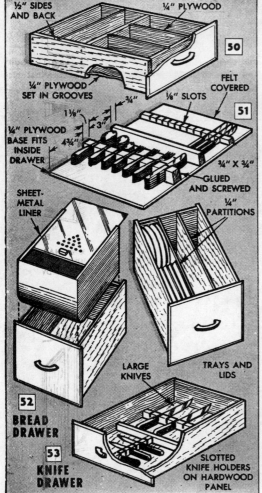

50
½" SIDES AND BACK
¼" PLYWOOD
¼" PLYWOOD SET IN GROOVES
¼" PLYWOOD BASE FITS INSIDE DRAWER

51
FELT COVERED
⅛" SLOTS
¾"
1⅛"
3"
4¾"
¾" X ¾"
GLUED AND SCREWED
¼" PARTITIONS

SHEET-METAL LINER

52 BREAD DRAWER

LARGE KNIVES
TRAYS AND LIDS

53 KNIFE DRAWER
SLOTTED KNIFE HOLDERS ON HARDWOOD PANEL

align it in perfect position. Now raise the sheet of plastic laminate and withdraw the paper 2 or 3 in. Where the paper has been withdrawn, press the laminate firmly into place. Then withdraw the paper completely and roll down the entire surface of the counter top with heavy pressure, covering every square inch. A rolling pin will serve for this job but a hand roller of narrower width will provide more concentrated pressure. (If use of the wrapping paper "slip sheet" is impossible, hold the plastic laminate sheet at a 45-deg. angle to the surface of the counter top, register it accurately, then lay it down into position and roll. Care in alignment is vitally important as most cements supplied with the laminates bond on contact and shifting to correct errors is difficult.) Areas not accessible with a roller should be tapped down. Place a smooth block of wood on the laminate and tap with a hammer. Finish by installing moldings.

Kitchen conveniences: There are many minor yet important things that you can do to get extra convenience and efficiency from your kitchen. If you don't have enough space for an extra table, the pull-out lapboard shown in Fig. 48 may be just the thing you need. Located right under two top drawers or a single long one, the board is installed in a base cabinet 26 to 28 in. from the floor. If you build the cabinet yourself, and you wish to include a lapboard, the cabinet front should have two crossrails instead of one, with sufficient space between them to accommodate the lapboard. Hardwood runners screwed to the ends slide on hardwood guides that are

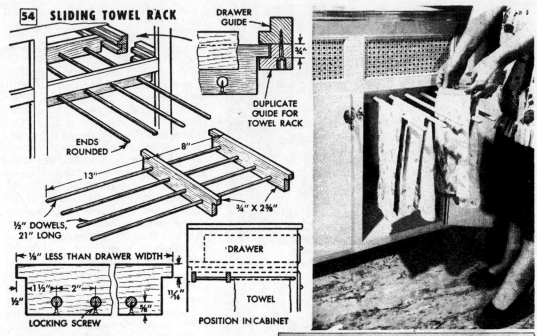

54 SLIDING TOWEL RACK

DRAWER GUIDE

DUPLICATE GUIDE FOR TOWEL RACK

ENDS ROUNDED

8"

13"

¾" X 2⅝"

½" DOWELS, 21" LONG

⅛" LESS THAN DRAWER WIDTH

1½" 2"

½"

11/16"

⅝"

LOCKING SCREW

DRAWER

TOWEL

POSITION IN CABINET

made just like regular drawer runners and are installed below them. The runners extend ⅛ in. below the panel and a clearance of 1/16 in. above and below the runners is required to prevent the board from rubbing against or binding between the crossrails. The partition between two drawers above a lapboard should be wide enough to serve as a hold-down for the board to prevent its tipping down when pulled out. The guides and hold-downs of the drawers above the board are screwed to the partition. Note how the front crossrails are mortised into the side rails as in detail B, Fig. 49, for maximum resistance to pressure.

Drawer arrangements: Partitioned drawers, Fig. 50, are convenient for storing everyday silverware, but the felt-covered holder shown in Fig. 51 offers better protection against scratching. Blocks slotted to hold the silverware are attached to a removable panel that fits inside the drawer. The felt is glued on, even in the knife, fork and spoon slots, but on the steak-knife rack the felt is just slit down the slots with a razor blade. Carving and paring knives can be stored in drawers with less risk of getting their sharp edges nicked and with less danger of cutting fingers if they are set with their sharp edges down in slotted holders as in Fig. 53. The holders are screwed to a removable panel of plywood or hardboard.

A deep drawer can be partitioned for storage of tins and lids. The partitions are held in grooves, metal channels or between lengths of ¼-in. quarter-round molding. Fig. 52 shows a sheet-metal bread-drawer

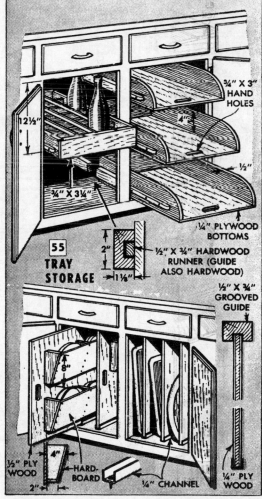

55 TRAY STORAGE

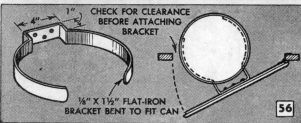

CHECK FOR CLEARANCE BEFORE ATTACHING BRACKET

⅛" X 1½" FLAT-IRON BRACKET BENT TO FIT CAN

56

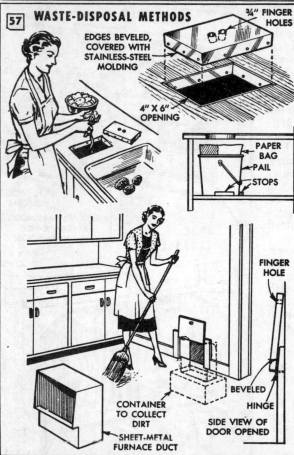

57 WASTE-DISPOSAL METHODS

¾" FINGER HOLES

EDGES BEVELED, COVERED WITH STAINLESS-STEEL MOLDING

4" X 6" OPENING

PAPER BAG

PAIL

STOPS

FINGER HOLE

BEVELED HINGE

SIDE VIEW OF DOOR OPENED

CONTAINER TO COLLECT DIRT

SHEET-METAL FURNACE DUCT

liner which can be purchased ready-made.

Sliding towel rack: Towels can be kept at hand but out of sight on a sliding towel rack in a base or sink cabinet, as in Fig. 54. The rack consists of a number of hardwood dowels fitting snugly in holes drilled in two crosspieces that slide on drawer guides. The guides of a drawer above the towel rack serve as hold-downs. In case there is no drawer above the rack, as in a sink cabinet, you will need rack guides having a U-shaped cross section. The front ends of the dowels are rounded and sandpapered smooth. Screws are driven through the crosspieces to keep the dowels in position and make the assembly rigid. Ventilation through the towel-rack compartment is highly desirable. Some manufacturers provide an electric heater and a circulating fan for towel compartments.

Other storage facilities: Vegetables and heavy cooking utensils such as skillets, and also empty beverage bottles, can be kept in orderly fashion if you provide sliding units in base cabinets as shown in Fig. 55. Hand holes are cut in the bottom of sliding shelves that have no front. For vegetables, you may prefer a drawer having a front, in which case a row of holes for air circulation should be bored in the sides near the lower edge just above the bottom. Hardwood strips on the sides of the units fit grooved hardwood guides as shown in the detail. Use of roller bearings on sliding shelves, as described earlier on page 1208, will greatly reduce friction. Divider strips on the unit for empty bottles provide individual wells for holding them.

To keep trays out of sight, set them vertically between partitions in a base cabinet as in Fig 55. The partitions may be held in channels or between molding strips. Shallow pans, lids and tins can be kept in pockets attached to vertical panels that slide in channels. The pockets can be attached to both sides of the panels. Hand holes are provided as shown.

Waste-disposal methods: One of the handiest places to hold a container to take table scraps, vegetable peelings, etc., is the cabinet door under a sink. It saves steps and avoids stooping. A simple arrangement consists of a rimmed container that can be held by a bracket bent to fit as in Fig. 56. Three screws hold the bracket to the cabinet door. Before attaching it, check for clearance when opening the door. Keep a waxed bag in the container for easy removal of contents to the outside waste can. The bag also eliminates constantly washing the container.

A somewhat similar idea is shown in the two upper details of Fig. 57. An opening is cut in a counter top to center directly over the container, which is set on a shelf below and is held in the proper position by stops nailed to the shelf. The edges of the opening are lined with stainless steel, which also is used on the edges and top surface of the hardwood-block cover. It fits flush with the counter surface and has two finger holes drilled at a slight angle toward each other. Cutting and chopping of vegetables, meat, etc., should be done on a hardwood board unless the counter itself is laminated hardwood.

Floor sweepings simply drop into a pan hung on the basement ceiling if you install a dust chute in the kitchen wall at floor level as shown in the detail below Fig. 57. Cut out the plaster, baseboard, floor boards in the partition, part of the sole plate, and a section of the basement ceiling to install a wall-register fitting of a warm-air furnace duct. Finish the job with a neat frame and provide a door, hinged at the top. By beveling the top of the frame, the door can swing back far enough to prevent it from dropping down of its own weight. A wall chute of this kind is preferable to an opening in the floor which entails accident risk.

Extra storage space: A separate shelf to store cups makes more space available for other dishes The cup shelf has a cleat at each end so that it is held by four shelf brackets which can be adjusted for height, Fig. 58. Similar narrow shelves can be used for tumblers.

Another convenience is a plate rail on a cabinet shelf, as in Fig. 59, for large serving dishes that cannot be stacked. The rail is merely a strip of wood nailed to the shelf. A long one can be located near the rear edge, and short ones at the

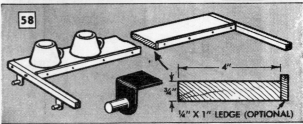

58

¼" X 1" LEDGE (OPTIONAL)

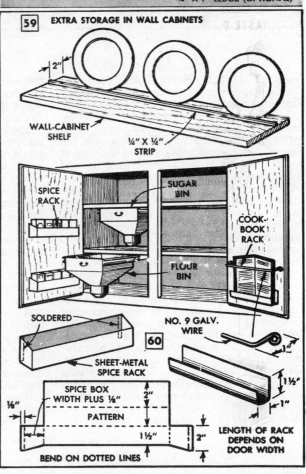

59 EXTRA STORAGE IN WALL CABINETS

2"

WALL-CABINET SHELF

¼" X ¼" STRIP

SPICE RACK

SUGAR BIN

COOK-BOOK RACK

FLOUR BIN

SOLDERED

NO. 9 GALV. WIRE

SHEET-METAL SPICE RACK

60

SPICE BOX WIDTH PLUS ⅛"

2"

⅛"

PATTERN

1½"

2"

BEND ON DOTTED LINES

1½"

1"

LENGTH OF RACK DEPENDS ON DOOR WIDTH

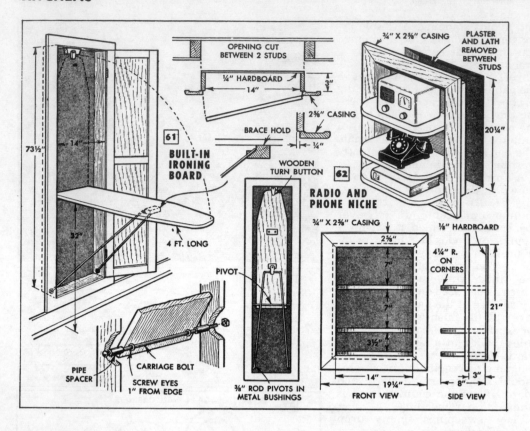

ends of a shelf. Ready-made flour and sugar dispensers can be attached to the underside of wall-cabinet shelves as in Fig. 60. This drawing also shows easily made spice-box racks which are attached to the doors between the shelf positions. Because the exact dimensions depend upon the size of spice containers commonly used in the kitchen, the drawing does not give all sizes. A piece of sheet metal is cut and bent as indicated and the tabs at the ends are soldered to the back. By the simple rack shown, recipe books can be held in open position on the inside of a cabinet door, where they are out of the way and not apt to be soiled, yet easily read while at work.

Built-in ironing board: You can purchase a ready-made cabinet-type ironing board or you can build one as shown in Fig. 61. It fits above the baseboard to avoid removing or cutting the board. Cut plaster from the wall between two studs at the most convenient location and then install the cabinet, nailing it through the casing to the studs with finishing nails. The board pivots on a ⅜-in. carriage bolt slipped through large screw eyes or eyebolts installed about 1 in. in at the wide end of the board. Although a 14-in. dimension is given for

the width of the cabinet, this will vary as the distance between wall studs is not always the same. Therefore, the opening in the wall should be cut first and the cabinet made to fit. If you find the studs to be 16 in. on centers, the cabinet will have to be made narrower than indicated. In some cases, where existing studs are not located where you prefer the ironing board, it may be necessary to straddle a stud and install headers and vertical members to provide the necessary framework for the cabinet Pipe spacers on the bolt keep the board centered. After the nut is turned on, peen the ends of the thread to lock the nut in place. Allow just enough clearance to permit the board to be raised and lowered without rubbing against the back of the cabinet.

A wooden turn button prevents the raised board from falling unexpectedly. A ⅜-in. steel rod, bent to a U shape as shown in the detail, provides sturdy bracing for the board when in use. The ends of the brace are bent outward to fit in metal bushings or sleeves in the cabinet sides at the bottom. The natural spring of the brace keeps the ends in place. The other end of the brace butts into a notched block on the

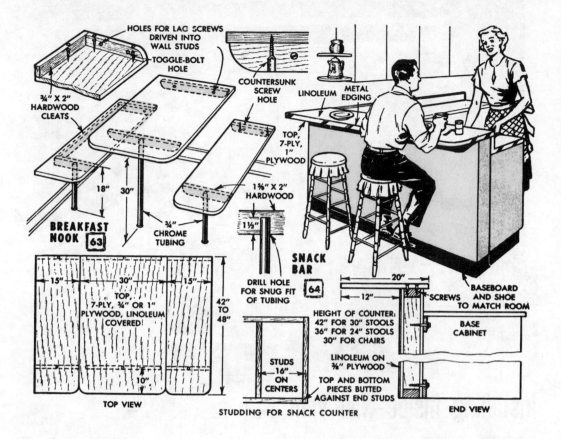

HOLES FOR LAG SCREWS DRIVEN INTO WALL STUDS

TOGGLE-BOLT HOLE

COUNTERSUNK SCREW HOLE

LINOLEUM   METAL EDGING

¾" X 2" HARDWOOD CLEATS

TOP, 7-PLY, 1" PLYWOOD

18"   30"

1⅝" X 2" HARDWOOD

BREAKFAST NOOK 63

¾" CHROME TUBING

1½"

SNACK BAR 64

DRILL HOLE FOR SNUG FIT OF TUBING

20"

12"

SCREWS

BASEBOARD AND SHOE TO MATCH ROOM

BASE CABINET

15"   30"   15"

TOP, 7-PLY, ¾" OR 1" PLYWOOD, LINOLEUM COVERED!

42" TO 48"

HEIGHT OF COUNTER: 42" FOR 30" STOOLS 36" FOR 24" STOOLS 30" FOR CHAIRS

LINOLEUM ON ⅜" PLYWOOD

STUDS 16" ON CENTERS

TOP AND BOTTOM PIECES BUTTED AGAINST END STUDS

10"

TOP VIEW

STUDDING FOR SNACK COUNTER

END VIEW

underside of the board. When not in use, a wooden turn button on the board keeps the brace from falling. An electric outlet should be provided in the inside of the cabinet at the top so that the ironing cord hangs out of the way.

Built-in radio and phone niche: Installed like the ironing-board cabinet, a wall niche as shown in Fig. 62 keeps a radio and phone out of the way, yet convenient. Install it at the right height for dialing. The shelves must extend beyond the casing to provide the necessary space and the corners are all rounded the same radius for good appearance. The niche should have an electric outlet for the radio, preferably at the top.

Breakfast nook: About the simplest construction for an attractive breakfast nook is shown in Fig. 63. Table and backless benches are cut from a single 4 x 5-ft. plywood panel. Hardwood cleats on the underside provide a means of sturdy support. The cleats used for attachment to walls are flush with the edges and are drilled for lag screws driven into wall studs. Bench cleats are attached with one lag screw and one toggle bolt as they are not wide enough to pass two studs. Where one bench fits against an end wall, a cleat is provided at

this wall edge also. A seat corner adjoining a wall is not rounded. Wider cleats located about 6 or 8 in. from the other end of table top and benches are bored centrally to take chrome legs. Since there are only three legs, floor cleaning is easy. Benches are simply enameled and the table top may be either painted or covered with linoleum.

Snack bar: Even though space is at a premium, you may still be able to install a three or four-stool snack bar. It can be attached to a wall with brackets or may extend into the room, backing against a base cabinet or range as in Fig. 64. For good support, build a wall of regular studs, including sole and top plate. Flat-headed wood screws, 3 in. long and spaced about 12 in. apart, hold the counter to the top plate. Studs are covered with plywood, and linoleum may be cemented over it on the counter side. The wall end of the counter is screwed to a cleat fastened to the wall with a lag screw and toggle bolt. The height of the counter may be varied according to the height of the stools. These, when not in use, are pushed under the counter.

Certain information courtesy Formica Co.

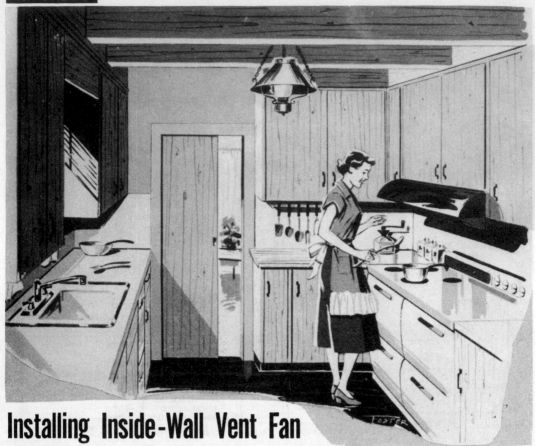

Installing Inside-Wall Vent Fan

WHEN a kitchen range is located on the inside wall of a two-story house, installing a vent fan might seem to be a problem if there is no way of running ducts up between the wall studs. Actually the installation is fairly simple, and also can add to the appearance of the kitchen. **The ducting is routed up through wall cabinets over the range, then through a false ceiling beam to the outside wall. Photographs on this and the facing page give a step-by-step description of a typical installation.** ★ ★ ★

First step in installation is to make cutouts in cabinet shelves for duct. Soffit also is opened

Next step, as shown below, is to attach vent hood, complete with fan and motor, to bottom of cabinet

Photos courtesy Western Pine Association

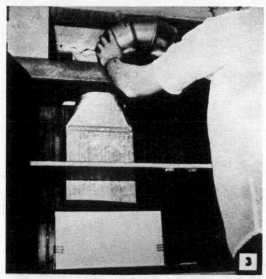

After hood is attached and ductwork run up through cabinet, right-angle elbow is installed in soffit space to route ducting horizontally across ceiling

Installation is now complete up to ceiling. Horizontal lengths of ducting now are fitted and run to opening that has been cut through outside wall

After ductwork across ceiling has been fitted and run to outside-wall opening, soffit face is cut out to accommodate ducting, then is replaced on soffit

Centered over the horizontal duct, a length of 1-in. stock is nailed to the ceiling to provide a means of supporting the "beam" to be fitted around the duct

Three sides of box that form simulated beam now are nailed around duct. Lower corners of box are mitered so assembled box will appear as solid wooden beam

Before horizontal run of ducting is installed, hole is cut through outside wall. End of duct then is protected by weatherproof louver or other device

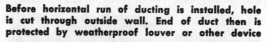

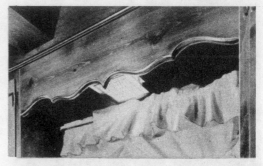

OVER-THE-SINK KITCHEN LIGHT

ANY KITCHEN remodeling plan should include adequate lighting over the sink. If an existing scroll-cut cornice under the sink soffit is deep enough, a flush light can be set in simply by installing a false ceiling behind the cornice. An opening is cut in the piece of wood used for the "ceiling" and the light is fitted into it. If the present cornice is too shallow to accept the light, it must be replaced with one of sufficient depth. First step in the operation is to hold the light in place, as in the upper left-hand photo, to determine its position. Measurements taken then are transferred to the ceiling board, and the opening is marked by using the light shell itself as a pattern, lower left-hand photo. A portable power jig or saber saw, speeds up the job of cutting the opening, lower right-hand photo, but it is only a little more work to drill holes in the four corners and cut between them with a keyhole saw. The detail shows how the ceiling board is positioned behind the cornice. Quarter-round molding can be used both to hold the ceiling in place and as a trim.

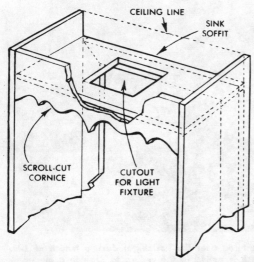

CEILING LINE

SINK SOFFIT

SCROLL-CUT CORNICE

CUTOUT FOR LIGHT FIXTURE

Detail above shows how false "ceiling" is located behind scrolled cornice to permit installing flush light. Below, light box is used to mark opening

Below, portable power saber saw makes quick work of cutting opening. Without power saw, drill holes in the corners, cut between them with keyhole saw

Photos and information courtesy Western Pine Association

Mounted on casters and with the drawer and cabinet accessible from both sides, the kitchen caddie also provides a portable work surface. When the maple top becomes scarred from use, it can be easily reversed or replaced

MATERIAL LIST

Maple

1 pc.—¾"x14½"x22½"—Top

Tempered Hardboard

2 pcs.—¼"x13½"x28"—End panels
1 pc.—¼"x15¼"x22½"—Bottom
4 pcs.—¼"x10¾"x19½"—Doors
2 pcs.—¼"x1"x18¼"—Door strips
4 pcs.—¼"x1½"x4½"—Door finger-grip backing
1 pc.—¼"x15"x19⅞"—Drawer bottom

White Pine, Basswood or Poplar

4 pcs.—¾"x3⅛"x13½"—End-frame tops and bottoms
4 pcs.—¾"x1¾"x33¼"—End-frame uprights
4 pcs.—¾"x1¼"x33¼"—Side-frame uprights
2 pcs.—¾"x1¼"x20½"—Top-frame facing strips
2 pcs.—¾"x6⅜"x20½"—Bottom side panels
2 pcs.—1¼"x1¾"x22½"—Top door slides
2 pcs.—1¾"x1¾"x22½"—Bottom door slides
2 pcs.—1¼"x2"x14½"—Top-frame ends
2 pcs.—¾"x1¾"x22½"—Top-frame sides
2 pcs.—¾"x2"x12⅞"—Drawer-frame ends
2 pcs.—¾"x1"x14½"—Side drawer guides
2 pcs.—¾"x1"x13"—Shelf cleats
4 pcs.—¾"x1"x18⅞"—End door-filler strips
4 pcs.—1¾"x4"x4"—Caster blocks
2 pcs.—¾"x3⅜"x20⅜"—Drawer fronts
2 pcs.—½"x3⅜"x15½"—Drawer sides
2 pcs.—1½"x2"x14"—Handles

Plywood

1 pc.—¾"x13"x23½"—Shelf
1 pc.—¼"x2⅝"x19⅞"—Drawer partition
4 pcs.—¼"x2⅝"x10¼"—Drawer partitions

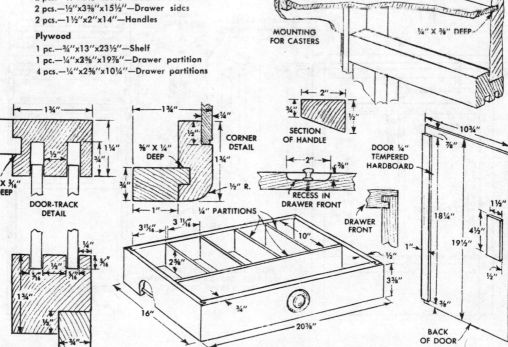

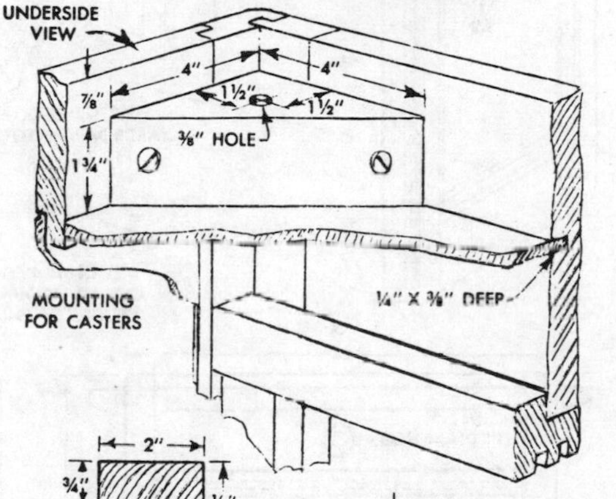

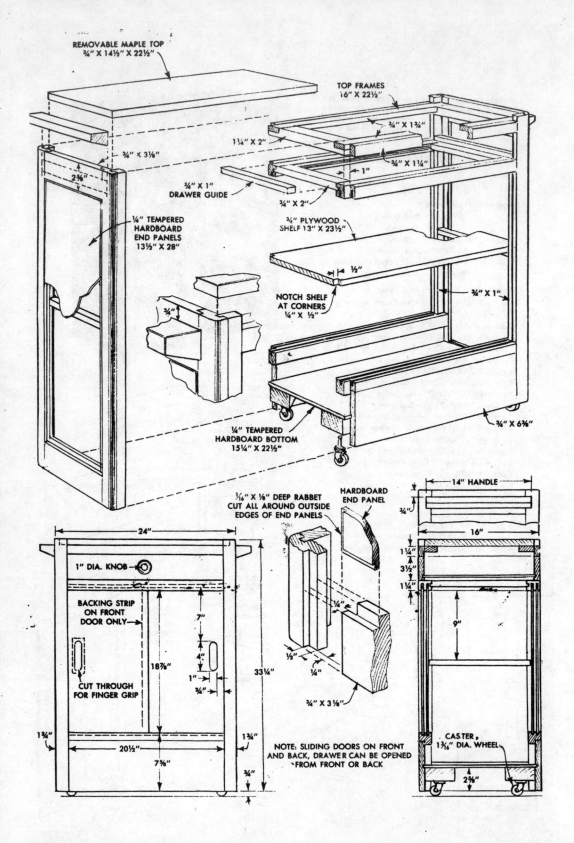

REMOVABLE MAPLE TOP
¾" X 14½" X 22½"

TOP FRAMES
16" X 22½"

¾" X 1¾"

1¼" X 2"

¾" X 1¼"

¾" X 3⅛"

1"

2⅜"

¾" X 1"
DRAWER GUIDE

¾" X 2"

¼" TEMPERED
HARDBOARD
END PANELS
13½" X 28"

¾" PLYWOOD
SHELF 13" X 23½"

½"

NOTCH SHELF
AT CORNERS
¼" X ½"

¾"

¾" X 1"

¼" TEMPERED
HARDBOARD BOTTOM
15¼" X 22½"

¾" X 6⅜"

1/16" X ⅛" DEEP RABBET
CUT ALL AROUND OUTSIDE
EDGES OF END PANELS

HARDBOARD
END PANEL

14" HANDLE

¾"

16"

24"

1" DIA. KNOB

¼"

1¼"

3½"

1¼"

BACKING STRIP
ON FRONT
DOOR ONLY

7"

4"

1"

¾"

½"

¼"

9"

18⅞"

33¼"

CUT THROUGH
FOR FINGER GRIP

¾" X 3⅛"

1¾"

20½"

1¾"

7⅝"

¾"

NOTE: SLIDING DOORS ON FRONT
AND BACK, DRAWER CAN BE OPENED
FROM FRONT OR BACK

CASTER,
1¾" DIA. WHEEL

2⅝"

KITCHEN ROLL-OUT CABINET

IS THERE A NARROW SPACE in your kitchen that seems destined to be wasted? Such a waste space often is found between the range and the sink or between a wall and a range or sink. Too small for a standard cabinet, the space often becomes a bothersome cleaning problem and adds nothing to the convenience or appearance of the kitchen.

One solution that puts this waste space to work is a roll-out shelf cabinet that is simple to build yet adds greatly to the accessible storage space. Made to fit the opening, the cabinet consists of three shelves that pull out like a drawer, rolling on rubber-wheeled casters. The casters are non-pivoting and should be placed as wide apart as possible to increase stability.

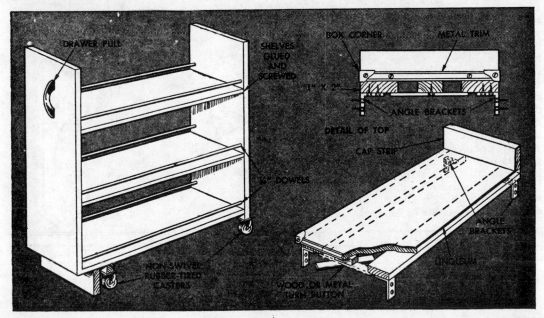

For the cabinet on page 1223, 8-in. pine boards were used throughout. The simple butt joints were glued and screwed for strength. The drawing shows the simple design of the cabinet. To prevent the stored items from sliding off the edges of the shelves, quarter-inch dowels are run along each side. The dowels are forced into holes drilled in the front and back uprights.

The top shelf, which is separate from the pull-out cabinet, rests on 1 x 2s at-tached to the sink and range with angle irons. If you prefer, the shelf can be supported at the rear by an angle iron screwed into the wall and at the front by a sheet-metal strap that slides into the joints between the top and sides of the range and sink. The shelf should be built so it can be easily removed for cleaning, as crumbs frequently lodge along its edges. Linoleum covering and metal trim add to its neatness and serviceability.

KITCHEN SHELVES

USUALLY a small hanging shelf is the answer to the decorative problem posed by a bare wall in the kitchen. Although pictured above as a china and knickknack shelf, this one, with its scrolled cornice, also serves equally well as a storage space for spices and condiments. The back is cut from ¾-in. plywood and all other parts are of ⅛ and ¼-in. plywood as indicated. Note especially the method of fitting the scrolled parts A, B and C. Part C is notched to fit inside the open end of the shelf while part B is an overlay. After sanding, join all parts with glue and brads and finish in the natural color of the wood with shellac, or in color with two coats of enamel.

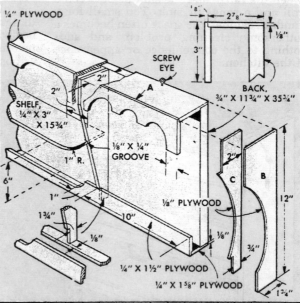

1" SQUARES

HIGHFLYING LIGHT KITES FROM JAPAN

By Hi Sibley

TRADITIONALLY EXPERT kitefliers, the Japanese have produced some interesting and unusual models. On the next two pages are plans for several of these kites, plus a fast-winding reel to keep the kites under control. With the exception of the large Daimyo kite, which requires ¼ x ¼-in. spruce or pine strips, all kites are made from 1⁄16 x 3⁄16-in. bamboo strips. Where curves are required, the bamboo first is heated over a lamp bulb or small flame, then is bent. All kites are covered with rice paper, obtainable at most hobby stores. Designs are painted on the paper with poster paint before it is applied. Cut the paper 1 in. larger, all around, than the frame, then fold it over and cement.

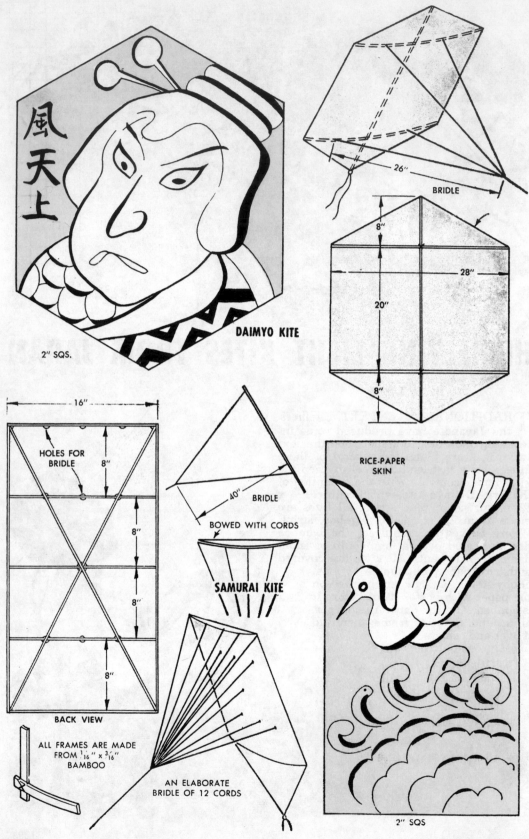

風天上

2″ SQS.

DAIMYO KITE

26″

BRIDLE

8″

28″

20″

8″

16″

HOLES FOR
BRIDLE

8″

8″

8″

8″

BACK VIEW

ALL FRAMES ARE MADE
FROM 1/16″ x 3/16″
BAMBOO

40″   BRIDLE

BOWED WITH CORDS

SAMURAI KITE

AN ELABORATE
BRIDLE OF 12 CORDS

RICE-PAPER
SKIN

2″ SQS

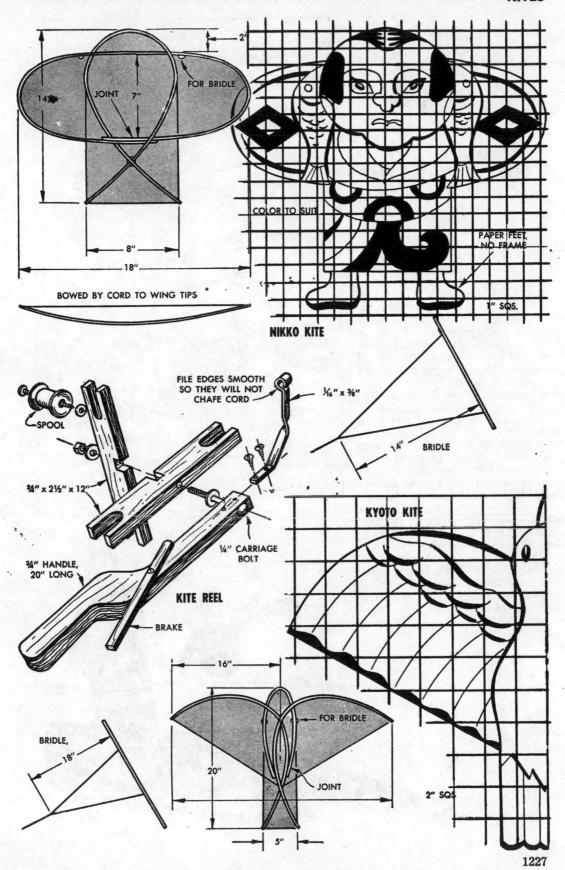

2"

FOR BRIDLE

14"

JOINT 7"

8"

18"

BOWED BY CORD TO WING TIPS

COLOR TO SUIT

PAPER FEET,
NO FRAME

1" SQS.

NIKKO KITE

FILE EDGES SMOOTH
SO THEY WILL NOT
CHAFE CORD

1/16" x 3/8"

SPOOL

14"

BRIDLE

¾" x 2½" x 12"

¼" CARRIAGE
BOLT

KYOTO KITE

¾" HANDLE,
20" LONG

BRAKE

KITE REEL

16"

FOR BRIDLE

BRIDLE,

18"

20"

JOINT

2" SQS

5"

THE **W**-KITE

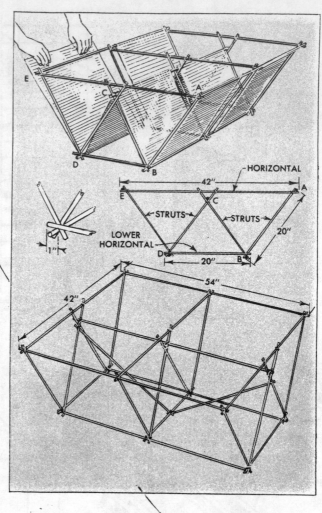

THE W-KITE, one of the highest fliers and most efficient climbers of all kites, combines the stability of the regular box kite and the strength of the triangular box kite. It flies well without a tail and, in a fair breeze, will "walk" right up to a spot almost directly overhead. It does not pull hard, as does the box, because it adjusts itself constantly. In a fair breeze, it can be fed into the air from the hand and brought back to the hand without ever touching the ground.

The frame is made of any light wood and covered with cellophane. The joints of the frame are tied with string or heavy thread and then coated with shellac or glue. The cellophane cover should not be pulled too tightly, as it may shrink. Where necessary, back the cellophane with a light network of thread tied to the frame. A four-legged bridle is used, the length of the top two legs being about the same as the kite's short struts. The method of attaching the bridle can be seen in the illustration. The size of the kite may be varied provided the proportions of the parts remain the same as pictured.

KNIVES FROM HACKSAW BLADES

STANDARD 1" POWER-HACKSAW BLADE

A B C

DEGREE OF BEVEL NEEDED
FOR VARIOUS TYPES OF CUT

③ ROUGH-GRIND TAPER ON SIDE OF FINE WHEEL

WELL tempered, razor-sharp knives that keep their keen edge can be ground from worn or broken power-hacksaw blades, obtainable at many machine shops. As these blades are made of hard steel alloy such as molybdenum, which is so tough that a file will not cut it, shaping the blades must be done on a wet grindstone or very lightly on an emery wheel. Heavy pressure results in overheating and withdrawing the temper from the steel, which renders the blade useless. When grinding, a blade should be dipped in warm water every half minute or so, but if it is hot enough to sizzle, allow it to cool in the air. Tempered steel should never be immersed in cold water while the metal is hot.

When grinding knives from hacksaw blades, the best procedure is to work on two or three blades at once. As soon as one becomes too warm for the fingers, lay it aside and work on the next. The carving-knife blade shown in Fig. 1, utilizes an entire hacksaw blade. Broken blades are used for shorter knives. Before you start grinding, the shape of the knife is outlined on the blade with a wax crayon, and a full-size pattern on paper should be made for checking. A fairly coarse wheel is used to blank the knife to shape.

Rough-grinding the tempered sides to remove excess material, which is a slow process, is done on the side of a fine wheel as shown in Fig. 3. As the blank gets thinner it tends to heat more rapidly and therefore it is necessary to take light cuts the entire length of the blade. Be sure to keep the blade moving rapidly, not letting it come to rest for an instant. First work on one side and then on the other to cut the two sides down evenly. Smoothing of the

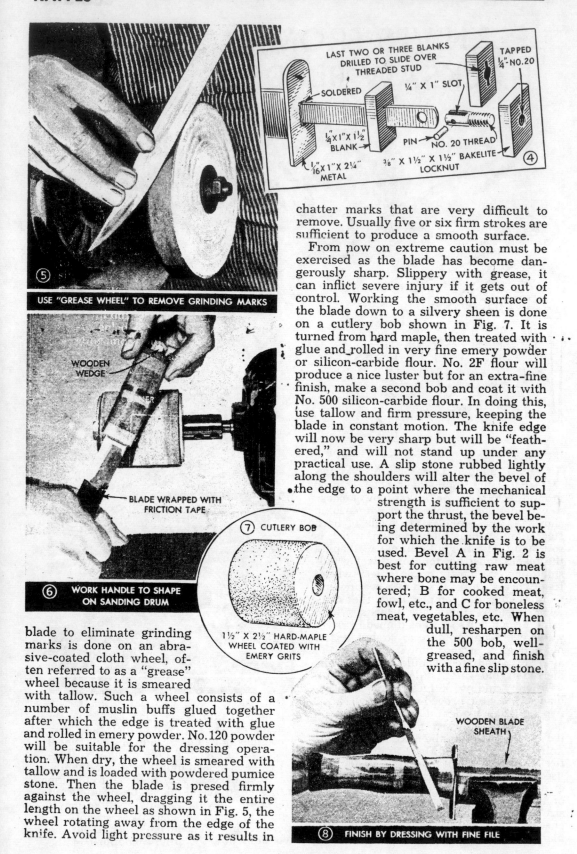

⑤ USE "GREASE WHEEL" TO REMOVE GRINDING MARKS

LAST TWO OR THREE BLANKS DRILLED TO SLIDE OVER THREADED STUD

TAPPED ¼"-NO.20

SOLDERED

¼" X 1" SLOT

¼"X 1"X 1½" BLANK

PIN

NO. 20 THREAD

1/16"X 1" X 2¼" METAL

3/8" X 1½" X 1½" BAKELITE LOCKNUT

④

WOODEN WEDGE

BLADE WRAPPED WITH FRICTION TAPE

⑥ WORK HANDLE TO SHAPE ON SANDING DRUM

⑦ CUTLERY BOB

1½" X 2½" HARD-MAPLE WHEEL COATED WITH EMERY GRITS

WOODEN BLADE SHEATH

⑧ FINISH BY DRESSING WITH FINE FILE

chatter marks that are very difficult to remove. Usually five or six firm strokes are sufficient to produce a smooth surface.

From now on extreme caution must be exercised as the blade has become dangerously sharp. Slippery with grease, it can inflict severe injury if it gets out of control. Working the smooth surface of the blade down to a silvery sheen is done on a cutlery bob shown in Fig. 7. It is turned from hard maple, then treated with glue and rolled in very fine emery powder or silicon-carbide flour. No. 2F flour will produce a nice luster but for an extra-fine finish, make a second bob and coat it with No. 500 silicon-carbide flour. In doing this, use tallow and firm pressure, keeping the blade in constant motion. The knife edge will now be very sharp but will be "feathered," and will not stand up under any practical use. A slip stone rubbed lightly along the shoulders will alter the bevel of the edge to a point where the mechanical strength is sufficient to support the thrust, the bevel being determined by the work for which the knife is to be used. Bevel A in Fig. 2 is best for cutting raw meat where bone may be encountered; B for cooked meat, fowl, etc., and C for boneless meat, vegetables, etc. When dull, resharpen on the 500 bob, well-greased, and finish with a fine slip stone.

blade to eliminate grinding marks is done on an abrasive-coated cloth wheel, often referred to as a "grease" wheel because it is smeared with tallow. Such a wheel consists of a number of muslin buffs glued together after which the edge is treated with glue and rolled in emery powder. No. 120 powder will be suitable for the dressing operation. When dry, the wheel is smeared with tallow and is loaded with powdered pumice stone. Then the blade is presed firmly against the wheel, dragging it the entire length on the wheel as shown in Fig. 5, the wheel rotating away from the edge of the knife. Avoid light pressure as it results in

It's Easy To Tie
KNOTS

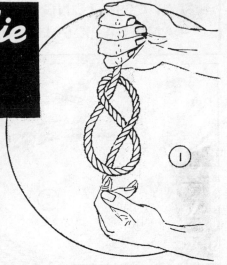

ALTHOUGH a piece of rope or cord has no separate parts such as top, bottom, or sides, in knot tying one has to think of a length of rope or cord as having three sections. These are the two ends and the standing part, Fig. 3. No matter how complicated the knot it consists basically of three turns, the bight, and the overhand and underhand loops. Certain knots are formed on the ends of separate ropes, others are tied on the standing part alone and some are tied with the end and the standing part. Knots also are formed with the separate end strands of a rope. Skilled users always "work" a new rope before putting it in service. "Working" a rope is simply a process of pulling, stretching, and gently twisting it throughout the length to take out the stiffness. A cotton-braided rope of the clothesline

Do not coil or store damp or wet rope. Dry in the sun and then coil and store in a dry place. Rope that is not to be used for some time should never be allowed to tangle and kink. Always coil it when dry so that it will pay out smoothly and evenly

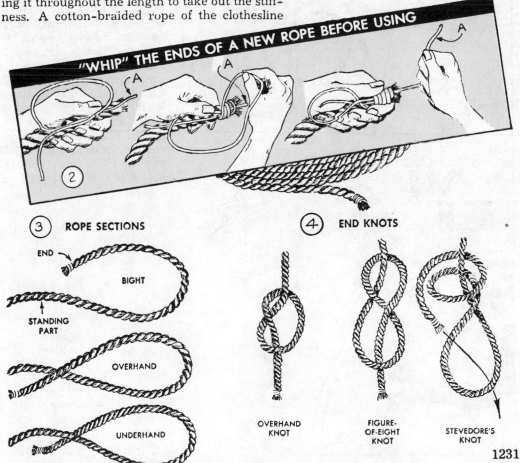

"WHIP" THE ENDS OF A NEW ROPE BEFORE USING

③ **ROPE SECTIONS**

END

BIGHT

STANDING PART

OVERHAND

UNDERHAND

④ **END KNOTS**

OVERHAND KNOT

FIGURE-OF-EIGHT KNOT

STEVEDORE'S KNOT

FLAT COIL, LONG COIL AND BACK SPLICE

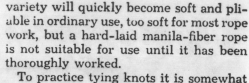

variety will quickly become soft and pliable in ordinary use, too soft for most rope work, but a hard-laid manila-fiber rope is not suitable for use until it has been thoroughly worked.

To practice tying knots it is somewhat handier to use a three-strand rope ⅜ in. in diameter and fifteen to twenty-five feet long. Work it well to take out the newness and stiffness then stretch it tight and run a piece of coarse cloth several times over the length of it. This will pick up the fine "slivers" of fiber which project from the surface of the strands. This will prevent any injury to your hands while gripping the rope tightly as is necessary in tying certain of the various knots. Although most of the knots detailed are shown tied with rope it should be remembered that most of them are just as effective when tied in any cord or twine of small diameter.

The ends of the rope should always be protected against fraying by whipping with cord, Fig. 2, by any one of the end knots, Figs. 1 and 4, or better still, when usage permits, by any one of the "stopper" knots detailed in Figs. 6, 7 and 8. These latter are known as the wall knot, Fig. 6, the single Matthew Walker knot, Fig. 7, and the crown knot or back splice, Fig. 8. The latter is a tricky one but the details A, B, C, D and E, show quite clearly how it is made and with the

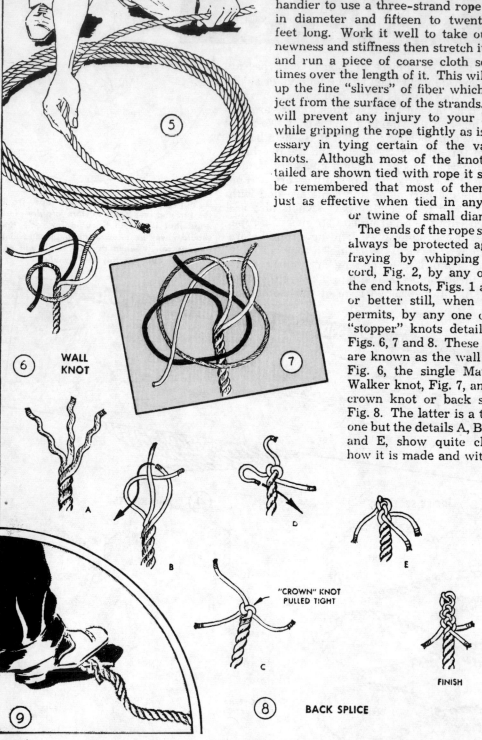

5

6 WALL KNOT

7

A

B

C "CROWN" KNOT PULLED TIGHT

D

E

FINISH

8 BACK SPLICE

9

rope in your hands and the strands unlaid as in the first step A, it becomes easier still. When you end the splice lay the knot on the floor and roll it with your foot as in Fig. 9. If you're careful, it finishes off the end with a neat, professional job. The trick in getting a neat tie of either of the knots shown in Figs. 6 and 7, is to "snug up" the tucked strands separately and by stages until all three are in place and equally tight. If desired, the projecting ends of the strands may be whipped as in Fig. 2.

Right at the beginning it's important that one know how to coil a rope properly. Fig. 5 shows how to lay up an average length of rope in a flat coil, also known as the deck coil. You begin by laying the outer circle first and then winding inward in a clockwise direction giving a half turn to the rope as each loop is laid. When the full length has been laid, tighten the coil by grasping the edges and twisting it counter-clockwise. On very long ropes the same procedure is used, except that the rope is coiled in several layers. An outer wall is coiled first and the inside is built up with successive windings one on top of the

VARIATIONS OF THE SQUARE KNOT

SHOESTRING KNOT ⑩

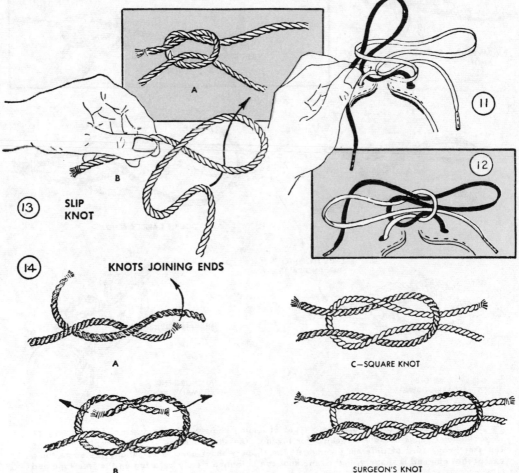

⑪

⑫

⑬ SLIP KNOT

A

B

⑭ KNOTS JOINING ENDS

A

B

C—SQUARE KNOT

SURGEON'S KNOT

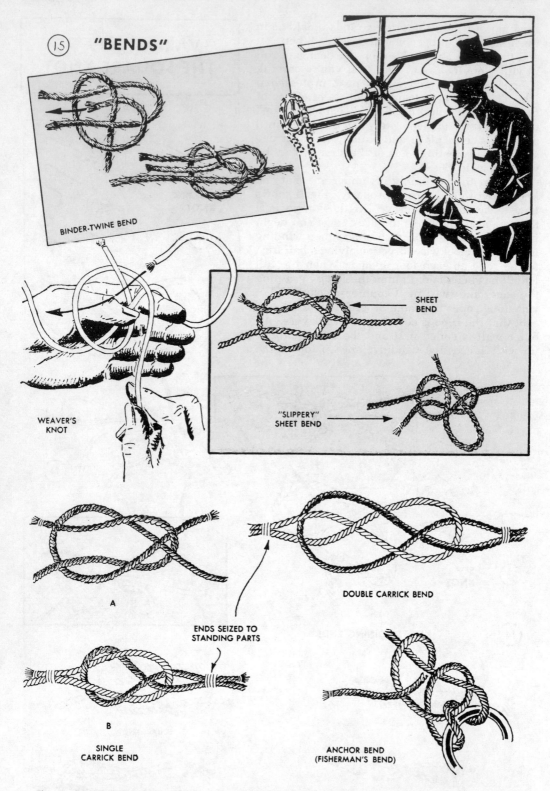

15 **"BENDS"**

BINDER-TWINE BEND

WEAVER'S
KNOT

SHEET
BEND

"SLIPPERY"
SHEET BEND

A

DOUBLE CARRICK BEND

ENDS SEIZED TO
STANDING PARTS

B

SINGLE
CARRICK BEND

ANCHOR BEND
(FISHERMAN'S BEND)

The single and double carrick bends are types of joining knots which are practical for use only on large-diameter ropes or hawsers joined for towing. The sheet bend is especially useful in joining ropes or heavy cord of different diameters. The slippery sheet bend is essentially the same thing except that one end is slippery, that is, the knot can be untied merely by a tug on the free rope end

TYING ROPES TO OBJECTS

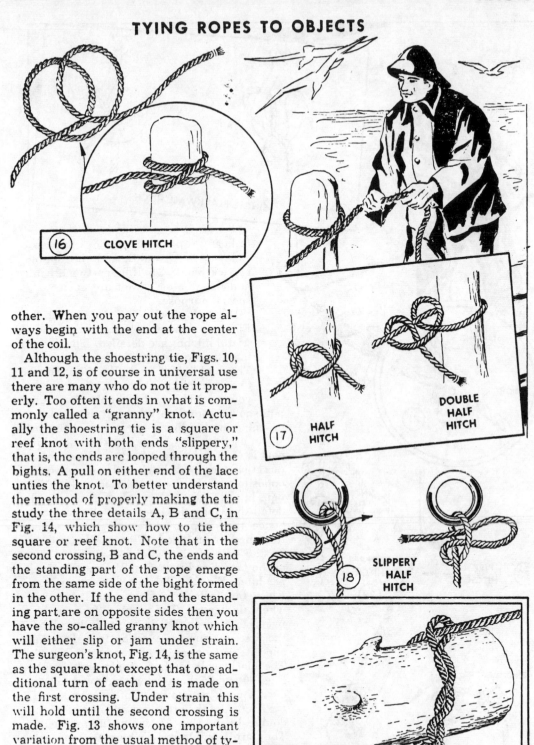

16   CLOVE HITCH

17   HALF HITCH

DOUBLE HALF HITCH

18   SLIPPERY HALF HITCH

19   TIMBER HITCH

other. When you pay out the rope always begin with the end at the center of the coil.

Although the shoestring tie, Figs. 10, 11 and 12, is of course in universal use there are many who do not tie it properly. Too often it ends in what is commonly called a "granny" knot. Actually the shoestring tie is a square or reef knot with both ends "slippery," that is, the ends are looped through the bights. A pull on either end of the lace unties the knot. To better understand the method of properly making the tie study the three details A, B and C, in Fig. 14, which show how to tie the square or reef knot. Note that in the second crossing, B and C, the ends and the standing part of the rope emerge from the same side of the bight formed in the other. If the end and the standing part are on opposite sides then you have the so-called granny knot which will either slip or jam under strain. The surgeon's knot, Fig. 14, is the same as the square knot except that one additional turn of each end is made on the first crossing. Under strain this will hold until the second crossing is made. Fig. 13 shows one important variation from the usual method of tying the common slip knot, Fig. 13, B. The latter is properly tied with the standing part as shown in detail B, and not with the end of the rope or cord as is so often done.

Fig. 15 details a number of "bends" which are used chiefly for joining ends

As will be seen from the above details, practically all the simple hitches are essentially the same, consisting fundamentally of turns about the object and loops in the free rope end. For the sake of clarity the timber hitch is shown above incomplete. It is ordinarily finished as in Fig. 22

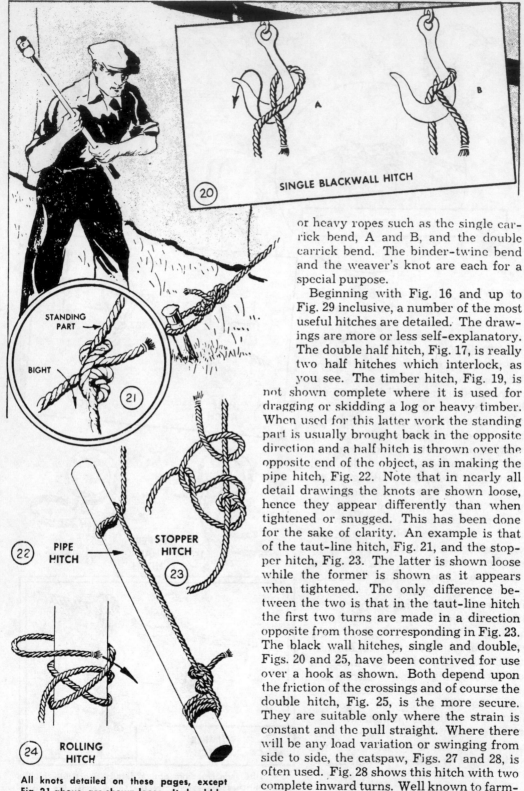

SINGLE BLACKWALL HITCH

STANDING PART

BIGHT

21

PIPE HITCH

22

STOPPER HITCH

23

ROLLING HITCH

24

All knots detailed on these pages, except Fig. 21 above, are shown loose. It should be remembered that when snugged or tightened they will appear somewhat different

or heavy ropes such as the single carrick bend, A and B, and the double carrick bend. The binder-twine bend and the weaver's knot are each for a special purpose.

Beginning with Fig. 16 and up to Fig. 29 inclusive, a number of the most useful hitches are detailed. The drawings are more or less self-explanatory. The double half hitch, Fig. 17, is really two half hitches which interlock, as you see. The timber hitch, Fig. 19, is not shown complete where it is used for dragging or skidding a log or heavy timber. When used for this latter work the standing part is usually brought back in the opposite direction and a half hitch is thrown over the opposite end of the object, as in making the pipe hitch, Fig. 22. Note that in nearly all detail drawings the knots are shown loose, hence they appear differently than when tightened or snugged. This has been done for the sake of clarity. An example is that of the taut-line hitch, Fig. 21, and the stopper hitch, Fig. 23. The latter is shown loose while the former is shown as it appears when tightened. The only difference between the two is that in the taut-line hitch the first two turns are made in a direction opposite from those corresponding in Fig. 23. The black wall hitches, single and double, Figs. 20 and 25, have been contrived for use over a hook as shown. Both depend upon the friction of the crossings and of course the double hitch, Fig. 25, is the more secure. They are suitable only where the strain is constant and the pull straight. Where there will be any load variation or swinging from side to side, the catspaw, Figs. 27 and 28, is often used. Fig. 28 shows this hitch with two complete inward turns. Well known to farmers and horsemen are the halter or hitching tie, Fig. 26, and the hackamore, Fig. 29. Both

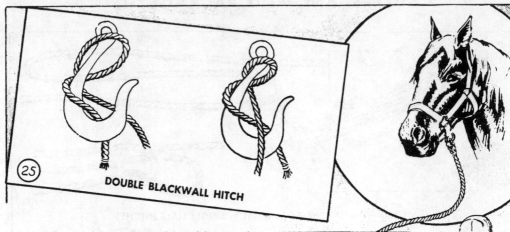

DOUBLE BLACKWALL HITCH

are widely used for tying Old Dobbin to the hitching post or the manger. Both have the feature of being easy to untie. The first is "locked" by passing the end through the bight as shown in the right-hand view. To untie, simply pull out the end and give it a light jerk. Note the similarity of the hackamore to the figure-of-eight knot in Fig. 3. Both knots are good ones to know as they are useful for other purposes.

When you need to shorten a rope without cutting it or you find a weak spot in a long rope which needs strengthening, then the sheepshank, Figs. 30 and 31, is the answer to the problem. Take up the slack as in the top detail, Fig. 30, then throw single or double half hitches over the loops as shown.

Everyone should know the trick of wrapping and tying a parcel post or express package securely. Fig. 32 details what is known as the packer's knot. It is simply a figure-of-eight knot with the end emerging parallel with the standing part. On square packages, place the loop over the package, center it, and pull tight to make the first crossing at right angles to the ends. Take the standing part down over one end and back to the first crossing. Take it over and under the first crossing, then around the opposite end and back to the starting point. To fasten the cord pull it tight and throw a series of half hitches as in Fig. 35. In tying a long rectangular package proceed as in Figs. 33 and 34, and finish as in Fig. 35.

If you ever chance to be faced with a sudden emergency where quick action with a rope may mean saving a life, you should know how to tie the various forms of the bowline knot, Figs. 36 to 40 inclusive. The single bowline or bowline loop is a most valuable and important knot as it forms a loop of any required size and the knot will

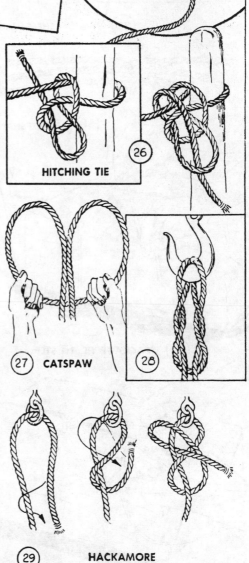

HITCHING TIE

CATSPAW

HACKAMORE

The single and double blackwall hitches hold securely when subjected to a continuous strain. However, they are safe for human life only when taken in the middle of a rope with both ends fast and supporting the load

SHEEPSHANK AND PACKAGE TIE

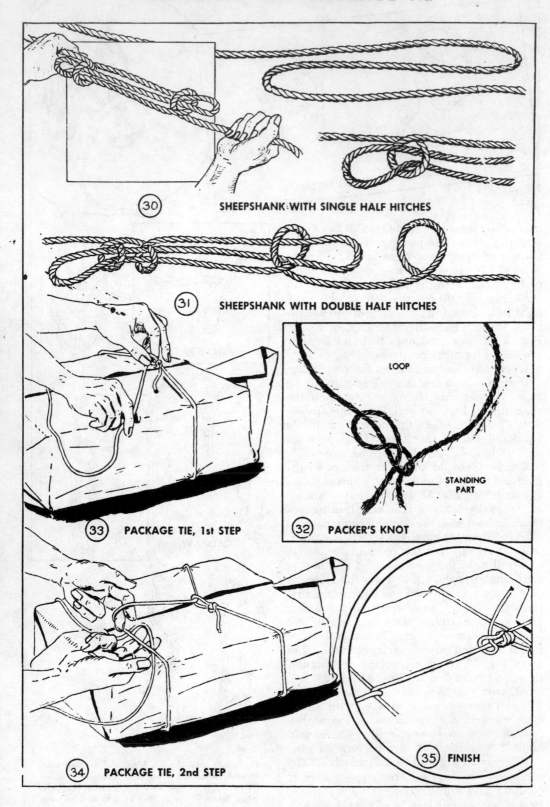

30 **SHEEPSHANK WITH SINGLE HALF HITCHES**

31 **SHEEPSHANK WITH DOUBLE HALF HITCHES**

33 **PACKAGE TIE, 1st STEP**

LOOP

STANDING PART

32 **PACKER'S KNOT**

34 **PACKAGE TIE, 2nd STEP**

35 **FINISH**

stand any strain the rope will bear without slipping or jamming. If one is familiar with it he can tie it in an instant and untie it almost as quickly. Although there are differing methods of tying the single bowline, that shown in Fig. 36 is one of the simplest and most common. In the Texas bowline, Fig. 37, the knot is partially formed on the standing part by passing a bight through the overhand loop, as in A and B, and then bringing the end back through the bight, C. A figure-of-eight or Matthew Walker knot in the end prevents the latter pulling out when the knot is snugged. In the double bowline, Fig. 38, A and B, the two loops are adjustable. One may sit in one loop while the other goes around the body, leaving hands and arms free. The bowline on a

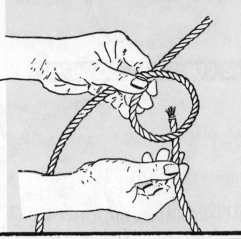

KNOTTING FIXED LOOPS

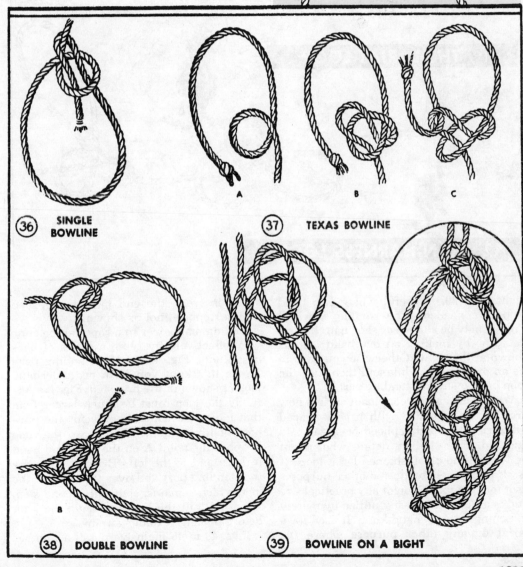

(36) **SINGLE BOWLINE**

(37) **TEXAS BOWLINE**

(38) **DOUBLE BOWLINE**

(39) **BOWLINE ON A BIGHT**

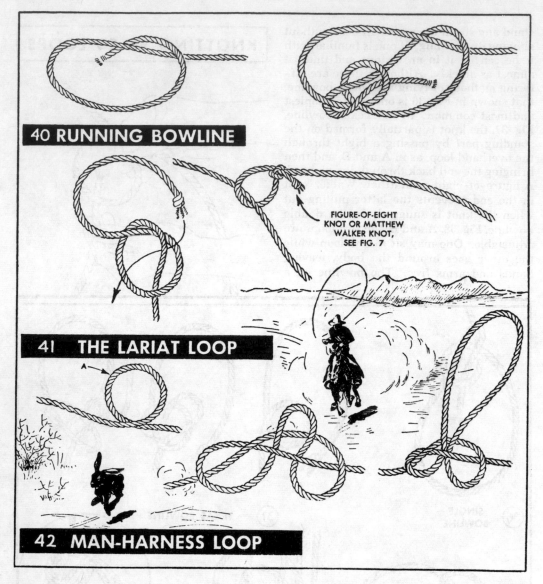

40 RUNNING BOWLINE

FIGURE-OF-EIGHT
KNOT OR MATTHEW
WALKER KNOT,
SEE FIG. 7

41 THE LARIAT LOOP

A

42 MAN-HARNESS LOOP

bight, Fig. 39, is useful where two fixed loops are needed. The running bowline, Fig. 40, may be started as shown in the first detail or by making an overhand loop as shown at the right. Otherwise you have to tie an ordinary bowline and then turn the loop back over the standing part.

When purchased readymade lariats now are usually provided with a pear-shaped brass ring or honda spliced or seized into one end. Fig. 41 then, details what might be termed the old-fashioned lariat loop. It is also an excellent tie for other purposes as it forms a fixed loop of any practical size and is quickly and easily untied by merely loosening the overhand knot. If used for a lariat or any other purpose where the

strain is great, the end must be finished with a stopper knot as shown.

Adding manpower to a rope can be done very effectively by tying a series of harness knots, Fig. 42, in the standing part. To tie this knot you form an underhand loop as shown in the first step, Fig. 42. Actually the loop must be much larger than that indicated, which is only for the purpose of illustration. Then grasp the rope at about the point A on the loop, and bend it down and to the left. Bring it up under the standing part and over that part of the loop which remains, as in the second step. Then pull out the loop and snug the knot before putting it under strain.

Figs. 43 to 46 inclusive detail a number

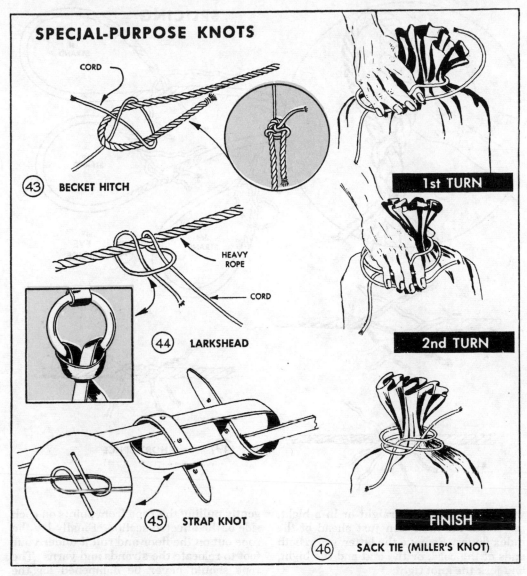

SPECIAL-PURPOSE KNOTS

CORD

(43) BECKET HITCH

HEAVY ROPE

CORD

(44) LARKSHEAD

(45) STRAP KNOT

1st TURN

2nd TURN

FINISH

(46) SACK TIE (MILLER'S KNOT)

of useful special-purpose knots. Where a long rope must be taken up a ladder to the top of a building it's much easier to pull the rope up after you get to the top than to carry it up. Attach a cord to one end of the rope with a becket hitch as in Fig. 43. This simple hitch has many other uses as you can see. It's handy where it is necessary to join the ends of ropes of different diameters, or where attaching a cord to a rope will serve some special purpose. Of the several applications and forms of the larkshead, Fig. 44, only two are shown. It's handy where necessary to attach a small rope to a large one along the standing part for a pull at right angles. It also is used when tying a rope to a ring or post. The Western saddle-girth hitch is really a

larkshead tied with the cinch strap, as you see in the left-hand detail, Fig. 44. Another strap knot, good to know in an emergency, is shown in Fig. 45. It consists of two interlocking half hitches and is particularly effective in joining the ends of flat straps. A wire splice can be made similarly as shown in the circular detail, Fig. 45. Most all farmers are familiar with the sack tie or miller's knot, Fig. 46, but campers, hikers, and others who handle sacks filled with fine material should know how to tie it. As you can see, it is similar to the clove hitch, Fig. 16, and is tied by first laying the starting end of the cord over the index finger as in the top detail. Two turns are then made, each passing under all four fingers as in the second view. Then draw the

SPLICING

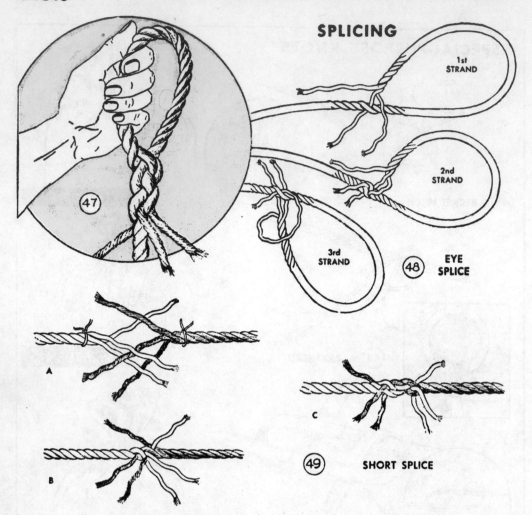

winding end, either straight or in a bight, up under the first turn just ahead of the index finger. Remove the latter, grasp both ends of the cord, or the end and the bight, and jerk the knot tight.

Now one thing to keep in mind: None of the knots described can ever be fully effective unless snugged up tight before putting under strain. Never trust a knot until you have made sure it is drawn tight. Remember, too, that the strength of the rope or cord in the knot is never as great as that of the standing part. All knots are shown tied on three-strand rope.

When rope is depended on to hold a given strain or load through knots it should be remembered that the strands and fibers within the knot tend to take a "set" where the rope is knotted for long periods of time. When untying such a knot be especially careful not to twist or kink the rope unduly, then carefully straighten the bends by

gently pulling the rope from points on each side of the affected section. Finally lay the rope out on the floor and roll it under your foot to relocate the strands and yarns. The rope should never be dampened for the purpose of straightening it.

Of all the rope splices the eye splice has the greatest appeal because of its neat, professional look. Fig. 48 shows one simple way to splice an eye in the end of a rope. The drawings are self-explanatory except perhaps for one point. Before tucking the third strand the loop or eye is turned over. After you have made two or more tucks, over and under the rope strands, the splice will tend to become bulky, as in Fig. 47. Snug up the unlaid strands separately, pulling equally on each until you get the knot tight and smooth. Then separate each strand into its individual yarns and cut away half the latter. Finish the tucking with the half strands. This trick tapers the

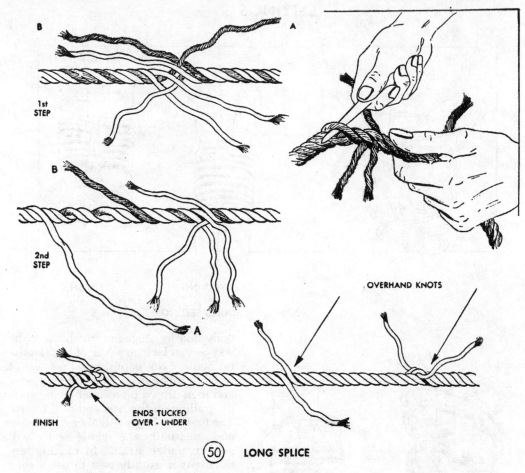

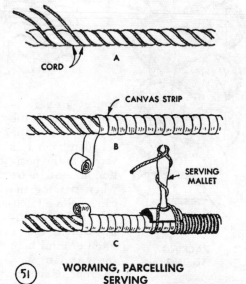

50 — **LONG SPLICE**

OVERHAND KNOTS

ENDS TUCKED OVER · UNDER

FINISH

CORD A

CANVAS STRIP

B

SERVING MALLET

C

51 — **WORMING, PARCELLING SERVING**

splice neatly. The short splice, A, B and C, Fig. 49, is a quick, effective method of splicing a long rope for practical purposes. Unlay 10 to 20 in. of the end strands and tie with a cord as at A to prevent further unlaying. Then simply place the unlaid ends together with the strands in the relation shown and tuck the strands of the left-hand rope over and under the strands of the right. Continue the procedure with the right-hand rope strands. Smooth by rolling on the floor with your foot. In the long splice, Fig. 50, strands are unlaid for a distance equal to 8 to 12 times the circumference of the rope. Place ends together, then unlay strand A and fill the space with strand B. Do the same with corresponding strands in the opposite direction. Finish with overhand knots and tucks as shown. Fig. 51, A, B and C, show the method of waterproofing a rope. The canvas strip B, is coated with white lead after which the cord, serving, is wound on with a special fixture or serving mallet, as shown. Figs. 51 and 53 detail the making of round and racking seizing, the latter method being used when rigging ropes together where strain on one is greater than on the other. In the round seizing the first winding is

SEIZINGS

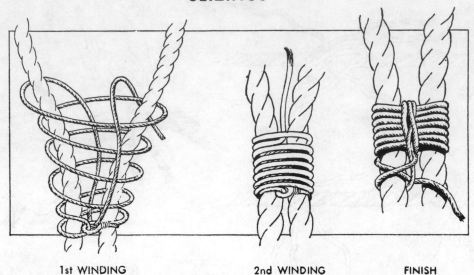

1st WINDING   2nd WINDING   FINISH

(52)   **ROUND SEIZING**

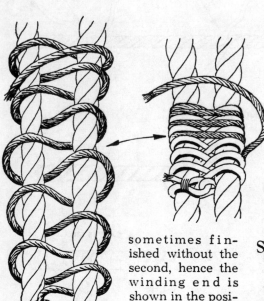

(53) **RACKING SEIZING**

ually and by stages in much the same way as you lace up a pair of high leather boots. No complicated series of loops of this nature can first be placed and then drawn up as a whole by simply pulling on the free end of the cord. The first few loops will always be loose and eventually the whole series will slacken under strain. In making any seizing it is usually best to use a cord not less than one-eighth of the diameter of the rope, although this is not a hard-and-fast rule. Although cotton cord may be used, cords of jute or sisal fibers are usually best for this purpose.

sometimes finished without the second, hence the winding end is shown in the position it would be when starting the center clove hitch. In either case, finish with a clove hitch around both the winding and the rope, as shown.

Making a neat seizing requires much the same skill and attention to details as making either a short or long splice. In Figs. 52 and 53 the loops are shown loose. The trick is to keep snugging the loops individ-

Singeing Hand Rope on Elevator Removes Projecting Fibers

Workmen who operate elevators of the type that have hand ropes will find it a good idea to keep them smooth and free of small projecting fibers. These can be removed easily

ELEVATOR ROPE

and quickly with the flame of an ordinary blowtorch, which is passed rapidly along the surface of the rope, taking care not to burn it.

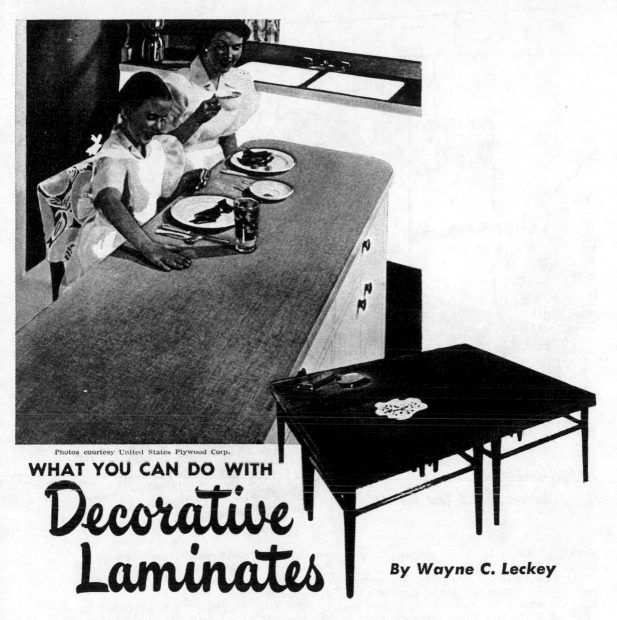

Photos courtesy United States Plywood Corp.

WHAT YOU CAN DO WITH
Decorative Laminates

By Wayne C. Leckey

M OST EVERYONE knows what usually happens when a frosty drink is placed on a highly polished table or a burning cigarette accidentally falls from an ash tray—the table top is ruined and a costly refinishing job is in order. Homeowners who have experienced this will be eager to learn of a comparatively new plastic material that literally defies marring. Called decorative laminate, this amazing plastic material will withstand most acids, will resist heat and cold and endure chemical action. It is virtually unstainable. It won't chip, scratch, craze when wet, or corrode when soft drinks, food or liquor is spilled on it. It requires no refinishing or polishing — just a quick wipe with a damp

WINDOW SILL

1245

COUNTER TOPS

DOORS

CABINETS

Applications
throughout the house

TABLE TOPS

cloth will bring back its original bright luster, year after year.

Familiar to many who first remember seeing it on restaurant tables and counter tops, decorative laminate, as its name implies, is a durable high-pressure plastic laminate with a decorative surface. It is made up of many layers of resin-soaked kraft paper and veneer which are fused together under intense heat and pressure. The laminations actually merge to form a new substance which is coated with a super-tough skin of clear plastic that locks in the color and pattern for life. Marketed under several different trade names, decorative laminate can be had in roll or sheet form and in a score of patterns and colors, including beautiful reproductions of rich mahogany, oak, prima vera and walnut wood grains. Available in various lengths and widths, decorative laminate also may be

purchased at lumberyards, ready bonded to ¾-in. plywood. Most linoleum stores carry laminates and the cement that's needed to apply them.

Decorative laminates are at home in every room of the house. On kitchen counters, cabinets and other work surfaces where cleanliness is a must, this miracle material provides a most practical covering. Liquids, grease and food particles leave no residue on its impervious glass-smooth surface. On furniture in the living room and bedroom, laminate fills the double function of fashion and lasting utility. A more practical top for a cocktail table could not be found. In the bathroom it does triple duty in repelling water, medicines and cosmetics. On a refreshment bar in the recreation room it comes through without a scratch or stain. Dated panel doors can be converted to beautiful flush doors by

COFFEE TABLES

There's a practical use for decorative laminates in every room of your home. Whether used on counter tops, cabinets, dinette and coffee tables, recreation-room bars or bathroom vanitories, this amazing material outshines and outlasts any other surfacing product. Practically indestructible, decorative laminates retain their glass-smooth luster indefinitely with a mere wipe of a damp cloth

Photo courtesy Midcontinent Adhesive Co.

covering them with any of the true wood-grain reproductions to be had. Window sills will stay permanently protected from the hot sun when surfaced with laminate. A section of a wall can be paneled in wood grain to give contrast to a papered or painted wall.

While decorative laminates have an exceptionally durable surface, it is not so hard that it cannot be damaged under certain conditions, and while it can stand constant abuse, one should avoid giving it unnecessary punishment. It is neither recommended nor necessary to clean the surface with gritty scouring powders—only a damp cloth is needed to clean it. Also, avoid placing a hot pressing iron directly on the laminate, or using it as a cutting surface. Always place a pad under a toaster, waffle iron, percolator or other hot appliance.

Heretofore, the application of decorative laminate has been limited to the furniture manufacturer having facilities for gluing and clamping the material securely to the surface. Now, thanks to the development of special "no clamp" adhesives, the application of decorative laminate can be done right at home with a few common hand tools. Of the several adhesives available, Roltite and Tapon were successfully tried by the author in bonding several different decorative laminates.

While laminates can be had in both roll and sheet form, the roll type is $\frac{1}{32}$ in. thick and the sheet type is $\frac{1}{16}$ in. thick. The thinner material is cut by merely scoring the top surface with an awl and then bending it upward to snap it off, whereas the heavier $\frac{1}{16}$-in. material must be cut with a fine-tooth (metal-cutting) keyhole saw, using downward strokes to avoid chipping. It is always best to cut the material about 1 in.

While not a sheet laminate but of the same durable quality, molded counter is available in 6-ft. lengths

oversize to be on the safe side if chipping should occur and also to have enough waste to later trim carefully to line. When it comes to actual application, the work should be done in a room temperature of at least 70 deg. F., and it is important, too, that the laminate be of room temperature. The cement must be applied warm, heating it beforehand in a pan of hot water until it is warm to the touch. All wood surfaces to be covered must be flat, clean and dry. If the surface has been painted or varnished, better results are had if the finish is removed. If the edges as well as the top surface are to be covered, the laminate is always applied to the edges first, using a cement of thicker consistency which is made specifically for edge work. Assuming that only the top and not the edge of a work counter is to be covered, first brush a coat of cement on the wood with a clean paintbrush and allow to dry at least 30 min. Then apply a second coat. While this is drying, brush a coat on the back of the laminate and allow all coats to dry not less than 30 min. There's no need to hurry, as the cement can be left to dry up to two hours and still be workable. To determine when the cement is dry enough to bond the laminate, test it with a piece of wrapping paper. If, after pressing it on the cement, it has a tendency to pull the cement away from the surface, the cement is not dry enough. If it is necessary to allow the cement to dry for a longer period than specified, it can be reactivated by applying another coat on top of the first one. Try to get an even coating over the entire area; too thin an application will result in dull spots.

Above, laminate makes excellent durable covering for traveling case, and a most practical surface material for a vanitory in a powder room as pictured below

These decorative laminate samples show four popular patterns which are available in variety of pastel shades and wood grains to suit any interior treatment

FOSTER

Because bonding is immediate and permanent when both cemented surfaces come in contact, wrapping paper is used as a separator to permit the laminate to be positioned and aligned properly. The paper is placed lightly over the cemented surface and the laminate placed on top of it. When in proper position, the laminate is raised slightly and the paper is withdrawn two or three inches. This allows a portion of the laminate to make contact with the coated surface, after which the paper is pulled out all the way. All that remains to be done is to roll the laminate firmly to assure over-all contact, and the bonding is completed. Trimming the edges back to line is done

Beautiful walls which require only a wipe of a cloth to clean are had by paneling a living room or den with rich wood grains of mahogany, walnut or oak

with the square edge of a single-cut file, working carefully and slowly to avoid chipping. If the laminate is to be covered with a metal or wooden edging, carefulness is not too important. If the edge of the laminate is not to be covered, the laminate is finally filed at a slight bevel, just enough to break the sharp corner. This is done with the flat side of the file as pictured. Don't worry about any excess cement on the surface, it is easily rubbed off with the fingers.

Remember that if the edge of the work is

Here are pictured the two methods recommended for cutting roll and sheet-type laminate. Roll type is scored with pointed tool like an awl or ice pick and bent upward to snap off. Sheet laminate is cut with a fine-tooth saw

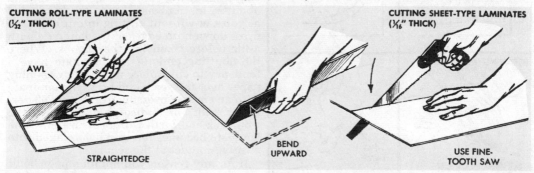

CUTTING ROLL-TYPE LAMINATES
(1/32" THICK)

AWL

STRAIGHTEDGE

BEND UPWARD

CUTTING SHEET-TYPE LAMINATES
(1/16" THICK)

USE FINE-TOOTH SAW

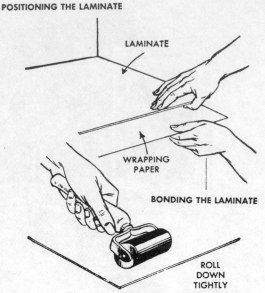

POSITIONING THE LAMINATE

LAMINATE

WRAPPING PAPER

BONDING THE LAMINATE

ROLL DOWN TIGHTLY

The cement is applied warm with a clean paintbrush and left to dry at least 30 min. Two coats are applied to the wooden surface and one to the laminate

Wrapping-paper separator permits laminate to be positioned on cemented surface prior to final bonding. Rolling with firm pressure assures positive contact

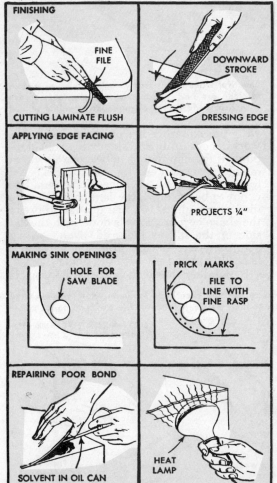

FINISHING

FINE FILE

CUTTING LAMINATE FLUSH

DOWNWARD STROKE

DRESSING EDGE

APPLYING EDGE FACING

PROJECTS ¼"

MAKING SINK OPENINGS

HOLE FOR SAW BLADE

PRICK MARKS

FILE TO LINE WITH FINE RASP

REPAIRING POOR BOND

SOLVENT IN OIL CAN

HEAT LAMP

to be covered, the edge is done first and then the top surface. Cut the laminate so that it will be flush with the bottom of the edge and wide enough to extend about ¼ in. above the top surface. Apply the cement as before, using a special and thicker cement (Tapon), and let dry. Then apply by aligning the laminate in position and tapping it in place with a hammer and a block of wood. Finally, the waste is filed off as before, flush with the top surface. Laminate covering the surface should always be laid to extend over the edge of the facing strip. If it is necessary to bend the facing strip around a corner, heat it at the bend with a heat lamp (never an open flame) to prevent surface cracking. Do not attempt to bend it around a sharp corner.

Where a seam must be used, abutting edges of the laminate are first placed face to face and both cut at one time. This is done by clamping the material between two hardwood boards having perfectly straight edges, allowing the laminate to extend about ¼ in. Saw as close to the hardwood as you can without cutting into it and then dress down both edges of the laminate with a file before removing the clamps. Where the abutting ends of the laminate have a tendency to curl, place a piece of wrapping paper over the seam and press the laminate with an electric pressing iron set at 200 deg. F., or "silk" on indicator dial. Move the iron back and forth with pressure until the laminate becomes hot and has relaxed into positive contact at the seam.

If for any reason you obtain a poor bond

CUTTING A SEAM

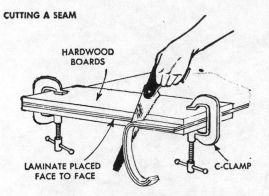

HARDWOOD BOARDS

LAMINATE PLACED FACE TO FACE

C-CLAMP

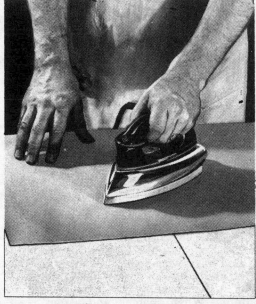

Abutting edges of a seam which have a tendency to curl, are heated with an iron to make pliable and pressed in contact with the cement-coated surface

or if a blister should develop under the laminate, the defective area generally can be repaired by heating it until hot (130 deg. F.). This relaxes the laminate and reactivates the cement film, after which mere pressure usually will rebond the spot. If not, a C-clamp and block of wood will do the trick where it is possible to clamp the work. In the case of a blister, heat and press the surface as described and then quickly chill the surface with ice. If it is necessary to remove the laminate completely, cement solvent applied with an oil can to the cement will soften it to the point where the laminate can be peeled carefully from the surface. In the case of some cements, it is recommended that repairs must be made within a few days of the original application, as the cement tends to vulcanize with age and prevents any repairs being made.

Where walls are perfectly straight and flat, the laminate can be applied directly. Otherwise, it is best to provide a smooth base of hardboard. If desired, hardboard panels can be purchased prebonded with laminate and ready for direct application. The left-hand photo below shows a wall covered with prebonded laminate.

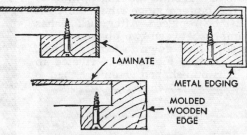

LAMINATE

METAL EDGING

MOLDED WOODEN EDGE

BUILT-UP EDGES AND EDGE TREATMENT

If you do not wish to face the edge of the work with laminate, the edge can be attractively concealed with either a metal or wooden molding. Note that laminate applied to the surface extends over facing strip

Photo courtesy Woodall Industries, Inc.

Photo courtesy The Formica Co.

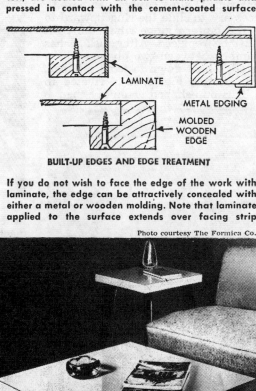

LAMPS—
Interior and
Exterior

BOTH THESE LAMPS are based on antique themes, yet either will go well with the style and furnishing of a modern home. The outside lamp, Fig. 1, is built around a lantern globe, as shown in Figs. 2 and 4, that can be purchased at most hardware stores. The components of the lamp are cut and shaped from aluminum, Figs. 4, 5, 7 and 8. Brass or copper also could be used because of their weather resistance and easy workability. When aluminum is used, rivets, screws and nuts employed in the assembly also should be of aluminum. When shaping and assembling the parts for the outdoor lamp, make sure that ring D slips easily over part C. It is necessary to slide the ring upward to remove the lantern globe when the light bulb must be replaced. After disk G has been clamped between two plywood disks and the edge bent down to form a flange, right-hand detail, Fig. 8, it is riveted to ring F. This cup-shaped assembly then is

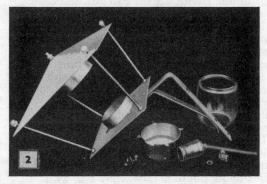

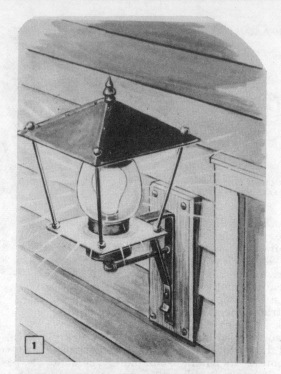

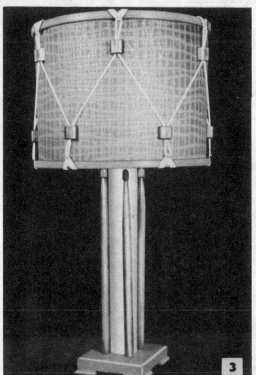

fastened to the lower surface of base B with machine screws and nuts. It is not riveted, as are the other components, because it may at some time be necessary to remove it to repair or replace the light socket. The socket is screwed to an assembly of 1/8-in. pipe and fittings, lower detail, Fig. 4, that is used to protect the wire leading into the house wall. A brass lamp finial is screwed to the center of the lamp cap, while the four supporting rods are capped with drilled and threaded brass balls, such as can be purchased at jewelers and lamp-supply houses.

The uniquely styled table lamp, Fig. 3, has a shade that suggests a Civil War drum, the four drum sticks around its column carrying out the theme, Fig. 6. Patterned translucent plastic is cemented to a pair of embroidery hoops to form a shade, a 1/2-in. lap being allowed on the plastic for

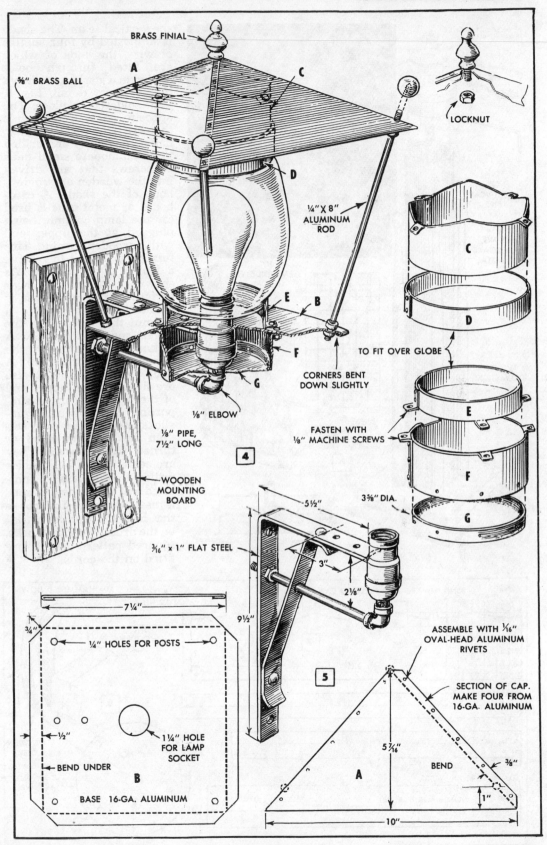

BRASS FINIAL

A

⅝" BRASS BALL

C

D

¼" X 8" ALUMINUM ROD

LOCKNUT

E

B

F

G

⅛" ELBOW

⅛" PIPE, 7½" LONG

WOODEN MOUNTING BOARD

TO FIT OVER GLOBE

FASTEN WITH ⅛" MACHINE SCREWS

3⅜" DIA.

4

5½"

3/16" x 1" FLAT STEEL

3"

2⅛"

9½"

ASSEMBLE WITH 1/16" OVAL-HEAD ALUMINUM RIVETS

5

SECTION OF CAP. MAKE FOUR FROM 16-GA. ALUMINUM

7¼"

¾"

¼" HOLES FOR POSTS

1¼" HOLE FOR LAMP SOCKET

½"

BEND UNDER

B

BASE 16-GA. ALUMINUM

CORNERS BENT DOWN SLIGHTLY

5 7/16"

A

BEND

⅜"

1"

10"

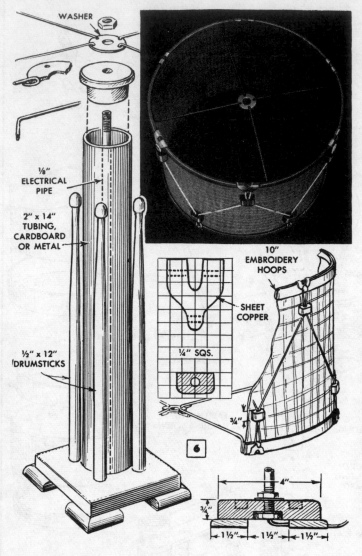

WASHER

⅛" ELECTRICAL PIPE

2" x 14" TUBING, CARDBOARD OR METAL

½" x 12" DRUMSTICKS

10" EMBROIDERY HOOPS

SHEET COPPER

¼" SQS.

6

¾"

4"

¾"

1½" 1½" 1½"

the vertical seam. The shade is supported by four lengths of wire, the ends of which are fitted through holes drilled in a washer, as shown in the upper detail, Fig. 6, then soldered in place. The opposite ends of the wires then are bent at right angles, flattened slightly and drilled to accommodate small nails or screws that are driven into the wooden embroidery hoop of the shade. A cardboard or metal tube is used for the lamp column, being plugged at the upper end with a wooden turning. This turning is drilled to receive a length of ⅛-in. pipe. As shown in Fig. 6, the lower surface of the lamp base is counterbored to receive a locknut that is fitted on the lower end of the pipe. A locknut also is fitted on the upper end of the pipe. A lamp harp and socket also are fitted on the upper end of the pipe, the former supporting the shade. Drumsticks used on the lamp column can be purchased or turned from dowels. They are cemented in blind holes drilled in the base as indicated in Fig. 6. Sheet copper is used to make the hooks that hold the "tuning cords" on the drum. Wooden blocks, squared pattern, Fig. 6, are fitted on the cords. ★ ★ ★

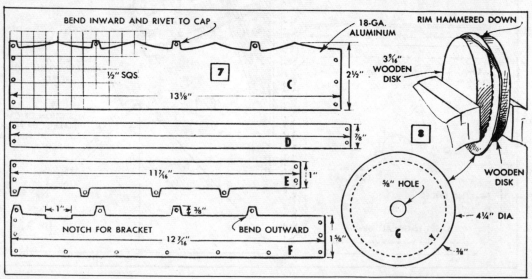

BEND INWARD AND RIVET TO CAP

18-GA. ALUMINUM

RIM HAMMERED DOWN

½" SQS.

7

C

2½"

13⅛"

3⅜₁₆" WOODEN DISK

8

D

⅜"

11⅞₁₆"

E

1"

WOODEN DISK

NOTCH FOR BRACKET

BEND OUTWARD

12⅞₁₆"

F

1"

⅜"

1⅝"

⅝" HOLE

G

4¼" DIA

⅜"

PLANTER YARD LIGHT

FOR SOMETHING UNIQUE in the way of a yard light, mount an ordinary yard lamp on a steel-angle post having a built-in planter. The angle is bent so that the bottom of the post flares outward, and the lower portions of the legs are embedded in a concrete base. The four lengths of angle used for the post are screwed to a 2-in.-square hardwood block at the top and are reinforced at a point just above the flare by a square brace made of flat iron. This is bolted to the legs. Each angle is cut lengthwise from the bottom upward for 3 or 4 in. so that one web of each leg can be bent at right angles to give greater support in the concrete base. The latter is poured in a wooden form, as in the lower right-hand detail. A nail keg is placed in the center of the form to leave an opening in which soil and plants can be added later. The post is held in place by a frame of 2 x 4s while the concrete is poured.

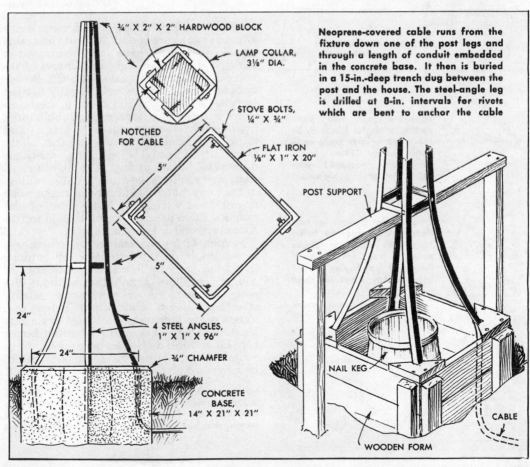

¾" X 2" X 2" HARDWOOD BLOCK

LAMP COLLAR, 3⅛" DIA.

NOTCHED FOR CABLE

STOVE BOLTS, ¼" X ¾"

FLAT IRON ⅛" X 1" X 20"

5"

5"

24"

24"

¾" CHAMFER

4 STEEL ANGLES, 1" X 1" X 96"

CONCRETE BASE, 14" X 21" X 21"

Neoprene-covered cable runs from the fixture down one of the post legs and through a length of conduit embedded in the concrete base. It then is buried in a 15-in.-deep trench dug between the post and the house. The steel-angle leg is drilled at 8-in. intervals for rivets which are bent to anchor the cable

POST SUPPORT

NAIL KEG

CABLE

WOODEN FORM

OUTDOOR LIGHTING

General Electric photo

150-W.
PROJECTOR
LAMP

Egg-crate roof over patio permits projector lamps to be concealed in open wells as in detail above. These lamps also come equipped with spikes for ground placement

Two popular fixtures for outdoor lighting are the bullet type with metal or plastic housing and the enclosed floodlight type having colored glass which snaps in place

Stonco Electric Products Co.

Chances are you'll enjoy your patio more after sundown when it is cool, and this means you will have to devote some thought to outdoor lighting. This will involve not only the patio, but the flower beds and play areas as well. A gaily lighted terrace or patio will add savor to food and spark to cookout entertaining. Bubble units fitted with 75-watt-reflector lamps and hung overhead as shown in the photo above, will provide exciting spotlight drama to buffet dining. The lightweight units are easily hung from a patio ceiling, or roof overhang. Lighting can make your flower beds a colorful focal point of the outdoor room at night if you embed mushroom-type fixtures among them.

Proper wiring, permanent or temporary, is essential for the extension of outdoor living at night. Permanent outlets, of course, facilitate installation without the potential hazards of temporary wiring stretched across walks and driveways. Fence posts, trees and buildings are a few locations where weatherproof outlet boxes can be mounted. Separate circuits, with switch control either inside or out, should be provided. It is always wise to turn off

Left, new floodlighting fixtures for patio lighting include surface-wall and through-wall mountings that do not require separate splice boxes. Full length, cast box covers hold up to four lampholders

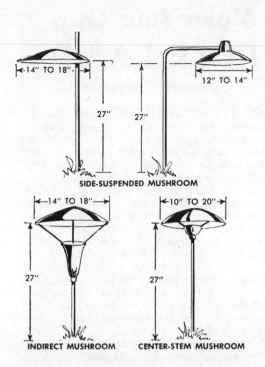

SIDE-SUSPENDED MUSHROOM

14" TO 18"   12" TO 14"   27"   27"

INDIRECT MUSHROOM   CENTER-STEM MUSHROOM

14" TO 18"   10" TO 20"   27"   27"

Sunshade umbrella by day becomes lighted canopy by night when an upturned reflector bulb is attached to supporting pole. Colored bulb is most effective

Courtesy General Electric Co.

Built-in step lights, louvered for light control, are excellent pathfinders when patio walk is adjacent to garage or house. Mount 18 in. above grade

or disconnect the circuit when changing bulbs or placing equipment. Portable cord sets specifically designed for outdoor use are available. These have molded junction and socket connections which insure that the cords will remain weatherproof. While not the neatest installation, overhead wiring is the simplest to install, compared to underground, when there are buildings or trees for support. Wires should be at least 8 ft. above the ground and supported about every 15 ft. with insulators. In the case of underground wiring, sand or light gravel around the wires will help water drainage, and boards over the wires will give further protection. Short conduit els guard wires above ground.

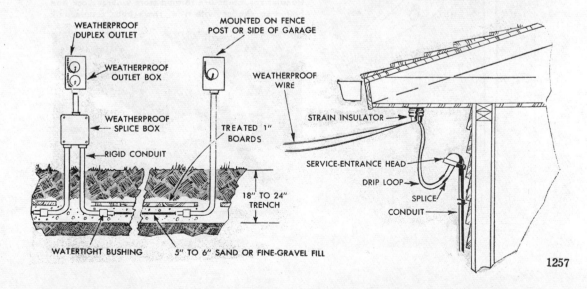

WEATHERPROOF DUPLEX OUTLET

WEATHERPROOF OUTLET BOX

WEATHERPROOF SPLICE BOX

RIGID CONDUIT

MOUNTED ON FENCE POST OR SIDE OF GARAGE

TREATED 1" BOARDS

WEATHERPROOF WIRE

STRAIN INSULATOR

SERVICE-ENTRANCE HEAD

DRIP LOOP

SPLICE

CONDUIT

18" TO 24" TRENCH

WATERTIGHT BUSHING   5" TO 6" SAND OR FINE-GRAVEL FILL

Make Your Own
POLE LAMP

By Ronald L. Anderson

FOR EFFECTIVE HIGHLIGHTING of special areas of interest in your living-room decor, here is a pole lamp with a cluster of three spotlights that you can make in a few evenings. Except for the spotlights, which are purchased ready-made, the lamp is made from stock materials using hand tools and a portable power drill as illustrated. Aluminum tubing is used for the pole of the lamp, with extension legs made of brass tubing and dowel stock fitted in the ends. The upper leg is spring-loaded like a pogo stick, so that the lamp pole can be gently wedged between the floor and ceiling at any desired location. To move the lamp you need only pull up on the pole and swing the lower end of it to one side.

To make the lamp, cut an 8-ft. length of 1¼-in. aluminum tubing to size and drill it to take the lights and fittings for the legs as indicated in Fig. 1. Then the upper and lower leg assemblies are made and installed in the tubing as detailed in Figs. 3 and 4. Note that the upper leg is not secured to the end dowel piece, to permit cylinderlike movement while both dowel pieces of the lower leg are secured to the pole and to the leg so that it remains in a fixed position. A 2-in. drain plug fastened to each leg end as in detail A, provides a nonslip contact with floor and ceiling. Wooden handles, shaped and cut to fit the contour and size of light shades, may be bolted to them for easier turning when hot, detail B and Fig. 2. ★ ★ ★

Handles for lamps are formed from walnut stock and bolted to shades with 1-in. stove bolts countersunk

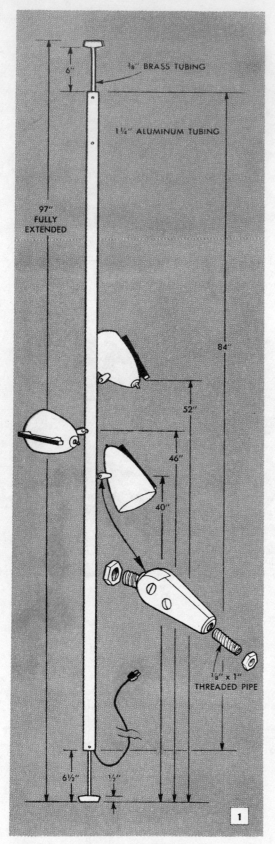

¾" BRASS TUBING

6"

1¼" ALUMINUM TUBING

97" FULLY EXTENDED

84"

52"

46"

40"

⅛" x 1" THREADED PIPE

6½" ½"

1

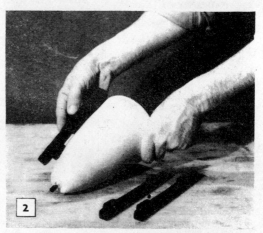

2

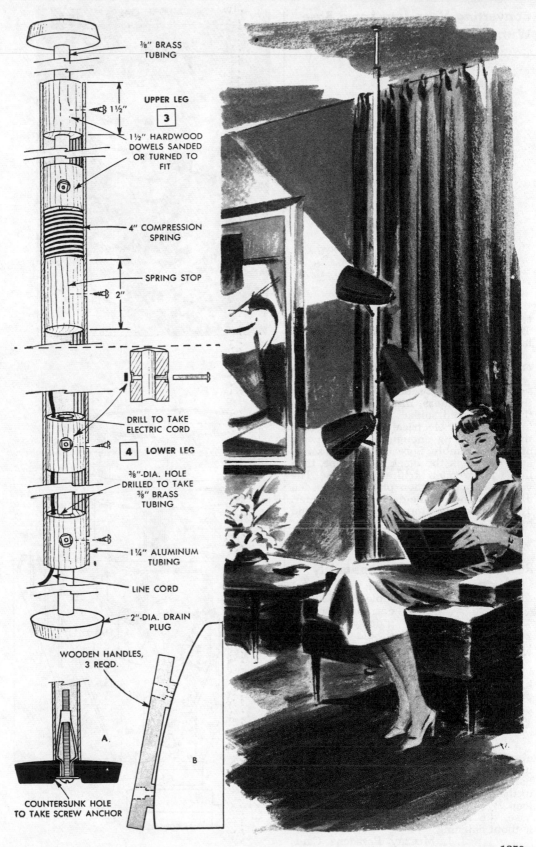

⅜" BRASS TUBING

UPPER LEG

3

⅛ × 1½"

1½" HARDWOOD DOWELS SANDED OR TURNED TO FIT

4" COMPRESSION SPRING

SPRING STOP

2"

DRILL TO TAKE ELECTRIC CORD

4 LOWER LEG

⅜"-DIA. HOLE DRILLED TO TAKE ⅜" BRASS TUBING

1¼" ALUMINUM TUBING

LINE CORD

2"-DIA. DRAIN PLUG

WOODEN HANDLES, 3 REQD.

A.

B

COUNTERSUNK HOLE TO TAKE SCREW ANCHOR

Converting Vase Into Lamp Base Without Drilling for Pipe or Wire

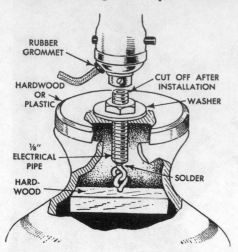

RUBBER GROMMET

CUT OFF AFTER INSTALLATION

HARDWOOD OR PLASTIC

WASHER

⅛" ELECTRICAL PIPE

HARD-WOOD

SOLDER

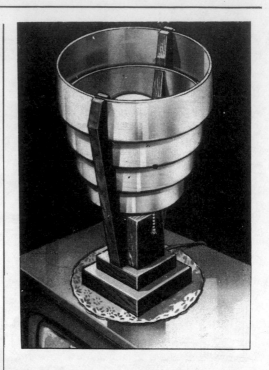

Many small-neck vases and fancy bottles can be converted into beautiful lamp bases. The problem generally is how to attach the lamp socket to the top without drilling a hole in the bottom of the bottle for a pipe and locknut. Here's a way that works perfectly. Cut a hardwood strip about ½-in. square, just long enough to catch inside the vase shoulders. Insert a screw eye in the middle and solder another screw eye into a length of electrical pipe, making sure the pipe is long enough to allow sawing off after assembly. Spread one of the screw eyes and hook the block to the pipe, then insert the wooden strip into the vase. The vase is capped with a plastic or wooden disk which has a hole drilled in the center. This disk is now slipped over the pipe and held by a washer and locknut.

Art Trauffer, McClelland, Iowa.

Rewire Ornamental Lamps Easily

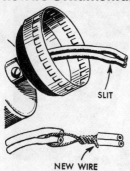

SLIT

NEW WIRE

An ornamental table or floor lamp can be rewired quickly by using the old wire to pull the new wire through the base and socket. Pull up enough of the old wire to trim it off and cut a slit between the two wires about ½ in. from the end. Bare about 2 in. of the new wire and taper the insulation down to the wire. Twist the bared wire tightly, pass it through the slit in the old wire and fasten it securely in a loop. By pulling on the old wire at the lamp base, the new wire will follow through without catching.

J. L. McClay, Pasadena, Calif.

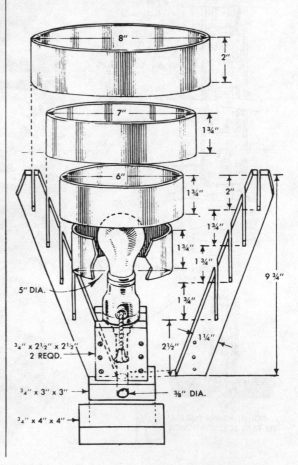

8"

2"

7"

1¾"

6"

1¾"

2"

1¾"

1¾"

1¾"

5" DIA.

1¾"

9¾"

¾" x 2½" x 2½" 2 REQD.

2½"

1¼"

¾" x 3" x 3"

⅜" DIA.

¾" x 4" x 4"

MODERN TV LAMPS

By M. C. Anderson

THE TWO LAMPS illustrated in this article are so easy to make that any homecraftsman can assemble both of them in one evening. Tiers of metal Venetian-blind slats that form the shade on the lamp shown on the opposite page direct most of the light upward, making it an ideal lamp for use where indirect lighting is desired. To make this lamp, simply cut the various members to size as shown in the details, and make the saw cuts in the arms that support the slats. The arms, cut from ¾-in. material, should be clamped together when making the saw cuts. Drill the hole in the base for the lamp cord. A pull-chain-type light socket screwed to a length of threaded electrical pipe which is clamped between the two vertical blocks of the base, completes the job. It is important to make the saw cuts exactly as indicated so that the shade tiers overlap ¼ in.

The lamp shown on this page requires even less time to make. Wooden dowels are used for uprights. Two pairs of embroidery hoops, of which the inner one of each pair is screwed to the uprights as shown, provide a means of clamping the translucent-plastic shade. Material for the latter is ob-

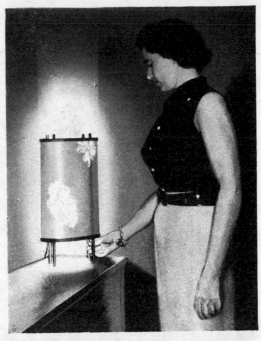

Low-wattage bulb in lamp produces soft glow for most effective display of design in plastic shade

tainable in most variety stores. The ends of the plastic lap ¼ in., the lap being centered over one of the dowels at the back of the lamp to prevent light leaks. Pilot holes are drilled for the screws to prevent splitting, and the heads are countersunk for proper clearance between hoops.　★ ★ ★

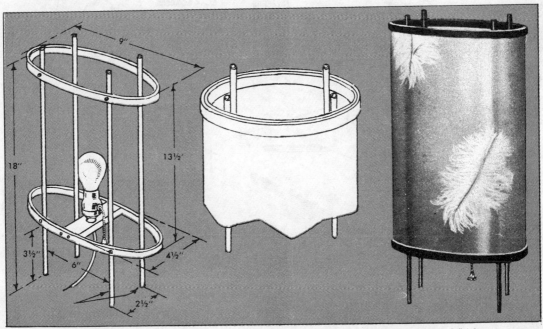

FLASK

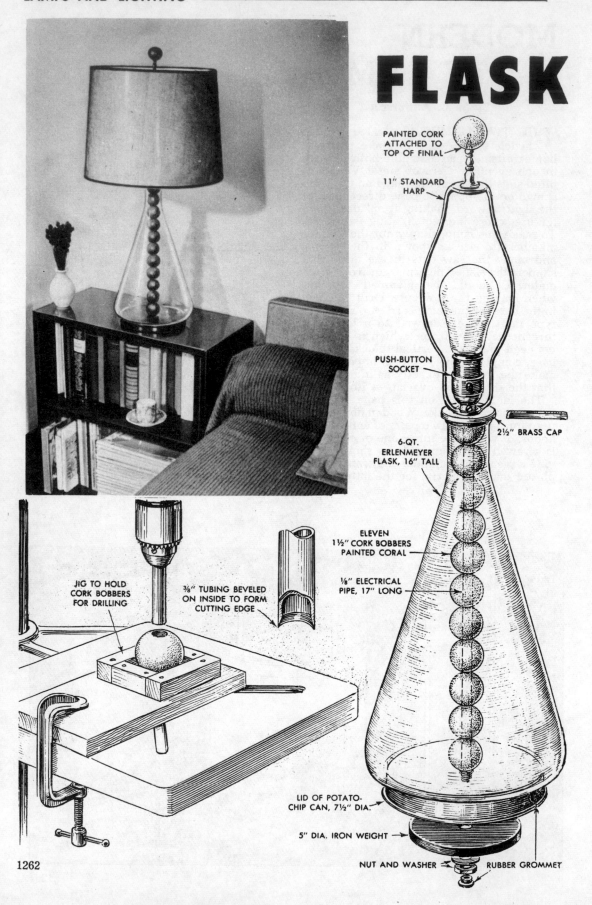

PAINTED CORK
ATTACHED TO
TOP OF FINIAL

11" STANDARD
HARP

PUSH-BUTTON
SOCKET

2½" BRASS CAP

6-QT.
ERLENMEYER
FLASK, 16" TALL

ELEVEN
1½" CORK BOBBERS
PAINTED CORAL

⅛" ELECTRICAL
PIPE, 17" LONG

JIG TO HOLD
CORK BOBBERS
FOR DRILLING

⅜" TUBING BEVELED
ON INSIDE TO FORM
CUTTING EDGE

LID OF POTATO-
CHIP CAN, 7½" DIA.

5" DIA. IRON WEIGHT

NUT AND WASHER

RUBBER GROMMET

LAMP

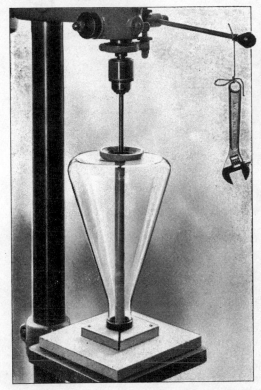

Wrench of sufficient weight to apply right amount of pressure for drilling glass is tied to handle of drill, so it can be run with minimum of attention

Here is a novelty-type lamp that is suitable for a bedroom, nursery, or den. Using a large flask as the basic unit on which standard lamp parts are assembled as shown, you can make a pair of the lamps in a few hours. A unique feature of the lamp is the column of painted cork fishing bobbers that are stacked on threaded electrical pipe fastened in the center of the flask. Not only do the bobbers conceal the lamp cord but they can be repainted any number of times to fit into the decor of any room. In most cases the same shade could be used.

Begin the lamp by drilling a ⅜-in. hole in each of the bobbers, using a jig and an improvised bit as shown in the detail on the opposite page. Next drill a ⅜-in. hole in the bottom of the flask to take one end of a 17-in. length of electrical pipe. A workable procedure for drilling glass is explained below. Since this job is the most time consuming of the project, make a jig to hold the flask in position on your drill-press table as shown in the photo. Meanwhile the rest of the assembly can be completed as shown in the drawing.

When painting the bobbers, string them on a taut wire and use a hat pin to hold and turn each one as paint is being brushed on them. The potato-chip can lid used for the base is painted flat black. If a 5-in. dia. iron disk base weight is unavailable, melt some lead and pour one directly in the lid.

Bob Joselyn, Chicago

HOW TO DRILL FLASK

About the easiest way of drilling a hole in glass is to chuck a length of brass tubing in a drill press and use a jig to hold the object while the relatively slow process of drilling or grinding is in progress. A weight, such as a wrench, is tied to the drill handle to apply sufficient pressure to grind away the glass without overheating or breaking it as in the photo above.

An oil-and-emery dust mixture confined to the drilling area by a putty dam as detailed at right, provides the abrasive. Slots cut in the end of the improvised bit help to circulate the mixture. This cools the glass and brings a constant supply of abrasive to the grinding surfaces of the bit. The drill must be run at slow speed to avoid overheating the glass, which might crack it.

When drilling a hole in the bottom of a thin-wall bottle or flask, the flat surface must be supported at a point directly under the bit to counter-balance pressure exerted by the drill. In the case of the flask illustrated, a prop consisting of a length of dowel with a rubber disk glued on each end

serves this purpose. The lower end of the dowel is fitted in a hole drilled in the bottom of the jig. The latter is made up of two squares of 1-in. lumber, the lower one of which is one piece. The upper square is sawed in half diagonally and notched at the center to clamp the neck of the flask when screwed to the bottom square. A portable power drill may be used for drilling glass in this manner but it is a tiresome job since the weight of the drill must be balanced carefully.

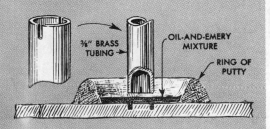

⅜" BRASS TUBING
OIL-AND-EMERY MIXTURE
RING OF PUTTY

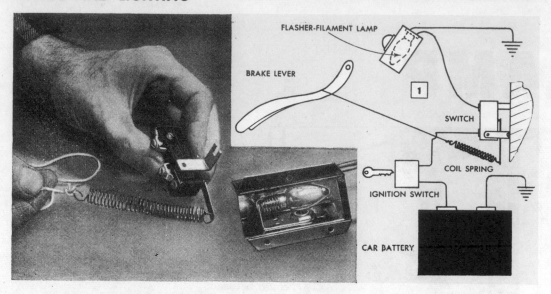

FLASHER-FILAMENT LAMP

BRAKE LEVER

1

SWITCH

COIL SPRING

IGNITION SWITCH

CAR BATTERY

Flashing Lamps Catch the Eye

By Walter E. Burton

THERE IS NO DOUBT that a flashing light is more effective as an "attention getter" than one that burns steadily. This factor is utilized every day in store signs, theater marquees and in turn indicators on automobiles. Although automatic, momentary-contact switches are used in these applications, a craftsman or hobbyist who has need for a flashing light can assemble one with only an off-on switch in the circuit. Incandescent electric lamps are available that have an automatic "switch" in the filament to make and break a circuit. Because the lamps require only from about 4 to 6 volts (12-volt lamps are to be available soon) they can be used in portable setups powered by dry cells or an automobile battery. For permanent installations, house current can be reduced with a stepdown transformer for the low-voltage lamps.

If you have ever driven with the parking brake of your car pulled on, you will appreciate the warning lamp shown in Fig. 1. When the brake handle is pulled, a spring-loaded, momentary-contact switch is closed and a light flashes on and off until the brake handle is moved to the "release" position, or the ignition switch is turned off. Switches of the type shown can be purchased at radio-supply houses, or regular parking-brake warning-light switches can be obtained at some auto-supply houses. A piece of sheet aluminum is shaped into a box that contains a socket to receive a G-E

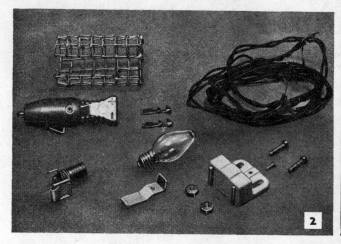

2

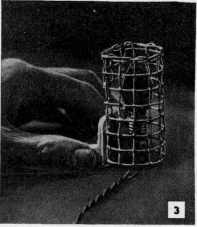

3

No. 405 flasher-filament lamp. If a 12-volt lamp is not available, a 30-ohm, 2-watt resistor can be wired in series with a 6-volt lamp when used in a car with a 12-volt ignition system. The box is attached to the lower edge of the instrument panel where it can be seen by the driver. The switch is mounted on the fire wall and is actuated by means of a length of fishline. A spring between the cord and switch prevents damage to the switch.

Figs. 2 and 3 show another application for flasher-filament lamps. In this auto-emergency light, a G-E No. D-25 lamp is used, it being available in colors. A No. 405 lamp also could be used if covered with a colored glass or plastic housing. The light itself consists of an L-shaped bracket to which is fastened a socket of the type used for radio pilot lights. The bracket is screwed to a magnetic cabinet latch which positions the light vertically when the unit is placed on a horizontal metal surface, such as a car roof. A piece of hardware cloth is shaped as a shield to protect the lamp. An 8-ft. length of 2-wire cord and an auto-accessory plug that fits the cigarette-lighter receptacle provide battery current to the lamp.

Youngsters with sidewalk cars want their vehicles to be as much like real cars as possible, and flasher-filament lamps can aid this wish for realism. Fig. 4 shows how two

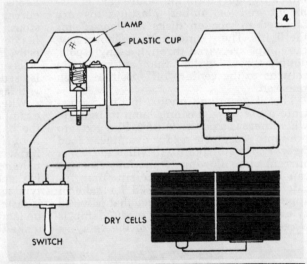

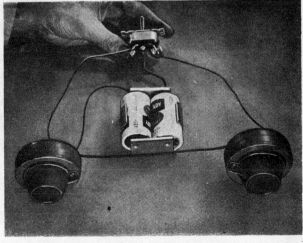

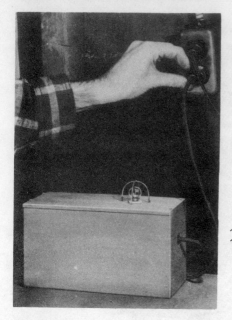

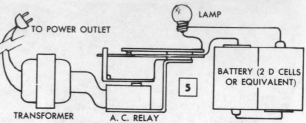

TO POWER OUTLET
LAMP
BATTERY (2 D CELLS OR EQUIVALENT)
5
TRANSFORMER
A. C. RELAY

G-E No. 406 lamps are employed as turn-indicator lights for a miniature car. Translucent red or amber plastic cups are screwed to wooden disks as "lenses" for the lights. The wiring diagram shows how the lamps are wired through a single-pole, double-throw switch that automatically returns to the center "off" position when released.

The diagram and photos in Fig. 5 illustrate a use for a flashing lamp to indicate when there is a power failure. Plugged into the same receptacle as, for example, a food freezer or water pump, it will warn when current stops flowing to the unit so steps can be taken to correct the situation. Inside a wooden cabinet—used for sake of appearance—is a transformer that is wired to a relay. A G-E No. 406 or 407 lamp is wired to the opposite side of the relay as

indicated. The relay is of the type that keeps the contact points open as long as current flows through it. When the current stops, the contacts close and the flasher-filament lamp then is energized by the dry cells. For the No. 406 lamp, two size-D dry cells are required. A 6-volt lantern battery is used with a No. 407, and this latter setup will last approximately twice as long.

Where a warning light is needed, for example, to indicate that someone is using the bathroom for a darkroom, the pin-up light in Figs. 6 and 7 does the job. A transformer reduces household current to 6 volts to power a No. 405 or D-25 lamp. An L-shaped bracket supports a socket of the type used for illuminating radio dials, and is fastened to an aluminum disk for a "pin up lamp" appearance. A small shade would make the lamp even more attractive. ★ ★ ★

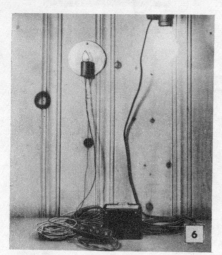

Gatepost Light Simulates Old Locomotive Headlamp

RESEMBLING the headlamp from an old wood-burning locomotive, this gatepost light was made by a model-railroad enthusiast to illuminate his house number. Smaller in size than the original lamp, the major construction change was substitution of electrical light for the kerosene lantern.

All metal parts are galvanized sheet metal which can be readily soldered. The base is assembled first from the three pieces marked A, B and C. Overlapping tabs are soldered to the adjoining piece. The light chamber is framed with ¾-in. galvanized angle and a faceplate of sheet metal in which a 5-in.-dia. hole has been cut. Fitted into the hole is a 2-in. length of stovepipe with ½-in. tabs cut along the inside edge. An aluminum reflector is hinged to the opposite side of the light chamber to provide access for changing the bulb. A spring catch locks it shut. Individual metal tabs, soldered to the frame, hold the front lens and side windows in place.

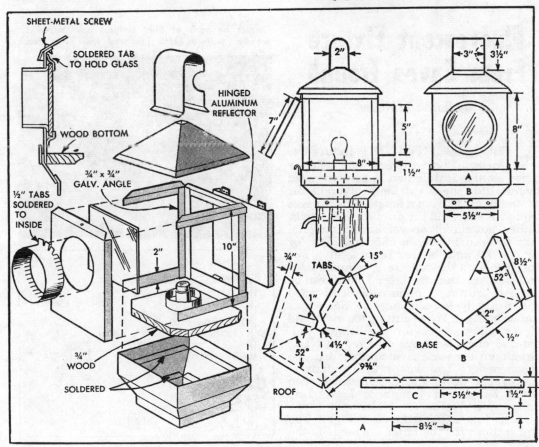

Flowerpot Lamp on Tripod Is Novel Planter

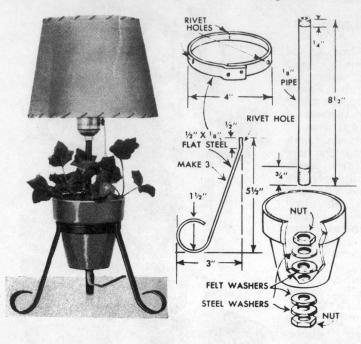

RIVET HOLES

4"

RIVET HOLE

½" X ⅛"
FLAT STEEL

MAKE 3

1½"

3"

⅛" PIPE

5½"

¾"

½"

8½"

¼"

NUT

FELT WASHERS

STEEL WASHERS

NUT

An interesting planter lamp can be made easily by mounting a pull-chain socket on a length of pipe fastened through the drain hole of a flowerpot set on a flat-steel tripod. Form the tripod legs by bending equal lengths of flat steel around a large iron shaft. Then rivet them to a steel ring that is dimensioned to fit under the rim of the flowerpot. Fasten a length of ⅛-in. pipe, threaded at both ends, in the drain hole of the pot and screw a pull-chain socket on the other end of the pipe. Wire the socket by running the cord up through the pipe. Add a plant and clip a shade over the bulb. Herbert Y. Moon, Orient, N. Y.

Fluorescent Fixture From Eaves Trough

By Ralph T. Moore

A FLUORESCENT-LIGHT fixture for a drawing board, over a workbench or other similar installation is easy to make by installing one or two lamps in a reflector assembly made from a length of 5-in. eaves trough as shown in the drawing and details. Either aluminum or galvanized material may be used, in lengths of 50 and 25 in. for 40 and 20-watt lamps, respectively. For end pieces on the reflectors, manufactured end caps are used, or the end pieces can be made by cutting a pattern block of wood and using it for shaping the flanges as shown in Fig. 1. When cutting the metal end pieces, allow ½ in. for the flanges. Galvanized end pieces are soldered in place, aluminum ones are riveted or bolted. To accommodate two lamps in one fixture, simply cut down the back sides of two equal lengths of trough to leave 1-in. flanges for riveting or soldering the two sections together, as shown in Fig. 3. The end sections for the latter are made in the

Flanges on ends of light fixtures are shaped on wooden pattern block jigsawed from 1-in. stock

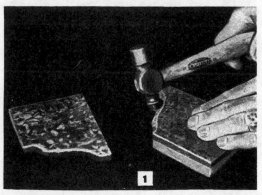

1

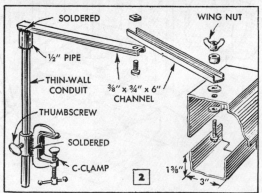

SOLDERED

WING NUT

½" PIPE

THIN-WALL CONDUIT

THUMBSCREW

SOLDERED

C-CLAMP

⅜" x ¾" x 6" CHANNEL

2

1⅜"

3"

same way as for a single-lamp fixture.

Installation of the lamp circuit, including two end sockets and one starter for each lamp and one ballast of suitable capacity for each fixture, is the same or similar for all fixtures. Follow the diagram for wiring printed on the ballast, or the one shown in the detail. After bolting the sockets, switch and ballast in place, a cover piece 1⅜ x 3 in. is formed from 28-ga. galvanized sheet steel and two cutouts made at one end of the cover to accommodate the socket and starter. This cover, the length of which is determined by the length of the lamp used, is then bolted to the reflector as indicated in the detail. Be sure to insulate all connections and electrical parts mounted on the fixture.

The completed fluorescent fixture can be screwed to a wall, ceiling or other place, or attached to the adjustable brackets, Fig. 2. A thumbscrew on the lower end of each bracket permits adjusting the light to the desired height. The channel-steel members are pivoted for easy adjustment on a horizontal plane. ★ ★ ★

To accommodate 20-watt lamp, a 25-in. length of eaves trough is required, 50-in. length for 40-watt lamp

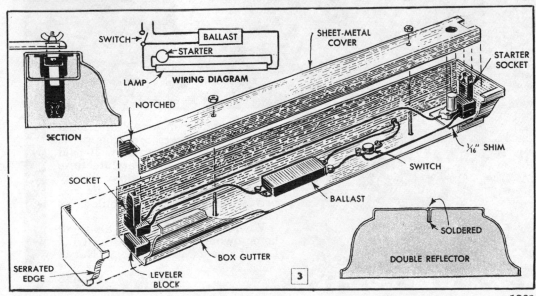

Charles G. Curtis Co.

Home Landscaping . . .

LANDSCAPING is an art. Professional landscape designers are among the most highly trained and well-paid experts in the field of architecture. They place the final stamp of beauty on large homes, estates, public and private buildings, parks, boulevards and golf courses.

Where does all this leave the small home owner who cannot afford the fees of a landscape architect? Not in

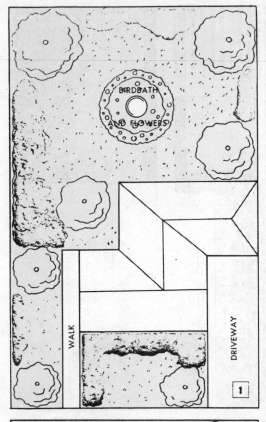

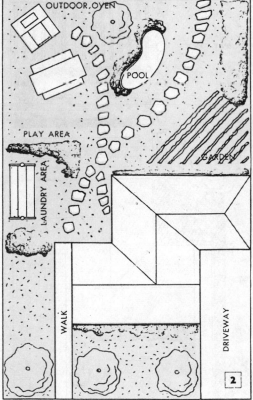

too bad a position, really. Landscape artists are sympathetic with the desire of the average homeowner for beauty on his small plot of land. They have offered generous advice and counsel, and set down general rules for the guidance of gardeners who wish to apply some of the principles of landscaping.

Everyone at one time or another has noted the raw and ugly appearance of a newly built house. However charmingly designed, the beauty of the house is marred by the bare scarred earth around the house and the blank skyline about and behind it. Let a little grass grow, however, and let but a few trees and shrubs be placed about it, and the house immediately acquires the beauty its designer intended to be revealed. Only a little haphazard growth will achieve much. Think, then, how much more will be done for such a house if the landscaping is well planned and well carried out!

Landscaping has a twofold purpose. The first—beauty—is obvious. The second—utility—will become apparent upon examination. Every home needs different treatment because the people who live in it are different from their neighbors in more or less degree. One family has small children, and will want at least some part of the home grounds devoted to space for playground equipment. One family is intensely interested in gardening; another is only mildly so. There will be a vast difference in their landscaping needs. The family requiring laundry space will have a problem not faced by the family owning a mechanical clothes drier or using a commercial laundry. Outdoor laundry-drying space must be planned carefully so that it is conveniently at hand and yet not too obtrusive. It must be attractively screened by some kind of planting, so as not to become an eyesore.

It is good to think of the home grounds as an outdoor living room. In it you will want everything that interests you in gracious outdoor living. In a limited space there will have to be compromises. Mother may have to sacrifice part of her flower-garden plans to space for a shuffleboard court or an outdoor oven. Father's allotment for a vegetable garden may have to yield to the desire of other members of the family for a rock garden or a garden pool.

To reach a compromise in this conflict of interests, careful planning is necessary. This planning should be done in several stages. The first step is the drawing of a rough sketch.

The rough: Begin your landscape plan with a blunt black pencil and a piece of paper on which you have drawn the boundaries of your lot in proportion. Make this space as small as practical—say about 2 by

4 in. if your lot is 50 by 100 ft. This won't give you any room for details, which is a desirable limitation at this stage. What you want to achieve is the "large form," or the general appearance your landscape will present. This, in the end, will be a more important factor for pleasing or unpleasing results than any of the details.

Block in the space taken by the house, garage, walks, driveways and other permanent fixtures. The area that remains is to be divided into two parts—planted space and free space. The planted space is, of course, for trees, shrubbery, flowers and vegetables. Free space will be allotted to lawn, play areas, laundry space and for similar purposes.

Using free movements (remember that here you can spoil only a small piece of paper), try to work out interesting shapes in and around the free space. Don't bother about professional landscape symbols—just use your own way of showing trees, shrubbery and other details.

Once started, you'll make a lot of these sketches. They will be very revealing. They will show weaknesses and impracticalities in the ideas you may have had before you put pencil to paper. And, as your pencil moves freely within the sketching space, other ideas will come. Save all the sketches, as you probably will want to combine two or more in your final rough plan. Here's an important tip—don't use the boundaries of your lot as *landscaping* boundaries. The shape of your lot is a space *within* which you work and not *about* which you plan. Try to keep away from straight lines in planning shrubbery and other plantings. Nature never plants in a straight line. And there will be enough planes provided by house, walks, driveway, etc., to guard against the possibility of curves becoming monotonous.

The plan: Now you're ready to take your plan out of the rough stage and into details. And we hope, for the sake of final effect, that you resolve (and stick to it) not to depart from the general curves of your rough as you plot the details.

Figs. 1 to 4 show four landscape plans drawn about similarly sized and placed house plans. Each plan places different emphasis on certain areas, although there are points of similarity which are made necessary by the layout of house and grounds. The number of variations is practically limitless, and there is no reason for your home, even though it may be of the same design and material as every other in your block, to present the same appearance as any neighbor's house.

The formal plan will be larger than the rough sketch—a scale of ¼ in. equals 1 ft. is suggested. Make an L-shaped scale ruler

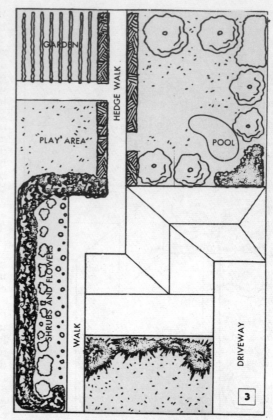

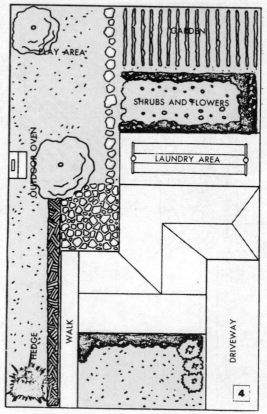

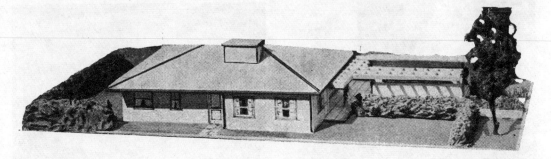

of a strip of heavy cardboard, marking both arms of the rule in feet at ¼-in. intervals. This rule will enable you easily to mark off space in square feet that you intend to devote to certain areas. Again block in the buildings, walks and drives, and outline the lawn space and other open areas with light pencil lines. Make your house plan detailed, with rooms, porches, doors and windows indicated, so that you can plan plantings near these carefully. Now treat each special area of planting space individually. You can forget about the whole plan now, since your rough sketch has assured the over-all effect.

In working out details within an area, remember that balance is wanted, but also that good balance is not always obtained by mathematical precision.

Planting trees in front of a picture window, for instance, does not mean that two trees of equal height should be placed at exactly located spots on either side, with a uniformly spaced line of shrubbery between. Two or three trees at one side of the window, with a shrubbery mass curving before the window and sweeping to meet a porch column, will provide more pleasing balance.

Shrubbery is more attractive in varying masses than in straight rows of uniform height. Two or three varieties of shrubs are better than a single kind if their shapes and textures harmonize. Choices for planting will be given later, but the way in which plantings are massed should be given some attention on your scale plan.

The model: You can, of course, proceed directly from plan to planting. But professional landscape artists recommend one more planning step—the construction of a scale-model house and grounds. A scale model gives a much more realistic forecast of the final effect than a two-dimensional plan, and may reveal defects in the original plan that will save you money.

To lay out a plan accurately to scale you will need a draftsman's T-square, a 45-deg. triangle, a pair of dividers, a small drawing board, thumbtacks and a triangular scale showing common scale reductions.

Begin by thumbtacking a piece of illustration board to the drawing board. Then, with the scale, lay out the size of the lot, using a scale of ¼ in. equals 1 ft. For some types of construction a scale reduction of ⅛ in. equals 1 ft. is practical. Mark the property boundaries on the board. Then, using the same scale reduction, lay out the floor plan of the house on another sheet of illustration board. Scale the thickness of the walls and mark the inside over-all di-

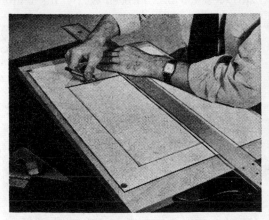

Lay out the exact scale size of your lot on heavy illustration board and mark boundary lines in pencil. Use the common reduction of ⅛ or ¼ in. to 1 ft.

Cut out the lot, using a metal-edged ruler and a sharp, thin-bladed knife. Hold the blade in a vertical plane so the edges of the board will be square on all sides

On another board lay out the house plan. Mark the partitions. Plan should be an exact scale reduction of the inside dimensions measured from wall to wall

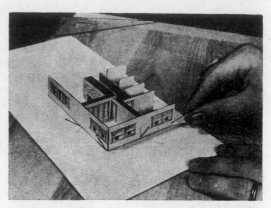

With walls and interior partitions cut to scale, the model may be assembled. Hold walls with pins while joining the partitions with airplane cement

mensions of the floor plan. Then cut on the inside lines. 'Cement this cutout in place on the plan of the lot in exactly the same location as the full-size house is to be. This method of cementing the floor-plan piece to the board on which the lot plan is laid out makes it easier to position the walls. Use your T-square and triangle to get parts laid out exactly at right angles and be careful about the measurements.

Next, determine the scale height of the outside walls and partitions. Mark off and cut strips of the illustration board so that you can cut pieces of partition and wall stock as required. Scale-sized windows and doors are represented by drawing the outlines directly on the walls with black ink, or with pencil. Assemble the parts and fasten them together with airplane cement, reinforcing the outer walls with common pins. On most plans you can cement all the partitions in place before setting the outside walls. At this stage, with the exterior walls in place, cut a ceiling piece of the exact outside dimensions of the floor plan so that it overlaps the thickness of the walls on all

sides. This gives you a foundation on which to build the roof. If the house has a boxed cornice, then the ceiling piece should extend beyond the outer walls a scale distance equal to the overhang of the cornice. Build the roof in sections, using small blocks of wood to elevate the sections to the correct pitch. Carve the chimney top from a small block of wood to scale size, score it, or line with ink to represent bricks, and cement it to the roof. Finally, cement the model house in proper position on the illustration board. Next, make and place the garage if this is separate from the house.

Cut green blotting paper to represent the open lawn areas of your landscape. Cement this in place. Hedges and shrubs can be worked out to scale with green modeling clay. Use crumpled colored crepe paper to represent flower beds. Trees can be represented by tiny artificial trees such as can be obtained in any dime store, or by sprigs of evergreen. Trellises, archways and fences may be carved from pine or balsa wood. Walks, drives and other concrete surfaces will be represented by the white

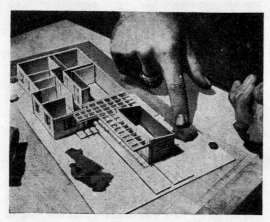

Colored modeling clay is used to form shrubbery and hedges. Strips cut from a sponge also can be used

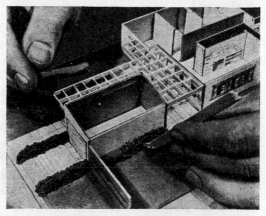

Finishing the modeling-clay shrubbery with the splintered end of a stick gives a realistic effect of foliage

Here trees and shrubbery have been combined to set off the house without spoiling architectural details

unadorned area of the illustration board.

Paint the model house and other appropriate parts of the layout with painter's oil colors thinned to an easy brushing consistency. Use soft-bristle brushes to spread the paint in a uniform coating on the smaller surfaces.

The scale layout may seem to be a lot of trouble. But it can be a lot of fun, and may save you some unpleasant shocks in the future. Don't forget to make your pieces scale correctly in height as well as in length and width.

Trees should be the first concern of your landscape plan. Trees will frame your picture, and can ruin it if located incorrectly. A small ranch house, for instance, will be dwarfed and its pleasing rambling effect destroyed by plantings of Lombardy poplars that eventually will grow to 70 ft. or higher. Smaller trees, placed advantageously, will make the house appear larger than it is. The shapes of trees also will have an important over-all effect on the picture. With a tall, narrow house, a broadening effect should be sought for in the over-all landscape plan. Trees of rounded form, in plantings leading the eye away from the corners of the house, will achieve this.

Tree shapes generally fall into one of the following classifications: pyramid, inverted pyramid, oval, columnar and clump. Pyramid trees include the cedar, fir, hemlock, pine, spruce and larch. Inverted pyramid shapes are assumed by the elm, honey locust and Japanese pagoda tree. The oak, maple and tulip are oval-shaped trees. Trees of the columnar type include the

This is wrong. Trees are planted too closely for future growth. The center one will block the window

Doorstep plantings must be chosen with care. Plant trees that will spread, rather than attain height

Paul Hadley

For the formal house—formal plantings. The several kinds of evergreens here have been trimmed to shape

KEY

1. Globe arborvitae **2. Pyramid arborvitae**

3. Dwarf juniper

Lombardy poplar, cypress and eucalyptus.

Clump trees are those which naturally grow with multiple trunks, or in close-growing groves, such as the birch, ash and willow. In addition, there are trees which are especially suited to being trimmed into fancy artificial shapes, such as the laurel, linden, plane and horse chestnut.

The shape and the eventual size of the mature trees will determine the general effect and character of the landscape picture. Be careful to allow for future growth, so that the trees will frame the house and not hide it. Locate the larger trees near the rear corners, so that they will extend their branches above the house, softening the harsh lines of roof and corners and showing the home to advantage. Trees should always appear to be associated with some other part of the grounds—either the house, other trees or a shrubbery mass. Landscape artists rarely put a lone tree in the center of open lawn.

Trees fall into two main groups—deciduous and evergreen. Evergreens keep their leaves or needles during winter, so that a continuously green foliage is maintained. But they present a cold and formal appearance in spring and midsummer, when other plantings are brilliant with blossoms and sparkling with foliage. So it is doubtful that you will want to confine your tree plantings solely to evergreens.

Most of your plantings should be native trees. This is important because native trees are used to the soil and climate of the region, and because they are less expensive. By keeping a lookout along the highway or in the woods, you can often find good specimens suitable for transplanting to your grounds in early spring or fall. (Don't be guilty of trespassing on private land or of robbing state preserves.)

With these general matters in mind, you are ready to choose your trees.

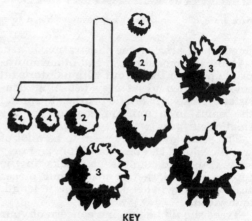

KEY

1. Pyramid arborvitae **2. Pyramid juniper**

3. Dwarf juniper **4. Globe arborvitae**

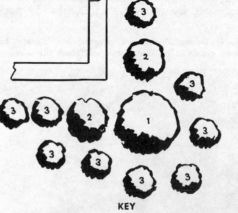

KEY

1. Pyramid arborvitae **2. Taper queen juniper**

3. Globe arborvitae

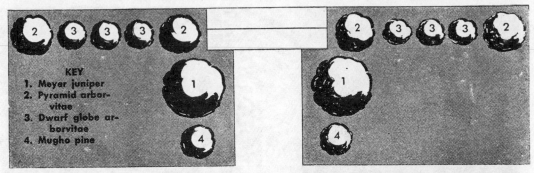

KEY
1. Meyer juniper
2. Pyramid arbor-
      vitae
3. Dwarf globe ar-
      borvitae
4. Mugho pine

When making a landscape plan, number the duplicate shrubs of a given variety. Where there are duplicates in a single group or in adjacent groups, it's quite important that the duplicates be of the same age and training

Shrubbery plantings not only add materially to the value of any home, large or small, but they give it that natural appearance so difficult to achieve in any other way. In making a selection for a given location, keep in mind the exposure, type of soil, appearance, and especially the spread and height of the shrubs when they have attained maximum growth. In some locations and for certain specific purposes, the relative rates of growth of a group of shrubs must be considered in the planning. Most of the extremely hardy shrubs grow very slowly, taking years to attain maximum height or spread. Others grow rapidly, taking only two or three seasons to reach tree size from a single nursery "whip." Certain varieties of slow growers have been designed by nature to withstand very severe cold without harm and without any additional protection. Some thrive in exposed positions in thin soils, while other more tender plants require sheltered locations and moist soils rich in plant foods. This wide variety gives you a choice of plants with size, color of foliage and bloom, and growth habits suitable for almost any plan, location and climatic conditions.

Corner plantings, using both tall, conical shrubs and the low-growing types, which spread a thick foliage only a few inches above the ground, are especially effective around small homes. Plan views of such plantings are shown in the keyed drawings. Usually, tall-growing shrubs are planted in the background and the lower varieties in the foreground in those arrangements where close grouping is necessary. Where shrubbery borders a walk, driveway or a terrace stairway, those bordering the stairway should be of the low-growing varieties, all specimens being of equal age at the time of planting. Where the stairway leads from a lower to a higher level of the garden or lawn and not directly into the house, the lower-level terminal planting usually is a low, spreading evergreen, the spreading junipers being especially suitable. At the top of such an arrangement the stairway row planting may properly terminate in a single taller specimen on each side. When making any closely grouped planting requiring the use of duplicate specimens, be sure that the duplicates are of the same age.

Border plantings, on the other hand, should not achieve the more geometric symmetry required near a building. Instead they should show the rambling out-

In corner plantings, left, low-growing shrubs with thick foliage ordinarily are planted in the foreground. Right, formal plantings require regular seasonal care. Trimming must be done repeatedly as growth progresses

Totty's

Above, a one-plant garden of assorted chrysanthemums. Below, a bed devoted entirely to floribunda roses

J. Horace McFarland

line often found in natural surroundings. The one exception, perhaps, is a hedge which also serves as a boundary between two properties. Here the planting may consist of individuals of a single variety of the same size and age, or two varieties of contrasting foliage if there is room.

It pays to buy balled stock for both individual plantings and also for the larger specimens in a group planting. Balled evergreens should be at least three years old. The five-year specimens of most varieties of evergreens cost more but these have had the benefit of two or three years' training in the nursery.

Smaller specimens dug from the nursery row are supplied with open-root systems packed in damp moss. These should be handled with the greatest care after unpacking to prevent the roots from drying out before the shrubs can be planted in a permanent location. If there are a number of shrubs such as a single lot of one variety for a long hedgerow, all those which cannot be planted immediately after unpacking should be "heeled" into moist soil. To do this dig a V-shaped trench in the garden and lay the shrubs side by side against one side of the trench with the roots at the bottom. Cover the roots and trunks some distance above the ground line with soil and pack it lightly. Soak the trench thoroughly. When you remove the shrubs from the trench, or the original packing, place the roots in a pail or tub filled with water.

Tall flowers can be blended effectively with a hedge to make a colorful background for informal gardens

U.S.D.A.

Flowers are the jewels in the setting provided by your trees and shrubbery. One important fact should be grasped by every home landscape designer—flowers have a place in every part of the home grounds, but they must be wisely selected and properly located to give the most pleasing effect. At the front of the house they should be used for foundation and shrubbery plantings. Almost never should they be placed in a bed in the middle of the yard. At the front, flowers are especially useful during the early days of a landscape. Use them to fill the bare spaces around and between plantings of shrubbery, which often are thin and ragged when new. Most flower plantings in the front should be those of long-season blooming habits, with a few tulips, daffodils and crocuses for early spring, and a few late flowers such as chrysanthemums for late fall. This will provide color for your front from early spring to the onset of winter.

You will use flowers sparingly in your front yard, but in the back you may splurge with blossoms. Plan your beds formally or informally according to the general theme of your landscape plan.

Formal balance is achieved by a geometric layout of beds or pathways between beds. Plantings should be balanced on either side of an imaginary center line through the whole garden area. An informal garden can be an irregular border containing masses of varieties of flowers which are backed up by a shrubbery border or a boundary fence. A massed flower garden should be near the living room of the house or an outdoor terrace. This will add greatly to the beauty of the surroundings. If the land area is large enough, several flower gardens may be planted. That nearest the house can be formal while those at greater distances can be informal. The shape of a flower garden is most pleasing when it is a little longer than wide (about one and one-half times the width). But longer rectangles, or even a square, can be made interesting with a little planning.

Use low-growing flowers to border walks and the open boundaries of a lawn. Use of flowers here is much better than the common practice of spading out the grass and leaving raw, open trenches at the sides of walks. Border flowers can also be combined with shrubs, either by planting the flowers in front of the shrubs or devoting sections of the shrub border to flowers.

Tall-stemmed flowers, such as the castor bean, cosmos, sunflower and basketflower, can be used as screens for temporary fences, or to hide rubbish burners, garbage cans and other unsightly objects.

The simplest garden to design and maintain is the one-plant garden. This may be a rose garden, an iris garden, a zinnia garden, a petunia garden or any one variety. Equipment, garden practices and controls can be standardized in a one-plant garden.

The one-color garden is a popular idea among home gardeners. Is blue your favorite color? Imagine, then, the pleasure you'll get from a flower bed the edging of which begins with pansies, violets and forget-me-nots, which rises in the middle ground to bachelor buttons, cornflowers and columbines and is topped by tall sweetpeas, delphiniums and asters. Or visualize multishades of yellow made by California poppies, dwarf marigolds, strawflowers, double buttercups, dahlias, nasturtiums and black-eyed Susans.

You should plan a separate area for cut flowers for indoor decoration. The grounds which do not furnish beauty for the home

Take advantage of nature's oddities. Here a large rock has been left to set off shrubbery plantings

Washington Commercial

Climbing vines add charm to any garden plan. They are especially useful for breaking up wall expanse

U.S.D.A.

A flagstone walk flanked by flowering shrubs leads to a rock garden. The treatment here is informal

interior are performing only half their function. The vegetable garden is an ideal place for growing cut flowers. The cultivation and plant food which a vegetable garden receives also makes flowers grow better. Another argument for a separate area for cut flowers is that the beauty of the decorative garden and border plantings may be destroyed by cutting blooms for the house.

Other landscape areas: With all the "greens" in your landscape picture taken care of, you are ready to plan in detail the other areas of your home grounds. A close budget may not permit the completion of all your wants within a year or two, but sooner or later you'll want to add lawn furniture, some garden ornaments, perhaps some playground equipment or possibly an outdoor kitchen. You'll have to decide whether you want flagstone walks or a grass path in and around your flower and vegetable gardens. Whether you want a fence or not will depend on whether you actually need one to confine pets or small children and on whether it will or will not add beauty to the grounds. On small lots, landscape gardeners sometimes are reluctant to recommend a fence unless it is a prime necessity. You may want to build a rock garden or a garden pool. There will be spots on your ground which can be enhanced by trellises and pergolas, although care must be taken that these garden furnishings are not overdone. If they are, the whole landscape scheme can be made to appear in extremely bad taste. Remember that outdoor cooking areas and game courts get hard use—for the sake of the rest of your lawn you'd better plan to pave these areas in concrete, asphalt, gravel or tanbark.